# HEAT

# HEAT

ARCHIE G. WORTHING
& DAVID HALLIDAY
UNIVERSITY OF PITTSBURGH

· 1948 ·

NEW YORK · JOHN WILEY & SONS, INC.
LONDON · CHAPMAN & HALL, LIMITED

PRINTED IN THE UNITED STATES OF AMERICA

# PREFACE

The phenomena of nature and of industry involve transformations which are associated with heat. They and the laws which interrelate them are the subject matter of this book. Obviously, a severe selection of material has been necessary. Throughout, in this process, we have kept in mind the desirability of basing the structure of the book on fundamental laws and principles and of choosing appropriate phenomena for their illustration.

The book includes material appropriate for a first undergraduate course to follow an introductory course in physics and for an advanced course for college seniors and early graduate students. Suggestions for some deletions for the earlier course will be found in fine print.

Experimental methods are emphasized. Frequently various methods of measurement of the same physical quantity are described. It is hoped that, thereby, on the one hand, the student will conclude that most phenomena may be viewed from more than one standpoint and, on the other hand, that research workers may find herein a first reference for available methods.

We have taken great care to be precise and consistent in our definitions and in the use of terms and symbols. We have treated the symbols used as physical quantities rather than as numerics, a common but not a general policy. We have distinguished between temperature and temperature difference (p. 23) and assumed the equality of the various expressions for a given temperature regardless of the units used. We have thereby eliminated many sources of confusion on the part of the user. With the hope of eliminating much of the widespread uncertainty in students' minds as to the distinction between mass and weight, we have introduced the verb "to mass" (p. 6) to apply to the action when the analytical balance is used. The verb "to weigh" has been reserved as appropriate for the action involving the spring balance. Although, in this book, we are ordinarily concerned with massing, the process of weighing arises occasionally. Other new points of view will appear to the reader.

v

The names, the life spans, the nationalities, and, for Americans, the institutional connections of various contributors to our knowledge of heat are recorded. Generally the originator of a method or a principle and/or one who has done an exceptionally good piece of work relating thereto have been so mentioned. Such information, showing that the sources of our knowledge are international and that contributions to it have been made with considerable frequency in recent years, is thought to be highly worth while. Without doubt, in the process of selection, the work done in our own nation has been overemphasized.

The authors are indebted to Professor O. H. Blackwood of the University of Pittsburgh and to Mr. Frank Benford of the Research Laboratory of the General Electric Company at Schenectady who read the whole of the manuscript, to Professor John A. Dent, a former colleague, now at the University of Florida, who criticized the chapter relating to heat engines, and to Sister Mary Eudes Clougherty who in addition to reading the manuscript worked nearly all the problems. Certainly, as a result of their efforts, the text has been much improved.

If the book is to improve with time, the help of the users will be necessary. Consequently, the authors will be grateful for notices of errors and suggestions for improvement.

A. G. WORTHING
DAVID HALLIDAY

# SOURCES MUCH CONSULTED IN
# THE PREPARATION OF
# THIS BOOK

(1) H. S. Allen and R. S. Maxwell, *A Textbook of Heat*, Macmillan and Co., 1939.

(2) H. Buckley, *A Short History of Physics*, Methuen and Co., 1927.

(3) F. Cajori, *A History of Physics*, Macmillan and Co., 1906.

(4) O. D. Chwolson, Vol. 3 of *Lehrbuch der Physik*, trans. from the Russian by E. Berg, Friedrich Vieweg und Sohn, 1905.

(5) James Cork, *Heat*, 2nd ed., John Wiley and Sons, 1942.

(6) Edwin Edser, *Heat for Advanced Students*, Macmillan and Co.

(7) A. Eucken, Vol. 8, pt. 1, *Wien-Harms Handbuch der Experimental Physik*, 1929.

(8) V. M. Faires, *Applied Thermodynamics*, Macmillan and Co., 1938.

(9) M. Fishenden and O. Saunders, *The Calculation of Heat Transmission*, His Majesty's Stationery Office, 1932.

(10) B. Haurowitz, *Dynamic Meteorology*, McGraw-Hill Book Co., 1941.

(11) J. H. Keenan and F. G. Keyes, *Thermodynamic Properties of Steam*, John Wiley and Sons, 1936.

(12) B. Lewis and G. von Elbe, *Combustion, Flames and Explosions of Gases*, Cambridge at the University Press, 1938.

(13) G. Lusk, *The Elements of the Science of Nutrition*, 4th ed., W. B. Saunders Co., 1928.

(14) W. H. McAdams, *Heat Transmission*, McGraw-Hill Book Co., 1933.

(15) G. Ribaud, *Traité de pyrométrie optique*, la Revue d'optique théorique et expérimentale, 1931.

(16) J. K. Roberts, *Heat and Thermodynamics*, Blackie and Son, 1940.

(17) M. Saha and B. N. Srivastava, *Textbook of Heat*, Indian Press, 1931.

(18) R. L. Weber, *Temperature Measurement and Control*, P. Blakiston's Son and Co., 1941.

(19) L. D. Weld and F. Palmer, *A Textbook of Modern Physics*, P. Blakiston's Son and Co., 1930.

(20) M. W. Zemansky, *Heat and Thermodynamics*, 2nd ed., McGraw-Hill Book Co., 1943.

(21) *American Men of Science*, 7th ed., Science Press, 1944.

(22) *Encyclopædia Britannica*, 11th ed., The Cambridge University Press, 1911.

(23) *International Critical Tables*, published for the National Research Council by McGraw-Hill Book Co., 1926.

(24) *Temperature, Its Measurement and Control in Science and Industry*, report of a symposium sponsored by the American Institute of Physics, the National Bureau of Standards, and the National Research Council, Reinhold Publishing Corp., 1941.

vii

# CONTENTS

# SYMBOLS AND QUANTITIES

| SYMBOL | QUANTITY DESIGNATED |
|---|---|
| $A$ | area, Helmholtz function |
| $a$ | van der Waals' internal pressure coefficient |
| $B$ | brightness |
| $\mathcal{B}$ | steradiancy |
| $b$ | van der Waals' volume coefficient |
| $C$ | thermal capacitance; product of specific heat and density; Curie constant |
| $c$ | specific heat; velocity of light; molecular velocity |
| $c_2$ | second radiation constant |
| $d$ | diameter; atomic spacing; deflection; thickness |
| $đ$ | inexact differential operator |
| $E$ | emf, illumination |
| $E_0$ | average translational kinetic energy of an ideal gas molecule at 0°C |
| $\varepsilon$ | irradiancy |
| $F$ | luminous flux, force |
| $f$ | force |
| $G$ | Gibbs' function |
| $g$ | acceleration of gravity |
| $H$ | enthalpy; magnetic field strength |
| $h$ | specific enthalpy; height; Planck's constant; film coefficient |
| $h'$ | transfer coefficient |
| $I$ | luminous intensity of a source; electric current; thermal current density |
| $\mathcal{I}$ | rate of supply of energy electrically to a filament per unit length |
| $i$ | current density |
| $J$ | mechanical equivalent of heat; radiant intensity of a source |
| $K$ | leakage modulus; thermometer scale correction constant; coefficient of performance of a refrigerator; departure coefficient |
| $k$ | Boltzmann's molecular constant; thermal conductivity; cooling constant; force constant |
| $L$ | length; heat of fusion; heat of vaporization; heat of transition; torque |
| $l$ | film thickness |
| $M$ | mass; elastic modulus |
| $m$ | mass |
| $N$ | number of molecules (steradiancy) |
| $N_0$ | Avogadro number |
| $n$ | number |
| $O$ | radiant output rate for a lamp filament mounted in a vacuum |
| $\Theta$ | rate of radiation of energy from a filament per unit length |
| $P$ | radiant flux |
| $p$ | pressure |

| SYMBOL | QUANTITY DESIGNATED |
|--------|---------------------|
| $Q$ | heat |
| $R$ | molar gas constant; electrical resistance; thermal resistance per unit area |
| $\mathcal{R}$ | radiancy |
| $r$ | radius, radial distance |
| $S$ | entropy; setting temperature of a differential thermometer; brightness temperature; speed of sound; stirring constant for a calorimeter |
| $s$ | area; specific entropy; specific gravity |
| $T$ | temperature |
| $t$ | time |
| $U$ | internal energy |
| $u$ | specific internal energy |
| $V$ | volume; potential difference |
| $v$ | specific volume |
| $W$ | work done by body or system under consideration |
| $w$ | weight |
| $X$ | unknown mass |
| $\alpha$ | linear expansivity, absorptance |
| $\alpha'$ | absorptivity |
| $\beta$ | volume expansivity |
| $\gamma$ | ratio of specific heats; degrees of freedom |
| $\delta$ | density; uncertainty of a measured quantity |
| $\epsilon$ | emittance |
| $\epsilon'$ | emissivity |
| $\zeta$ | resistivity |
| $\eta$ | efficiency; Reynolds number; free expansion coefficient |
| $\Theta$ | Debye temperature |
| $\theta$ | angle; scale reading, temperature difference |
| $\kappa$ | compressibility; thermal diffusivity |
| $\lambda$ | wavelength; mean free path |
| $\mu$ | porous plug effect |
| $\nu$ | frequency; viscosity |
| $\rho$ | resistivity; reflectance |
| $\rho'$ | reflectivity |
| $\sigma$ | fourth-power radiation constant |
| $\tau$ | transmittance |
| $\varphi$ | radiant flux; plane angle; Bragg angle; thermal resistance |
| $\omega$ | solid angle; plane angular velocity |
| $\chi$ | paramagnetic susceptibility |

# CHAPTER I

## SOME LABORATORY PROCEDURES

**1. Introduction.** It is the experience of the authors that, in the laboratory, students often lose valuable time or use it to too little advantage. The main purpose of this chapter is to offer some general instructions, which, it is hoped, will enable the student to use his available time more wisely. Among other things we shall consider certain procedures, precautions, and corrections for the accurate determination of a pressure, a mass, or a temperature; how to record data obtained; how to plot them if necessary; how to obtain needed equations; how to treat data in order both to obtain a reasonable result and to determine how much of a computed result is of significance; and how to present a reasonable report. Even with these suggestions, a certain portion of the time will undoubtedly still be spent inadvisedly, but, the authors hope, not so much so.

Of all procedures for laboratory experimentation, none takes precedence over that of obtaining at the beginning a clear understanding of the problem at hand and of the proposed method of solution.

**2. Determining Pressures.** Pressures are commonly expressed in mm-Hg or cm-Hg, though often the $dy/cm^2$, the $lb/in.^2$, and the A (atmosphere) are used. Carelessly, however, many express pressures in cm without realization of the need to use instead cm-Hg (centimeter-of-mercury), to be precise. The cm by itself is never more than a length unit. How the two are connected is readily shown. From elementary physics we have for hydrostatic pressure, as a basic relation,

$$p = h\delta g \tag{1}$$

of which $p$, $h$, $\delta$, and $g$ in order represent hydrostatic pressure, height of liquid column, density of liquid, and acceleration of gravity. Where $h$, $\delta$, and $g$ are measured in cm, $gm/cm^3$, and $cm/sec^2$, a consistent unit for $p$ is the $dy/cm^2$. But $p$ may be and usually is expressed in other units. As has been indicated above, the cm-Hg is one such unit. By definition, the cm-Hg is the hydrostatic pressure due to a column of mercury just 1 cm high for standard conditions as to $\delta$ and $g$, that is $\delta_0$ and $g_0$, or 13.5951 $gm/cm^3$ and 980.665 $cm/sec^2$. Thus

$$1.00000 \text{ cm-Hg} = 1.00000 \text{ cm} \times \delta_0 g_0 \tag{2}$$

It is characteristic of definitions and defining relations that the thing defined may always be replaced by the definition. In accord therewith and in view of Eq. 2 we may, therefore, at any time, replace the cm-Hg by $\delta_0 g_0$ cm or the cm by cm-Hg/$(\delta_0 g_0)$. The fact that the numeric in front of the cm-Hg, when representing the pressure due to a column of mercury under standard conditions, is the same as that in front of the cm in the expression for the height is very convenient but does not identify the $p$ as an $h$. The student who perceives these distinctions and makes use of them consistently will save himself much confusion. It is to be emphasized similarly that the atmosphere, A, is a precise unit whose value is 760.00 mm-Hg and that a 760.00-mm column of mercury indicates such a pressure only when the conditions as to $\delta$ and $g$ are standard.

Often when using a mercury manometer, we measure the difference in heights of two mercury columns in cm, perhaps, and then say that the pressure difference is that same number of cm-Hg. This, however, is acceptable only as a first approximation. For a precise determination, several things must be taken into account. Some are: (1) the method of reading the positions of the tops of the columns; (2) the similarity or dissimilarity of these upper boundary surfaces; (3) the uniformity of temperature of the mercury columns; (4) the correctness of the length-measuring instrument; (5) the correction to standard conditions as to temperature and gravitational field strength.

**3. Reading the Position of Tops of Mercury Columns.** Where the position of the top of a mercury column in a glass tube with respect to a scale firmly fixed behind or preferably beside the glass tube to the closest 0.2 mm suffices, a good method makes use of a paper straight edge. The paper should be held just above the mercury meniscus, horizontal and tangent to the mercury surface when viewed horizontally. It is then rather easy to read the position of the top of the column with reasonable accuracy.

For a higher precision, something of the nature of a cathetometer is desirable. Sometimes, with the further aid of a telescope with cross hairs mounted on the cathetometer, the transfer of the position of the meniscus top to a scale is easily accomplished. Occasionally, however, because of the high reflectivity of the meniscus surface, difficulty is experienced in locating the exact meniscus top. Then, particularly if it is possible to reach the tops of the two menisci with a prong or prongs inserted from the tops of the tubes, an electrical contact method may be used. In such case it is desirable to take several readings alternately on the left and on the right meniscus tops at regular time intervals. Only successions of readings that show consistency are to be accepted, and, to take account in part of some possible gradual change, each succession accepted should be limited generally to an odd number of readings. By so doing, one insures that the mean for the readings on the left will correspond to the same instant, time centroid, as does the mean for the readings on the right. That such a succession is desirable if not essential is apparent from the following diagram.

$$a$$
$$b$$
$$\text{time centroid} \ldots \ldots \ldots c \ldots \ldots \ldots$$
$$e \qquad\qquad d$$

To illustrate the foregoing, consider the following succession of readings, which were taken alternately left and right and approximately equally spaced in times of taking.

| LEFT | RIGHT |
|---|---|
| 0.502 mm | 0.343 mm |
| .530 | .355 |
| .513 | .359 |
| .522 | .366 |
| .529 | .373 |
| .535 | |

Starting with a reading on the left, we find one reading, the second on the left, which does not fit into the series. We therefore ignore the first three readings and seek an acceptable odd-number succession from the remainder. Such a succession may start with reading 0.355 mm or 0.513 mm or even with a later reading. Starting with the 0.355-mm reading and ending the succession with the final reading on the right, we obtain an average of 0.363 mm for those on the right. Correspondingly, the three included readings on the left have an average of 0.521 mm. As they should, these averages correspond in time of taking to the same instant, namely the instant the 0.522-mm reading was taken. The difference between the averages is 0.158 mm. Using a succession of seven readings beginning with 0.513 mm, we obtain the nearly identical value 0.159 mm. When an odd-number succession of readings is taken, it matters not whether the first reading is on the right or on the left.

**4. The Similarity of Menisci at the Tops of the Mercury Columns.** An obvious requirement for equal menisci in any instance is that the glass tubes have equal diameters in the regions where the menisci are present. Other obvious requirements are equal temperatures, equal purity of mercury, and equal cleanliness of tubes. These are here taken for granted. Even then, difficulties appear.

When mercury is caused to move up or down a capillary tube, there is a tendency for the mercury at the edge of the meniscus to drag. With downward motion, the meniscus is overly flat; with upward motion, the meniscus is overly convex. With change of pressure, the two menisci of a manometer usually experience these opposite effects. One method of overcoming this difficulty is to have a screw volume control for the mercury in the manometer so that by means of it, at the conclusion of a pressure change, the same final motions may be produced at the same time in both capillaries. It is better, however, to have the tubing so large, at least where the meniscus readings are made, that the shape of a meniscus does not appreciably affect the height of the meniscus at its center. A combination of these precautions is sometimes desirable.

In barometers where differences in radii for the two free ends occur, the zeros of the length scales are adjusted by the makers to yield the readings that would be obtained were the cross sections of the tubes so large that menisci effects would be absent. Errors due to a failure to make this correction complete, as well as those due to the pressure of a small amount of gas in the space above the mercury and to certain other sources, are combined under the term instrument error. Where high precision is desired this must be taken into account.

**5. The Uniformity of Temperature of the Mercury Columns.** That non-uniformity leads to error is evident. It is best to try for uniformity of temperature. Where impossible, corrections for this defect, if required, should be made in accord with that shown below in correcting to a standard temperature condition.

**6. The Correctness of the Length-Measuring Instrument.** Scales of ordinary wooden meter sticks can hardly be expected to yield differences closer than 0.1 mm or 0.2 mm under the best conditions. Metal scales are better, but for accurate results they should be calibrated, and, if calibrated at one temperature and used at another, corrections should be made for the difference. In so doing it should be remembered that, if a scale is used at a higher temperature than the calibration temperature, the actual difference in level between the two menisci will be greater than the apparent difference.

**7. The Correction to Standard Conditions as to Temperature and Gravitational Field Strength.** With the factors already noted properly taken into account, there still remain two corrections to be considered before the difference in height of two menisci can be translated into standard pressure units. One correction is for the change in density of the mercury from its actual value, $\delta$, when the difference in height is determined, to its standard value at 0°C, namely $\delta_0$; the other is for the deviation of the gravitational field strength $g$ at the place where the measurements are made from the standard value $g_0$. Let $p'$ be the apparent but uncorrected pressure and $p$ the corrected pressure. Further let $h'$ represent the height difference as read on the scale, assumed correct at 0°C,* and $h$ the actual difference in height between the menisci. Starting with the defining equation for pressure and applying the above mentioned corrections, we obtain

$$p = h\delta g = h'\delta_0 g_0(1 + \bar{\alpha}_s\theta)\,\frac{1}{1 + \bar{\beta}_l\theta}\left(1 - \frac{g_0 - g}{g_0}\right) \qquad (3)$$

$$= p'\left[1 - (\bar{\beta}_l - \bar{\alpha}_s)\theta - \frac{g_0 - g}{g_0}\right]$$

where $\theta$ is the temperature interval between the temperature occurring and the standard 0°C, $\bar{\alpha}_s$ the linear expansivity of the scale, and $\bar{\beta}_l$ the volume expansivity of the manometer liquid. Eq. 3 applies, of course, to barometric pressure readings as well as to other pressure determinations.

For a brass scale, $\bar{\alpha}_s$ is $19 \times 10^{-6}$ 1/C°; for mercury $\bar{\beta}_l$ is $180 \times 10^{-6}$ 1/C°.† The standard value for $g_0$ is 980.665 cm/sec², and, of course, $g$ varies from place to place. On the second floor of Thaw Hall at the University of Pittsburgh, it is 980.11 cm/sec². For this place the factor $(g_0 - g)/g_0$ is 0.00056. A reading of 740.32 mm-Hg obtained there with a barometer having a brass scale, when the temperature is 25°C, yields when corrected

$$p = 740.32 \text{ mm-Hg}\left(1 - 161 \times 10^{-6}\frac{1}{\text{C}°} \times 25\text{ C}° - 0.00056\right) \qquad (4)$$

$$= 740.32 \text{ mm-Hg } (1 - 0.00458) = 736.92 \text{ mm-Hg}$$

The correction to $p'$ is seen to be quite appreciable. Often tables are provided for the user's convenience.

**8. Measuring Pressure by Means of Boiling Water.** The connection between boiling-point temperature and atmospheric pressure for a pure liquid is so definite that it is possible to determine atmospheric pressures by means of observed boiling points for a liquid of known characteristics. As one of several substances, very pure water is particularly satisfactory. By definition, its boiling point at a pressure of a standard atmosphere is 100.000°C. The rate of change of pressure at this temperature with change of boiling point is about 27 mm-Hg/K°. To obtain a pressure

---

* The standard temperature for scale reduction for barometers with scales calibrated in inches is 62°F, not that of melting ice. Peculiarly, however, the correction for the mercury expansion is made with reference to 32°F.

† See p. 23 for the significance of the degree sign following the C as in 1/C°.

close to atmospheric, to within 0.03 mm-Hg, say, it is necessary to measure the boiling point to within 0.030 mm-Hg/(27 mm-Hg/K°) or 0.001 K°. With an electrical resistance thermometer, this is quite possible. The value obtained is at once free from corrections such as those for the deviation of $g$ from $g_0$ and for the expansion of a measuring scale. Apparatus developed for this purpose by the Polish physical chemist W. Swietoslawski (1881–   ) is shown later as Fig. 11 of Chapter X.

In operation, water in $A$ is heated electrically and, in the form of bubbles of vapor and liquid, is thrown against tube $B$ containing the resistance thermometer immersed in mercury. Some vapor, condensing in $C$, runs down and leaks through a small orifice at $D$ to return to the main supply. It is necessary to keep the heating rate adjusted so that the rate of return of drops of water at $D$ falls within certain limits.

## 9. Massing.* Spring balances and platform balances are often satisfactory for mass determinations. All depends on the precision required. Where mass determinations to within 10 mg or better are desired, it is usually necessary to use an equal-arm chemical balance and sometimes to make corrections for the buoyancy exerted by the atmosphere on the body massed and on the so-called "weights," really mass standards.

## 10. Single Massing. In single massing, it is common to determine (1) a point of rest $d_1$ for no load; (2) a point of rest $d_2$ with the body of unknown mass $X$ in one pan, and with the several other bodies of known masses, to give a combined known mass $M$ nearly balancing the unknown mass, in the other pan; and (3) for balance-sensitivity purposes, a point of rest $d_3$ for a condition similar to that just stated but with a small known mass, $m$, say 1 mg or 2 mg, added to or taken from the known mass. Where precision is desired, these points of rest are determined by the swing method. With the balance cage

---

* Weighing is the term commonly used for what is here denoted as massing. The reason for adopting massing is the confusion that has resulted from the use of the term weighing when the mass of a body is the quantity sought. It is argued that actually, with an analytical beam balance, we weigh a body, that is, we measure the earth pull on it, and later compute its mass. It would be more true to say that we compare the weight of a body with that of a standard body or bodies and then deduce a conclusion as to the mass of the body. Seldom, using a beam balance, do we ever determine the actual magnitude of the earth pull or weight. With the spring balance it is different. For the process involved then, the term weighing may well be retained, for primarily a weight is obtained and the mass, if wanted, must be computed. The use of the term weighing in connection with beam balances, however, is contrary to our policy of nomenclature in other fields. Using a thermometer, one never compares the expansion of mercury with that of glass; he measures temperatures instead. Using an ammeter, one never measures the torques of interacting magnetic fields; he measures electric currents instead. Using a spectrograph, one never measures the deviation and the dispersion of a beam of light; he measures wavelengths instead. It is the final result of the process that determines the description of the process. For that reason we should say that we *mass* a body rather than *weigh* a body when we use an analytical beam balance.

closed and air drafts eliminated, the balance beam supports are lowered, the beam is set in motion, and a succession of pointer deflections, alternately to the right and to the left, is taken. From these a succession containing an odd number of readings, say 3, 5, or 7, is selected. Averages of left and right readings are taken separately, and then these two averages are averaged for the point of rest. Thus from the succession

| LEFT | RIGHT |
|------|-------|
| $-3.2$ | $+7.4$ |
| $-2.1$ | $+6.2$ |
| $-1.1$ | $+5.1$ |
| $-0.1$ | |

one may obtain three successions of 5 to be treated separately, or one may take all in a single group. From the uniform variation in differences, it is apparent that each odd-numbered group will be satisfactory. The point of rest, $+2.3$, is obtained in a manner similar to that described above for the determination of the difference in heights of two mercury menisci.

Given the points of rest $d_1$, $d_2$, and $d_3$, the known mass $M$, and the small mass $m$, one may obtain the mass of the unknown body $X$, except for buoyancy effects, from

$$X = M \pm \frac{d_2 - d_1}{d_3 - d_2} m \qquad (5)$$

Whether to use the plus or the minus for the correction depends on which pan of the balance the unknown body is placed upon, and on whether $m$ was added to or taken from $M$ in determining $d_3$. How to make correction for buoyancy will appear later (p. 8).

**11. Double Massing.** For very high precision, double massing is desirable. It tends to eliminate (1) the effects of slight differences in the lengths of the arms of the equal-arm balance and (2) the effect of a possible change in the normal rest point with change in load. When the method is properly carried out, it involves just the same number of determinations of points of rest as does single massing. The only increase in work arises from the single interchanging of the $X$ and the $M$ bodies.

Using this method, one does not determine a "no-load" point of rest. As above, let $X$ represent the unknown mass, $M$ the sum of the known masses used to obtain an approximate balance, and $m$ a small mass used for a sensitivity determination. As suggested by Fig. 1, one determines a $d_A$, a $d_B$, and a $d_C$. For the present, the effects of atmospheric buoyancy on the bodies in both pans are disregarded. It is evident then that, if $d_A$ should equal $d_B$, $X$ would equal $M$. It is also evident that, as diagrammed, $M$ is greater than $X$ and that the amount by which it is greater is the mass $\Delta M$ which when taken from $M$ will cause the point of rest to shift the distance $(d_B - d_A)/2$. Its

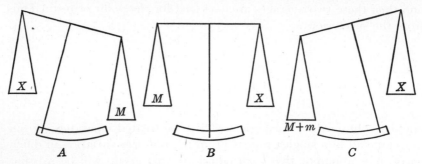

FIG. 1. Points of rest positions for double massing

magnitude, as will be seen, involves the sensitivity for the loaded balance, namely $(d_C - d_B)/m$. Except for buoyancy effects, there follows, for the case diagrammed in Fig. 1,

$$X = M - \Delta M = M - \frac{d_B - d_A}{2} \frac{m}{d_C - d_B} \qquad (6)$$

**12. Corrections for Buoyancy.** Both the body of unknown mass and the bodies of mass $M$ are buoyed up by the atmosphere in which they are immersed. With $V_X$ and $V_M$ representing volumes and $\delta_a$ the density of the displaced air, the resulting apparent losses of mass are $V_X\delta_a$ and $V_M\delta_a$. The consequent correction $\Delta X$ to be added algebraically to values for $X$ obtained with the aid of Eq. 6 or Eq. 5 is given closely by

$$\Delta X = (V_X - V_M)\delta_a = M\delta_a\left(\frac{1}{\delta_X} - \frac{1}{\delta_M}\right) \qquad (7)$$

where $\delta_X$, $\delta_M$, and $\delta_a$ represent in order the densities of the body of unknown mass, the standard bodies of mass $M$, and the air. Suppose in a special case that $\delta_X$, $\delta_M$, and $\delta_a$ are respectively 1.0 gm/cm$^3$, 8.4 gm/cm$^3$, and 0.0012 gm/cm$^3$, and that $M$ equals 200 gm; $\Delta X$ is then 0.212 gm. If $\delta_X$ and $\delta_M$ are equal, $\Delta X$ becomes zero.

**13. Determining Temperatures.** We here give consideration only to the reading of mercury-in-glass thermometers, for the question of determining temperatures by means of other thermometers forms a large part of the following chapter.

We shall assume well-seasoned thermometers such as are commonly used in laboratory and in industry. Temperature readings should be taken with the following facts in mind.

1. Most of the less expensive common thermometers with scales ranging from −5°C to 105°C are factory calibrated for complete immersion at 0°C and 100°C only, and have the space on the stem between corresponding marks divided up evenly on the assumption that the bore is exactly uniform.

2. Some thermometers of the better types are calibrated at several points but always for complete immersion unless a complete etched ring shows at the 20°C mark or elsewhere. In that case the calibration is for immersion to that ring only and for a certain ambient temperature.

A so-called stem correction must be applied to the reading of a scale which has been calibrated for total immersion but which for some reason is used partially immersed, in order to take account of the differential expansion between the glass of the stem and the contained mercury. The equation giving this stem correction $\Delta T$ is

$$\Delta T = KN(T_b - T_s) \tag{8}$$

$T_b$ and $T_s$ are the bulb and stem temperatures. $N$ is the temperature interval corresponding to a shift of the top of the mercury thread from the top surface of the liquid around the bulb to its position at temperature $T_b$. $K$ is a constant characteristic of mercury and of the stem glass. For ordinary thermometers its value is 0.00016 1/C° or 0.000089 1/F°. A thermometer whose bulb is at 100°C but whose capillary is for the most part at room temperature may give on this account an indication that is more than a degree in error. This error increases about as the square of the difference between bulb and ambient temperatures. For a bulb temperature of 400°C, it may amount to as much as 25 C°.

3. Due to an atmosphere of nitrogen above the mercury column, large variations of pressure occur inside a thermometer. Consequent bulb distortions may be the source of appreciable errors if the stem condition during use differs appreciably from that during calibration.

4. The mercury well of a thermometer intended for high temperatures may be permanently changed, without breakage occurring, if the thermometer is heated beyond the range for which it is intended. The attached scale thereafter is of little use, however, without recalibration.

5. Sensitive thermometers with large thin-walled mercury wells may have their indications vary on account of difference of internal and

external pressures resulting from changes in position or of the density of the liquids being tested. A shift merely from a vertical to a horizontal position sometimes produces an appreciable effect.

6. During rapid heating or cooling, not only will the temperature of the thermometer differ from the surroundings whose temperature it is assumed to measure, but also the mean temperature of the glass walls of the bulb will differ from that of the contained mercury. Depending on the temperature change, the nature of the surroundings,

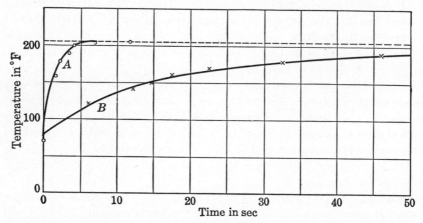

FIG. 2. The temperature indications of a mercury-in-glass thermometer, originally at about 75 °F, as a function of time after being thrust into (A) boiling water and (B) oil at the same temperature. (By permission, Howe and Boelter in *The Symposium on Temperature—Its Measurement and Control in Science and Industry*, p. 337, New York, Reinhold Publishing Corp., 1941.)

the stirring, and other factors, a time varying from some seconds to some minutes may be expected before the final temperature will be approximately attained (Fig. 2).

7. The glass of a thermometer on heating or cooling, particularly when changing through a considerable range of temperature, requires appreciable time for final adjustment to the new temperature. For a well-aged thermometer with a 0°C to 105°C range, the depression of the ice point, as it is called, following heating to 100°C and subsequent cooling to 0°C is of the order of 0.1 C°. Such changes, however, are temporary, and usually the effect disappears gradually, but completely, within a few days.

8. All thermometers undergo permanent changes with time. To reduce the aging effect, high-grade thermometers are artificially aged by the manufacturers by being held at high temperatures for prolonged intervals. However, aging is never complete. Whatever

changes occur are effectively limited to the bulb, and a calibration once properly made can be used thereafter even with the occurrence of such permanent changes. It is merely necessary to add, to the original calibration differences throughout the scale, the change that is found at any time at some one point, say 0°C.

9. The plane of the graduated scale usually differs from that containing the mercury thread. On this account, the line of sight of the observer when making a reading should be perpendicular to the length of the capillary tube.

10. At most a thermometer measures its own temperature.

**14. Recording Data.** It is a common experience for those writing up reports of experimental work to find (1) that more experimental data are desired; (2) that certain data are missing; (3) that more of the original data (see below) are needed. To some extent, at least, these deficiencies can be anticipated. The most important method of anticipation consists of obtaining a clear conception of the problem in advance of taking measurements. However, the matter of particular interest here is the recording of data.

*All original data* should be recorded. To illustrate, if one is concerned with an interval of time that is obtained by subtracting one time reading, an original datum, from another, he should record on his data sheet both those time readings. By so doing he reduces the chance for error in taking a difference, a datum that is not original, at least to the extent that an available check on the taking of the difference continues to be possible.

If the measurements involve decimals, a zero in the last measured place should be recorded as zero. In a series of measurements involving the same number of decimal places for the unit used, a number with one decimal place lacking can seldom be ascribed later, with certainty, to a failure to record a final zero rather than to an accidental failure to record a digit in any of the other decimal places.

It is generally desirable to have recorded data show the order of taking measurements. Occasionally that order is important. But, most of all, the record should be so clear that it cannot be misinterpreted later.

**15. Plotting Data.** Often, for some reason, the data taken in an experiment or a portion of it must be graphed. The following are some suggestions to aid in the construction of graphs from which conclusions may be drawn or which can serve as tools for further experimentation. See Fig. 3 in this connection.

1. A graph constructed for another's consideration, or for one's own future use, should carry a descriptive statement giving essential facts

regarding it so that it may be understood by one familiar with the field with little or no extra reading.

2. Generally, values of the variable viewed as the independent variable should be plotted as abscissas, along the $x$-axis.

3. The scales chosen for the coordinates should be convenient. Scales are usually satisfactory in this respect if the determination of

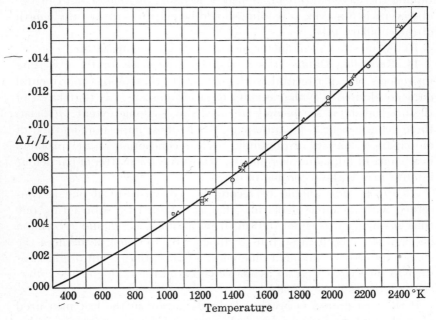

FIG. 3. A graph showing $\Delta L/L = f(T)$ for molybdenum.

the coordinates of a point on the plot chosen at random, and not at main cross lines, is simple and convenient. If the common cross-section paper with ten spaces between main division lines equally separated is used, those main division lines should generally correspond to rounded or whole-number values; and the differences between the values for two adjacent, main division lines should be 1, 2, 2.5, 4, 5, or 10, or 1000 or 0.1, etc., times some convenient rounded value. Seldom if ever are differences of 3, 6, 7, 8, 9, or of any other number not mentioned just above found to be anything but sources of annoyance.

4. If the relation between the plotted variables does not differ greatly from a straight line, a very common occurrence in the study of heat, the spaces allotted to the independent and the dependent variables should not differ greatly.

5. Subject to the condition that it is not desirable to have scales so open that the uncertainties of measurement correspond to more than half of the distance between successive main division lines on the coordinate paper, the scales should be so chosen as to cover nearly the whole of a coordinate sheet. Sometimes single end points may be plotted in the margin for the sake of covering the sheet and obtaining a convenient scale.

6. Generally, only every main division line or every second main division line should have the value assigned it indicated in the margin at one end of the line.

7. The quantities plotted and the units in which they are expressed should be written on the margins below or to one side of the cross-sectioned space.

8. All observed values should be indicated by one or more types of symbols, such as $\odot$, $\bullet$, $\times$, $+$, and $\Delta$. Only one type of symbol should be used in connection with a particular relation unless there is some reason for distinguishing certain observed values from others.

9. Curves that are drawn to represent a relation indicated by the plotted points should generally be drawn as narrow lines with the aid of transparent, fixed-form curves (ship's curves represent one group). When drawing a curve, it is well to remember that end points are often end points because of difficulties of measurement, and that then they are less exact than are other points and should be given less consideration.

**16. Obtaining Equations.** Often the result of a test is best expressed by means of an equation. At other times equations expressing the relations between observed quantities are needed in the process of arriving at the results of tests. Here we shall consider the method of arriving at such equations.

In many cases, the desired equations are of a form in which $y$ is expressed as a power series of $x$, thus

$$y = a + bx + cx^2 + dx^3 + \cdots \tag{9}$$

We shall consider three simple cases using determinants, where the constants to be determined are (1) $a$ and $b$; (2) $a$, $b$, and $c$; and (3) $b$, $c$, and $d$. The problem in each case consists of finding the equation of a curve that will pass through arbitrarily chosen points, as many in number as the number of constants to be determined. For case (1), the curve is a straight line, and in theory any two points may be chosen. For cases (2) and (3), three points must be chosen. It is always desirable to choose points that are well separated to represent the whole range and which lend themselves to easy computation. Where $(x_1, y_1)$, $(x_2, y_2)$, $(x_3, y_3)$, etc., represent the points, the equations corresponding to the three cases in order, when expressed in determinant form, are:

$$\begin{vmatrix} y & 1 & x \\ y_1 & 1 & x_1 \\ y_2 & 1 & x_2 \end{vmatrix} = 0 \tag{10}$$

$$\begin{vmatrix} y & 1 & x & x^2 \\ y_1 & 1 & x_1 & x_1^2 \\ y_2 & 1 & x_2 & x_2^2 \\ y_3 & 1 & x_3 & x_3^2 \end{vmatrix} = 0 \tag{11}$$

and

$$\begin{vmatrix} y & x & x^2 & x^3 \\ y_1 & x_1 & x_1^2 & x_1^3 \\ y_2 & x_2 & x_2^2 & x_2^3 \\ y_3 & x_3 & x_3^2 & x_3^3 \end{vmatrix} = 0 \tag{12}$$

These determinants, when expanded, yield values for $a$, $b$, $c$, and $d$ in terms of $y_1$, $y_2$, etc., and $x_1$, $x_2$, etc. See Appendix IV.

Those not familiar with determinants may use the longer method of solving simultaneous equations. For case (2) they are

$$y_1 = a + bx_1 + cx_1^2 \tag{13}$$

$$y_2 = a + bx_2 + cx_2^2 \tag{14}$$

$$y_3 = a + bx_3 + cx_3^2 \tag{15}$$

Let us apply the foregoing to the derivation of an equation for the curve of Fig. 3, expressing $\Delta L/L$ as a function of $(T - 300°K)$. This means that $a$ is necessarily zero. Let us assume that terms beyond the third power of $(T - 300°K)$ are negligible and that the equation is to have the form

$$\frac{\Delta L}{L} = b(T - 300°K) + c(T - 300°K)^2 + d(T - 300°K)^3 \tag{16}$$

Since only three constants are to be determined, it is only necessary to choose three points on the plot through which the curve shall pass. From the standpoint of ease of computation and of representation of the whole range, points corresponding to 1000°K, 1700°K, and 2400°K may well be chosen. The point corresponding to 300°K was used, in fact, when it was decided that the equation should take the form of Eq. 16, in which $a$ is zero. We thus have for the points chosen

$$\Delta L/L \qquad (T - 300°K)$$

$$0.0040 \qquad 700 \text{ K}°$$
$$.0091 \qquad 1400 \text{ K}°$$
$$.0153 \qquad 2100 \text{ K}°$$

In determinant form the equation is

$$\begin{vmatrix} \Delta L/L & (T - 300°K) & (T - 300°K)^2 & (T - 300°K)^3 \\ 0.0040 & 700 \text{ K}° & (700 \text{ K}°)^2 & (700 \text{ K}°)^3 \\ 0.0091 & 1400 \text{ K}° & (1400 \text{ K}°)^2 & (1400 \text{ K}°)^3 \\ 0.0153 & 2100 \text{ K}° & (2100 \text{ K}°)^2 & (2100 \text{ K}°)^3 \end{vmatrix} = 0 \tag{17}$$

When expanded, this equation takes the form of Eq. 16 with actual values appearing for $b$, $c$, and $d$.

However, much time may be saved by introducing $x = \dfrac{T - 300°\text{K}}{700 \text{ K}°}$ as a new variable. Eq. 17 is thereby replaced by

$$\begin{vmatrix} \Delta L/L & x & x^2 & x^3 \\ 0.0040 & 1 & 1 & 1 \\ .0091 & 2 & 4 & 8 \\ .0153 & 3 & 9 & 27 \end{vmatrix} = 0 \tag{18}$$

Solution yields

$$\frac{\Delta L}{L} = 0.00345x + 0.00055x^2$$

$$= 4.97 \times 10^{-6}\, \frac{1}{\text{K}°}\, (T - 300°\text{K}) + 1.12 \times 10^{-9}\, \frac{1}{\text{K}°^2}\, (T - 300°\text{K})^2 \tag{19}$$

Note that, when in succession the values 1, 2, and 3 are substituted for $x$ in this expression, 0.0040, 0.0091, and 0.0153 are obtained. This check insures that no error has been made in evaluating the determinant. It is always advisable to make such a check. For the points chosen, the coefficient $d$, Eq. 19, has turned out to be zero, a decidedly unusual occurrence. Had three other points been chosen with values for $\Delta L/L$ read with the same precision, a relatively small value would undoubtedly have been obtained for $d$. In addition to the checks indicated, it is obviously desirable to check additionally at some midpoints of the curve.

The significance of the constants in an equation of this kind will be discussed in a later chapter.

## 17. The Precision of Computed Results.

Only a few important suggestions will be given. Full treatment requires much more space than is justifiable here.

In what follows we shall not use the technical terms probable error and standard deviation. One reason is that ordinarily, in laboratory work connected with a heat course for students, time prevents the taking of sufficient readings to yield significant probable errors or standard deviations. Nevertheless the student should gain some idea of the accuracy of a result which he has obtained. For this purpose, we introduce, without precise definition, the concept of "uncertainty" for a measured quantity. As the general symbol for it we shall use $\delta$. Thus we shall represent an uncertainty in $T$ by $\delta T$, in $L$ by $\delta L$, etc. What the uncertainty is, in many cases, will be very much a matter of opinion. Despite that, opinions should be formed. For a temperature measurement, using a common $-5°C$ to $105°C$ mercury-in-glass thermometer graduated in degrees, a $\delta T$ of 0.1 C° must be expected even when conditions are excellent. If conditions are not excellent $\delta T$ may be twice or even five times as great. To this uncertainty should be added that which is due to the scale, if known. The $\delta I$ for an electric-current reading, similarly under the most favorable conditions as to steadiness of current and illumination of scale, is at least $\frac{1}{10}$ of the value of the smallest division.

Some principles relating to uncertainties, stated without proof, are:

1. The uncertainty for the average of $n$ measurements of a quantity, each with the same uncertainty, is $1/\sqrt{n}$ times the uncertainty of a single measurement. If $\delta T$ for each of 10 measurements of a temperature is 0.2 C°, the $\delta T$ for the average should be $1/\sqrt{10} \times 0.2$ C° or 0.06 C°.

2. The uncertainty of either a sum or a difference is the square root of the sum of the squares of the absolute uncertainties. Where, for instance,

$$z = y - x \tag{20}$$

$$\delta z = \sqrt{\delta y^2 + \delta x^2} \tag{21}$$

If $y$, $\delta y$, $x$, and $\delta x$ in order are 30.7 cm, 0.3 cm, 1.54 cm, and 0.05 cm, then $z$ and $\delta z$ are 29.2 cm and $\sqrt{(0.3 \text{ cm})^2 + (0.05 \text{ cm})^2}$ or 0.3 cm.

3. The fractional uncertainty for the inverse of a quantity is the same as the fractional uncertainty for the quantity. Thus, if $\delta T/T$ is 0.003, then $\delta(1/T)/(1/T)$ is also 0.003. Note that $T$, if a temperature, in cases like this, must be measured from the absolute zero.

4. The fractional uncertainty for the product of quantities that are multiplied together is the square root of the sum of the squares of the fractional uncertainties for the quantities multiplied. Since division by a quantity is merely multiplication by its inverse, this rule includes division also. If

$$w = \frac{xy}{z} \tag{22}$$

then

$$\frac{\delta w}{w} = \sqrt{\left(\frac{\delta x}{x}\right)^2 + \left(\frac{\delta y}{y}\right)^2 + \left(\frac{\delta z}{z}\right)^2} \tag{23}$$

5. The fractional uncertainty for the $n$th power or the $m$th root of a quantity is $n$ times or $1/m$ times the fractional uncertainty for the quantity. Thus, where

$$y = x^4 \tag{24}$$

$$\frac{\delta y}{y} = \frac{4\delta x}{x} \tag{25}$$

These principles combined suffice, for the most part, in arriving at a reasonable value for the uncertainty of a computed result.

**18. A Report of an Experiment.** As far as a student is concerned, the principal values for the presentation of laboratory reports seem to be:

1. The clarity of understanding that comes with the expression of the ideas in a rational form in writing.

2. The training for the future that comes with the presentation of reports concerning work done.

What, in a general way, should be included in a report depends somewhat on the value of a comprehensive report on an experiment already worked in contrast with that of the performance of an additional experiment. The time factor is very important. As a minimum, a report where instruction sheets are issued should include:

1. Title of experiment.

2. Incidental information—date of performance, name of partner, date of completion of write-up, etc.

3. Condensed statement of purpose.

4. Condensed statement of method.

5. Data taken during performance of the experiment.

6. Sample computations, if necessary, showing uncertainties involved.

7. Plots and tabulations where desirable.

8. Results of the experiment and their probable uncertainties.

9. Discussion of the significance of the results obtained unless they are self-evident.

10. Signature of the one performing and writing up the experiment.

As one general consideration, it should be kept in mind that a report is well done only when the person for whom it is intended is able to get from it the complete message clearly and with reasonable ease.

## PROBLEMS

**1.** Express a pressure of 1 standard atmosphere in mm-Hg, $dy/cm^2$, and $lb/in.^2$ correct to 1 part in 10,000.

**2.** Express in mm-Hg and atmospheres the pressure corresponding to that due to a barometric mercury column whose height, measured with a brass scale, appears to be 736.15 mm, given that $T$ is 25 °C, that $g$ is 980.11 $cm/sec^2$, and that the scale is correct at 0 °C. Assume the instrument error to be zero.

**3.** Where $g$ is 980.00 $cm/sec^2$ and $T$ is 32 °C, what should be the uncorrected height of a mercury column measured with a brass scale correct at 0 °C, that will yield a pressure of 750.00 mm-Hg? Disregard the possible error due to a curved meniscus.

**4.** In a double-massing determination of mass, with $M$ and $m$ equal to 2.3250 gm and 2.0 mg and with 8.40 $gm/cm^3$, 1.25 $gm/cm^3$, and 0.00122 $gm/cm^3$ as the densities of the standard masses, the body being massed, and the atmosphere, the swing readings for conditions $A$, $B$, and $C$ (see Fig. 1) are:

| | $A$ | | $B$ | | $C$ |
|---|---|---|---|---|---|
| LEFT | RIGHT | LEFT | RIGHT | LEFT | RIGHT |
| −7.3 | +4.2 | −3.3 | +3.1 | −0.8 | +4.1 |
| −6.2 | +3.2 | −2.7 | +2.5 | −0.2 | +3.4 |
| −5.0 | | −2.2 | | +0.3 | |

What is the mass of the body being massed?

**5.** Osborne and Meyers of the National Bureau of Standards give the following data for the variation of the boiling point of water with pressure.

| $p$ in mm-Hg | $T$ in °C | $p$ in mm-Hg | $T$ in °C |
|---|---|---|---|
| 800 | 101.443 | 700 | 97.712 |
| 780 | 100.729 | 680 | 96.914 |
| 760 | 100.000 | 660 | 96.095 |
| 740 | 99.255 | 640 | 95.256 |
| 720 | 98.492 | | |

Graph these data in accord with suggestions given in the text.

**6.** Assuming a relation of the form

$$T = T_0 + a(p_0 - p) + b(p_0 - p)^2$$

where $T$ represents the boiling point at pressure $p$, and $T_0$ and $p_0$ the values for standard conditions, compute an equation of the type indicated, using the data of problem 5.

**7.** What scale correction should be applied to 60°C and 80°C readings obtained with an ordinary 0°C–105°C total immersion thermometer when, with an ambient temperature of 25°C, the thermometer is immersed only to the 5°C scale mark?

**8.** What scale error is made when a partial 20°C immersion thermometer calibrated for an ambient temperature of 20°C is used as a total immersion thermometer to measure a temperature of 100°C?

# CHAPTER II

## TEMPERATURE AND ITS MEASUREMENT

**1. Introduction.** Beginning with Planck's introduction of the quantum concept in 1900, the years that have followed have seen tremendous advances in physics. There has been much revamping of old concepts as well as development of some that are entirely new. Throughout this period, however, some basic concepts have maintained their original significances fairly well. Among these is the concept of temperature.

Prequantum thermometers, in principle, are much the same as those we use now. Of course, improvements in instruments and technique have been great, and certain entirely new methods of measurement, for example, the velocity-of-sound method, have been developed. Of the various thermometer scales in existence then and now, one, that based on entropy considerations, had been singled out as the most fundamental. It is still so considered.

When, however, one considers the temperatures that have been produced and measured, one sees a pronounced change from the 1900 status. In 1896, the English chemist Sir James Dewar (1842–1923) had liquefied hydrogen, and in 1899 he had obtained it in solid form at a temperature of about 16°K. Only in 1908 did the physicist H. Kamerlingh Onnes (1853–1926) liquefy helium at the University of Leyden in Holland at a temperature of about 4°K. Eighteen years later, in 1926, W. H. Keesom (1876– ) obtained solid helium in the same laboratory. An evident goal was the absolute zero. With the freezing of helium, the practical limit in this direction seemed near; but, with the introduction of demagnetization methods, it has become possible to go to within a few hundredths of a degree of the goal. Most interesting, in this extremely low-temperature field, are the previously unsuspected properties of matter which were discovered, among them the superconductivity (electrical) of many metals and the tendency of liquid helium II to flow automatically out over the edges of a flask in apparent contradiction to gravitational laws. Some of these characteristics of matter will be discussed later.

On the high-temperature side, the highest that had been produced by 1900 was that of the positive crater of the carbon arc, about

19

3800°K. Following this, in succeeding years, higher temperatures that have been measured are those of exploding wires by J. A. Anderson (1876– ) at the Mt. Wilson Observatory in 1920, yielding momentarily about 20,000°K, and those in the path of the arc discharge by C. G. Suits (1905– ) at the General Electric Laboratories in Schenectady in 1935, yielding sustained values of about 10,000°K. Before 1900 the surface layers of the sun were known to have a temperature of about 6000°K, and it seemed that the internal temperatures of stellar bodies were outside the realm of consideration. Today, however, it seems possible to conclude that temperatures of the order of 10,000,000°K and greater really exist within star interiors. Such temperatures are also produced during the explosion of atomic bombs.

There has been development, also, with regard to the temperature concept itself, as will appear in the following section.

**2. What is Temperature?** In attempting a definition of *temperature as a physically measurable quantity*, we meet with the difficulty that is experienced in attempting to define other basic terms such as length, time, and mass or force. Logically simpler terms are not available, and we content ourselves with descriptive but inadequate statements. One such is the statement that temperature is that property of bodies whose variations in the bodies about us are commonly associated with warmth and coldness. A more elegant statement, not intended as a definition, is that presented by Mark Zemansky * (1901– ) of the College of the City of New York: "The temperature of a system is a property that determines whether or not a system is in thermal equilibrium with other systems." What is implied by thermal equilibrium need not be considered here. As a definition, the statement fails in that it offers no suggestion as to evaluation procedure. To illustrate, consistent with either statement, it would be possible to evaluate temperatures in such a way that in place of $T$ to the first power in our ideal gas law

$$pv = RT \tag{1}$$

we might have $T^2$ or $T^{1/4}$. The statements may be true and helpful in describing the concept, but they are not definitions.

Frequently it has been said that the temperatures of bodies are just measures of the average translational kinetic energies of their molecules. On this basis, it would be possible to say, for instance, that 0°C is the same as $5.66 \times 10^{-14}$ erg/molecule. Actually we might safely follow the suggested plan were our attention confined to gases and the temperatures were not too close to the absolute zero. When,

* M. Zemansky, *Heat and Thermodynamics*, 2nd ed., Chapter I, New York, McGraw-Hill Book Co., 1943.

however, attention is given to liquids and solids, the range of failure, in accord with quantum considerations, reaches in several instances to room temperatures and higher. How great the failure may be depends on the substance. Under such conditions, it is possible on the bringing of two such bodies in contact to have the net transfer of heat from what, judged by the mean molecular translational energies, is the apparent low-temperature body to the high-temperature body. See in this connection a paper by one of the authors * where this and other possibilities are considered.

Despite our inability to formulate a precise definition of temperature, we find it possible to define temperature scales precisely and to make precise measurements of temperature.

**3. The Zeroth Law of Thermodynamics.** This law was formally listed as such only recently, many years after the formal stating of the first and second laws of thermodynamics, which we shall consider later. The zeroth law states: "Two systems in thermal equilibrium with a third are in thermal equilibrium with each other." For a statement of what is implied by the term thermal equilibrium reference may be made to Zemansky's discussion.

Without the detailed reasoning, we shall pass to a corollary of the zeroth law, namely: "An isolated, inextensible system tends with time toward an equilibrium condition with a constant temperature throughout." By an isolated system is meant one that does not receive energy from or transmit energy to other bodies or systems. Though often idealized for discussion purposes, such isolation is seldom completely realized.

Consider, as an example, the mixing of two liquids and the determination of the resultant temperature by means of a thermometer. The two liquids, their containers, and the thermometer together represent the system we would isolate. Depending on precautions taken, the leakage of heat into or out from the system may be moderate, small, or very small. Correspondingly, after a certain time, the temperature variations in the system will be moderate, small, or very small. Depending on the precision desired for the temperature itself, we either assume the corollary fulfilled satisfactorily and take the thermometer reading as the desired temperature, or we attempt to make corrections for leakages and possible stirring effects in order to obtain the temperature that would result were the corollary specifications completely fulfilled. These considerations enter wherever a temperature is measured. In the form of its corollary, the zeroth law is basic to the development of the subject of heat.

* A. G. Worthing, *Am. J. Phys.*, 8, 28, 1940.

**4. Definitions.** The *standard atmosphere* as a unit of pressure is the hydrostatic pressure due to a 760.000-mm layer of mercury of density 13.5951 gm/cm$^3$ at a place where gravity is 980.665 cm/sec$^2$. Ordinarily we specify that the mercury shall have a temperature of 0.000°C instead of specifying its density. Strictly, this procedure is illogical since it uses the quantity 0.000°C, which in turn requires the concept of the standard atmosphere for its definition.

It is common, when expressing a pressure in terms of the mm-Hg or other, similar unit, to do so with the understanding that, in accord with the basic relation $p = h\delta g$, the number of mm-Hg is the same as the number of mm of difference of level only when the conditions of density and of gravity are standard. We shall follow this custom. Conversely, in determining pressures by means of barometers or liquid manometers, one must correct observed differences in level for variations in gravity as well as for variations in temperature.

The probable magnitude of gravity corrections is too little appreciated. In the Heat Laboratory of the University of Pittsburgh, for instance, where $g$ is 980.11 cm/sec$^2$, the corrections on that account are negative and range from 0.40 to 0.42 mm-Hg.

The *ice point* or 0.000°C, as specified by the present International Temperature Scale adopted in 1927, is the "temperature of equilibrium between ice and air-saturated water at normal atmospheric pressure." The condition of air saturation, easy to realize and difficult to prevent, as shown by H. W. Foote (1875–1942), chemist, and G. Leopold of Yale University in 1926, yields a temperature for the ice point about 0.0023 C° lower than that experienced with air-free water and ice.

The *steam point* or 100.000°C is the equilibrium temperature of pure liquid water and its vapor when the vapor pressure is a standard atmosphere. This temperature is often referred to as the boiling point of water.

**5. Types of Temperature Scales.** There are four temperature scales in common use. The Fahrenheit is the oldest. It was planned by the German manufacturer of meteorological instruments, Gabriel Fahrenheit (1686–1736). The zero of the scale was arbitrary; 32 degrees was taken as the temperature of melting ice and 212 as that of boiling water under standard conditions. The second oldest scale, the Centigrade, also has an arbitrarily chosen zero. It is the joint product of the Swedish astronomer Andreas Celsius (1701–1744) and his colleague Märten Stromer. Initially, as planned by Celsius, the 0 reading referred to the boiling point of water and the 100 reading to the temperature of melting ice. The reversal to yield the scale that we now know as the Centigrade was made by Stromer after Celsius' death.

The other two temperature scales are the Kelvin and the Rankine, after the English physicist Lord Kelvin (1824–1907) and the English engineer W. J. M. Rankine (1820–1872). Both start from the absolute zero of temperature, below which no temperature is possible. Both depend on thermodynamic considerations and could be developed only after the establishment of certain thermodynamic principles (p. 265). The Kelvin scale, often called the absolute Centigrade scale, has the same unit of temperature difference. Similarly, the Rankine scale is often called the absolute Fahrenheit scale and has the same unit of temperature difference.

The relation of the four temperature scales to one another is shown in Table I. Among other things, note that the numeric part of a Kelvin temperature reading is always 273.16 greater than that for the corresponding Centigrade reading. Likewise, the numeric part of a Rankine temperature reading is always 459.69 greater than that for the corresponding Fahrenheit reading.

TABLE I

FOUR COMMON TYPES OF TEMPERATURE SCALES AND CERTAIN
CORRESPONDING TEMPERATURES

| Temperature | Centigrade | Kelvin (Absolute Centigrade) | Fahrenheit | Rankine (Absolute Fahrenheit) |
|---|---|---|---|---|
| Steam point | 100.000°C | 373.16°K | 212.000°F | 671.69°R |
| Ice point | 0.000 | 273.16 | 32.000 | 491.69 |
| Absolute zero | −273.16 | 0.00 | −459.69 | 0.00 |

It is convenient to observe the policy, when expressing *a temperature*, of following the numeric with one of the common symbols °C, °K, etc.; and, when expressing *a difference of temperature*, of using the less common symbols C°, K°, etc. Thus the difference between 50°C and 20°C is 30 C°. The reason for this policy is seen when one compares the following two equations, both of which follow from Table I:

$$212°F = 100°C \tag{2}$$

$$180 \ F° = 100 \ C° \tag{3}$$

With the degree signs of Eq. 3 preceding the F and the C, there would be obvious contradiction.

For the convenient transfer of temperatures from one type of scale to another, conversion factors are used. Two such, both equal to unity, as are all conversion factors, are obtained by dividing both sides of Eq. 3 by 100 C° and 180 F° in turn, thus

$$\frac{9 \text{ F}°}{5 \text{ C}°} = 1 = \frac{5 \text{ C}°}{9 \text{ F}°} \tag{4}$$

Illustrating the use of these factors in transfers, we write

$$95°F = 32°F + 63 \text{ F}° \left(\frac{5 \text{ C}°}{9 \text{ F}°}\right) = 0°C + 35 \text{ C}° = 35°C \tag{5}$$

$$445°C = 0°C + 445 \text{ C}° \left(\frac{9 \text{ F}°}{5 \text{ C}°}\right) = 32°F + 801 \text{ F}° = 833°F \tag{6}$$

Note that both the 95°F and the 445°C are equated to a temperature plus a change in temperature, and that to the latter only have the conversion factors of Eq. 4 been applied. As illustrations of transfers between the common and the absolute scales, we have,

$$85°C = 273°K + 85 \text{ K}° = 358°K \tag{7}$$

$$1000°R = 32°F + (1000 - 492)\text{F}° = 540°F \tag{8}$$

**6. Some Instrument Types and Their Common Temperature Ranges.** In theory, for each type of measurement of a property of a substance for which measurable changes occur with changes in temperature, there is a potential method of measuring temperatures. However, for one reason or another, only a few are used to any extent. Some are indicated in Table II, together with their common usable ranges.

TABLE II

SOME COMMON METHODS OF MEASURING TEMPERATURES AND THEIR
APPROXIMATE RANGES

| Method | Approximate Range | |
|---|---|---|
| Mercury-in-glass thermometer | −38°C | 550°C |
| Alcohol-in-glass thermometer | −80°C | 100°C |
| Toluol-in-glass thermometer | −95.1°C | 100°C |
| Constant-volume gas thermometer | 4°K | 1850°K |
| Vapor thermometer | 2°K | 200°C |
| Bimetallic thermometer | Limited by melting points of metals | |
| Thermocouple | 20°K | 1800°K |
| Resistance thermometer | 0.8°K | 1800°K or more |
| Total radiation pyrometer | 100°C | Up |
| Velocity of sound | No limits | |
| Thermodynamic | No limits | |
| Optical pyrometer | 700°C | Up |

**7. The Mercury-in-Glass Thermometer.** These thermometers are the most common of all thermometers. The instrument always has a bulb and a fine capillary (Fig. 1). Its principle of operation depends on the *differential* expansion between mercury and glass with change

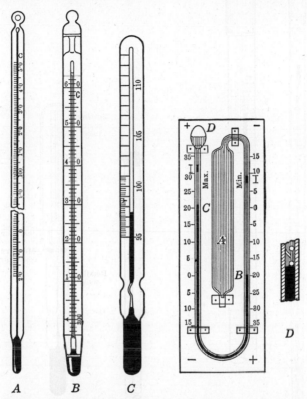

FIG. 1. Various types of mercury-in-glass thermometers. (*A*) An ordinary laboratory type (courtesy of the Brooklyn Thermometer Co.). (*B*) A nitrogen-filled limited-range type reading from 300°C to 360°C (courtesy of the Brooklyn Thermometer Co.). (*C*) A clinical type. (*D*) A maximum-minimum type (by permission, J. M. Cork, *Heat*, 2nd ed., New York, John Wiley and Sons, 1942).

in temperature. How the mercury is forced as a fine thread of liquid up a capillary tube is evident. The fractional expansion of mercury on being heated from 0°C to 100°C is about 0.018; that of the thermometer glass, about 0.003. Consider a thermometer with a 750-mm³ bulb and a capillary of 20-cm length between the 0°C and the 100°C lines; it is easy to compute that the volume of the 20-cm length of capillary is about 11.2 mm³ and that its diameter is about 0.27 mm. So fine is the thread that a magnifier is necessary to view it. This the

maker provides when he shapes the glass of the capillary tube. With
the eye properly located, the thread of mercury appears as a rather

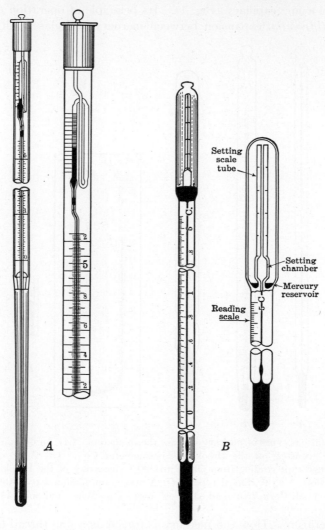

FIG. 2. Two types of difference thermometers with enlarged views of auxiliary
mercury reservoir and setting chamber. (*A*) A standard Beckmann thermometer
(courtesy of the Brooklyn Thermometer Co.). (*B*) A Philadelphia thermometer
(courtesy of the Precision Instrument Co., Chicago, Ill.).

wide band convenient for reading. Further details as to the construction and the use of mercury-in-glass thermometers are given in Chapter
I, under the heading "Determining Temperatures."

Of the many special types of mercury-in-glass thermometers, we need to consider but two. One is the maximum-reading instrument known as the *common fever thermometer*. Its capillary is contracted near the bulb. The opening is sufficiently large to permit mercury to be forced through, but also sufficiently small to make it impossible, when the mercury in the bulb contracts, for the cohesive force between the two segments of thread at the constriction to withdraw the thread from beyond. To return the thread to the bulb after a reading, the inertia of the mercury thread is used and the thermometer is swung rapidly in a curved path.

The second special type to be mentioned is the *difference thermometer* frequently referred to as the Beckmann thermometer (Fig. 2). It is intended for the precise measurement of small temperature differences. It has a large bulb, a relatively fine capillary, and only a moderate length. Its scale, of the order of 30 cm in length, covers a range of only 5 C° or 6 C° and is graduated to read directly to 0.01 C°. At the upper end of the scale, there is an auxiliary reservoir for storing mercury in excess of what may be used for any particular temperature range.

Using a difference thermometer designed to operate between 0°C and 100°C, consider the procedure one follows in order to read temperature differences in the region between 50°C and 55°C. Starting with an excessive supply of mercury in the bulb, one gives the bulb a preliminary heating in water or otherwise to about 56°C or 57°C. Some of the mercury is forced into the auxiliary reservoir where it is trapped. The method of trapping varies with the design. In some instruments it is done by holding the thermometer upright, cooling the bulb after the necessary preliminary heating, and tapping the stem at the proper time. It is then ready for use in the desired range. The actual temperature at which the mercury thread just reaches to the zero of the scale is called the "setting temperature." It is ordinarily obtained with the aid of a less sensitive thermometer. To return the mercury in the auxiliary chamber to the bulb, the bulb must first be heated until there is union of the mercury parts. Then, with the thermometer in an approximately normal position, the bulb is cooled once more. This time, if all goes well, the auxiliary chamber may be drained partially or completely.

Since, for the different setting temperatures of a Beckmann thermometer, there are different amounts of mercury in the bulb, the temperature-difference scale that is valid for one range will not serve without correction for another range. In effect a transfer of scale calibration from that for the customary standard setting temperature of 20°C to that for another temperature is necessary. The theory underlying such a transfer involves only normal expansivities of mercury and of glass. It is, however, rather tedious and involved, and we shall here merely indicate how to make such a transfer. In so doing, use is made of a standard table (Table III) of setting factors which is based on 0.000183 1/C° and 0.000025 1/C° as the volume expansivities of mercury and of thermometer glass.

Table III has been computed on the assumption of complete immersion of the thermometer for all temperature measurements. It shows that, if the scale divisions are correct for a setting temperature of 20°C., they are uniformly too large for all higher and too small for all lower setting temperatures. For example, for a setting temperature of 70°C, one needs to multiply the apparent temperature interval as read from the scale by the setting factor 1.0125 to obtain the true temperature interval. An apparent difference of 4.250 C°, in the 70°C to 75°C range, as read, corresponds to an actual difference of 4.303 C°. If, however, when used with a 70°C setting temperature, the stem is immersed in the liquid only to the zero of the scale and the temperature of the stem differs from that of the liquid, a separate additional stem correction should be made. For standard immersions to the zero of the scale, stem corrections are given by

$$\text{Stem correction} = K(\theta_2 - \theta_1)(S + \theta_2 + \theta_1 - T_0) \qquad (9)$$

where $S$ is the setting temperature, $T_0$ the stem temperature, $\theta_2$ and $\theta_1$ the upper and the lower scale readings, and $K$ the excess of the volume expansivity of mercury over that of the thermometer glass, 0.000158 1/C° for ordinary Beckmann thermometers.

TABLE III

SETTING FACTORS FOR BECKMANN THERMOMETERS FOR VARIOUS SETTING TEMPERATURES, AS USED BY THE NATIONAL BUREAU OF STANDARDS

| Setting Temperature | Setting Factor | Setting Temperature | Setting Factor |
|---|---|---|---|
| 0°C | 0.9931 | 55°C | 1.0094 |
| 5 | 0.9950 | 60 | 1.0105 |
| 10 | 0.9968 | 65 | 1.0115 |
| 15 | 0.9985 | 70 | 1.0125 |
| 20 | 1.0000 | 75 | 1.0134 |
| 25 | 1.0015 | 80 | 1.0143 |
| 30 | 1.0029 | 85 | 1.0152 |
| 35 | 1.0043 | 90 | 1.0161 |
| 40 | 1.0056 | 95 | 1.0169 |
| 45 | 1.0069 | 100 | 1.0177 |
| 50 | 1.0082 | | |

Let us illustrate the application of the foregoing to a particular thermometer with scale calibrated by the National Bureau of Standards, which with a setting temperature $S$ of 42°C and a stem temperature $T_0$ of 27°C yielded scale readings $\theta_2$ and $\theta_1$ of 4.327 C° and 1.365 C°. We have

| | |
|---|---|
| Scale error correction at $\theta_2$ less that at $\theta_1$ (from certificate issued for the particular thermometer by the National Bureau of Standards) | 0.007 C° |
| $(\theta_2 - \theta_1)_0$, as read | 2.962 C° |
| $(\theta_2 - \theta_1)_c$, as corrected for scale error | 2.969 C° |
| Setting factor, $f$ (see Table III) | 1.0061 |
| $f(\theta_2 - \theta_1)_c$ | 2.987 C° |
| $S + \theta_2 + \theta_1 - T_0$ | 21 C° |
| $K(\theta_2 - \theta_1)_c(S + \theta_2 + \theta_1 - T_0)$, stem correction | +0.010 C° |
| Corrected temperature interval | 2.997 C° |

The total correction in this example is +0.035 C°.

If, as is sometimes difficult to avoid, the immersion is only part way to the zero of the scale, account should be taken in high-precision work of any difference that may exist between the temperatures of this part and of the liquid whose temperature is being measured.

The upper limit of the standard Beckmann thermometer just described is about 100°C. By filling the space above the mercury with an inert gas at high pressure an extension of this limit to 300°C has been achieved in a recently developed Philadelphia differential thermometer (Fig. 2).

**8. Alcohol-in-Glass and Toluol-in-Glass Thermometers.** These thermometers operate on the same principle as the mercury-in-glass thermometer, but, because of the lower freezing points of the liquids, −114°C for alcohol and −92°C for toluol, they may be used to measure considerably lower temperatures. Further, because of the considerably greater expansivities of these liquids, the capillaries required by them are not as small as for corresponding mercury-in-glass thermometers. As a result the reading of their scales is somewhat easier, particularly if, as is usual, the liquids are colored. On the other hand, the expansivities of alcohol and toluol are less uniform than that of mercury; also the boiling points of these liquids are much lower than that of mercury and their upper limits for operation (appreciably higher than their normal boiling points) are much reduced.

## 9. Constant-Volume Gas Thermometers.

There are two types of gas thermometers, the constant-volume and the constant-pressure types. Except for determinations of the ice point on the absolute scales, the constant-volume thermometers are used to almost the complete exclusion of the constant-pressure ones, mainly because the latter are difficult to manipulate. Here the constant-volume type only will be discussed in some detail.

The constant-volume gas thermometer is used mainly for the accurate determination of certain boiling, melting, and transformation points. Convenient calibration points for other, more convenient temperature-measuring devices are thereby provided. Its use depends on the fact that, at sufficiently low pressures, many actual gases obey the relation

$$pv = RT \tag{10}$$

with rather high precision.

A temperature determination by means of a constant-volume gas thermometer requires three measurements of the gas pressure in the bulb. One is made with the bulb immersed in the material whose temperature is sought. The second and third are for calibration purposes and are made with the bulb first in melting ice and then in the vapor in equilibrium with boiling water under standard conditions. Let these three pressures be $p$, $p_0$, and $p_{100}$, and the corresponding temperatures $T$, $T_0$, and $T_{100}$. Then, assuming Eq. 10 to hold, we have

$$\frac{T - T_0}{T_{100} - T_0} = \frac{p - p_0}{p_{100} - p_0} \tag{11}$$

from which $T - T_0$, the Centigrade temperature, may be found. For convenience, depending on the range, reference points other than the ice and steam points may be used.  In the last analysis, however, one must refer all temperatures to these fundamental points to which values have been arbitrarily assigned.

So far as the gas is an ideal gas, Eq. 11 reduces to

$$\frac{T}{T_0} = \frac{p}{p_0} \tag{12}$$

of which $T$ and $T_0$ are to be reckoned from the absolute zero.  Granted that the value of the ice point $T_0$ is known sufficiently accurately, Eq. 12 may be used in place of Eq. 11.  Experimentally doing this eliminates troubles due to atmospheric pressure and other variations at the steam point.

The dependence of the thermometer indications on the kind of gas used is shown in Table IV.

TABLE IV

The Variations in Measured Temperatures Expected with Change of Gas in a Constant-Volume Gas Thermometer, at Two Temperatures, on the Assumption that Eq. 11 Applies in Each Instance.[1]

(At 0°C, the pressure in each instance is 1000 mm-Hg.)

| Gas | $T_1$ in °C | $T_2$ in °C |
|---|---|---|
| Hydrogen | 50.003 | 199.976 |
| Helium | 50.001 | 199.994 |
| Neon | 50.001 | 199.997 |
| Nitrogen | 50.010 | 199.978 |
| Oxygen | 50.016 | 199.929 |
| Argon | 50.014 | 199.971 |
| Air | 50.013 | 199.976 |

[1] Zemansky, *Heat and Thermodynamics*, p. 10, New York, McGraw-Hill Book Co., 1937.

With progressively reduced pressures, the temperature agreement using different gases becomes progressively better, suggesting that, as the pressure approaches zero, all gases become ideal and obey Eq. 10 exactly.

Fig. 3 shows a constant-volume gas thermometer like that used by the French physicist P. Chappuis (1855–  ) at the International Bureau of Weights and Measures near Paris in 1884 in a study of mercury-in-glass thermometers.  The bulb of the gas thermometer, $A$, was of platinum-iridium alloy, 110 cm long and 3.6 cm in diameter. It is shown in a horizontal position in a tank of stirred liquid.  The capillary leading from this bulb to and through the metal plug $P$ was

1 m long by 0.7 mm in diameter. Plug $P$, which completely closed tube $B$, carried a small pointed index on its lower side. Whenever adjustments were made previous to the taking of pressure readings, the mercury in column $B$ was raised into contact with it. Such adjustments were brought about by raising or lowering the mercury reservoir $C$. Pressures in excess of atmospheric were represented by the distance

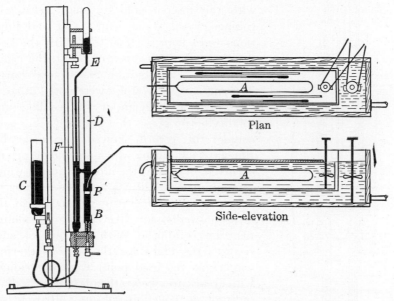

Fig. 3. A constant-volume gas thermometer used by Chappius at the International Bureau of Weights and Measures near Paris in a study of mercury-in-glass thermometers (by permission, E. Griffiths, *Methods of Measuring Temperature*, London, Charles Griffin and Co., 1925).

from the tip of the index to the mercury level in $D$. It was convenient, however, since total pressures were desired, to eliminate this reading by introducing barometer tube $E$ into mercury column $F$. Then, with the beginning of the barometer scale adjusted to be on a level with the index tip, the desired pressures, except for normal corrections, were measured directly. After the measurement of the needed pressures, temperatures were computed in accord with Eq. 11 or 12.

Outstanding work with the constant-volume gas thermometer was carried out by geophysicist A. L. Day (1869–   ) and physical chemist R. B. Sosman (1881–   ) at the Geophysical Laboratory in Washington. They determined the melting points of a number of pure metals. Among them, the determination for gold is particularly important.

In the process of determining the gold point, the normal melting point of gold, Day and Sosman first placed in an electrical furnace (Fig. 4) a small crucible containing pure gold in which were immersed the hot junctions of several platinum, platinum-10% rhodium thermocouples. The immersed ends were protected from contact with the molten gold by small refractory tubings closed at one end. The cold junctions were kept at 0.00°C. With the gold definitely above its melting point, the crucible and its contents were cooled very slowly. The emf's of the couples were noted at regular intervals throughout the cooling and solidifying processes that followed. For each couple, the record showed a considerable time interval during which no change of emf occurred. This was the interval during which the gold was solidifying and maintaining its constancy of temperature by means of the heat normally set free whenever molten material solidifies. With the aid of such records, the emf's for the various thermocouples at the gold point were determined with great care. Next, the platinum-rhodium bulb of a constant-volume, nitrogen gas thermometer of special design (Fig. 5), with the hot junctions of the thermocouples in close juxtaposition to various points on its surface, was enclosed in an air-tight furnace. The temperature of the furnace was then raised until the mean emf of the couples was that previously found for the solidifying gold. The bulb and its contents were then at the melting point of pure gold. The pressure exerted by the gas in the bulb was determined and the temperature was computed in the customary manner. Since the temperature was beyond any previous thermocouple-calibration range, the observed emf's were useless for direct temperature determinations. The thermocouples served only as transfer devices.

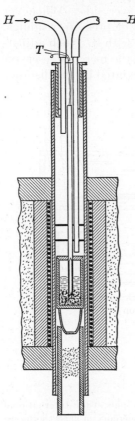

FIG. 4. The furnace used by Day and Sosman for determining the melting points of metals including that of gold. *T*—thermo-element wires; *H*—tubes used for maintaining a hydrogen or a nitrogen atmosphere within the furnace. (By permission, A. L. Day and R. B. Sosman, *High Temperature Gas Thermometry*, p. 83, Carnegie Institution of Washington, 1911.)

Corrections were made by Day and Sosman to take account of (1) the lower temperature of the gas in the capillary; (2) the change in the volume of the bulb with change in temperature; and (3) the departure

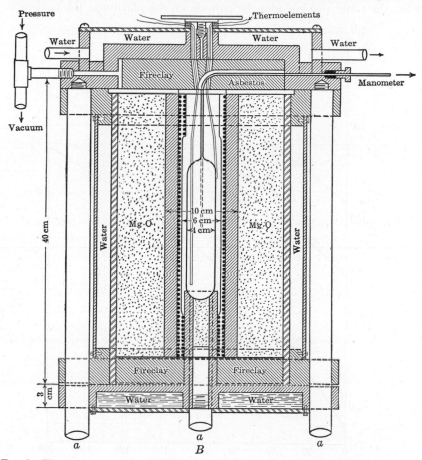

FIG. 5. The platinum-rhodium bulb of the gas thermometer used by Day and Sosman showing the location of two of the twelve thermojunctions. The bulb is shown in place in a closed furnace provided with means for keeping the surrounding pressure the same as that inside the bulb. (By permission, A. L. Day and R. B. Sosman, *High Temperature Gas Thermometry*, p. 54, Carnegie Institution of Washington, 1911.)

of the gas from the ideal gas law. Possible errors due to distortion of the bulb because of differences between the inside and outside pressures were eliminated by an arrangement for maintaining these two pressures at the same value. The value of the gold point arrived at by Day and Sosman, as a consequence of this attention to experimental details, finds universal acceptance.

In Table V are listed several normal melting or solidification points and several normal boiling points, most of which have been determined with constant-volume gas thermometers. Though determined otherwise, the table also includes the palladium, the platinum, the tungsten,

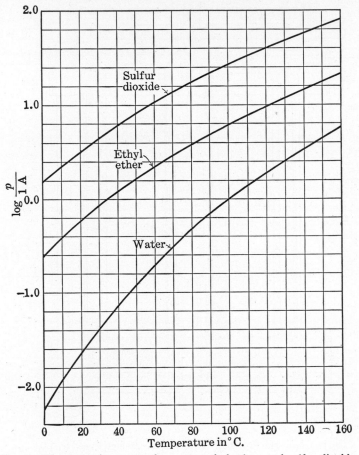

FIG. 6. Vapor-tension curves for water, ethyl ether, and sulfur dioxide.

the ice, and the steam points, the last two of which values are what they are by definition.

**10. Vapor-Pressure Thermometers.** In a closed space containing only a liquid and its vapor in equilibrium, molecules of the vapor are constantly leaving and returning to the free surface of the liquid at a common rate, which is determined by the characteristics of the liquid and the temperature of the enclosure. In the space above the liquid these molecules form a gas whose pressure, known as the vapor tension

## TABLE V

PARTIAL LIST OF NORMAL MELTING, FREEZING, AND SUBLIMING POINTS, MOST OF WHICH HAVE BEEN DETERMINED WITH THE AID OF CONSTANT-VOLUME GAS THERMOMETERS

| Substance | Phenomenon | Temperature in °C | Temperature in °K |
|---|---|---|---|
| Helium | λ transformation [1] | −270.97 | 2.19 |
| Helium | Boiling | −268.97 | 4.19 |
| Hydrogen | Boiling | −252.76 | 20.40 |
| Neon | Boiling | −245.99 | 27.1 |
| Nitrogen | Boiling | −193.9 | 77.3 |
| Oxygen | Boiling [2] | −182.97 | 90.19 |
| Carbon dioxide | Subliming | −78.5 | 194.7 |
| Mercury | Freezing | 38.87 | 234.3 |
| Water | Freezing [2] | 0.000 | 273.16 |
| Water | Boiling [2] | 100.000 | 373.16 |
| Naphthalene | Boiling | 217.96 | 491.12 |
| Tin | Freezing | 231.9 | 505.1 |
| Benzophenone | Boiling | 305.9 | 571.1 |
| Cadmium | Freezing [2] | 320.9 | 594.1 |
| Lead | Freezing | 327.35 | 600.51 |
| Zinc | Freezing [2] | 419.5 | 692.6 |
| Sulfur | Boiling [2] | 444.60 | 717.76 |
| Quartz | α β transition [3] | 573.3 | 846.5 |
| Antimony | Freezing [2] | 630.5 | 903.7 |
| Aluminum | Freezing | 660.15 | 933.31 |
| Potassium chloride | Freezing | 770.2 | 1043.4 |
| Copper-silver eutectic [4] | Freezing | 778.8 | 1052.0 |
| Silver | Freezing [2] | 960.5 | 1233.7 |
| Gold | Freezing [2] | 1063.0 | 1336.0 |
| Copper | Freezing | 1083 | 1356 |
| Palladium | Melting | 1555 | 1828 [5] |
| Platinum | Melting | 1773 | 2046 [5] |
| Tungsten | Melting | 3400 | 3670 [5] |

[1] A transition point between two different forms of liquid helium.

[2] Adopted as an international standard temperature at the Seventh International Conference on Weights and Measures. Of these the ice and steam points were fixed by definitions.

[3] This temperature is the starting temperature for a transition from one solid phase to another, which occurs as heat is added. The reverse transition occurs at a less definite, lower temperature.

[4] An alloy consisting of 28.1% copper by mass.

[5] A change of the second radiation constant, $c_2$ (see p. 444), from 14,320 $\mu K°$ to 14,385 $\mu K°$, as proposed in 1941 by R. T. Birge (1887–   ), physicist, of the University of California, automatically changes these values to 1825°K, 2041°K, and 3640°K.

of the liquid, is likewise characteristic of the liquid and the temperature of the enclosure.   As shown in Fig. 6 for water, ethyl ether, and sulfur dioxide, such vapor tensions increase with temperature and are single-

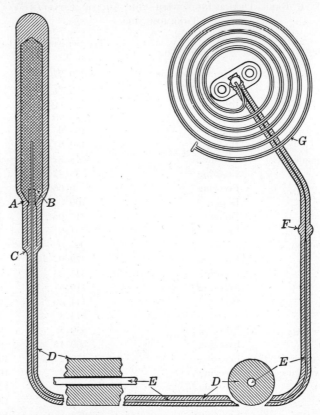

Fig. 7.   An industrial all-liquid thermometer, the power plant of an industrial "distant-recording" or "distant-indicating" mercury thermometer.   Vapor and gas thermometers differ from the above essentially in having all but a small portion of bulb $A$ filled with a liquid and its vapor or with a gas. In this particular system, a core $E$, having special properties, partially fills the capillary tubing stretching from $A$ to the gage $G$, which responds to pressure changes brought about by the temperature changes experienced by bulb $A$.   Its purpose is to nullify the effects of the changes in temperature of the capillary surroundings. Other types of "distant-recording" thermometers meet this difficulty differently.   (Courtesy of the Taylor Instrument Co.)

valued.   It follows that, for a given liquid, variations in such vapor tensions may be used to measure temperature.

Fig. 7, except as noted in its legend, shows the construction of such a thermometer.   Variations in the temperature of bulb $A$ cause changes in vapor pressure which are transmitted through the liquid $B$, commonly mercury, to gage $G$. This gage usually consists of a coiled hollow tube of elliptical cross section. Pressure variations cause it to coil or uncoil, thus producing motion of an attached pointer (not shown in the figure). The instrument may be made an indicating, a recording, or a controlling device.

In practice the boiling-point temperatures actually produced during calibrations differ from those listed in Table V because the pressures in general are not a standard atmosphere. Actual temperatures occurring may be computed from

$$T = T_0 + a(p_0 - p) + b(p_0 - p)^2 \qquad (13)$$

where $T_0$ is the temperature listed in Table VI, $p_0$ is 760 mm-Hg, and $a$ and $b$ are constants similar to those listed for three substances in Table VI.

### TABLE VI

CONSTANTS OF EQ. 13 FOR USE WITH CERTAIN SUBSTANCES IN OBTAINING CORRECTIONS TO APPLY TO OBSERVED BOILING POINTS BECAUSE OF VARIATIONS IN PRESSURE

For water, temperatures predicted are correct to within 0.01 C° for values of $p_0 - p$ not greater than ±50 mm-Hg.

| Substance | $T_0$ °C | $a$ C° mm-Hg | $b$ C° mm-Hg² |
|---|---|---|---|
| Water | 100.000 | −0.03686 | −0.0000202 |
| Naphthalene [1] | 217.96 | −0.0583 | −0.000031 |
| Sulfur | 444.60 | −0.0908 | −0.000048 |

[1] For naphthalene, international agreement assumes a type of equation different from Eq. 13. Correction constants assuming Eq. 13 are given here, however, because of their greater ease of application.

**11. Bimetallic Thermometers.** Two strips of material with different expansivities, e.g., brass and iron, cut to the same size and soldered or riveted together form the essential part of this type of thermometer. With a temperature rise, such a composite strip will bend toward the component that has the smaller expansivity. If one end is attached rigidly to a support, it is plain that each position of the free end corresponds to a separate definite temperature. In actual construction the motion of the free end is usually transmitted by a link-and-chain mechanism to a spring-controlled pointer. Calibration is necessary to coordinate the angular position of the pointer with the temperature of the composite strip.

A very convenient, indicating, bimetallic, immersion thermometer was devised about 1940. The composite strip is wound to form a compound coil of three coaxial helixes (Fig. 8). Enclosed in stainless steel and unaffected by exposures to temperatures considerably in excess of their normal ranges, these thermometers seem to be exceptionally rugged. Given a 2-in. immersion in liquids and a 4-in.

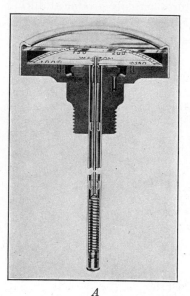
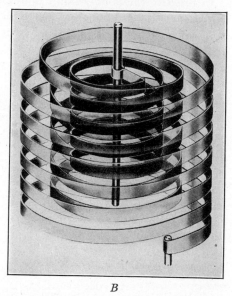

A                                B

FIG. 8. The Weston bimetallic thermometer. (*A*) A sectional view of the instrument. (*B*) A magnified view of the bimetallic coil. (Courtesy of the Weston Instrument Co.)

immersion in gases, an accuracy of $\frac{1}{2}\%$ of the range over the entire scale is guaranteed by the maker for the common laboratory type of thermometer.

A similar type of instrument, known as a thermoregulator, is frequently used in maintaining temperatures within certain limits. Contact points are placed on each side of the composite strip and so adjusted that no contact occurs between the strip and either of the points when the temperature falls within the two prescribed limits. When a contact occurs, an electrical circuit is closed and an external controlling device is operated.

**12. Thermoelectric Thermometers.** A thermocouple or "thermel," the term applied by many users, consists of two wires of different metals joined to each other at their ends. When a temperature difference between the junctions is produced, an emf known as a *thermo-*

*electric emf* is set up in the circuit. It may be measured directly with a potentiometer or a millivoltmeter. Such a thermocouple together with the apparatus for measuring the emf's produced, particularly when the indications of the measuring instruments give values for temperatures directly, is called a thermoelectric thermometer.

### TABLE VII

CORRESPONDING VALUES OF TEMPERATURE AND EMF FOR VARIOUS TYPES OF THERMOCOUPLES

Note the two sets of values for two different iron-Constantan couples. (W. F. Roeser, *J. Applied Phys.*, **11**, 388, 1940, and G. R. Fitterer, *Inst.*, **13**, 157, 1940.)

| Temperature °C | 90% Platinum-10% Rhodium to Platinum mv | 87% Platinum-13% Rhodium to Platinum mv | Chromel-P to Alumel mv | Iron to Constantan | | Copper to Constantan mv | Carbon to Silicon Carbide mv |
|---|---|---|---|---|---|---|---|
| | | | | A mv | B mv | | |
| −200 | | | −5.75 | −8.27 | | −5.539 | |
| −100 | | | −3.49 | −4.82 | | −3.349 | |
| 0 | 0.000 | 0.000 | 0.00 | 0.00 | 0.00 | 0.000 | |
| +100 | +0.643 | +0.646 | +4.10 | +5.40 | +5.28 | +4.276 | |
| 200 | 1.436 | 1.464 | 8.13 | 10.99 | 10.78 | 9.285 | |
| 300 | 2.315 | 2.394 | 12.21 | 16.56 | 16.30 | 14.859 | |
| 400 | 3.250 | 3.398 | 16.39 | 22.07 | 21.82 | 20.865 | |
| 500 | 4.219 | 4.454 | 20.64 | 27.50 | 27.39 | | |
| 600 | 5.222 | 5.561 | 24.90 | 33.27 | 33.16 | | |
| 700 | 6.260 | 6.720 | 29.14 | 39.30 | 39.19 | | 207 |
| 800 | 7.330 | 7.927 | 33.31 | 45.72 | 45.48 | | 237 |
| 900 | 8.434 | 9.177 | 37.36 | 52.29 | 51.82 | | 267 |
| 1000 | 9.569 | 10.470 | 41.31 | 58.22 | 58.16 | | 297 |
| 1100 | 10.736 | 11.811 | 45.14 | | 64.50 | | 327 |
| 1200 | 11.924 | 13.181 | 48.85 | | | | 357 |
| 1300 | 13.120 | 14.562 | 52.41 | | | | 387 |
| 1400 | 14.312 | 15.940 | 55.81 | | | | 417 |
| 1500 | 15.498 | 17.316 | | | | | 447 |
| 1600 | 16.674 | 18.679 | | | | | 477 |
| 1700 | 17.841 | 20.032 | | | | | 507 |
| 1800 | | | | | | | 537 |
| 1900 | | | | | | | 567 |
| 2000 | | | | | | | 597 |

Along with the platinum resistance thermometer, the thermocouple with one wire of pure platinum and the other of 90% platinum and 10% rhodium forms a convenient secondary standard of thermometry and is sufficiently accurate for most measurements. Such couples together with platinum to 87% platinum-13% rhodium couples are used chiefly in precise scientific work and are called *noble-metal couples* to distinguish them from the iron-Constantan, copper-Constantan, Chromel-Alumel, and similar *base-metal couples* that are more readily adaptable to less precise scientific and industrial uses. The choice of materials for a given thermocouple is influenced also by the temperature range.

## TABLE VIII

COMMON TYPES OF THERMOCOUPLES AND THE TEMPERATURE RANGES
IN WHICH THEY ARE USED

(In part as given by W. F. Roeser, National Bureau of Standards, *J. Applied Phys.*, **11**, 388, 1940.)

| Type | Usual Temperature Range °C | Usual Temperature Range °F | Maximum Temperature °C | Maximum Temperature °F |
|---|---|---|---|---|
| Platinum to platinum rhodium | 0 to 1450 | 0 to 2650 | 1700 | 3100 |
| Chromel-P to Alumel | −200 to 1200 | −300 to 2200 | 1350 | 2450 |
| Iron to Constantan | −200 to 750 | −300 to 1400 | 1000 | 1800 |
| Copper to Constantan | −200 to 350 | −300 to 650 | 600 | 1100 |
| Carbon to silicon carbide | 1000 to 1800 | 1800 to 3200 | 2600(?) | 4600(?) |

When, as is usual, the cold junction of a couple is kept at 0°C, the emf developed in a platinum to platinum-10% rhodium couple as a

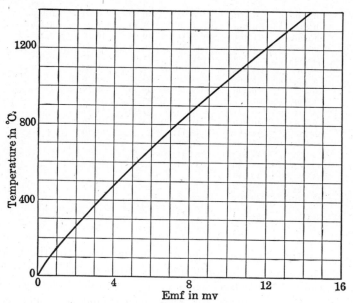

FIG. 9. The emf calibration of a platinum to 90% platinum-10% rhodium thermocouple with the reference junction at 0°C (by permission, Roeser, *The Symposium on Temperature—Its Measurement and Control in Science and Industry*, p. 194, New York, Reinhold Publishing Corp., 1941).

function of the difference in temperature between the junctions is that shown in Fig. 9. If some other temperature than 0°C is selected for the cold junction, the thermal emf's measured need a corresponding correction. If 100°C is used as such temperature, the emf's obtained with a platinum to 90% platinum-10% rhodium thermocouple, for instance, must be increased by 0.643 mv before the data of Fig. 9 may be used. Some potentiometers (Fig. 10) intended for thermocouple use are provided with devices that, when adjusted by hand or automatically to correspond to the temperature of the surroundings, automatically make this correction.

The procedure for calibrating consists of (1) measuring the emf's obtained with the cold junction at 0°C and the hot junction at several known fixed temperatures in the desired range; (2) evaluating, with the aid of these data, the constants of an empirical formula selected to represent them; and (3) computing a table or graphing a figure to show directly temperature differences corresponding to an observed thermal emf. A formula sometimes used in connection with such calibration is of the type

$$E = a\,\Delta T + b(\Delta T)^2 + c(\Delta T)^3 \quad (14)$$

of which $E$ is the thermal emf and $\Delta T$ is the difference in temperature between the hot and the cold junctions. This equation is usually applicable only over restricted ranges.

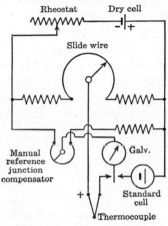

FIG. 10. The circuit of a commercial thermocouple potentiometer containing a hand-operated compensator for the reference-junction temperature. A device to shift the compensator effectively to its zero position when the standard cell switch is closed is not shown. (Courtesy of the Leeds and Northrup Co.)

Once a calibration chart or graph has been obtained for a particular couple, the procedure for determining a temperature with the aid of the chart is obvious. With the cold junction at a known temperature and the hot junction at the temperature to be measured, the thermal emf of the couple is measured, the cold-junction correction is applied, and the corresponding high temperature is read from the calibration chart or graph. Thermocouples used near the upper limits of their ranges, in contact with certain substances or in certain gases or vapors, are likely to have their calibrations altered. After such use, they should be recalibrated or replaced if reliable results are desired.

The term *thermoelectric power* is defined as the limit of the ratio of the change in thermoelectric emf to the change in temperature producing it, as both approach zero. It is frequently used and is usually specified in $\mu v/C°$. It may be found by differentiating Eq. 14 with respect to $\Delta T$.  Given its average value between two calibration points, one may determine intervening temperatures with an accuracy sufficient for many purposes by assuming a linear relationship between temperature difference and emf.  Thus, if an iron-Constantan couple has an average thermoelectric power of 7.9 $\mu$v/C° over the range 100°C to 200°C, and the emf is 643 $\mu$v when the hot junction is at 100°C and the cold junction is at 0°C, an emf of 992 $\mu$v would indicate for the hot junction a temperature of

$$100°C + 349\ \mu v \left(\frac{1\ C°}{7.9\ \mu v}\right) = 144°C \tag{15}$$

Note that the term thermoelectric power is a misnomer since emf/(temperature difference) is not a power unit.  In general, the thermoelectric powers of base-metal couples are considerably higher than those of the noble-metal couples.

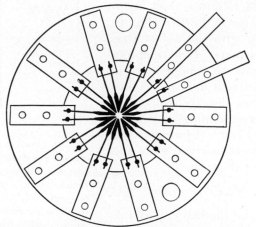

FIG. 11.  The thermopile of the Brown Instrument Co. radiation pyrometer.  The flattened spear-headed portions near the center are the hot junctions.  The metal straps at the outer ends of the thermocouple wires form the cold junctions.  The straps are fastened to an annular ring of mica.  (Courtesy of the Brown Instrument Co.)

The thermocouple is widely used in industry both as an indicating and as a recording instrument, the hot junction being encased in a cylindrical metallic or porcelain sheath and imbedded directly in a furnace roof or wall.  For other uses the hot junction can be welded directly onto a metallic surface whose temperature is to be measured. One distinct advantage of this instrument over other thermometers is the lack of appreciable time lag in its actual attainment of the temperature which it is to measure.  This is a consequence of the small amount of metal that must be put in thermal equilibrium with the body whose temperature is desired.  For the measurement of very low temperatures, a copper to Constantan couple has been used with fair success as low as −255°C.

*The thermopile* (Fig. **11**), used for the measurement of very small temperature differences, consists of a set of bars of two dissimilar metals so joined together that, if a temperature difference exists between the two sets of junctions, the thermal emf's developed are additive. This makes for great sensitivity. The thermopile has been used for comparing the intensities of various regions of spectra of radiant energy.

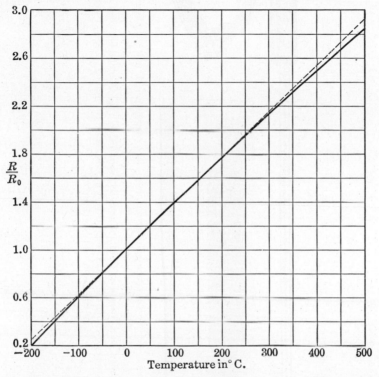

FIG. 12. The resistance of a very pure platinum resistance thermometer as a function of temperature.

**13. Resistance Thermometers.** The electrical resistance thermometer depends on the fact that the electrical resistances of most metals change with temperature. Once the resistance of a specimen of a substance is known at various temperatures, the specimen can be used as a thermometer. Platinum wire is often so used because of its chemical stability at ordinary and at high temperatures and because of the purity with which it can be obtained. For high precision in a specified range, it is almost universally used. The temperature variation of resistance for the wire of a particular platinum resistance thermometer is shown in Fig. 12.

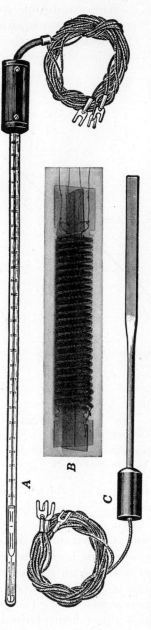

Fig. 13. Platinum resistance thermometers. (*A*) A glass-enclosed thermometer. The overall length not including leads is 46 cm; the diameter of the Pyrex glass tubing is 7 mm. (*B*) A magnified view of the sensitive portion of the thermometer shown in *A*. It is about 2 cm long. The platinum wire is twice coiled on a cross-mica form and is nearly strain free. (*C*) A metal-enclosed thermometer. The overall length is about 30 cm, and the housing covering the sensitive portion, which is about 10 cm long, is only 2 mm thick. (Courtesy of the Leeds and Northrup Co.)

A typical platinum resistance thermometer (see Fig. 13) consists of a coil of fine platinum wire loosely wound to prevent strain on a mica or unglazed porcelain frame and enclosed in a sheath of glass, porcelain, quartz, or some high-melting alloy to protect the platinum from the contaminating action of the fumes and flames. Though sometimes sealed in, the platinum wire is usually exposed to the air.

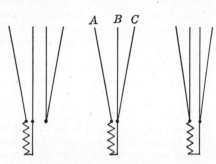

Three types of connections for such thermometers are common (Fig. 14). Two have four leads, the other three. The purpose in each type is the elimination of resistances other than that due to the coil only.

FIG. 14.   Three types of lead connections used in platinum resistance thermometers.

To obtain the coil resistance of a three-lead type, for example, one may measure successively, using a standard Wheatstone bridge or its equivalent, the resistances between points $(A, B)$ and $(B, C)$ in Fig. 14. If the leads to $A$ and to $C$ are electrically similar and have the same temperature distribution, the coil resistance is given by the difference of these two readings. However, using the Wheatstone bridge circuit of Fig. 15, one obtains the coil resistance of a three-lead thermometer with but a single measurement. From the figure it is clear that, if as before the leads to $A$ and to $C$ have the same resistance and if $R_1$ and $R_2$ are equal, the coil resistance $X$ will be equal to $R_3$ when the bridge is balanced. Similar arrangements are possible with the four-lead types.

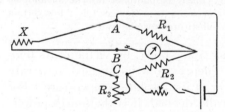

FIG. 15.  A Wheatstone bridge circuit for measuring the coil resistance of a three-lead resistance thermometer.  $A$, $B$, and $C$ indicate the lead terminals.  Resistances $R_1$ and $R_2$ are equal.  When the bridge is balanced, resistance $X$ equals resistance $R_3$.

In 1927, with the unanimous adoption of the International Temperature Scale, the platinum resistance thermometer was standardized as the instrument to be used in national standardizing laboratories for determining temperatures between $-190°C$ and $+660°C$.  The rules governing its use were:

"From the ice point to 660°C the temperature $t$ * is deduced from the resistance

* The $t$ here obviously has the significance of $T - T_0$, with $T_0$ equal to 0°C.

$R_t$ of a standard platinum resistance thermometer by means of the formula

$$R_t = R_0(1 + At + Bt^2)$$        (16)

The constants $R_0$, $A$, and $B$ of this formula are to be determined by calibration at the ice, steam, and sulfur points, respectively.

"The purity and physical condition of the platinum of which the thermometer is made should be such that the ratio $R_t/R_0$ shall not be less than 1.390 for $t = 100\,°C$ and 2.645 for $t = 444.6\,°C$.

"From $-190°$ to the ice point, the temperature $t$ is deduced from the resistance $R_t$ of a standard platinum resistance thermometer by means of the formula

$$R_t = R_0[1 + At + Bt^2 + C(t - 100)t^3]$$        (17)

The constants $R_0$, $A$, and $B$ are to be determined as specified above, and the additional constant $C$ is determined by calibration at the oxygen point.

"The standard thermometer for use below 0°C must, in addition, have a ratio $R_t/R_0$ less than 0.250 for $t = -183°$."

The approximate resistance-temperature relation expected for a resistance thermometer containing very pure platinum is shown in Fig. 12. Often, for metals, a linear dependence in accord with

$$R = R_0[1 + a(T - T_0)]$$        (18)

is assumed for the resistance-temperature relation. To what extent such assumption fails for platinum is shown by the dashed line of Fig. 12, for which an $a$ has been selected that yields a correct value for the ratio $R_{200°C}/R_{0°C}$.

For still lower temperatures, when platinum is used, an empirical calibration is needed for each specimen. Below about 10°K the platinum thermometer fails badly, largely because of the rapid assumption of superconductivity. Here instead, resistance thermometers of lead and particularly of phosphor bronze, an alloy of copper and tin, have been used with fair accuracy to as low as 1°K. For certain uses, nickel and palladium are sometimes substituted for platinum.

## 14. Total-Radiation Pyrometers.

Each body, by virtue of its temperature, is constantly radiating energy from its surface at a rate roughly proportional to some power of its absolute temperature. For the idealized blackbody as technically defined, it is the fourth power. For other bodies the power varies widely, depending on the material, its temperature, and the condition of its surface. However, the rate of emission of energy per unit of area, that is its radiancy, is never greater than the radiancy of a blackbody at the same temperature. For this reason the blackbody, which represents the upper limit of all bodies for the emission of radiant energy, is taken as a standard and other bodies are compared with it.

The fourth-power-temperature relationship, which strictly holds for blackbodies only, underlies total-radiation pyrometry. The instruments used in this field are called total-radiation pyrometers, and their indications, except for losses, are strictly proportional to the rate of reception of radiant energy from the body or bodies on which they are sighted less their rate of radiation back to that body or those bodies. A total-radiation pyrometer, designed by the French physicist Charles Féry, is shown in Fig. 16. It is a fairly close approximation to the theoretical ideal in that its responses are nearly non-selective with respect to wavelength.

Radiation from the body whose temperature is sought is reflected from the front surface of a gold-plated, concave mirror and focused on the junction of a thermo-couple $D$, placed just behind a hole in two inclined mirrors and connected through binding posts $BB$ to a millivoltmeter or a gal-vanometer. If the instrument is not in adjustment, an observer, sighting through the eyepiece, sees the upper and lower halves of the field of view displaced with respect to each other by the mirrors. By adjusting the focusing pinion, the radiation may be brought to a focus on

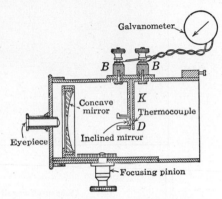

Fig. 16.  A Féry total-radiation pyrometer.

the junction at $D$. When this has been done, the two halves of the field of view will appear normally aligned.

The total-radiation pyrometers, common in industry (Fig. 17), differ from the Féry type principally in having quartz or glass covers over the openings through which the radiations enter, to prevent the en-trance of dust and destructive fumes.

A total-radiation pyrometer is calibrated by (1) sighting it at the interior of a uniformly heated, nearly enclosed, opaque-walled cavity held in succession at various arbitrarily selected temperatures, which are usually determined with the aid of calibrated thermocouples; (2) noting the indications of the thermocouple or thermopile forming a part of the pyrometer; and (3) constructing a graph or chart showing such indications as a function of the cavity temperature.

Temperatures as measured with a total-radiation pyrometer are correct only so far as the radiation from the body whose temperature is to be measured is similar to that from a calibration cavity. The temperature assigned to any particular radiancy is that of a blackbody possessing the radiancy in question. The temperature first obtained with a radiation pyrometer is ordinarily not the true temperature but instead what is called the "radiation temperature" of the body. However, if properly obtained, it is never higher than the true temperature of the body.   In order to obtain a true temperature from a radiation temperature, one must use the total emittance of the body.   (See

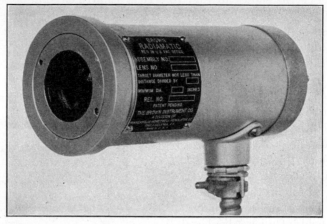

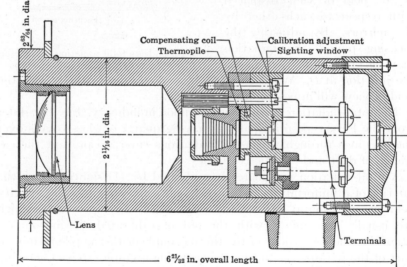

FIG. 17.   A total-radiation pyrometer (courtesy of the Brown Instrument Co.).

chapter on radiant energy.)   Frequently the interior of an industrial furnace approaches blackbody cavity conditions so closely that its radiation temperature differs but little from its true temperature.

Except for the rather small orifice through which radiation comes from the body being studied, the radiation-receiving element of a total-radiation pyrometer should be surrounded by material at some constant known temperature. With this condition fulfilled, the response of the radiation-receiving element, $d$, for a receiver of the Féry type, is given by

$$d = c(T_R{}^4 + \tilde{\rho}T_0{}^4 - T_0{}^4) \qquad (19)$$

where $T_0$ is the surrounding temperature, $T_R$ the radiation temperature of the body sighted on, $\tilde{\rho}$ the reflectance of that body for radiant energy from the surroundings, and $c$ a proportionality constant. For $T_0 = 300°K$ and $T_R = 400°K$, one sees by simple computation that the receiver reradiates to the hot body about 30% of what it receives. However, for $T_0 = 300°K$ and $T_R = 1200°K$, the percentage is less than ½% and the $T_0{}^4$ terms are nearly negligible. Further details regarding radiation pyrometry, particularly such as involve total emissivities and total emittances, will be given in the chapter on radiant energy.

**15. Optical Pyrometers.** With the aid of these devices, one ordinarily compares the brightness, a quantity frequently expressed in

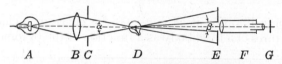

$$A \qquad B\ C \qquad D \qquad\qquad E \quad F \quad G$$

FIG. 18. The construction of a disappearing-filament optical pyrometer. The pyrometer proper extends from $B$ to $G$. $A$ is a source under observation, $B$ an objective lens, $C$ a diaphragm limiting the cone of entering rays, $D$ a pyrometer lamp with a filament whose brightness may be varied by means of an electric current, $E$ a diaphragm limiting the cone of rays entering the eyepiece $F$, $G$ a colored filter transmitting a rather narrow range of wavelengths of light. (A. G. Worthing and W. E. Forsythe, *Phys. Rev.*, **4**, 163, 1914.)

candles/cm$^2$, for a short range of wavelengths in the visible region, of the body whose temperature is desired with that of a calibrated source. In the disappearing-filament type of instrument (Figs. 18 to 20), this calibrated source is the filament of a small, low-voltage, incandescent lamp, located in the focal plane of a telescope, which in use is focused on the body whose temperature is to be measured. By varying the lamp current, the filament can be made to appear brighter or less bright than the image of the body or to disappear against it (Fig. 21). The filament current at disappearance is the indication used in determining a temperature. As will be described in the chapter on radiant energy, an interesting variation occurs when the temperature of a flame is sought.

An optical pyrometer may be calibrated (1) by comparison with a standard calibrated pyrometer; (2) by a method much like that given for the total radiation pyrometer; or (3) by the application of Wien's distribution law for blackbody radiation in the form presented in

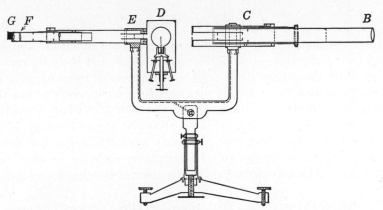

FIG. 19. A research type of disappearing-filament optical pyrometer. The lettering corresponds to that of Fig. 18. (W. E. Forsythe, *Astrophys. J.*, **43**, 295, 1916.)

Eq. 20. The calibration itself consists of a curve or a chart showing the temperatures of a blackbody as a function of the pyrometer current

FIG. 20. A commercial type of disappearing-filament optical pyrometer (courtesy of the Leeds and Northrup Co.).

at disappearance. Using the pyrometer whose calibration is that plotted in Fig. 22, assume that one obtains, on sighting the pyrometer on a particular luminous body, a pyrometer current of 350 ma at disappearance. It follows that the corresponding temperature for a blackbody having the same brightness is 1562°K. As for the radiation

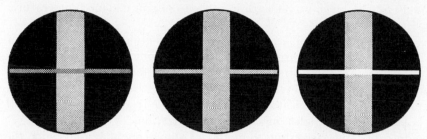

FIG. 21. Field of view of a disappearing-filament optical pyrometer for conditions where the brightness of the pyrometer filament is, from left to right, too low, just right, and too great.

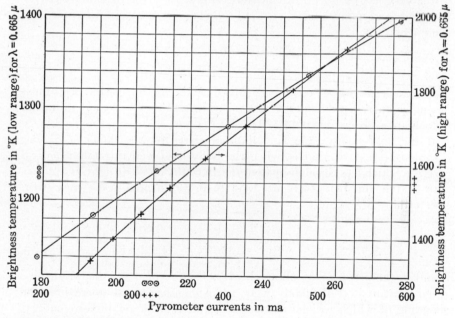

FIG. 22. A calibration curve for a disappearing-filament optical pyrometer at λ = 0.665 μ showing the temperature of a blackbody source, towards which the pyrometer is sighted, as a function of the pyrometer lamp current for disappearance of the pyrometer filament against the blackbody background, for temperatures below 1400°K and for temperatures above 1300°K.

pyrometer, the temperature read from the calibration graph is ordinarily less than the true temperature of the body. It is referred to as the "brightness temperature" for a certain wavelength, the average for the narrow band of wavelengths that is used.

Given the brightness temperature of a self-luminous body for a certain wavelength, one must have also the spectral emittance of that body for the given wavelength in order to obtain its true temperature. (See p. 447.)

The compact form, ruggedness of construction, and simplicity of operation of the disappearing-filament pyrometer have led to its extensive use in industry for measuring the temperatures of furnaces, molten metal, and metals in various stages of heat treatment. Also, the precision of which it is capable has made it an indispensable tool in many precise, high-temperature investigations.

In calibrating according to method 3 above, one may determine the brightness temperature of a body for a given wavelength by determining its relative spectral brightness (spectral because of limitation to a very narrow spectral band) in terms of that of a blackbody cavity at the gold point and then applying Wien's law (see Chapter 13), namely

$$\ln \frac{B_\lambda}{B_{0\lambda}} = - \frac{c_2}{\lambda}\left(\frac{1}{S_\lambda} - \frac{1}{S_0}\right) \tag{20}$$

where $B_\lambda$ is the spectral brightness of the body, $S_\lambda$ its brightness temperature, $\lambda$ the effective wavelength, and $c_2$ the second radiation constant whose value is $14{,}320\ \mu K^\circ$. $B_{0\lambda}$ and $S_0$ refer to the blackbody at the gold point, $1336^\circ K$. Suppose that, for $\lambda = 0.665\ \mu$, $B_\lambda/B_{0\lambda}$ should be just 10, that is, when the body is viewed through a neutral screen which lets through just one-tenth of the incident light, it appears to match the blackbody at $1336^\circ K$ in brightness. We may then determine $S_\lambda$. Thus,

$$\frac{1}{S_\lambda} = \frac{1}{S_0} - \frac{\lambda}{c_2} \ln \frac{B_\lambda}{B_{0\lambda}} = \frac{1}{1336^\circ K} - \frac{0.665\ \mu}{14{,}320\ \mu K^\circ} \ln 10 \tag{21}$$

and a temperature of about $1557^\circ K$ is obtained as the brightness temperature. If the body were tungsten, its true temperature, the finding of which will be discussed in the chapter on radiant energy, would be $1652^\circ K$. In that chapter also it will be shown how an optical pyrometer may be used to measure flame temperatures.

### 16. Speed-of-Sound Thermometry.
The speed with which a sound wave travels through an ideal gas is shown in elementary textbooks to be given by

$$S = \sqrt{\frac{\gamma p}{\delta}} \tag{22}$$

where $\gamma$ is the ratio of the specific heat of the gas at constant pressure to that at constant volume, $p$ the pressure exerted by it, and $\delta$ its density. This may be rewritten as

$$S = \sqrt{\gamma RT} \tag{23}$$

where $R$ is the universal gas constant (1.986 cal/mol K°) and $T$ is the absolute temperature of the gas. Thus, to the extent that a gas is ideal and that $\gamma$ is independent of the temperature, the absolute temperature of a gas may be found, by means of Eq. 23, from measurements of the speed of sound. C. G. Suits (1905–  ) of the General Electric Co. at Schenectady has used this method to measure the temperatures of the gases in various arc streams. For a 6-amp copper arc, for instance, a temperature of 4200°K ± 200 K° was found.

**17. Interferometer Thermometry.** Since the index of refraction of a gas varies with its density, and the density of a gas at constant pressure varies inversely as the temperature, one would expect distortions in the fringe patterns seen when the path of only one of the two interfering beams of an interferometer contains a gas in which appreciable temperature variations are present. Such is the case. Actually under certain conditions the distortions are so definite that they can be used to determine temperature variations. This will be discussed further in the chapter on convection.

**18. Seger Cones and Tempilstiks.** In the ceramic industry, it is common to place in the kiln a series of triangular clay cones of various compositions and certain

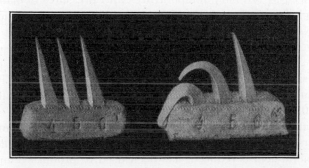

FIG. 23. A Seger cone series as introduced into and as taken from a potter's kiln. Cones 4, 5, and 6 mounted in plaques with tilts of 8° with the vertical and heated at a rate of 20 C° per hour deform and reach positions with tips touching their plaques at temperatures of about 1165°C, 1180°C, and 1190°C. (Courtesy of G. A. Bole of the Edward Orton, Jr., Ceramic Foundation, Columbus, Ohio.)

height-to-width ratios mounted in a clay plaque and tilted at an angle of about 8°. Under the combined influence of time and temperature, certain of these cones will deform and bend over (Fig. 23), passing through the critical position in which the tip of the cone lies in the plane of the base. A calibration cone gives an approximate indication of kiln temperature. Experience has shown that its behavior depends not only on time but also on the entire thermal history of the kiln after the introduction of the cone. Although pyrometric cones do not measure temperatures with any precision, and are not intended to do so, they are invaluable in indicating the so-called "heat-work" condition of the kiln and are used as controls in various ceramic processes.

Somewhat similar to Seger cones in operating principle are the crayons known as Tempilstiks. A mark on a piece of metal, porcelain, or glass made with such a crayon has the normal mat appearance produced by any crayon; but, as soon as the melting point of its characteristic constituent has been attained, the mark glistens in the manner of melted material. Different Tempilstiks have melting points at approximately 50 F° intervals ranging from 125°F to 700°F.

It should be obvious that any property of a body whatsoever, provided its magnitude depends only or very largely on temperature, can be used to measure temperature. The instruments described are based on properties most commonly employed, but the list is by no means conclusive. As examples, a device designed to measure the natural frequency of mechanical vibration of a certain type of crystal, the surface tension of a certain liquid, or the emf of a certain electric cell might, if necessary, be calibrated to serve as a thermometer.

**19. Low-Temperature Thermometry.** The experimental difficulties encountered in thermometry increase enormously as the temperature is lowered. The constant-volume helium thermometer may be used with ordinary precautions down to the normal boiling point of helium, 4.220°K. From this point down to about 1°K, the difficulty of measuring the reduced pressures and the dominance of certain effects which are unnoticed at ordinary temperatures and pressures demand a very special technique. For this region, following the usual practice, the constant-volume helium thermometer is used to calibrate several secondary thermometers of which the helium vapor-pressure thermometer, the copper-Constantan thermocouple, and the phosphor bronze resistance thermometer are the most common. With them, temperatures as low as 0.8°K can be measured with a probable accuracy of 0.01 K°.

The phenomenon of magnetic cooling, i.e., the drop in temperature that occurs in a paramagnetic solid in a strong magnetic field when that magnetic field is reduced, has been used to produce temperatures much below 1°K. Curie's* law,

$$T = \frac{C}{\chi} \tag{24}$$

where $T$ is the temperature of the substance, $C$ the Curie constant, and $\chi$ the paramagnetic susceptibility (the ratio of the magnetic moment per unit volume of the specimen to the magnetic field strength) of the specimen used, provides the means for approximating the temperatures attained. This law, generally applicable at room temperatures, is rather closely obeyed at very low temperatures (around 1°K) by a restricted number of paramagnetic salts. With

---

* Pierre Curie (1859–1906) announced the law in 1895. In 1903, one-half of the Nobel prize in physics was awarded to him and his wife, Marie Curie.

such a salt, the procedure for obtaining and measuring the very low temperature consists of (1) cooling some of the salt while in a very strong externally produced magnetic field to a temperature of the order of 1.2°K, with the aid of liquid helium; (2) evacuating the space surrounding the salt; (3) reducing the external magnetic field to nearly zero; (4) measuring the paramagnetic susceptibility $\chi$ of the salt in the reduced field; (5) computing a so-called Curie temperature using Eq. 24; and (6) applying, with the aid of thermodynamic considerations too advanced to consider here, a correction to the Curie temperature to obtain the true temperature attained. Using dilute chromic alum, workers at the University of Leyden have obtained a value of 0.0047°K on the Curie scale.

**20. Thermometry in Industry.** Thermometers designed for industrial use must generally be of rugged and fool-proof construction; they must be easy to read as well as direct reading. For particular purposes they must be able to endure lengthy exposure to corrosive liquids or vapors or to high temperatures without requiring frequent recalibration. Frequently they must be of the recording and/or controlling types. In partial compensation, neither great precision nor a high degree of adaptibility is usually required.

Base-metal thermocouples are used in the steel industry to maintain constant temperatures in the large annealing furnaces. Temperatures of batches of molten metal or of ingots during the forging, rolling, or heat-treating processes are observed with optical and radiation pyrometers. Thermocouples are also used to reverse automatically the direction of gas flow in regenerative open-hearth furnaces when the emergent hot gases have raised the chambers at one end of the furnace to a certain predetermined temperature. Also the successful production of pottery, glassware, and many ceramic products depends largely on the ability of the maker to produce and maintain certain definite temperature conditions. Recording vapor (Fig. 7), gas, or mercury thermometers are frequently placed in special wells in pipe lines, thus providing a continuous record of the temperature variation of the material in the pipe at that particular position.

Most chemical processes are critically dependent on temperature, and many special forms of thermometers have been devised to meet the varied demands. A particular example is a thermocouple with a hot junction in the form of a small, thin, circular disk designed for measuring the surface temperatures of molds in which various plastics are pressed. Another is a thermocouple with a hot junction enclosed in a long, slender needle for measuring temperatures in the interiors of blocks of raw rubber. It may easily be supposed that the ability of industry to keep pace with scientific achievement is due in great part to the development of adequate temperature-measuring and -controlling devices.

## PROBLEMS

**1.** The gold point as determined by Day and Sosman was found to be 1063.0°C. Express this in terms of the Kelvin, the Fahrenheit, and the Rankine scales.

**2.** The temperature of the surface layers of the sun is about 6000°K. What is this on the Fahrenheit scale?

**3.** What are the normal boiling points of helium, hydrogen, and oxygen on the Fahrenheit and the Rankine scales? (See Table V.)

**4.** If one ignores the setting factor and stem corrections when using a Beckmann thermometer with a scale that is correct for a setting temperature of 20°C, about what percentage errors on temperature differences might one expect for temperature differences of about 4 C° measured in the neighborhood of 50°C and 0°C? Assume that the thermometer is immersed to the zero of the scale only and that the stem temperature is 25°C.

**5.** A constant-volume gas thermometer calibration, when corrections are made for small sources of discrepancy, shows a pressure of 1000.00 mm-Hg at 0.000°C and 1366.08 mm-Hg at 100.000°C. What are the expected corrected pressures at the helium, the hydrogen, the sulfur, and the silver points?

**6.** In a determination of the sulfur point, using a constant-volume nitrogen thermometer, a corrected pressure of 750.0 mm-Hg at 0.000°C and an uncorrected pressure of 1944.0 mm-Hg at the sulfur point were obtained. About what should the correction to the uncorrected pressure be?

**7.** What is the expected boiling point for sulfur on a hot summer's day when the uncorrected barometer reading is 725.2 mm-Hg and the temperature is 36.0°C at a place where $g$ is 979.50 cm/sec$^2$? What is it when, at the same place in winter, the uncorrected reading is 751.5 mm-Hg and the temperature is −15°C?

**8.** A Bourdon pressure gage, having a scale calibrated to read absolute pressures up to 100 lb/in.$^2$, is to be used as part of an ethyl ether vapor thermometer. The connecting tube is filled with mercury, and the effective mercury level in the gage is 102 cm higher than the mercury level in the bulb containing the ether. To what temperatures of the bulb chamber will gage indications of 0 lb/in.$^2$, 20 lb/in.$^2$, 60 lb/in.$^2$, and 100 lb/in.$^2$ correspond?

**9.** Using data given in Table VII, compute, for a platinum to 90% platinum-10% rhodium couple with one junction at 0°C, the constants for an equation of the type

$$E = a + b(T - 700°C) + c(T - 700°C)^2$$

using values corresponding to 400°C, 700°C, and 1000°C. Compute, with its aid, values of $E$ for 0°C, 200°C, 600°C, 800°C, and 1200°C. Check the computed values. Note the variations from the values given in the table. If possible use the determinant method.

**10.** Plot a curve for a Chromel-P to Alumel thermocouple showing corrections that must be applied to the first-order approximation

$$T - 0°C = 24.5 \frac{C°}{mv} E$$

to obtain the standard values shown in Table VII.

**11.** Using data given in Fig. 12 compute the constants for an equation for a platinum resistance thermometer of the type

$$R = R_0[1 + a\,\Delta T + b(\Delta T)^2]$$

for the range 0° to 600°C.

**12.** In an experiment on heats of dilution involving two adjacent, nearly identical chambers with a separating wall containing 987 pairs of junctions of a Constantan to Chromel-P thermopile, with alternate junctions facing oppositely, as constructed in the Physical Chemistry Department of the University of Pittsburgh, it was found that an emf of 0.018 $\mu v$ could be detected with certainty. With a thermoelectric power of 70 $\mu v/C°$ for a single couple, what difference in temperature between the contents of the two chambers could be detected with certainty?

**13.** A galvanometer connected to a total-radiation pyrometer of the Féry type experiences a deflection of 5.0 divisions when the pyrometer, whose temperature is 27°C, is sighted properly on the interior of a blackbody cavity at 100°C. What are the deflections expected when the cavity is successively at 227°C, 527°C, and 1027°C? For a blackbody, $\not{\sigma}$ of Eq. 19 is, of course, zero.

**14.** What are the brightness temperatures at 0.665 $\mu$ for two bodies whose spectral brightnesses at that wavelength are respectively 50 times and ⅟₅₀ of that of a blackbody at the gold point?

**15.** At wavelength 0.665 $\mu$, what are the ratios of the spectral brightnesses of blackbodies at the palladium point and the platinum point to that of a blackbody at the gold point?

**16.** Given that the density of nitrogen under standard conditions is 0.00125 gm/cm³, compute the velocity of sound in an arc stream in nitrogen whose temperature is 6500°K, on the assumption of complete dissociation at that temperature.

**17.** With the aid of Fig. 22 and Table V determine, in terms of the spectral brightness at $\lambda = 0.665$ $\mu$ of a blackbody at the gold point, the corresponding spectral brightnesses of a blackbody at the silver point, the palladium point, and, by a slight extrapolation, the platinum point. Note that successive points on the graph correspond to temperatures with spectral brightnesses having a ratio of just 2. Check these values using Wien's equation.

# CHAPTER III

## THE EXPANSIVITIES OF SOLIDS AND LIQUIDS

**1. Introduction.** The fact that bodies generally expand with increase in temperature is well known; that this characteristic involves many problems in industry is also well known, but to what extent and how frequently is not generally appreciated. However, applications of such knowledge are perhaps more general than in any other subdivision in heat. In long bridge structures, of the suspension type particularly, it is necessary to provide for length expansions and contractions. At each end of the Golden Gate Bridge at San Francisco, overlapping aprons are provided in the roadway able to take care of a length expansion for the bridge roadway of 4 to 6 ft. Moreover, on account of the contractions and expansions of the supporting cables, the clearance at the center of the bridge, between it and the water below, is from 8 to 10 ft less in hot weather than in cold weather.

In the manufacture of incandescent lamps, a wire was developed to replace the costly platinum used in early lamps for carrying the heating current through the glass of the bulb to the incandescent filament. Platinum has almost the same expansion characteristics as had the lamp glass formerly used and could serve as lead-in wires without danger of breakage to the glass, or of developing a leak for air from the outside, both during manufacture and afterwards. To replace the platinum, a so-called "Dumet wire" (two-metal wire) was developed. It consisted of a solid core of a nickel-steel alloy covered with a sheath of copper. The tendency of the nickel-steel to expand with temperature is much less than that of glass, that of copper much greater. By the proper adjustment of the amounts of copper and nickel steel that are soldered together, the expansion characteristics of any glass can be duplicated reasonably closely. In addition, because of the tendency of copper to adhere to glass, this industrial application resulted in a lead-in wire not only less expensive but also more satisfactory than the original platinum. Kovar and Fernico are two alloys that have been developed for similar use with certain harder, more resistant glasses. Fig. 1 shows how closely the relative expansion of Kovar matches that of the glass to which it was designed to seal.

Other obvious industrial applications occur in connection with the pendulums of astronomical clocks, the balance wheels of watches, the enamel on kitchen utensils, the pistons and cylinders of automobile engines, rapid heating and rapid cooling of refractories and glassware, expansion joints in gas pipe lines, and dental cements and enamels.

How differently various materials expand on heating is shown in Fig. 2. In agreement with what is suggested, it is certainly the usual, if not the universal, characteristic of elements in solid or liquid form to expand on heating. For compounds and solutions, including solid solutions, the same characteristic is generally though not universally observed. We have the well-known exceptions of liquid water below 4°C and of certain nickel-steel alloys at ordinary temperatures.

Fig. 2A and B also shows certain other rather common characteristics: (1) The expansivities of liquids are generally much greater than those of solids. (2) With an increase in temperature, the expansion rate usually increases gradually. This will be obvious to the reader who, with his eye slightly above the plane of the paper, sights along the various curves. However, at temperatures which represent points of transition from the solid to

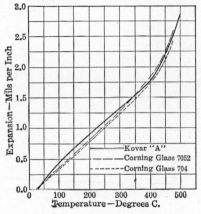

FIG. 1. The thermal expansion of Kovar "A," an iron, cobalt, nickel alloy, and of the two glasses into which it was designed to seal (courtesy of Stupakoff Ceramic and Manufacturing Co.).

liquid, from one solid form to another, or indeed from one liquid form to another, both the change and the rate of change may be abrupt.

**2. Linear Expansions.** It is common to write, as the expansion equation of a rod,*

$$l = l_0 \, (1 + \bar{\alpha} \, \Delta T) \tag{1}$$

where $l_0$ is the length at 0°C, 0°F, 300°K, or some other convenient temperature, $l$ the length at a temperature differing from this initial temperature by $\Delta T$ and $\bar{\alpha}$ the average linear expansivity for the specified temperature interval. Rearrangement gives

$$\bar{\alpha} = \frac{l - l_0}{l_0} \frac{1}{\Delta T} = \frac{1}{l_0} \frac{\Delta l}{\Delta T} \tag{2}$$

* The symbol $\Delta$ preceding the symbol for a quantity together with that symbol represents a change in the value of that quantity. In comparison with that quantity, it is ordinarily thought to be rather small. This limitation will not be observed strictly in this book. An illustration is $\Delta T$ of Eq. 2.

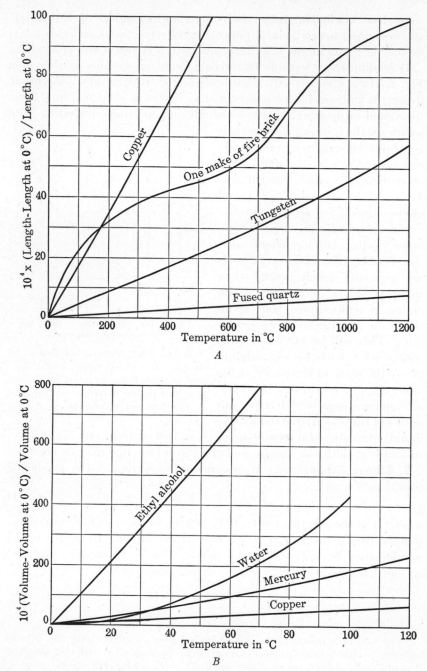

Fig. 2. *A*. Linear expansions of four solids. *B*. Volume expansions of three liquids together with the volume expansion of copper for comparison.

A linear expansivity for a solid describes a basic characteristic, namely its fractional change in length per unit change of temperature. Accordingly an average linear expansivity of $16.8 \times 10^{-6}$ $1/C°$ for copper between 0°C and 100°C indicates that, on the average, between 0°C and 100°C a copper rod expands 0.0000168 of its length at 0°C for an increase of 1 C° in temperature.

It is to be emphasized that, while $\bar{a}$ represents an average, there are various kinds of averages. As used here, it is the average which yields a correct value for the total change in length on going from the lower temperature limit to the higher.

For more exact purposes Eqs. 1 and 2 are not sufficient. The exact expressions needed are obtained by introducing terms with higher powers in the right-hand member of Eq. 1. Thus, with a slight rearrangement, we have

$$\frac{l - l_0}{l_0} = a_1(T - T_0) + a_2(T - T_0)^2 + a_3(T - T_0)^3 + \cdots \quad (3)$$

where $a_1$, $a_2$, etc., are constants characteristic of the material and the reference temperature, $T_0$, at which the length is $l_0$. As $T_0$ we commonly select 0°C, 0°F, 300°K, or 32°F, though any temperature whatever may be so used.

Eq. 3 may also be written

$$\frac{\Delta l}{l_0} = a_1 \Delta T + a_2(\Delta T)^2 + a_3(\Delta T)^3 \cdots \quad (4)$$

In the case of tungsten, three terms suffice for the range 300°K < $T$ < 3000°K. With 300°K as $T_0$, the values of $a_1$, $a_2$, and $a_3$ are $4.44 \times 10^{-6}$ $1/K°$, $0.045 \times 10^{-9}$ $1/K°^2$, and $0.220 \times 10^{-12}$ $1/K°^3$.

The $a_1$ term of Eq. 4 represents the major part of a fractional expansion, for small and even moderate values of $\Delta T$. The $a_2$, $a_3$, etc., terms are ordinarily but not always successively smaller and represent corrections to take account of the failure of the $a_1$ term to represent the whole. One may view the terms containing $a_1$, $a_2$, and $a_3$ as representing successively the first-, second-, and third-order corrections to the length at $T_0$, for the obtaining of the length at $T$. For tungsten heated from 300°K to 2300°K, these terms in order yield 0.00888, 0.00018, and 0.00176. For temperatures in the neighborhood of $T_0$, the $a_2$ and $a_3$ terms may be disregarded. For the limiting case, that is, for the region about $T_0$, we write *

$$\alpha_{T_0} = \left[\frac{1}{l}\frac{dl}{dT}\right]_{T_0} = a_1 \quad (5)$$

* For those unfamiliar with calculus, $dl/dT$ is defined as the limiting value of $\Delta l/\Delta T$, as $\Delta T$ approaches zero.

The constant $a_1$ is strictly the *linear expansivity at $T_0$*. Thus the linear expansivity of tungsten at 300°K is 4.44 × 10$^{-6}$ 1/K°. For a graph showing $\Delta l/l_0 = f(T)$, $a_1$ is the physical slope of the curve at $T_0$. Which of the foregoing equations is selected for use depends on the problem at hand and on the accuracy desired.

The procedure for evaluating $a_1$, $a_2$, and $a_3$ includes (1) selecting a $T_0$; (2) determining and plotting the relative expansions $\Delta l/l_0$ as a function of $(T - T_0)$; (3) drawing in the best smooth curve to represent the results; (4) reading from the curve relative expansions corresponding to three conveniently chosen round-numbered values of $(T - T_0)$; and (5) finally proceeding, as shown in Chapter I, to obtain an equation of the type of Eq. 3. The procedure for Eq. 1 is obvious.

**3. Surface and Volume Expansions.** Similar in all respects to the linear-expansion relations just discussed are additional relations involving surface and volume expansions, namely,

$$\frac{\Delta A}{A_0} = b_1(T - T_0) + b_2(T - T_0)^2 + b_3(T - T_0)^3 + \cdots \qquad (6)$$

$$b_1 = \left[\frac{1}{A}\frac{dA}{dT}\right]_{T_0} \qquad (7)$$

$$\frac{\Delta V}{V_0} = c_1(T - T_0) + c_2(T - T_0)^2 + c_3(T - T_0)^3 + \cdots \qquad (8)$$

$$c_1 = \left[\frac{1}{V}\frac{dV}{dT}\right]_{T_0} \qquad (9)$$

where $b_1$ and $c_1$ are the surface and volume expansivities at the temperature $T_0$. As for $a_1$, a normal unit for $b_1$ and $c_1$ is the 1/C° or 1/K°. Calculation procedures are exactly the same as those for the $a$'s.

Eqs. 8 and 9 apply to liquids as well as to solids. Obviously, however, Eqs. 1 to 7 as applied to liquids are without significance, except for some few very special instances. For this reason, when the expansivity of a liquid is spoken of, the volume or bulk expansivity is obviously meant. Corresponding to the $\bar{\alpha}$ of Eqs. 1 and 2, we have for the mean volume expansivity $\bar{\beta}$,

$$V = V_0(1 + \bar{\beta}\,\Delta T) \qquad (10)$$

$$\bar{\beta} = \frac{V - V_0}{V_0}\frac{1}{\Delta T} = \frac{\Delta V}{V_0}\frac{1}{\Delta T} \qquad (11)$$

Simple relations exist between the constants $a_1$, $b_1$, and $c_1$ of isotropic solids. Here we may write

$$A = k_1 l^2 \tag{12}$$

$$V = k_2 l^3 \tag{13}$$

where $l$ is an arbitrarily chosen linear dimension and $k_1$ and $k_2$ are two numerical constants. If the surface and volume of a sphere are considered, $l$ being taken as the radius, $k_1$ and $k_2$ have the values $4\pi$ and $4\pi/3$. To show the relations between the $a$'s and $b$'s, one conveniently rewrites Eqs. 3 and 6 as

$$l = l_0[1 + a_1(T - T_0) + a_2(T - T_0)^2 + a_3(T - T_0)^3 + \cdots] \tag{14}$$

$$A = A_0[1 + b_1(T - T_0) + b_2(T - T_0)^2 + b_3(T - T_0)^3 + \cdots] \tag{15}$$

From Eqs. 12 and 14 we then obtain

$$A = k_1 l_0^2[1 + 2a_1(T - T_0) - (a_1^2 + 2a_2)(T - T_0)^2 + \cdots] \tag{16}$$

If $(T - T_0)$ is not too large, we have as a close approximation

$$b_1 = 2a_1 \tag{17}$$

From similar considerations, there follows

$$c_1 = 3a_1 \tag{18}$$

For anisotropic substances, evidently

$$b_1 = a_1' + a_1'' \tag{19}$$

$$c_1 = a_1' + a_1'' + a_1''' \tag{20}$$

where $a_1'$, $a_1''$, and $a_1'''$ are the values of $a_1$ that correspond to three, appropriate, mutually perpendicular directions within the solid.

## METHODS OF MEASUREMENT FOR LIQUIDS

**4. Specific-Gravity Method.** This method depends on the fact that, with expansion and change of density of a liquid with change of temperature, the apparent loss of mass experienced by a sinker massed in it will change accordingly. Corrections, of course, must be made for any change of volume the sinker may experience.

Consider an Invar sinker of assumed negligible expansivity. Let its apparent losses of mass be $\Delta m_0$ and $\Delta m$ when massed while immersed in the liquid at the lower and the upper limiting temperatures $T_0$ and $T$ of the temperature range $\Delta T$, or $T - T_0$. With $\delta_0$ and $\delta$ representing the densities of the liquid at $T_0$ and $T$, we may write, since the variation of density with temperature is just the inverse of that for volume,

$$\frac{\delta_0}{\delta} = \frac{\Delta m_0}{\Delta m} = \frac{1 + \bar{\beta}_l \, \Delta T}{1} \tag{21}$$

and

$$\bar{\beta}_l = \frac{1}{\Delta T} \left( \frac{\Delta m_0}{\Delta m} - 1 \right) \tag{22}$$

In illustration, consider the determination of $\bar{\beta}_l$ for ethyl alcohol. Using an Invar sinker whose mass is just 20.000 gm, assume that, immersed in alcohol at 10.00°C and 20.00°C, it has "apparent" losses of mass of 1.9946 gm and 1.9734 gm respectively. We have at once, for the range 10°C to 20°C,

$$\bar{\beta}_l = \frac{1}{10.00 \text{ C}°} \left( \frac{1.9946 \text{ gm}}{1.9734 \text{ gm}} - 1 \right) = 1.074 \times 10^{-3} \text{ 1/C}° \tag{23}$$

The method is simple and has the accuracy of massing.

**5. The Envelope Method.** This method is sometimes called the "weight-thermometer" method. The liquid being investigated is contained in a vessel of glass or other material (Fig. 3), which is closed except for a capillary tube of small dimensions that may be firmly fused or sealed to the container or removable, as in a pycnometer bottle. For a liquid whose expansivity exceeds that of the container, one procedure is the following. $V_0$ is the volume of the container at the lower limiting temperature $T_0$ of the temperature interval $\Delta T$. The average container expansivity $\bar{\beta}_c$ for the interval will be assumed as known or readily obtainable. One first completely fills the container with the liquid at temperature $T_0$ and determines $m$, the mass of the liquid thus contained. Then, with suitable arrangements for catching the liquid squeezed out, the container and liquid are heated to the upper limiting temperature $T$ of the interval $\Delta T$ and $\Delta m$, the mass of the liquid squeezed out, is measured. Finally the average expansivity of the liquid $\bar{\beta}_l$ for the interval $\Delta T$ is determined in accord with the following. Equating the volume of the expanded liquid to the combined volume of the expanded container and the liquid which was squeezed out, we have

$$V_0(1 + \bar{\beta}_l \, \Delta T) = V_0(1 + \bar{\beta}_c \, \Delta T) + \frac{\Delta m}{m - \Delta m} V_0(1 + \bar{\beta}_c \, \Delta T) \tag{24}$$

Solution of this equation for $\bar{\beta}_l$ yields

$$\bar{\beta}_l = \bar{\beta}_c + \frac{1}{\Delta T} \frac{\Delta m}{m - \Delta m} (1 + \bar{\beta}_c \, \Delta T) \tag{25}$$

Replacing $\Delta m/(m - \Delta m)$ by the approximation $(\Delta m/m)(1 + \Delta m/m)$, we obtain

$$\bar{\beta}_l = \bar{\beta}_c + \frac{1}{\Delta T}\frac{\Delta m}{m}\left(1 + \frac{\Delta m}{m} + \bar{\beta}_c\,\Delta T\right) \qquad (26)$$

As a first rather rough approximation, the quantity in parentheses may be replaced by 1.

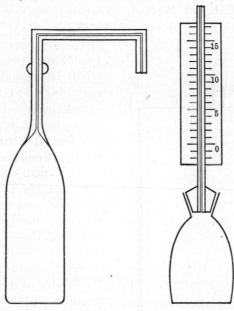

Fig. 3. Vessels for use in connection with the envelope method of measuring the volume expansivities of liquids. That at the right is known as a pycnometer.

To illustrate this method, consider the determination of $\bar{\beta}_l$ for mercury for the range 0°C to 100°C using a Pyrex glass container for which $\bar{\beta}_c$ is $9.6 \times 10^{-6}$ 1/C°. Assume that $V_0$ is just 100 cm³; then $m$ and $\Delta m$ will be found to be 1359.5 gm and 23.00 gm. It follows that

$$\bar{\beta}_l = [9.6 + 169(1 + 0.0169 + 0.0010)] \times 10^{-6} \text{ 1/C}°$$

$$= 182 \times 10^{-6} \text{ 1/C}° \quad (27)$$

An obvious modification of the procedure described employs a calibrated pycnometer. The method consists of (1) filling the pycnometer with the liquid at temperature $T_0$ up to some specific scale division of the capillary; (2) heating the whole to a temperature $T$; (3) noting on the calibration scale the expansion of the liquid in excess of that of the pycnometer $\Delta V$; and (4) solving for $\bar{\beta}_l$ of the liquid, using the following approximate relation, which is based on Eq. 26,

$$\bar{\beta}_l = \bar{\beta}_c + \frac{\Delta V}{V_0\,\Delta T} \tag{28}$$

of which $V_0$ and $\bar{\beta}_c$ have the meanings given above.

6. **Balanced-Columns Method.** This method, first applied by the French scientists P. L. Dulong (1785–1838) and A. T. Petit (1791–1820), was improved by another French scientist, H. V. Regnault (1810–1878), and applied to mercury about 1847. A convenient arrangement of apparatus is shown in Fig. 4. It was planned for a temperature interval extending from the temperature of a convenient circulating cold-water supply to that of steam. The limits of the interval may be conveniently changed by changing the circulating liquid. The cross sections of columns $M$ and $N$ should be so large that the heights of the liquids in those columns will not be affected by surface-tension forces.

If water is used as the circulating liquid, the two mercury columns $P$ and $Q$ are brought initially to the same temperature by means of the circulating water. The tops of the columns in $M$ and $N$ should then be at the same level. A cathetometer with auxiliary apparatus including metal prongs for making electrical contacts at the tops of the menisci is very satisfactory for the test. If the tops are not at the same level in any particular instance, a search should be made for an air bubble or some cause of stoppage of flow of mercury. With the tops of the columns at the same level, one passes steam or water at some other temperature through the space surrounding one column, say $Q$, while continuing to pass water at a desired low temperature

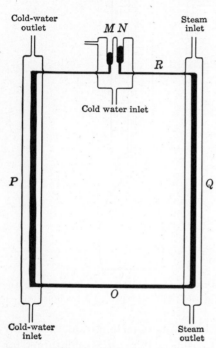

FIG. 4.   Diagram of Regnault apparatus for the convenient determination of expansivities of liquids.

around column $P$ and the two short columns $M$ and $N$. When a steady state has been attained, determinations are made of the distance $L$ between the centers of the small horizontal tubes $O$ and $R$, of the distance $h$ between the two surface levels in $M$ and $N$, and of the two temperatures $T_P$ and $T_Q$.

Whatever the temperatures $T_P$ and $T_Q$, it is evident that the hydrostatic pressures at $O$ via $MPO$ and via $NQO$ are equal. The pressure due to column $h$ in $N$, except for possible slight differences in the lengths of $P$ and $Q$, is necessarily equal to that due to column $P$ less that due to column $Q$. Representing by $\delta_Q$ the density of the liquid in $Q$, and by $\delta_P$ that in columns $P$, $M$, and $N$, we may write

$$Lg(\delta_P - \delta_Q) = hg\delta_P \qquad (29)$$

There follow

$$\frac{h}{L} = 1 - \frac{\delta_Q}{\delta_P} = 1 - \frac{v_P}{v_Q} = 1 - \frac{1}{1 + \bar{\beta}(T_Q - T_P)} \qquad (30)$$

and finally

$$\bar{\beta} = \frac{1}{T_Q - T_P}\frac{h}{L - h} = \frac{1}{\Delta T}\frac{h}{L - h} \qquad (31)$$

It is evident that the precision of a $\bar{\beta}$ obtained by the balanced-arm method will depend on the accuracy with which $h$ is measured and that this will increase proportionally with $L$. However, a long column for $L$ will introduce complications because of changes of density due to high pressures. To obviate this difficulty while retaining the advantage of a large $L$, physicists H. L. Callendar (1863–1930) and Moss in London and P. E. Chappuis (1855– ) in France used a series connection (Fig. 5) of hot and cold columns. All the hot columns were side by side in a well-stirred, hot-oil, constant-temperature bath. Similarly the cold columns were kept side by side in another bath. Callendar and Moss used six pairs of hot and cold columns each 2 m long. Chappuis used seven pairs each 1 m long. Their results are regarded as highly accurate. See Table I for specific volumes and densities of mercury and two other liquids.

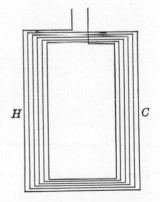

FIG. 5. Arrangement of hot ($H$) and cold ($C$) tubes used by Callendar and Moss and by Chappuis in their applications of the balanced columns method to the determination of $\bar{\beta}$ for a liquid.

## TABLE I

### THE SPECIFIC VOLUMES AND DENSITIES OF THREE LIQUIDS AT VARIOUS TEMPERATURES

(*International Critical Tables*, **2,** 458, as to mercury and water; *Nat. Bur. Standards Bull.*, **9:** 327, 1913, as to ethyl alcohol.)

| $T$ °C | Mercury | | Water | | Ethyl Alcohol | |
|---|---|---|---|---|---|---|
| | $v$ cm³/gm | $\delta$ gm/cm³ | $v$ cm³/gm | $\delta$ gm/cm³ | $v$ cm³/gm | $\delta$ gm/cm³ |
| −30 | 0.073154 | 13.6698 | | | | |
| −20 | 73287 | .6450 | | | | |
| −10 | 73420 | .6202 | 1.0021 | 0.9979 | | |
| 0 | 73554 | .5955 | .00021 | .99979 | 1.2403 | 0.80628 |
| 10 | 73687 | .5709 | .00035 | .99965 | .2534 | .79784 |
| 20 | 73821 | .5463 | .00184 | .99816 | .2669 | .78934 |
| 30 | 73955 | .5218 | .00442 | .99560 | .2808 | .78075 |
| 40 | 74089 | .4973 | .00789 | .99217 | .2953 | .77203 |
| 50 | 74223 | .4729 | .0121 | .9880 | .3098 | .7367 |
| 60 | 74357 | .4486 | .0171 | .9832 | .325 | .7547 |
| 70 | 74492 | .4243 | .0228 | .9777 | .341 | .7457 |
| 80 | 74626 | .4001 | .0290 | .9719 | | |
| 90 | 74761 | .3759 | .0359 | .9653 | | |
| 100 | 74896 | .3518 | .0435 | .9583 | | |
| 150 | 75575 | .2319 | .0906 | .9169 | | |
| 200 | 76262 | .1127 | .1565 | .8646 | | |
| 250 | 76960 | 12.9938 | .2512 | .7992 | | |
| 300 | 77672 | .8747 | .4036 | .7124 | | |
| 350 | 78403 | .7546 | .741 | .574 | | |
| 357.1 | 78509 | .7374 | | | | |
| 374.15 | | | 3.1 | .32 | | |

## METHODS OF MEASUREMENT FOR SOLIDS

**7. Selection of a Method.** The method to be used in obtaining the linear expansivity of a solid depends on the form in which the body or material is obtainable, the temperature range, the apparatus available, the precision required, the desires of the experimenter, and perhaps other factors. If the material is in the form of fine powder, the X-ray method would seem to be the only one possible. If it is in the form of small balls or rods of dimensions not larger than a few millimeters or a centimeter in diameter or length, the interference method is highly acceptable. For specimens in the form of rods of appreciable length, the comparator, the optical-lever, the quartz-furnace, and the specific-gravity methods are available. For specimens in wire form, the vertical-comparator, the optical-lever, the pycnometer, and the interference methods may be used. For irregularly shaped bodies too short for the application of certain rod methods, the specific-gravity method is particularly applicable if a suitable liquid is available. What form the specimen shall take is often, but not always, a matter of choice.

**8. The Comparator Method.** This method is applicable to specimens in rod and in wire form. If in rod form, the specimen, with scratches near its ends perpendicular to its length, may be conveniently mounted horizontally on two supports in an enclosure or bath

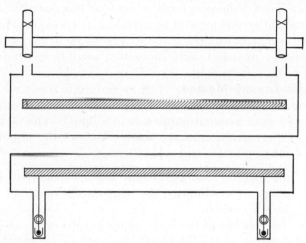

FIG. 6. Diagram of apparatus for a comparator method of measuring linear expansivities, showing (above) two microscopes mounted on an Invar bar and pointed toward fine scratches near the end of the rod under study in a furnace, and (below) an improved arrangement in which two fine weighted wires attached near the ends of the bar under study extend downwards from the furnace into closed side arms with windows for microscope observations.

whose temperature may be altered as desired (Fig. 6). Traveling microscopes mounted on Invar or other material of extremely low expansivity serve in the recording of the positions of the scratches at the different observation temperatures. Later the furnace or bath is shifted aside laterally and replaced by a standard scale at the temperature desired. How the length, the changes in length with changes of temperature, and the linear expansivity are then obtained is evident (Eq. 2).

A modification used at the National Bureau of Standards in Washington employs two fine straight wires fastened near the ends of the specimen. These wires (Fig. 6), extending downward outside the hot portion of the furnace into side arms, support bodies immersed in oil which serve to keep the wires straight and to damp out all vibrations that might otherwise be present.   Observations are made of the separation of the fine wires through windows in the side arms.   Compared with the scratch method just described, there are the evident advantages (1) of having the furnace closed, (2) of having the measuring apparatus as a whole farther away from the hot furnace, and (3) of being able to bring the measuring microscopes close to the wires whose positions are being measured.   Procedures otherwise are generally the same.

If the specimen is in wire form, a more or less continuous support with some slight stretching will be needed if the wire is kept horizontal.   Sometimes, particularly if the wire is to be heated to incandescence, it may be mounted vertically with a small body attached at its lower end to keep it straight.

**9. Specific-Gravity Method.**   The procedure is the same as in the specific-gravity method for liquids.   It involves the measurement of an apparent loss of mass on immersion in a liquid.   One is interested, however, in the expansion of the solid.   That of the liquid must be known and taken into account.   Let

$m$ = the mass of the body whose linear expansivity is desired.

$T_0$, $T$ = temperatures limiting the temperature range $\Delta T$ for which an $\bar{\alpha}$ is desired.

$V_0$, $V$ = the volumes of the body at temperatures $T_0$ and $T$.

$\delta_0$, $\delta$ = densities of the liquid at temperatures $T_0$ and $T$.

$s_0$, $s$ = the specific gravities of the body at $T_0$ and $T$ in terms of the liquid at $T_0$ and $T$.

By the well-known process of massing the body in air, correcting for its buoyancy when necessary, and then in the liquid, whatever the temperature, the specific gravity of the body with respect to the liquid is obtained.   Once the values $s_0$ and $s$ are thus determined, we make use of the defining relation for specific gravity, obtaining

$$\frac{m}{V_0} = s_0 \delta_0 \tag{32}$$

and

$$\frac{m}{V} = s\delta \tag{33}$$

There follow

$$\frac{V}{V_0} = 1 + \bar{\beta}\,\Delta T = \frac{s_0 \delta_0}{s\delta} \tag{34}$$

and

$$\bar{\alpha} = \frac{\bar{\beta}}{3} = \frac{1}{3\,\Delta T}\left(\frac{s_0 \delta_0}{s\delta} - 1\right) \tag{35}$$

Let us apply the foregoing to a determination of $\bar{\alpha}$ for copper for the range 10°C to 50°C, using water as the liquid. Given that 200.000 gm is the mass of a copper block, and that 0.99965 gm/cm$^3$ and 0.98807 gm/cm$^3$ are the densities of water at 10°C and at 50°C, one obtains 22.4052 gm and 22.1883 gm as the apparent losses of mass or, what is the same, the masses of the water displaced for the same two temperatures. The corresponding value for $s_0$ and $s$ are 8.9265 and 9.0138. Insertion of these values in Eq. 35 leads to $16.63 \times 10^{-6}$ 1/C° as the desired $\bar{\alpha}$.

**10. Dulong and Petit's Pycnometer Method.** This method is a variation of the envelope method for liquids. At a desired initial low temperature, a pycnometer of known volume and volume expansivity, containing a portion of the solid either in one or many pieces, is filled to some reference mark with a measured volume of a liquid of known volume expansivity. The whole is then heated to another temperature, and the volume of the liquid forced beyond the reference mark is measured. The initial volume of the container less that of the enclosed liquid is the volume occupied by the solid at the initial temperature. Similarly the final volume of the container plus that of the liquid forced beyond the reference mark less the expanded volume of the liquid initially in the pycnometer is the final volume of the solid. With $s$, $c$, and $l$ as subscripts referring to the solid, the container, and the liquid, let

$V_{0s}$, $V_{0c}$, $V_{0l}$ = initial volumes.
$V_s$, $V_c$, $V_l$ = final volumes.
$\Delta V_l$ = the increase in the volume of the liquid.
$m$ = the mass of the liquid.
$\Delta m$ = the mass of liquid forced beyond the initial reference mark.

There follow

$$\dot{V}_{0s} = V_{0c} - V_{0l} \tag{36}$$

$$V_s = V_c - (V_l - \Delta V_l) \tag{37}$$

$$V_s - V_{0s} = (V_c - V_{0c}) - (V_l - V_{0l}) + \Delta V_l \tag{38}$$

$$= (V_{0c}\bar{\beta}_c - V_{0l}\bar{\beta}_l) \Delta T + \frac{\Delta m}{m} V_{0l}(1 + \bar{\beta}_l \Delta T)$$

and, finally,

$$\bar{\beta}_s = \frac{V_s - V_{0s}}{V_{0s} \Delta T} = \frac{V_{0c}\bar{\beta}_c - V_{0l}\bar{\beta}_l}{V_{0s}} + \frac{\Delta m}{m} \frac{V_{0l}}{V_{0s}} \frac{(1 + \bar{\beta}_l \Delta T)}{\Delta T} \tag{39}$$

**11. Henning's Quartz-Furnace Method.** Described by the German physicist Fritz Henning (1877–   ) in 1907, this method is intended for material in rod form which is to be carried to high temperatures. As shown in Fig. 7, the rod is mounted between fused-quartz supports inside an electrically heated fused-quartz tube. The quartz rod resting on the specimen being studied carries an etched scale at its upper end, as also does the top of the inclosing tube. The tube and contents are immersed in a constant-temperature bath to half the height of the rod with the etched scale. It is assumed that this rod and the portion of the tube just outside it expand equally with increase of temperature. Consequently, by microscopic observations of the two etched scales, it is possible to determine the changes in length of a uniformly heated specimen compared with those for an initially equal length of the fused quartz surrounding it. Temperatures are determined by thermocouples (not shown) mounted with hot junctions inside the quartz tube. The length changes for the quartz are necessarily derived from a separate study by some other method. Once the change in length of a specimen of known length at a given temperature is known, a value for $\bar{a}$ is obtainable at once.

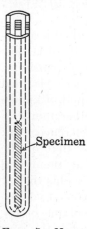

FIG. 7. Henning's quartz furnace for measuring linear expansivities at high temperatures.

Reasons for the quartz tube are: (1) up to certain limits, it can be maintained for a considerable time at a high temperature without distortion; (2) at these high temperatures it does not react with the atmosphere or give off vapors which will react with the specimens likely to be used; (3) its linear expansivity is relatively very small so that errors due to incorrect accounting for the lack of uniformity of temperature along the quartz tube and the quartz support rods will result in negligible or at least much reduced errors in the linear expansivity sought.

**12. The Optical-Lever Method for Rods and Wires.** This method uses the well-known magnifying properties of the optical lever. Fig. 8 shows an arrangement suitable for use with a wire which may be heated electrically and whose temperature is a known function of its resistance. The wire whose expansion is measured is that between the rigid support $A$ and block $B$. The block is free to move vertically. For precise work, potentiometer readings of current and potential difference serve for the necessary resistance measurements. Expansions $\Delta l$ are given by

$$\frac{\Delta l}{a} = (\tan \varphi - \tan \varphi_0) \tag{40}$$

where $a$ is the perpendicular distance from the support point under the mirror $M$ of the lever $L$ to the line joining the two points resting on block $B$, and $\varphi$ the angle shown in the figure.

To take account of the fact that the wire is cooled in the neighborhoods of $A$ and $B$ by thermal conduction, one must make measurements on two lengths of wire that are quite different. The difference between the two $\Delta l$'s for the same heating current yields the true expansion of a uniformly heated length of wire, that given by the difference between the two lengths. That this is so will appear from a consideration of Fig. 9. At $A$ the variation in temperature along a uniform electrically heated wire is shown. One sees two end regions of gradually changing reduced temperatures and a rather long central region of uniform high temperature. At $B$, a similar variation is shown for another wire for which the sole difference is one of length. Obviously the end-cooled regions for this shorter wire duplicate the temperature-expansion effects occurring in the corresponding equal lengths of the longer wire. Obviously, also, if one puts into Eq. 2 the difference in the overall expansions for $\Delta l$, the $\bar{\alpha}$ so determined will refer to a wire passing from one known uniform temperature to another.

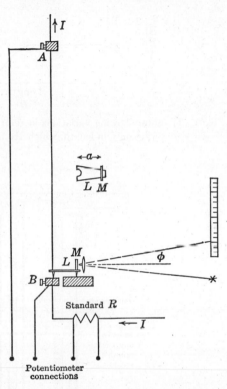

FIG. 8.  Diagram showing arrangements for measuring linear expansivities of a wire or rod by the optical-lever method.

**13. Roberts' Optical-Lever Method for Small Specimens.**  The application of the optical-lever method to the determination of expansivities of small specimens seems to have been made first by J. K. Roberts (1897–1944) of the Cavendish Laboratory, in England. A diagram of the apparatus is shown in Fig. 10; the optical system used by him was much like that shown in conjunction with Fig. 12. Certain details

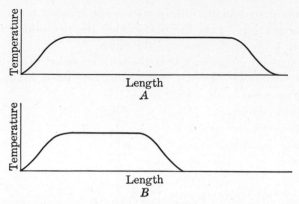

FIG. 9.   Diagram showing variations in temperature with respect to length for two wires, differing only in length, which are heated by the same electric current.

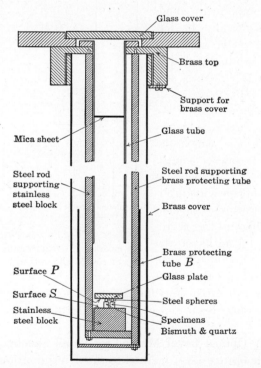

FIG. 10.   Furnace arrangement used by J. K. Roberts in his study of the expansivity of bismuth, using an optical-lever method.   (*Proc. Roy. Soc. London, A,* **106,** 385, 1924.)

of construction and operation as stated by Roberts * in connection with a determination of the expansivity of bismuth follow.

"The bismuth and quartz specimens, which were of the same size (5 to 10 mm) and which were optically flat, were placed side by side on the polished surface of the stainless steel block *S*. A glass plate *P*, which was slightly wedge-shaped, rested on three ³⁄₃₂-in. steel spheres, which were firmly set in a phosphor-bronze plate.

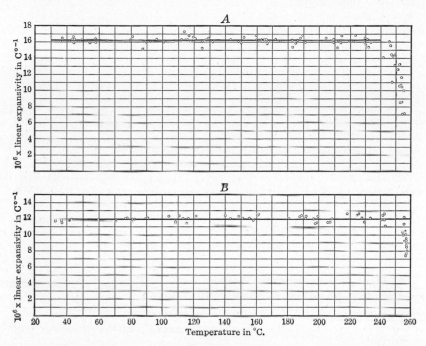

FIG. 11. Results obtained by J. K. Roberts, using the apparatus of Fig. 10 for the linear expansivities of a bismuth crystal (*A*) parallel to its axis, (*B*) perpendicular to its axis. See the text for an explanation of the occurrence above 240°C of decreasing values with approach to the melting point. (*Proc. Roy. Soc. London*, *A*, **106**, 385, 1924.)

The spheres rested on pieces of thin microscope cover-glass placed on the top of the specimens. These prevented the spheres from pressing into the bismuth at the higher temperatures.

"The different expansions of the bismuth and quartz specimens caused the angle between the lower surface of *P* and the surface of *S* to vary with temperature. This variation was determined by measuring the angle between the reflections of a parallel beam of light from these surfaces. Any effect due to the unequal expansion of the supports was eliminated as it affected both surfaces equally.

* Roberts, J. K., *Heat and Thermodynamics*, 3rd ed., p. 210, London, Blackie and Son, 1940.

"A cylindrical brass tube closed at the bottom served as container. This tube was carried on supports attached to the brass top. A heating coil was wound over the whole length of the container.

"In all experiments of this kind, whether the interference method or the optical lever method is employed, convection currents are a serious source of trouble, as they spoil the definition. They were eliminated by surrounding the specimens by a brass tube $B$, and by passing the light down to the reflecting surfaces through a glass tube as shown in the figure."

Roberts also stated, "With such an arrangement a relative change of length of the specimens of $3 \times 10^{-6}$ cm could be measured; this is about the same as can be done with an interference method." (See the next section.)

The results of Roberts' study of bismuth are shown in Fig. 11. For temperatures below about 240°C, the linear expansivities both parallel to and perpendicular to the axis of a crystal are shown not to vary appreciably with change of temperature. In this respect, bismuth differs from most other elements. Parallel to the axis, $\alpha_{||}$ is $16.2 \times 10^{-6}$ 1/C°; perpendicular to the axis, $\alpha_{\perp}$ is $12.1 \times 10^{-6}$ 1/C°. Above 240°C, both $\alpha_{||}$ and $\alpha_{\perp}$ decrease markedly with increase in temperature as the melting point, about 270°C, is approached. The significance of this variation is not entirely certain. To Roberts, it seemed most probable that, if strictly pure bismuth could have been tested, the expansivities would have been found to remain constant up to the melting point. Atoms of an impurity in a crystal lattice, in accord with certain support given by X-ray diffraction results, were assumed to leave their normal lattice positions and to move about much as in a liquid. A consequent anticipation of the change of volume that occurs on melting may be expected. With bismuth, as with water, there is a rather large shrinkage on melting; and, on the basis of the foregoing, the decrease in linear expansivities found above 240°C may well be ascribed to probable impurities.

**14. Fizeau's Interference Method.** This method, devised by the French physicist A. H. L. Fizeau (1819–1896), is especially adapted to small specimens. A diagrammatic sketch of the apparatus is shown in Fig. 12. Two fused-quartz wedges $a$ and $a'$, with surfaces ground plane and polished, are shown separated by a tubular specimen $b$ whose linear expansivity is desired. The light source, preferably one yielding separate spectral lines, should be located at the focus of the lens $L$ so that the beam reflected from the prism $P$ to the quartz-wedge system may be composed of so-called parallel rays. If the surfaces of the quartz plates facing one another are nearly parallel and if the orientation of the wedge system is correct, two nearly parallel beams, those reflected from the nearly parallel wedge surfaces in contact with the specimen, will be reflected to the 50% reflecting small-angled outer wedge $W$, the monochromatic filter $F$, and the telescope $T$. In use, the wedge system is commonly kept in an evacuated enclosure which may be heated electrically to desired temperatures.

In operation with the telescope focused on one of the nearly parallel wedge surfaces, the user sees a field somewhat like that shown at $B$ in the figure. As indicated by optical theory, these dark and bright streaks, frequently referred to as fringes, result from the interference of the beam reflected from the upper of the two nearly parallel surfaces with that from the lower.  Actually the transition from brightness to darkness is gradual.  How great the brightness contrast may be will depend in part on the smallness of the opening in diaphragm $D$.

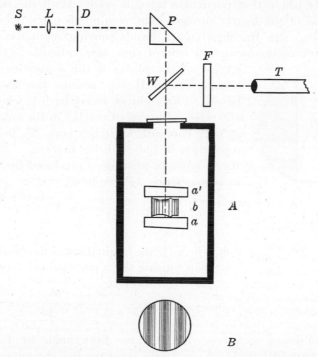

F$_{IG.}$ 12.  $A$. Arrangement of parts for Fizeau's interference method for measuring the linear expansivity of a tubular specimen.  $B$. The appearance of the field when in adjustment.

Because strictly parallel rays are impossible of realization, it may be shown that this brightness contrast depends also on the separation between the nearly parallel reflecting surfaces.  The less the separation, the greater is the contrast.  For this reason, it is a rather common procedure, where possible, to include, for a test of the kind being described, a quartz plate whose thickness is nearly that of the separation between the parallel surfaces.  It is placed on the lower wedge, and the fringes that are observed are those formed by the beams of light reflected from its upper surface and the lower surface of the upper wedge.

In direction the interference fringes are parallel to the line of intersection of the reflecting planes extended.  Further, except for the effect due to the well-known half-wavelength change of phase at one of the reflecting surfaces, the number of bands, counting a dark and a light streak as one band, that exists in the field between that intersection and any particular band seen through the telescope represents the number of half wavelengths of light that make up the separation of the plates where that particular band is seen. With the increasing separation of the quartz surfaces that results when the specimen is heated, one sees the interference bands moving regularly in some particular direction across the field of view, perpendicular to the inter-

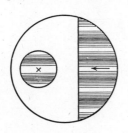

section of the planes if the separating body is homogeneous. If one counts the number of bands, $n$, for light of wavelength $\lambda$, which actually pass a convenient marker in the field, he can at once compute what has been the increase in separation in line with his marker. With $\Delta l$ as the increase in separation produced by a change in temperature $\Delta T$, we have

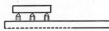

$$\Delta l = \frac{n\lambda}{2} \qquad (41)$$

FIG. 13. The interference field in Nix and MacNair's automatic temperature and expansion recorder.

and, where $l$ is the original linear dimension of the specimen causing the separation, we have finally

$$\bar{\alpha} = \frac{1}{l}\frac{\Delta l}{\Delta T} = \frac{n\lambda}{2l\,\Delta T} \qquad (42)$$

An interesting variation (Fig. 13) has been made by F. C. Nix (1905– ) and W. A. MacNair (1901– ) of the Bell Telephone Laboratories. The lower quartz wedge was made to extend laterally on one side beyond the upper wedge. This extension, ground flat and polished on both sides, was adjusted so that light beams were reflected also from its upper and lower surfaces into the field of view. Interference band shifts were observable there also. They corresponded to the expansion of the quartz. The expansivity of quartz being known from other work, changes in temperature could be determined with the aid of these observed shifts. Applying this plan to an experiment necessitating slow heating over a period of days, Nix and MacNair set up a device which photographed the field of view at regular intervals. One part of their film gave, in effect, a record of temperature as indicated by the regular interference bands just discussed. On the other part there was a record of expansion for the specimen. The two records together showed how the length varied as a function of both temperature and time. Figs. 14 and 15 represent the results of a very well-carried-out study of copper and nickel. The full lines are based

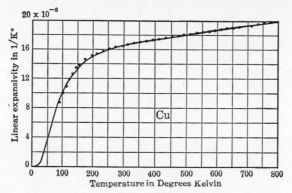

FIG. 14. Nix and MacNair's results for the linear expansivity of copper as a function of temperature. The full line is based on a theory by Grueneisen. (*Phys. Rev.*, **60**, 597, 1941.)

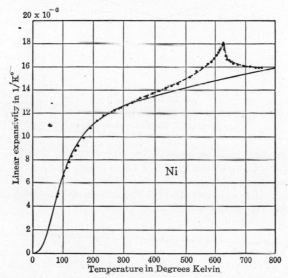

FIG. 15. Nix and MacNair's results for the linear expansivity of nickel as a function of temperature. The full line is based on a theory by Grueneisen. (*Phys. Rev.*, **60**, 597, 1941.)

on a theory, to be discussed later, developed by the German physicist Grueneisen (1877–   ).

I. G. Priest (1886–1932) at the Bureau of Standards in Washington in 1920 showed that changes in the length of a specimen may be computed from changes of the width of the interference bands or fringes, as well as from the number that have passed a cross hair.

Fizeau's method is much used in industry and in pure science research.

**15. The X-Ray Method.** This method is applicable to very small bodies possessing crystalline structures. Sometimes a single crystal is used, but more often the body is polycrystalline. Still more often a compressed aggregate of pulverized crystals is used. In the latter two cases, dependence is placed on the random arrangement of the small crystals. However, the underlying theory is the same.

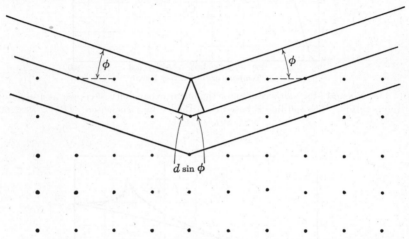

FIG. 16. The reflection of a monochromatic beam of X-rays by a simple cubic crystal in accord with the Bragg law.

Given a crystalline array of atoms, as shown in Fig. 16, with a beam of monochromatic X-rays of wavelength $\lambda$ incident on an atomic plane at the glancing angle $\varphi$, a reflected beam at the emergent glancing angle $\varphi$ is observed provided the W. L. Bragg (1890– ) relation, named after the English physicist and Nobel prize winner of 1915 who first stated it, is fulfilled, that is, when

$$n\lambda = 2d \sin \varphi \tag{43}$$

With change in $d$, the atomic layer spacing, with temperature, a change of incident glancing angle is required if a reflected beam is to be obtained. For the same $\lambda$ and $n$, this condition requires that $d \sin \varphi$ be constant with change of temperature. There follow

$$\frac{d}{d_0} = \frac{\sin \varphi_0}{\sin \varphi} \tag{44}$$

$$\bar{\alpha} = \frac{d - d_0}{d_0(T - T_0)} = \frac{\sin \varphi_0 - \sin \varphi}{\Delta T \sin \varphi} \tag{45}$$

According to the Bragg procedure in which a single crystal is used, one varies $\varphi$ until the ionization chamber with its narrow slit opening, always oriented to receive

X-rays reflected in accord with the Bragg law, shows a maximum response. Measurement, for a single crystal at two temperatures $T_0$ and $T$, of the angles $\varphi_0$ and $\varphi$ yields the necessary data for the computation of the desired $\bar{\alpha}$.

Since $\sin \varphi_0$ and $\sin \varphi$ differ by a small amount only, Eq. 45 may be simplified by replacing $\varphi$ in the numerator by $(\varphi_0 + \Delta\varphi)$, expanding $\sin (\varphi_0 + \Delta\varphi)$, and replacing $\sin \Delta\varphi$ and $\cos \Delta\varphi$ therein by the approximations $\Delta\varphi$ and $1 - (\Delta\varphi)^2/2$. We then have

$$\bar{\alpha} = \frac{\Delta\varphi(\Delta\varphi \sin \varphi_0 - 2 \cos \varphi_0)}{2 \, \Delta T \sin \varphi} \tag{46}$$

As long as $\Delta\varphi$, which is nearly always negative, is not greater than $1°$, the approximation of Eq. 46 is valid to better than 1 part in 1000. Generally, Eq. 46 is found more satisfactory for computational purposes than is Eq. 45. Inspection will show that, for equal accuracies of result, Eq. 45 requires tables with sines of angles given to the extent of five, or more probably six, significant digits, whereas Eq. 46 will require tables with only three or at most four significant figures. It is interesting that the X-ray wavelength and the atomic-layer spacing are both absent from Eqs. 45 and 46.

In an application to a single crystal of aluminum, Cu $K\alpha$ X-rays were reflected from a certain set of atomic planes. At $20.0°C$, a strong reflection was noted at $\varphi_0 = 10.9681°$. With heating of the crystal to $310.0°C$, the strong reflection shifted to $\varphi = 10.8866°$, yielding a $\Delta\varphi$ of $-0.0815°(= -0.001425$ rad.). Substituting in Eq. 46, we have

$$\bar{\alpha} = \frac{(-0.00143)(-0.00143 \sin 10.97° - 2 \cos 10.97°)}{2 \times 290.0 \, C° \times \sin 10.89°} = 25.6 \times 10^{-6} \, 1/C° \tag{47}$$

For use with the Debye-Scherrer-Hull * (1884– , 1890– , 1880– ) procedure, the material is usually formed into a short rod less than a millimeter in diameter and about a millimeter in length. It is immaterial whether the specimen is normally polycrystalline as received or is formed by mixing pulverized material with some organic binder and squeezed through a die to give it the desired shape. Mounted and rotated in the axis of a cylindrical X-ray camera, the specimen is exposed to a very narrow, nearly parallel beam of X-rays, obtained with the aid of small limiting diaphragms. As a joint consequence of the rotation of the specimen and the nearly random orientation of the small crystals, large numbers of minute crystals are at all times in position to satisfy the Bragg law. The radiation so reflected goes to form the X-ray spectrum of the specimen which is photographed on a film located on the inner wall of the cylindrical camera. A spectrum of platinum obtained in this manner is shown in Fig. 17.

With change of temperature, the accompanying change in an X-ray spectrum, if the crystal structure itself does not change, is a change of separation of the lines. From the positions of these lines with respect to the path of the incident beam, it is possible to compute $\varphi_0$ and $\varphi$ and to determine $\bar{\alpha}$ for the material. Each line on the pattern may be used to determine an $\bar{\alpha}$, which will be characteristic of the substance

---

* Peter Debye, a Hollander by birth who did much of his scientific work in Germany and was awarded a Nobel prize in chemistry in 1936, has been in the United States at Cornell University since 1940. Scherrer is a Swiss physicist. A. W. Hull is a physicist in the Research Laboratories of the General Electric Co. at Schenectady, N. Y.

for length changes in a direction normal to the atomic planes associated with the line. Frequently the $\bar{\alpha}$'s for different axes differ. Such materials are anisotropic.

X-ray values for $\bar{\alpha}$ depend only on changes in the lattice constants; most other types of values for $\bar{\alpha}$ depend additionally on any progressive change of the mosaic structure and of the number of vacant spaces in the atomic lattices. Accordingly X-ray expansivities do not always check precisely with values determined otherwise. Except where the crystalline structure is microscopically uniform, X-ray values for expansivities are to be viewed as somewhat uncertain.

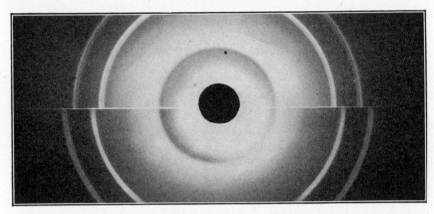

FIG. 17. X-ray diffraction patterns of a platinum wire at room temperature and at an elevated temperature, showing expansion effects.

**16. The Electron-Diffraction Method.** Though it has been employed but little in the measurement of expansivities, the electron-diffraction method would seem to be perfectly feasible. The theory is exactly the same as for the X-ray method, with the understanding that the wavelength of an impinging electron is given by $h/mv$, where $h$ is the Planck constant and $mv$ the electron's linear momentum. Since electrons penetrate most substances but a very short distance, they can give information regarding only surface layers or thin films. For these the method would seem to be especially suitable.

**17. Some Results of Expansivity Measurements.** Results for solids and liquids will be found in the Appendix. Certain generalizations of measurements have already been noted. They are: (1) The expansivities of liquids are generally greater than those of solids. (2) With increase in temperature the expansivities of materials generally increase. Other generalizations have also been found. As tabulated in the Appendix and as shown in Fig. 18, (3) the higher the melting point of a metal the smaller generally is its average linear expansivity for the range 0°C to 100°C. This relation might be expected since a high melting point means that at room temperatures the interatomic binding forces are relatively great, and that, for a given rise in temperature, the separating effects due to the increased agitation of the component atoms will be relatively small. As Fig. 18 shows, there are exceptions, as for tantalum, to this general rule. (4) The expansivities of pure metals tend toward zero at 0°K. (5) On the basis of assumed attrac-

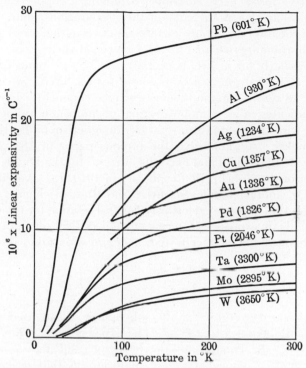

Fig. 18. A graph showing a general interdependence of linear expansivities and melting-point temperatures for metals.

tive and repulsive forces between atoms in a substance, E. Grueneisen (1877– ), a German physicist, developed the relation

$$\alpha = \frac{c_v}{3Q_0 \left[1 - \dfrac{m + n + 3}{6} \dfrac{u}{Q_0}\right]^2} \tag{48}$$

of which $c_v$, $u$, and $Q_0$ are the constant-volume specific heat, the specific internal energy (see Chapter IX), and a constant which may be computed for the substance being discussed; and $m$ and $n$ are the exponents of the attractive and repulsive terms in expressions relating the potential energy of the atoms of a monatomic solid to the distances separating its vibrating atoms. For copper, Nix and MacNair found that values of 13.8 for $m + n$ and of $120 \times 10^3$ cal/gm-atom for $Q_0$ yield the full line of Fig. 14. The fit is surprisingly good. If $m$ is now taken as 3, as is customary, $n$ becomes 10.8. The interpretation is that probably the attractive forces between copper atoms in a copper solid fall off with atom separation as the cube of their separations, that is as $1/r^3$, and that probably the repulsive forces between the same atoms increase with atom approach as the 10.8 power of their separation or as $1/r^{10.8}$. Similarly for nickel, as best values, 21 was found for $m + n$, and $151.5 \times 10^3$ cal/gm-atom was found for $Q_0$. With $m$ equal to 3, a value of 18 results for the inverse distance exponent. However, as Fig. 15 indicates, a certain interesting phenomenon thought to be associated with the disappearance of ferromagnetism on heating shows up with nickel. (6) Following the famous paper of 1881, "On the Continuity of the Liquid and Gaseous States," by the Dutch physicist and winner of the Nobel prize for physics in 1910, J. D. van der Waals (1837–1923), another famous scientist, the Russian chemist D. Mendeleff (1834–1907), suggested a simple general relation for the expansivities of liquids, $\beta$, expressed in terms of their critical temperatures, $T_c$. Slightly changed and as later tested, his expression takes the form

$$\frac{1 + \beta T}{T_c} = A \qquad (49)$$

of which $A$ is a constant. For the substances investigated, $A$ is said to vary from about 1.5 to 2.1 (7) The expansion behaviors of alloys vary greatly. (8) Though not the only such substance, water is a notable exception among non-alloy materials in that it expands on cooling from 4°C to 0°C.


## INDUSTRIAL APPLICATIONS

**18. The Suspension Bridge.** Unloaded, the cables of a suspension bridge assume the form of a catenary. Loaded so that each equal horizontal element carries the same load, a cable assumes the form of a parabola, a shape which is closely realized in actual structures (Fig. 19). Here we shall assume it to be rigidly true. With the lowest point of the cable in the span as the origin, and with $x$ and $y$ representing horizontal and vertical distances, one has for the length along a cable from the origin to some chosen point, say the top of one of the towers, $l$,

$$l = x\left(1 + \frac{2y^2}{3x^2} + \frac{7}{20}\frac{y^4}{x^4}\cdots\right) \qquad (50)$$

Ordinarily the term $\frac{7}{20}\, y^4/x^4$ is negligible. Differentiation and re-arrangement, subject to the condition of a constant separation between the towers supporting the cable ($x$ constant), yields, as a close approximation,

$$dy = \frac{3x}{4y}\left(1 - \frac{21}{20}\frac{y^2}{x^2}\right)dl \qquad (51)$$

Given $\bar{a}$, $x$, and $y$ for some particular temperature, it is easy to compute the change of sag for the cable for any probable change of temperature.

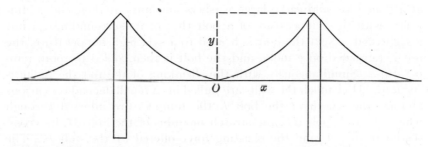

FIG. 19.  Diagram to illustrate the effects of thermal changes in suspension bridges.

**19. Dumet Lead-in Wires for Incandescent Lamps.** The general purpose and the construction of Dumet wire have been noted at the beginning of this chapter. It remains to consider what the radial dimensions of the nickel-steel core and copper sleeve shall be. It is evident that the Dumet wire must safely fill the channel it occupies in the glass. Throughout the interval during which the glass and wire are cooling down from the temperature at which the seal is made to room temperature, the cross section of the wire must equal that of the channel. Clearly we are concerned with cross-sectional surface expansions. Let $\bar{\alpha}_1$, $\bar{\alpha}_2$, and $\bar{\alpha}_3$ represent respectively the linear expansivities of the nickel steel, the copper, and the glass. One seeks the ratio $x$ of the radius of the nickel-steel core to that of the finished Dumet wire $r$. From the standpoint of surface expansions, we have, for the increases in cross-sectional area per unit temperature change,

$$2\bar{\alpha}_1\,\pi(xr)^2 + 2\bar{\alpha}_2\,\pi(r^2 - x^2 r^2) = 2\bar{\alpha}_3\,\pi r^2 \qquad (52)$$

and, solving for $x$,

$$x = \sqrt{\frac{\bar{\alpha}_2 - \bar{\alpha}_3}{\bar{\alpha}_2 - \bar{\alpha}_1}} \qquad (53)$$

In what precedes, it has been tacitly assumed that the expansions of the core, the sleeve, and the channel along the length of the wire are immaterial.  Such is not the case.  With increase of temperature the sleeve and the core through being attached to each other cannot expand normally.  Although all three parts may be free from strain at some one temperature, they cannot be thus generally.  Fortunately, all substances including glass can be strained and distorted to some extent without being damaged.

**20. Structural Tie Bolts.**  Occasionally one sees an old building which, in danger of destruction from bulging laterally, has been protected by means of long bolts which pass centrally through the building at a floor level and carry large washers and nuts at their ends.  Initially, with the temperature of a bolt that of its surroundings, a nut is tightened.  Next the bolt is heated to a safe high temperature, the nut is tightened once more, and the bolt is then cooled to room temperature.  Simultaneously with the shrinking of the rod the bulge is reduced.  How much the walls are pulled in, $\Delta'l$, will depend on various factors: the length of the bolt $l$, the temperature interval through which the rod cools $\Delta T$, the stretch modulus of the bolt $M$, its cross-sectional area $A$, and the resisting force offered by the wall $F$.  The maximum force available for pulling the walls together $F_m$ and the force experienced by the rod $F$ after cooling are both readily computed.  Representing further by $\Delta l$ the normal contraction for a cooling $\Delta T$, were there no resisting force, we have

$$F_m = MA \frac{\Delta l}{l} = MA\bar{\alpha}\,\Delta T \tag{54}$$

$$F = \frac{MA(\Delta l - \Delta'l)}{l} = MA\left(\bar{\alpha}\,\Delta T - \frac{\Delta'l}{l}\right) \tag{55}$$

When the necessary characteristics of a tie bolt, the temperature change $\Delta T$, and the fractional contraction experienced $\Delta'l/l$ are given, one can readily compute the resisting force $F$.  Thus, for a 1.0-in. steel tie bolt, 30 ft long with $M = 29 \times 10^6$ lb/in.$^2$ and $\bar{\alpha} = 6.9 \times 10^{-6}$ 1/F°, cooled from 1000°F to 100°F, we find that, if the contraction is to be prevented, the required resisting force $F_m$ is

$$F_m = (29 \times 10^6 \text{ lb/in.}^2)\left(\frac{\pi}{4} \times 1.0 \text{ in.}^2\right)(6.9 \times 10^{-6} \text{ 1/F°})(900 \text{ F°})$$
$$= 140,000 \text{ lb} \tag{56}$$

If instead unrestrained cooling is permitted, a contraction of 2.2 in. occurs.  On the other hand, if the bolt contracts 1.0 in. only, the tension remaining in the rod at 100°F is, as given by Eq. 55,

$$F = (29 \times 10^6 \text{ lb/in.}^2) \left( \frac{\pi}{4} \times 1.0 \text{ in.}^2 \right) \left( \frac{2.2 \text{ in. } - 1.0 \text{ in.}}{30 \times 12 \text{ in.}} \right)$$

$$= 75,000 \text{ lb} \quad (57)$$

Similar considerations apply to steel railway rails which are fastened end to end or indeed laid in continuous pieces of the order of a mile in length. They must stand the tensions and compressions arising with chilling or heating to reduced or to elevated temperatures.

**21. Astronomical Clocks.** For the highly precise measurement of time needed in astronomical research, extremely high-grade clocks are required. Pendulums whose periods are not at all, or only very slightly, dependent on temperature changes are needed. The common solution of the problem involves linear expansivities.

The condition sought for the pendulum is a constant separation between the point of suspension $P$ and the center of oscillation $Q$, a point in the bob determined by the dimensions of the pendulum and the distribution of the matter composing it. How this may be accomplished is shown in Fig. 20. The main pendulum rod of steel supports at its lower end a metal plate which carries two glass tubes partially filled with mercury. With increase of temperature the effect of the expansion of the steel is to lengthen the pendulum and thus to lower the center of oscillation, but that of the expansion of the mercury, which is relatively much larger, raises it. With a proper adjustment of the length of the mercury column, the shift of the center of oscillation with change of temperature is made equal, or nearly equal, to zero. Let $L$ be the length $PQ$, $l$ the length $PR$, and $l'$ the length $RS$. Further assume the lateral expansion of the glass tubes to be negligible (this is not essential). The condition of constancy of $L$ requires that the length $PS$ shall contract with increase of temperature. In effect, it must possess a certain negative linear expansivity $\bar{\alpha}_1$.

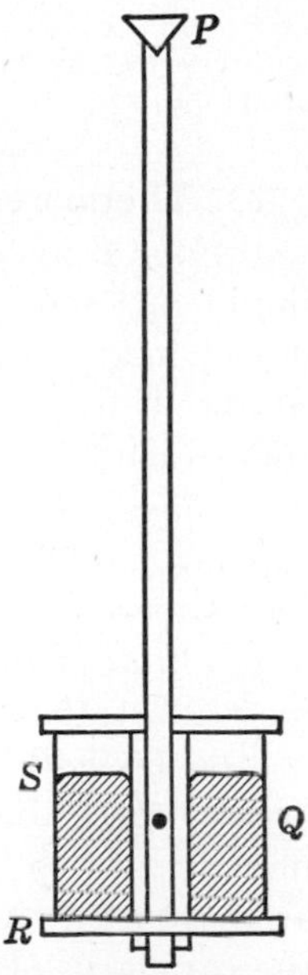

With $\bar{\alpha}$ as the linear expansivity of the steel support rod and $\bar{\beta}$ as the volume expansivity of mercury, also its effective linear expansivity since the mercury can expand in one direction only, we have as a necessary relation

$$l\bar{\alpha}\,\Delta T - l'\bar{\beta}\,\Delta T = (l - l')\bar{\alpha}_1\,\Delta T \quad (58)$$

$$l' = \left( \frac{\bar{\alpha} - \bar{\alpha}_1}{\bar{\beta} - \bar{\alpha}_1} \right) l \quad (59)$$

What $\bar{\alpha}_1$ should be to maintain $L$ constant may be computed or determined experimentally.

FIG. 20. Diagram of the pendulum of an astronomical clock with mercury-filled tubes to protect against the effects of changes of temperature.

**22. Compensated Balance Wheels.**  When the temperature of the balance wheel of a watch is raised, the natural period of vibration of wheel and spring is changed because (1) the rim of the wheel expands, thereby increasing its moment of inertia, and (2) the spring constant of the hairspring changes.  In order that the watch may keep time accurately, we can select the hairspring of some nickel-steel alloy whose spring constant increases with temperature so that, over a restricted temperature range, effects (1) and (2) closely annul each other.  If the spring is made from a material such that its spring constant decreases with temperature rise, effects (1) and (2) are additive.  When temperature compensation is desired, a common procedure is to make the rim of the wheel of two semicircular, bimetallic strips, each supported at one end only.  So arranged, the bending inward of these strips with rise in temperature compensates, over a restricted range, the combined effects of (1) and (2).

**23. Thermoregulators.**  For controlling the temperature of a fluid bath, one conveniently uses the relative expansion characteristic of a liquid enclosed in a solid container in contact with the fluid.  One such device installed in a water bath in the Physical Chemistry Laboratory at the University of Pittsburgh is capable of controlling the bath temperature to about 0.0007 C°.  It consists of a 0.5-in.-internal-diameter coiled copper tubing 33 ft long, filled with toluene.  The relative expansion on heating of the toluene with respect to its copper container forces mercury to rise in a small attached 0.50-mm capillary.  At the upper limit of the temperature interval for which the thermoregulator may be set, the mercury closes an electric circuit and a small amount of cold water is thereupon added to the bath.  A small heater is continuously operated in the bath to yield a slow temperature rise when the mercury switch is open.  The sensitivity $S$ of such a device is expressed as the bath temperature change per unit change of mercury level in the capillary.  If temperature change $\Delta T$ produces a mercury shift $h$ and if $\bar\beta$ and $V_0$ are the volume expansivity of the regulator liquid and the initial volume of the container, then

$$V_0\bar\beta \ \Delta T \ = \ h\frac{\pi}{4}\,d^2 \tag{60}$$

whence

$$S \ = \ \frac{\Delta T}{h} \ = \ \frac{\pi d^2}{4V_0\bar\beta} \tag{61}$$

For the device described ($V = 1.3$ l and $\bar\beta = 1.03 \times 10^{-3}$ 1/C°), the sensitivity $S$ is 0.00015 C°/mm.

**24. Low-Expansivity Alloys.**  For many uses such as surveyors' chains and secondary standards of length, where it is desired to minimize thermal expansion effects, a low-expansivity alloy such as Invar is used. By varying the composition, alloys can be designed so as to have a low expansivity over a selected temperature range. Expansivities for various nickel-steel alloys, of which that containing 63.5% iron and 36.5% nickel by weight is Invar, are given in Fig. 21. The expansivity of Invar in the region 20°C–150°C is very low.

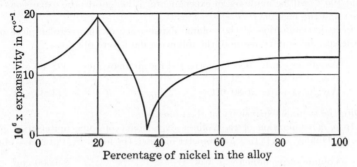

FIG. 21. The expansivities of nickel-steel alloys at ordinary temperatures as a function of the nickel content. The variations indicated in the neighborhoods of 20% and 36% are probably different from the true variations. The particular alloy having a 36.5% nickel content is known as Invar.

## PROBLEMS

**1.** The relative lengths of a tungsten wire at 300°K, 500°K, and 1000°K are 1.00000, 1.00089, and 1.00321. Using 300°K as $T_0$ but disregarding terms beyond the second order in the expansion of Eq. 3, what values are obtained for $a_1$ and $a_2$ for tungsten? How do these values compare with those stated in the text which are based on the inclusion of a third-order term?

**2.** Using the results of problem 1, determine the average linear expansivities for tungsten for the temperature ranges 300°K to 500°K and 300°K to 1000°K, also the expansivities at 300°K, 500°K, and 1000°K.

**3.** Given that the differential volume expansivity for the mercury and the glass of a mercury-in-glass thermometer is 0.00016 1/C°, determine for an ordinary 0°C to 100°C thermometer the approximate ratio of the volume of the thermometer bulb to that of a length of capillary corresponding to 1 C°.

**4.** In a determination of the volume expansivity of mercury using the balanced-column method, the length of the single heated mercury arm composed of Pyrex glass was found to be 62.50 cm at 20°C. What is the difference in height expected at the tops of the two mercury columns when the two temperatures are 20.0°C and 250.0°C? What error results from an error of 0.2 cm in the 62.5-cm determination?

**5.** Using data given for mercury determine the constants $a$ and $b$ of the equation

$$\frac{\Delta V}{V_0} = a(T - 0°C) + b(T - 0°C)^2$$

so as to give agreement with values reported there for 0°C, 100°C, and 200°C. How do the relative expansions $\Delta V/V$ computed for changes from 0°C to 20° and from 0°C to 80°C check with what may be deduced directly from the table?

**6.** A so-called liter flask composed of laboratory Pyrex having a linear expansivity of $3.2 \times 10^{-6}$ 1/C° with a 20°C-calibration ring about a neck 1.00 cm² in cross section is graduated to yield just 1 kg of water at 20°C. What masses of water will fill the flask to the calibration ring at temperatures of 0°C and 100°C?

**7.** A 25-cm³ pycnometer of laboratory Pyrex (see problem 6) calibrated at 20°C is used to measure mercury. What errors in the masses of mercury measured out at 0°C and 100°C will be made by an experimenter if he ignores the expansions of both the glass and the mercury?

**8.** In a determination of the volume expansivity of an irregular piece of rock, using the specific-gravity method, the following data were obtained:

Weight in air at 20.0°C (corrected for air buoyancy)  395.00 gwt
Weight in water at 20.0°C                              271.50 gwt
Weight in water at 80.0°C                              274.35 gwt

Compute the volume expansivity of the mineral.

**9.** In a determination of the volume expansivity of some material in granular form using Dulong and Petit's pycnometer method, the following data were obtained:

Volume of pycnometer at 0°C          8.0000 cm³
Volume of mercury added at 0°C       3.0000 cm³
Mass of mercury forced out at 100°C  0.6684 gm

Given that the average volume expansivity of the material of the pycnometer was $21.3 \times 10^{-6}$ 1/C°, compute the average volume expansivity of the granular material for the temperature range 0°C to 100°C.

**10.** In his report on bismuth, Roberts, using an optical-lever method, stated that a relative change of length for his specimens of $3 \times 10^{-6}$ cm was measurable. Assuming 10-mm long blocks of bismuth and fused quartz, a separation of 5.0 mm for the steel sphere centers, and an optical lever arm of 0.50 cm, obtain the just determinable corresponding angle of tilt for the plate on top of his specimens and the corresponding change of temperature for them. For bismuth use the expansivity parallel to the axis.

**11.** With a Fizeau apparatus, the expansion of a platinum wire 2.00 mm in diameter is studied. It is found, on heating the furnace containing the wire from 20°C to 270°C, that 16.50 fringes of the mercury green line 5461 Å shift across the cross-hair intersection in the field of view. What is the average linear expansivity that is to be computed?

**12.** Using Fe Kα radiation ($\lambda = 1.934$ Å), it was found that the expansion perpendicular to the 114 planes of magnesium produced on heating from 66°C to 104°C caused a Bragg glancing-angle shift from 73° 9.4′ to 72° 47.8′. What is the linear expansivity of magnesium in the direction considered?

**13.** Given that, when Mo Kα radiation of wavelength 0.7078 Å is used with tungsten at 20°C, a Bragg glancing angle of 65° 6.0′ is observed and that the linear expansivity of tungsten between 20°C and 120°C is $4.44 \times 10^{-6}$ 1/C°, compute the expected glancing angle when the temperature is 100°C.

**14.** The distance between the towers at the ends of the main span of the Golden Gate Bridge at San Francisco is 4200 ft. The sag of the cable halfway between the towers at normal temperature, say 50°F, is 470 ft. Given a linear expansivity of $6.5 \times 10^{-6}$ 1/F° for the cable, compute the change in length of the cable between the towers and the change in sag midway between for a temperature change from −30°F to 110°F.

**15.** The lead-in wires of ordinary incandescent lamps consist of a copper sleeve soldered to a nickel-steel core. With average linear expansivities for nickel steel, copper, and lamp-stem glass for the range 0°C to 300°C of about $5.9 \times 10^{-6}$ 1/C°, $16.6 \times 10^{-6}$ 1/C°, and $9.2 \times 10^{-6}$ 1/C° and with the requirements that the lead-in wire shall have the same radial expansivity as has the lamp-stem glass, what is the expected ratio of core diameter to wire diameter? Disregard effects that might result from the failure of the copper and nickel steel to expand freely along the length of the wire.

**16.** A steel bolt 30 ft long and of 2-in.$^2$ cross section is used in an attempt to draw together the bulging walls of a building. With the rod at an average temperature of 300°C, the nuts at the ends are set snugly and the bolt thereafter cools to 20°C. At this temperature it is found that the bulging has been reduced by approximately 1 in. Given that the linear expansivity of the steel is $11.7 \times 10^{-6}$ 1/C° and that its stretch (Young's) modulus is 14,000 tons wt/in.$^2$, compute the stress existing in the rod at the lower temperature.

**17.** Given $11.5 \times 10^{-6}$ 1/C° as the linear expansivity for the steel rod of an astronomical clock, $175 \times 10^{-6}$ 1/C° as the apparent volume expansivity of mercury, altered to take account of the expansion of the glass containers, and $-5.5 \times 10^{-6}$ 1/C° as that for the space between the knife-edge support and top mercury surfaces, compute the ratio of the length of the mercury columns to that of the pendulum's steel rod.

**18.** Given that the linear expansivity for certain steel rails used in a streetcar line is $6.5 \times 10^{-6}$ 1/F°, that their stretch modulus is 15,000 tons wt/in.$^2$, and that their elastic stretch limit is 30 tons wt/in.$^2$, show whether or not the rails, if laid and welded end-to-end when at 60°F, will hold without breaking at $-25$°F.

# CHAPTER IV

## THE DYNAMICAL THEORY OF HEAT

**1. Introduction.**  The tendency to explain phenomena by means of a few simple assumptions has been characteristic of the scientists of all periods.  A tendency to maintain a point of view, once adopted, seems equally characteristic.  Both statements are strikingly illustrated in the evolution of our concept of heat.

Among the obvious phenomena in the field of heat, which one might seek to explain on a simple basis are, (1) that, when hot and cold bodies are brought into contact, one loses heat to the other, (2) that, when bodies, particularly gases, are compressed, they become warmer, (3) that friction and abrasion result in the appearance of heat, (4) that bodies are heated when exposed to the radiation from hotter bodies, the sun, for example, (5) that heat must be supplied to solids to melt them, and (6) that gases and vapors in the vicinity of hot bodies tend to rise.  Given these phenomena at a time when thermometers were unknown, it is not difficult to comprehend why heat, or caloric as it was called, should have been conceived as a fluid (1) which could be neither created nor destroyed, (2) which was without weight, in fact, with something of an anti-weight characteristic, (3) which would pass through the air from a hot source to a cooler absorbing body without appreciable interference, (4) which, though penetrating all bodies, could nevertheless be squeezed out on compression, and (5) which, because of a possibility of becoming *latent* between the component particles of a body, could be made *sensible* by friction and by abrasion.

It is not surprising that objections to the caloric concept should have developed.  The English scientist Robert Boyle (1627–1691) expressed his objection clearly when he said, ". . . for whilst at every blow of the hammer, the nail enters farther and farther into the wood, the motion that is produced is chiefly progressive, and is of the whole nail tending one way; whereas, when that motion is stopped, then the impulse given by the stroke, being unable either to drive the nail further on, or destroy its entireness, must be spent in making a various, vehement and intensive commotion of the parts among themselves, and in such an one we formerly observed the nature of heat to consist." The great Sir Isaac Newton (1642–1727) and others added their arguments in favor of a mechanical theory. Nevertheless, the material caloric theory was the one that found favor generally in scientific minds up to near the middle of the nineteenth century.

The real beginning of the overthrow of the caloric theory began when the expatriated American, Count Rumford (1753–1814), published in 1798 his celebrated experiment in which he used a blunt boring tool to drill a cannon barrel immersed in water. In $2\frac{1}{2}$ hours, with a production of about 10 oz of finely powdered turnings, he brought the gun barrel and 18.8 pd * of cold water to the boiling point of the water. He also showed that the specific heat of the turnings was the same as that of an equal mass of the unmachined material.

Could he have further shown that the net amount of heat necessary to convert the turnings into a single solid was nil or approximately so, his case against caloric would have been perfect. Summarizing his results, Rumford said, " . . . we must not forget *that most remarkable circumstance* that the source of the heat generated by friction in these experiments appeared evidently to be *inexhaustible* . . . anything which any *insulated* body or system of bodies can continue to furnish *without limitation* cannot possibly be a material substance." (The italics are Rumford's.)

Expressed in terms of present-day units, the results of his measurements indicate that 1 calory of heat is equivalent to about 5.45 joules, a value about 30% too high.†

The year following the publication of Rumford's paper, and probably stimulated by its appearance, Humphry Davy (1778–1829), a young man who later became a leading English scientist, performed an experiment, which might have been crucial had sufficient precautions been taken to win the confidence of the scientists of his time. He liquefied ice by rubbing two pieces together. It was well known that ordinarily a considerable amount of heat must be supplied to ice from external sources to melt it. But, in Davy's experiment, there had been no such external source, and the only explanation that seemed plausible was that the heat had been created by friction.

Both Rumford and Davy believed in heat as a "mode of motion"; but how to measure that motion quantitatively was not apparent, and

---

* In this text, as in our daily life, the word pound will be used with two meanings. There will be a definite distinction, however. Almost always, if not always, the forms of expression will involve the abbreviations pd for a mass unit and lb for a force unit. Their connection is defined by Newton's second law of motion. It is

$$1 \text{ lb} = 1 \text{ pd} \times 1 \text{ grav} = 1 \text{ pd} \times 32.2 \text{ ft/sec}^2$$

† See P. S. Epstein's *Textbook of Thermodynamics*, pp. 27–37, New York, John Wiley and Sons, 1937. An excellent brief account of the history of the first law of thermodynamics is to be found on these pages.

the caloric concept though shaken continued in favor. Even the French engineer Sadi Carnot (1796–1832), in discussing the great principle which bears his name and which we shall discuss at some length in the chapter on thermodynamics, said, "The production of mechanical work by steam engines is thus not due to a real consumption of caloric but to its transfer from a hot body to a cold body." At the time of his early death, however, Carnot had concluded that caloric did not actually exist.

In 1839, the French engineer Marc Seguin carried out certain experiments in an attempt to determine the thermal equivalence of mechanical work. His work convinced him that such an equivalence existed but the results themselves seemed far from satisfactory to Seguin himself, and his contribution to the work-heat question has almost been forgotten.

In 1842, J. R. Mayer (1814–1878), a German physician, deduced from the well-known principle "cause equals effect" that the heat produced by mechanical work is directly related to the amount of work performed. From the work done in compressing a gas and the heat produced thereby, he deduced for the quantity now known as the mechanical equivalent of heat a value of 3.6 joules per calory, which is about 15% low.

One year later James Prescott Joule (1818–1889), in England, made his first report on an extended series of determinations of the same ratio, which seem to have been begun in 1840. His first results varied widely, but, with successive repetitions, there was great improvement. Eventually in 1849 as a result of three different sets of measurements involving the friction of water, of mercury, and of cast iron he obtained values which checked within about ⅓%. From that time on, caloric, except in the minds of a few, was mainly of historic value. However, only with the passing on of the then older generation of physicists and chemists did the mechanical concept of heat actually become universal.

**2. Joule's Experiment.** The arrangement of parts as used by Joule is shown in Fig. 1. Two rope-suspended bodies $B$, $B$, on being released, caused the central spindle $F$ to revolve. Connected to this spindle at its lower end but inside a calorimeter, $C$, was a set of paddles which rotated between fixed blades projecting inward from the calorimeter wall, an arrangement which insured that the water was thoroughly stirred. A ratchet attachment, not shown, permitted raising the fallen bodies to their original positions without any action taking place within the calorimeter. The heat developed by the stirring was obtained from measurements of the mass of water $m$ in the calorimeter, the water equivalent of the calorimeter itself, $m'$, and the rise in temperature of the whole, $\Delta T$. Similarly the amount of work performed during the stirring was taken as the loss in potential energy of the two falling bodies of combined weight $Mg$ which moved downward a distance $h$. Equating the two, Joule obtained

$$Mgh = (m + m')c \, \Delta T \qquad (1)$$

or, as it is often now written for a certain convenience,

$$Mgh = J(m + m')c \, \Delta T \qquad (2)$$

of which $c$ is the specific heat * of water, and $J$, thus abbreviated in honor of Joule, is the mechanical equivalent.

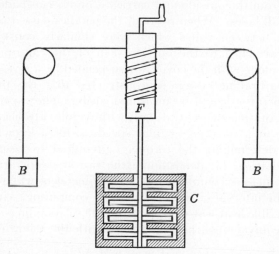

FIG. 1.   Joule's arrangement of apparatus for determining the mechanical equivalent of heat.

Obviously corrections were needed in Joule's work (1) for the cooling of the calorimeter by convection and by radiation, (2) on account of the kinetic energy possessed by the falling bodies when they reached the floor, (3) on account of the stretch in the supporting cords, (4) because of the friction in the pulleys, and (5) because of energy lost due to vibration. According to Edser's textbook on heat, Joule used a thermometer reading to $\frac{1}{360}$ C°. The water equivalent of the calorimeter and contents was 6316 gm, the combined mass of the falling bodies was 26,320 gm, the distance of fall for each of twenty falls was

* Elementary knowledge of specific heats is here assumed. See p. 112 for a definition.

160.5 cm, and the rise in temperature was 0.3129 C°.  Substitution in (2) gives

$$J = \frac{26{,}320 \text{ gm} \times 980.6 \text{ cm/sec}^2 \times 20 \times 160.5 \text{ cm}}{6316 \text{ gm} \times 1.000 \text{ cal/(gm C}°) \times 0.3129 \text{ C}°}$$

$$= 4.19 \times 10^7 \text{ ergs/calory} = 4.19 \text{ joules/calory} \qquad (3)$$

**3. Rowland's Experiment.**  In 1879, H. A. Rowland (1848–1901) of Johns Hopkins University published the result of his repetition of the mechanical equivalent of heat experiment.  His procedure was a considerable improvement over Joule's.  A sketch of his apparatus is shown in Fig. 2.  The central shaft, which in operation was rotated by a belt-connected engine, extended through the bottom of the calorimeter from the outside and carried a number of paddles pierced by many small holes.  When rotated, the paddles passed as in Joule's arrangement between vanes which were similarly constructed, but which were attached to the outside shell of the calorimeter.  This outside shell along with the cover was suspended by a torsion wire and attached to a braking system so constructed that the torque experienced in operation could be measured easily.  The experiment consisted of (1) rotating the central shaft with paddles attached by means of an engine at a constant angular speed, $\omega$, for a known length of time, $t$, (2) determining the torque, $L$, required to keep the outer shell from rotating, (3) determining the rise in temperature, $\Delta T$, of the water of mass $m$ contained in the calorimeter of water equivalent $m'$, during the interval of rotation, and (4) computing, with a correction for a possible heat leakage to or from the surroundings, the desired mechanical equivalent of heat in accord with the following equation

$$L\omega t = J(m + m')c \, \Delta T \qquad (4)$$

of which $c$ is the specific heat of the water.  Rowland obtained $4.179 \times 10^7$ ergs/calory, a value about 0.3% less than Joule's.

**4. Magnetic and Electric Methods of Determining $J$.**  Radiation and conduction losses and losses due to friction between moving parts which enter as troublemakers in all determinations of $J$ are considerably reduced by the application of magnetic and electric methods.

If a metal block is placed in a rotating magnetic field, heat is developed by the eddy currents produced.  The idea of equating this heat to the work done in rotating the magnetic field was suggested by Baille and Ch. Féry in France in 1898.  A device (Fig. 3) satisfactory for carrying out the method was later utilized in 1927 by James Cork (1894–   ) of the University of Michigan.  As shown, the metal block is supported in a Dewar flask, for the purpose of reducing radiation losses, and is kept in a stationary position during operation by means of a shaft-and-pulley arrangement to which the necessary torque may be applied.  The quantities to be measured are

(1) the torque, $L$, required to keep the block from rotating, (2) the total angle, $\omega t$, through which the magnetic field has been rotated, and (3) the amount of heat, $mc\,\Delta T$, developed in the metal block. It is interesting that the strength of the

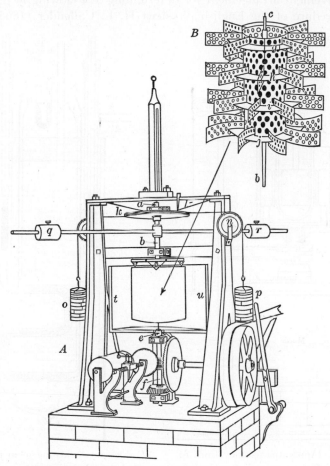

FIG. 2. *A*. Rowland's arrangement of apparatus for determining the mechanical equivalent of heat (Cork's *Heat*, 2nd ed., p. 176, New York, John Wiley & Sons, 1942). *B*. Details of construction of the central shaft with paddles attached (*Proc. Am. Acad. of Arts and Sciences*, **15**, 75, 1879).

magnetic field need not be measured. Eq. 4, with $c$ now referring to the specific heat of iron, applies here as for Rowland's method. The same year that Cork made a report of his work in America, a very careful study using the same method was reported by T. H. Laby (1880–  ) and E. O. Hercus (1891–  ) in Australia.

A convenient, precise method for the determination of $J$, nearly free from losses due to friction between moving parts, becomes available if the measured quantity of heat is produced by doing electrical work instead of mechanical work. In this method it is necessary to know the relation between the unit of electrical work (the international joule) and the unit of mechanical work (the absolute joule.) *

A convenient arrangement for determining $J$, following in principle the procedure of the English physicist H. L. Callender (1863–1930)

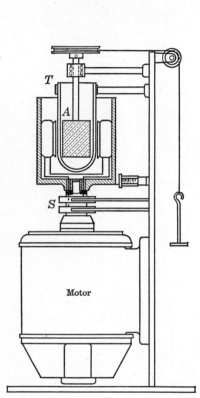

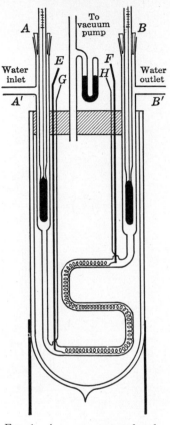

Fig. 3. Apparatus used by Cork to determine the mechanical equivalent of heat (by permission, J. M. Cork, *Heat,* 1st ed., p. 137, New York, John Wiley & Sons, 1933).

Fig. 4. An arrangement for the electrical determination of the mechanical equivalent of heat.

and his Canadian associate of McGill University in Montreal H. T. Barnes (1873–  ) reported in 1899, which makes use of differential thermometers or thermocouples, is shown in Fig. 4. In a Dewar flask,

* Previous to 1940, the international joule was greater than the absolute joule by about 0.034%. Beginning with 1940, it had been intended to change certain electrical units so that the electrical unit of work would likewise be the absolute joule. This plan, prevented by World War II, has now (1947) been put into effect.

there is mounted a coil of "resistance" wire, similar to that used in ordinary radiant heaters. It is enclosed in glass tubing whose ends are shaped to receive thermometers $A$, $B$, or thermocouple junctions, and to admit at $A'$ and to discharge at $B'$ a constant stream of water whose increase in temperature, $\Delta T$, on passage through the flask may be accurately measured. $E$ and $F$ represent leads for the heating current $I$, and $G$ and $H$ potential leads for measuring the potential difference, $V$, between the points where the heating current enters and leaves the "resistance" wire. The space surrounding the glass tubing inside the flask should be evacuated, and the glass tubing itself may well be silvered to reduce radiation losses.

In operation, one adjusts the water current, $m/t$, and the electric current, $I$, to a suitable steady value yielding a conveniently large temperature difference, $\Delta T$, such as will tend toward accuracy in the final determination of $J$, without causing an excessive radiation loss from the surroundings about $B$ to the surroundings about $A$. The equation leading to $J$ is

$$Jc \frac{m}{t} \Delta T = IV \tag{5}$$

of which $c$ is the specific heat of water.

Using the principle of the electrical method but not the apparatus described, an accurate determination of $J$ was made by W. Jaeger (1862– ) and H. v. Steinwehr in Germany in 1921. The evaluation of $J$ has been the subject of many highly accurate researches using various techniques in addition to those described.

**5. The Accepted Values and the Significance of $J$.** Before giving a precise value for $J$, it is necessary to consider how the calory is to be defined. Shall it be the amount of heat required to raise a gram of water from just 0°C to just 1°C, or from just 3.5°C to just 4.5°C, or from just 14.5°C to just 15.5°C, or $\frac{1}{100}$ of the amount of heat required to raise a gram of water from just 0°C to just 100°C, or perhaps something else? As is indicated in Fig. 5, taken from a 1939 report by N. S. Osborne (1875– ), H. F. Stimson (1890– ), and D. C. Ginnings (1905– ) of the National Bureau of Standards at Washington, variations of the order of 1% for the associated numerics are obtained depending on the choice. For the most commonly used, so-called 15°C-calory, $cal_{15}$, the value reported in 1939 as most probable by the National Bureau of Standards is $4.1858 \times 10^7$ ergs/$cal_{15}$ or 4.1858 *

* R. T. Birge (1887– ) of the University of California, in connection with a report in 1941 on fundamental units in physics, concluded that 4.1855 abs joules/$cal_{15}$ is a most probable value for $J$.

absolute joules/cal$_{15}$ or 4.1850 international joules/cal$_{15}$. The change from 4.1858 to 4.1850 results from the fact that the international joule of electrical measurements is 1.00019 times that of the absolute joule of mechanical measurements.

Designation of the mechanical equivalent of heat by $J$ seems to imply that it is a physical quantity. However, if heat may be viewed as energy which, when added to a body, shows up as energy of motion

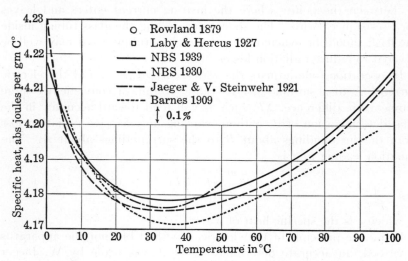

FIG. 5. Comparison of values of specific heat of water as obtained by various observers, including the 1939 recommendation of the National Bureau of Standards (Osborne, Stimson, and Ginnings, *J. Research, Natl. Bur. Standards,* **23,** 246, 1939).

and of position of the molecules and atoms of a body in accord with what has been said above, such a view of the nature of $J$ is hardly tenable. Instead, it is to be viewed as a conversion factor for converting expressions of energy stated in heat units into expressions stated in mechanical units. Written as the fraction 4.186 joules/1 cal with the numerator and denominator equal, $J$, like all conversion factors, is a convenient method of writing unity. Other, similar conversion factors based on experiment are 980.665 dy/gwt, 1000.028 cm³/liter, 0.99986 absolute ampere/international ampere, etc. In accord with the foregoing, we may write

$$80.0 \text{ cal} = 80.0 \text{ cal} \times J = 80.0 \text{ cal} \times 4.186 \frac{\text{joules}}{\text{cal}} = 335 \text{ joules} \quad (6)$$

Since 80.0 cal are equal to 335 joules, $J$ can have no other value than unity.

**6. First Law of Thermodynamics.** During the period 1840 to 1860, while concepts of heat and of energy were developing, there was much confusion of thought among leading physicists with regard to matters which seem simple to us now. One of the questions much discussed related to the possibility of perpetual motion. The work of Mayer and Joule, discussed above, as well as that of the great German physiologist, physicist, and mathematician Herman v. Helmholtz (1821–1894), the English engineer M. Rankine (1820–1872), the great English physicist Lord Kelvin (1824–1907), the Danish engineer L. A. Colding (1815–1888), the German physicist R. Clausius (1822–1888), and others, resulted in the formulation of the first two laws of thermodynamics. The third law was to wait for nearly three-fourths of a century, the zeroth law still longer. All these laws are generalizations of experience and cannot be deduced from more fundamental principles.

At present, we are able to consider only the first law. It states, in the words of Lord Kelvin, that, "When equal quantities of mechanical effect are produced by any means whatever from purely thermal effects, equal quantities of heat are put out of existence or are generated." This is definite recognition of the concept that heat is energy, the term invented to express a characteristic of bodies associated with the mechanical work which they can perform. Later this law was expanded to include all processes whatever, whether a heat exchange was involved or not. As such the principle is known as the conservation of energy. Acceptance of this principle denied, of course, the possibility of a "perpetual motion of the first kind" (perpetual motions of two other kinds will be discussed in Chapter IX), which was based on an assumed possible, continuous creation of energy for the performance of work.

In equation form, the first law of thermodynamics is usually written as

$$Q = \Delta U + W \tag{7}$$

where $Q$ represents the heat added to a body or system, while $\Delta U$ represents the increase in internal energy of and $W$ the work performed by the body or system in consequence of the addition of $Q$. To illustrate, as will be shown later, if, to 1 gm of water at 100°C and 1 A, one adds 540 cal of heat, the water will be completely vaporized, its internal energy will have increased by about 500 cal, and about 40 cal of work will be performed by the expanding water and water vapor.

**7. What is Heat?** All users of the term heat agree in saying that heat is energy. However, as to what energy shall be called heat, there is much confusion. A term closely associated with heat is internal energy. This term is self-explanatory and, with regard to its significance, there is no confusion. It has been mentioned in connection with Eq. 7 above. According to present conceptions, the internal energy a body possesses may be subdivided into: (1) the translational kinetic energy of its molecules, (2) the rotational kinetic energy of its molecules, (3) the intermolecular potential energy of its molecules, (4) the intramolecular vibrational energy of its atoms, (5) the radiant energy encompassed within its boundaries, and (6) various other energies associated with its atoms, their component parts, their structure, etc.

Some authors associate the term heat with the first item listed, others associate the term with the first two items only, others with all six items, while still others, in effect, include as heat possessed by a body certain work which it may have performed in expanding against external forces. Illustrating the last-mentioned usage, some would say that a gram of steam at 100°C and atmospheric pressure contains 540 cal of heat in excess of that possessed by a gram of water under the same conditions. Actually, however, the internal energy change accompanying the change from liquid to steam is only about 500 cal, in accord with what has been said above.

The confusion regarding heat is concerned wholly with discussions of stored energy and will disappear if the term is limited to energy in the process of transfer from one body to another because of a temperature difference. Such limitation would be in accord with usage in most instances. Fortunately this usage is quite in accord with the fundamental thermodynamic relation, Eq. 7, and the great superstructure of thermodynamics which is based on it. This procedure, as M. W. Zemansky (1900–   ) of the College of the City of New York has indicated in his *Heat and Thermodynamics*, 1st ed., suggests a similarity of relation for heat and internal energy much like that for rain and the water of a lake into which the rain is falling. The water that is rain while falling ceases to be rain the instant it merges with the lake water. With the foregoing in mind, the authors will attempt to limit the usage of the term heat to energy in process of transfer because of a temperature difference. Such, however, is the power of a habit of years' standing that the realization of such usage will probably be only partial.

**8. Thermal Processes Involving Mechanical Work.** Of the great number of thermal processes involving work, only a few need consideration here. Generally they will be characterized by some one or more conditions being maintained constant. Among the physical quantities involved in expressing such conditions, we have pressure $p$, temperature $T$, volume $V$, specific volume $v$ (or density $\delta$ since $\delta = 1/v$), internal energy $U$, entropy $S$, enthalpy $H$ (often but illogically called total heat), magnetic field strength also represented by $H$ (a symbol difficulty occurs when mentioned together with enthalpy), and electric field strength $E$. To these in astronomical considerations, gravitational field strength $g$ may be added. Values of $U$, $S$, and $H$ per unit mass are commonly represented by $u$, $s$, and $h$ and are referred to as specific internal energy, specific entropy, and specific enthalpy. Not all these quantities are independent of each other; enthalpy, for instance, is defined as $U + pV$.

Though thermal processes involving other quantities are physically of great interest, we shall restrict most of our considerations to those involving $p$, $v$, and $T$ only. Ordinarily we shall tacitly assume that certain quantities do not vary. As processes, we shall particularly consider those characterized by (1) a constant temperature (isothermal), (2) a constant pressure (isobaric or isopiestic), (3) a constant volume (isometric or isovolumic), (4) a constant entropy (isoentropic or reversible adiabatic), (5) a constant internal energy, $uV$, known as a free expansion (isenergic or irreversible adiabatic), (6) a constant enthalpy, $U + pV$, known as a porous plug expansion or throttling process. In illustrating these processes, it is convenient to consider a gas and to use a so-called $pV$ diagram for indicating changes.

Most of the processes mentioned involve the performance of work. How to determine the amount performed and to represent it on diagrams is important. Accordingly, before giving any detailed consideration to the processes, we shall discuss the methods of computing and of representing such work graphically and also certain associated units of measurements.

**9. Determination of Mechanical Work Performed.** Curiously there is uncertainty as to what is meant by the statement that a certain amount of work has been done. For this a rather common form of misstatement is responsible. We often say, for instance, that 100 ft-lb of energy appear as work. In so doing, we speak as though work were a form of energy coordinate with kinetic energy, potential energy, heat, etc. Actually what is meant is that 100 ft-lb of kinetic, potential, heat, etc., energy initially in some one body or group of bodies is transferred to some other body or group of bodies to appear there as kinetic, potential, heat, etc., energy by a process or processes that are not dependent upon a temperature difference. To say that 100 ft-lb of work have been performed by or on a given body is in agreement with this point of view and is justifiable. To say that 100 ft-lb of work appear in connection with a certain process is misleading and consequently unjustifiable.

When work, mechanical or of other type, is performed during a thermal process, it is important to know whether it is performed *by the body* experiencing the process or *on that body*. By general agreement, the distinction is based upon whether or not the displacements experienced by the body and the forces exerted by it are the same in direction or reversed. When work is done by the body, the displacements have the same directions as the forces exerted by the body have, and we often say that the body has done a positive amount of work. When work is done on a body, the displacements are necessarily opposite in direction to the directions of the forces exerted by the body, and we often say that the body has done a negative amount of work or that work has been done on the body. Except as energy may somehow be supplied to the body, performance of work *by the body* will be at the expense of its supply of internal energy. Except as energy may somehow be removed from the body, performance of work *on the body* will add to its supply of internal energy.

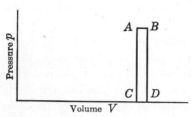

FIG. 6. A $p$-$V$ diagram for representing the positive work done by freezing water during freezing and the negative work done by melting ice, or, what is the same, the positive work done on ice by its surroundings, during melting.

Consider the $pV$ (pressure-volume) diagram of Fig. 6 for freezing water or melting ice carried out under the condition of both constant temperature and constant pressure. Let $A$ represent the condition as to $p$ and $V$ for a certain amount of water which is about to freeze and $B$ the corresponding condition for the ice just after freezing is complete. During the process of freezing, the pressure remains $p$ and the volume increases from $V_A$ to $V_B$, that is, by $\Delta V$. The work done, obviously mechanical work in this instance, is done by the water and is equal to $p \, \Delta V$.

That $p \, \Delta V$ represents work may be readily seen by viewing $p$ as $F/s$ and $\Delta V$ as $s \, \Delta l$, where $F$ represents the force exerted normal to area $s$ and $\Delta l$ a displacement in the same direction. The product $P \, \Delta V$, as seen, reduces to $F \, \Delta l$. In the diagram this work is represented by the area $ABDCA$. If $p$ is 1.000 A (1.000 atmosphere) and $V_A$ is 1000 cm$^3$, $V_B$ will be about 1090 cm$^3$ and the work done by the freezing water against external forces will be

$$W = 90 \text{ A cm}^3 \doteq 9.1 \text{ joules} \tag{8}$$

How the transfer from A cm$^3$ to joules is accomplished is discussed below. If the process is reversed and the same amount of ice is melted, external forces will perform 9.1 joules of work on it as it melts.

During freezing, water performs work at the expense of its own internal energy. During melting, energy supplied by external forces is added to the internal energy supply of the water (Eq. 7).

Usually, instead of plotting $p = f(V)$ as in Fig. 6, one plots $p = f(v)$, where $v$ is the specific volume. The plot then depends on the material and the process but not on the amount of material concerned. In accord therewith, we say that the work done against external forces per unit mass by water on freezing is 9.1 joules/kg.

**10. Units of Pressure, Mass, Specific Volume, and Work.** In practice, the same physical quantities are expressed in different problems in terms of different units. Despite this, the equations developed should be perfectly general and should hold regardless of the units specified. Mother Nature in her reckoning is not troubled by units. We, however, needing the units, will find it most convenient to consider them carefully.

As units of pressure, $p$, we shall use the mm-Hg, the dy/cm$^2$, the bar of the meteorologist, the lb/in.$^2$,[*] and the standard atmosphere,[†] A, which is based on 980.665 cm/sec$^2$ as the standard value for $g$. Their relation to one another is given by

$$1.00000 \text{ A} = 14.696 \text{ lb/in.}^2 * = 760.000 \text{ mm-Hg}$$

$$= 1.013246 \times 10^6 \text{ dy/cm}^2 = 1.013246 \text{ bar} \quad (9)$$

As units of mass, $m$, we shall use the gm, the kg, the pd,[*] the gm-mol, and the pd-mol. The relation of one to another of the first three is given by

$$1.00000 \text{ kg} = 1000.00 \text{ gm} = 2.2045 \text{ pd} * \quad (10)$$

A mass in gm-mol, or merely in mol as it will be commonly used in this book, can be obtained at any time with the aid of the molecular weight of the substance which is used as a conversion factor. Thus for oxygen

$$480 \text{ gm} = 480 \text{ gm} \times \frac{1.0000 \text{ mol}}{32.000 \text{ gm}} = 15.00 \text{ mol} \quad (11)$$

Volume relations are given by

$$1.00000 \text{ gmv} = 22.4140 \text{ liters} = 22,4146 \text{ cm}^3 = 1367.8 \text{ in.}^3 \quad (12)$$

---

* See footnote on p. 93.

† Another pressure unit, the 45° atmosphere, is based on 980.616 cm/sec$^2$ as the value of $g$ at 45° latitude and sea level. It will not be used in this book.

As units of specific volume, $v$, we shall use the $cm^3/gm$, the liter/gm, the in.$^3$/pd, the liter/mol, and the gmv/mol. The last two of these are frequently referred to as molal volume units.

As is evident from the above, one must distinguish, in precise work, between the milliliter, which is defined as $\frac{1}{1000}$ part of the volume of 1.00000 kg of pure water at 3.98°C, and the cubic centimeter, which is defined in terms of the standard meter. The relation is

$$1.000000 \text{ cm}^3 = 0.999972 \text{ ml} \tag{13}$$

The work units that are convenient depend upon the pressure and volume units used. They are the erg, the joule, the li-A, the calory, the ft-lb, and the btu. Determining their relations to one another is left for a problem.

Directly dependent upon the work units are the units used in the evaluation of $R$, the universal gas constant. The simplest expression for its value depends on the usual statement of the ideal gas law which, when rearranged, gives

$$R = \frac{pv}{T} \tag{14}$$

Introducing $v$ in the form of a molal volume and applying standard conditions, we have at once

$$R = \frac{1 \text{ A} \times 1 \text{ gmv/mol}}{273.16°\text{K}} = 0.0036609 \frac{\text{A gmv}}{\text{mol K}°} \tag{15}$$

The unit (A gmv)/(mol K°) may now be changed as desired. For example,

$$R = 0.0036609 \frac{\text{A gmv}}{\text{mol K}°} \times 1.01325 \times 10^6 \frac{(\text{dy/cm}^2)}{\text{A}} \times 22{,}414 \frac{\text{cm}^3}{\text{gmv}} \tag{16}$$

$$= 8.3142 \times 10^7 \text{ ergs/(mol K°)} = 8.3142 \text{ joules/(mol K°)}$$

$$= 1.9863 * \text{cal}_{15}/(\text{mol K}°)$$

**11. Isothermal Processes.** Isothermal or constant-temperature processes are common. Among those occurring most often, we have the freezing of water, the melting of ice, the boiling of water, and the condensing of steam. Similar changes for other substances, the drawing of steam into an engine cylinder, the charging of a storage battery, the dissolving of salt in water, the curdling of milk, and a host of other

---

* Birge (see footnote on p. 99) suggests $1.9864_7$ cal$_{15}$/(mol K°) as a most probable value for $R$.

processes provided their temperatures are maintained constant, belong to this class. Many, but not all, such processes are accompanied by expansions or contractions and consequently the performance of work.

One instance of work performed during an isothermal process has been discussed in connection with Fig. 6. Often, however, the situation differs in that the pressure does not remain constant. Such is the case for a gas. As shown in Fig. 7, when an ideal gas undergoes a gradual isothermal expansion, as from $A$ to $B$, the pressure decreases gradually in such fashion that the product $pv$ remains constant. Since

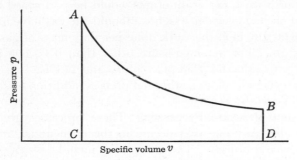

FIG. 7. A $p$-$v$ diagram for an ideal gas undergoing a reversible isothermal change of volume.

$v$ represents a volume per unit mass rather than the actual volume of a given amount of gas the product $p \, \Delta v$ represents work done per unit mass and will normally be expressed in ergs/gm or, more often still, in joules/mol. The work per unit mass, done by the gas, assumed ideal, as it passes from $A$ to $B$ is given by the integral $\int_{v_A}^{v_B} p \, dv$ * and is represented by the area $ABDCA$. For the ideal gas at constant temperature, we have

$$pv = k \tag{17}$$

For a temperature of 0°C, $k$ has the value $RT_0$, where $R$ is the universal gas constant and $T_0$ is 273.16°K. The work per unit mass done in this case is

$$\frac{W}{m} = \int_{v_A}^{v_B} p \, dv = RT_0 \int_{v_A}^{v_B} \frac{dv}{v} = RT_0 \ln \frac{v_B}{v_A} \tag{18}$$

* For those who have not studied calculus, it may be said that this integral represents the limiting value for the sum, as $n$ becomes indefinitely large, of the terms $p_1 \, dv$, $p_2 \, dv$, $p_3 \, dv \cdots p_n \, dv$, where $dv$ is $1/n$th of $(v_B - v_A)$, the total change in $v$, and where $p_1$, $p_2$, $p_3$, etc., are the average pressures, as represented by the curve $AB$, corresponding to the first, the second, the third, etc., $dv$ taken in order in going from $A$ to $B$.

If, in addition to $T_0$, specific volumes of 1.00 gmv/mol and 2.00 gmv/mol are specified, the work per unit mass becomes

$$\frac{W}{m} = \frac{1}{273} \frac{A \text{ gmv}}{\text{mol K}^\circ} \times 273^\circ K \ln 2.00$$

$$= 0.693 \frac{A \text{ gmv}}{\text{mol}} = 1570 \frac{\text{joules}}{\text{mol}} \tag{19}$$

Just how much work per gram of gas would be performed by the gas will depend on its molecular weight. Should the gas have a molecular weight of 32.0 gm/mol, the work done per unit mass of gas would be 49.0 joules/gm. For a temperature other than 0°C, one introduces the appropriate value for $T$ in place of $T_0$ and 273°K.

In the carrying out of an isothermal process, addition or subtraction of heat will generally occur.

**12. Constant-Pressure Processes.** These processes are the most familiar of all. Any one that occurs in the open under atmospheric pressure is such a process. The group may include, of course, certain processes included under other classifications. The melting of ice, the freezing of water, etc., discussed in connection with Fig. 6 are specific illustrations. As shown in that figure, the work performed by the body or on the body is then the constant pressure times the change in volume. Normally these processes involve a transfer of heat.

**13. Constant-Volume Processes.** These processes often take place inside rigid containers. They usually involve pressure changes. The process which the gas in the bulb of a constant-volume gas thermometer undergoes on heating is an illustration of the rigid-container type. Other illustrations occur in combustions in bomb calorimeters, in cases of diffusion without change of volume, and in the rearrangement of atoms in certain crystalline substances at what are called lambda points (see later). No work is done against outside forces. Normally, heat exchanges are involved.

**14. Reversible Adiabatic Processes.** Very often the word "reversible" is omitted in describing these processes. They are then described merely as adiabatic. These processes involve no heat exchange. The condition of being reversible means that by slight changes of conditions, e.g., the pressure, the process may be caused to proceed in the reverse direction. An instance of a close approach to a reversible process in nature is the rising of air at the center of a cyclonic whirl where normally, without the addition or subtraction of heat, the air changes from one condition with respect to pressure and temperature to another. That it is reversible is shown by the fact that, with but a slight change in the vertical pressure gradient, there is the neighboring anticyclonic whirl with its movement of air downward. Illustrations of adiabatic processes in industry are common. Those connected with the operation of engines will be discussed more fully later.

**15. Free Expansion.** Were a gas-filled incandescent lamp placed inside an air-tight chamber, the surrounding air removed by a vacuum pump, and the glass of the lamp bulb broken, the argon-nitrogen mixture within would expand freely to fill the air-tight chamber. This process would be a free expansion. It is not reversible. No work is done against external forces. Many actual processes, which we treat as reversibly adiabatic, or reversibly isothermal, etc., are actually to a slight extent free expansion processes.

**16. Porous-Plug Expansion.** When air or other gas is permitted to pass from a region of one constant pressure through a small orifice or a porous plug to another region with a lower pressure which is also maintained constant, we have a porous-plug expansion. This process is not reversible. It differs from a free expansion in that the expanding gas in a porous-plug expansion does work on the gas at the lower pressure in shoving it out of the way and in that work must be done on the gas when at the higher pressure in order to maintain that pressure. This process is of considerable economic importance in the liquefaction of gases from the air and in the drying of steam for use in engines. It will be discussed at some length in the chapter relating to gases.

## PROBLEMS

**1.** In a particular experiment for the determination of the mechanical equivalent of heat, two bodies with a combined mass of 19.74 kg fell a distance of 107.0 cm thirty times in succession and caused a 0.2503-C° temperature rise of the calorimeter and contents whose combined water equivalent was 5.920 kg. What value for $J$ do these data yield? Assume 980.5 cm/sec² as the acceleration of gravity.

**2.** An experimenter, using Rowland's method for determining $J$, finds that a calorimeter and contents with a water equivalent of 3.50 kg are heated at a rate of 0.250 C°/min in the neighborhood of 15°C when the central shaft and paddles are rotated at a rate of 240 rpm. What, except for the effects of losses, must be the necessary torque to maintain the calorimeter shell and attached vanes at rest? Express the result in m-kgwt/rad and in joules/rad.

**3.** An experimenter, using Rowland's method for determining $J$, finds that a calorimeter and contents with a water equivalent of 6.25 pd are heated through a range of 2.50 F° in the neighborhood of 60°F during an interval of 6.00 min when the paddle shaft is rotated at a rate of 180 rpm and the resisting torque is 1.79 ft-lb/rad. What is the value of $J$ that results?

**4.** An experimenter, using the magnetic method of Laby and Hercus and of Cork, found that a resisting torque of 500 gwt-cm/rad was required for a particular case when the motor was operating at a speed of 1725 rpm. What was the rate of development of heat in the metal block?

**5.** In planning for an experiment employing the electric method of determining $J$, a 25.0-ohm resistance wire is to be used. About what must be the heating current through the wire and the potential drop between its terminals in order that just 4.50-C° increase of temperature of the water may be produced when the water flows through at a rate of 0.600 liter/min?

**6.** Determine, with the aid of Table I of Chapter III, the fractional part of the specific heat of water at 100°C that results from the work done by water on expanding against the atmosphere.

**7.** Fill out the accompanying chart to an accuracy of 1 part in 1000. Keep this chart for future reference.

|          | erg | joule | calory | li-A | gmv-A | ft-lb | btu |
|----------|-----|-------|--------|------|-------|-------|-----|
| 1 erg =   |     |       |        |      |       |       |     |
| 1 joule = |     |       |        |      |       |       |     |
| 1 calory =|     |       |        |      |       |       |     |
| 1 li-A =  |     |       |        |      |       |       |     |
| 1 gmv-A = |     |       |        |      |       |       |     |
| 1 ft-lb = |     |       |        |      |       |       |     |
| 1 btu =   |     |       |        |      |       |       |     |

**8.** Express the value of $R$ to 1 part in 1000 in

$$\frac{\text{gmv-A}}{\text{mol K}°}, \frac{\text{li-A}}{\text{mol K}°}, \frac{\text{joule}}{\text{mol K}°}, \frac{\text{erg}}{\text{mol K}°}, \frac{\text{ft-lb}}{\text{pd-mol R}°}, \frac{\text{btu}}{\text{pd-mol R}°}$$

Keep these data for future reference.

**9.** Water, vaporizing at a pressure of just 1 A and 100°C, changes in specific volume from 1.043 cm³/gm to 1677 cm³/gm. What fractional part of the heat of vaporization of water (540 cal/gm) is accounted for by the work done in pushing the atmosphere back?

**10.** A gram of water vapor at 100°C and 1.00 A is expanded isothermally until the pressure is 0.50 A. What work is done by the water vapor? Boyle's law holds for this condition.

**11.** Assuming Boyle's law to hold, compute the work done in compressing isothermally 1 mol of hydrogen at 0°C and 1 A to 5 A. Repeat for 1 mol of helium.

**12.** The American Falls at Niagara is 162 ft high. What increase in temperature might be expected for the water on going over the falls? What factors might prevent the realization of this temperature change?

**13.** Express in kilocalories and btu's the amount of kinetic energy possessed by a 10-in., 300-pd projectile moving with a velocity of 2800 ft/sec. The energy associated with the rotation of the bullet is comparatively negligible.

# CHAPTER V

## CALORIMETRY

**1. Introduction.** Heat measurements are highly important in science and in industry. Sometimes we are concerned with the quantity of heat that may be supplied, principally for storage purposes temporarily or otherwise, to a given amount of material, as for instance the fluid used in the cooling of an airplane engine. The specific heat of the material, expressing the quantity of heat that must be supplied per unit mass and unit temperature change, is a characteristic of the material which is then of great interest. At other times we are concerned with the quantity of heat that is developed by a chemical reaction, as from burning coal gas; or the quantity of heat absorbed with a change of state, as for melting ice or vaporizing water; or the rate of transmission of heat through a body, as through the walls of a refrigerator; or the rate of transfer of internal energy from one body to another by radiation, as in industrial heat interchangers. These last-mentioned processes deal with special characteristics of materials, namely heats of combustion, heats of fusion, heats of vaporization, thermal conductivities, radiant emissivities, and absorptivities. Methods of measuring and of application of such characteristics form much of the subject matter of the chapters that follow.

A determination of one of the above-named characteristics always involves in some form a measurement of energy that has been produced or transferred. In the way of methods, there are several that are reliable and approved. Which one shall be used in any particular instance will depend on the specific problem, the apparatus available, and the will of those who direct the experiment.

The theory and practice of making measurements of quantities of heat is generally classed as calorimetry. In this chapter we discuss certain of the well-recognized methods. It should be understood, however, that, with regard to certain details, different experimenters differ and that only in the rare case can one truthfully say that his preferred procedure yields, within the limits of experimental procedure, exactly what is sought.

**2. Definitions.** The most common units of heat quantity employed in scientific and engineering work are the calory, already defined in Chapter IV, and the *British thermal unit*, or for short the btu.

The calory is defined as the amount of heat required to raise 1 gm of pure water from 14.5°C to 15.5°C when the pressure is 1 A. Similarly, the btu is defined as the quantity of heat required to raise the temperature of 1 pd of pure water from 59.5°F to 60.5°F when the pressure is 1 A.

In addition to these definitions of units, discussions of calorimetry require the defining of certain physical quantities, in particular the specific heat of a substance, the thermal capacitance of a body, and the water equivalent of a body.

The *specific heat of a substance* at any temperature and pressure for a specified condition during heating is defined as the quantity of heat which must be added per unit mass of the substance and per unit temperature rise. The defining equation is

$$c = \frac{Q}{m \, \Delta T} \tag{1}$$

Common units are the cal/(gm C°), the btu/(pd F°),* and the joule/(gm K°). If the unit of mass chosen is the gram-atom or the mole, the specific heat is known as the *atomic heat* or the *molecular heat*, respectively. The units are then the cal/(gram-atom C°) etc. Theory and methods of measurement are considered in the following chapter.

The *thermal capacitance* or, as frequently called, the *heat capacity of a body* is defined as the product of its mass and its specific heat. It is commonly expressed in cal/K° and in btu/F°. It is a characteristic of a particular body and not of a particular substance as is specific heat.

The *water equivalent* of a body is defined as the product of the mass of the body by the ratio of its specific heat to that of water. Its units are those of mass. In any system of units where the specific heat of water is by definition one unit, the numerics accompanying expressions for the thermal capacitance and the water equivalent of a body will be identical. Thus the thermal capacitance of a 20-pd block of iron is about 2.25 btu/F°, and its water equivalent is likewise about 2.25 pd.

**3. General Considerations Regarding Methods.** A measurement of heat in calorimetry is usually based on one of two general relations.

* See footnote, p. 93.

According to the first, the heat $Q$ under consideration is equated to that required to raise or lower the calorimetric substance and its container and certain accessory material through a certain range of temperature $\Delta T$. Thus

$$Q = (mc + m'c') \, \Delta T \tag{2}$$

of which $mc$ is thermal capacitance of the calorimetric substance and $m'c'$ that of the container and accessory material. In case water is used, Eq. 2 may be written as

$$Q = (m + m_w')c_w \, \Delta T \tag{3}$$

where $m_w'$ is the water equivalent of the container and the accessory material and $c_w$ the specific heat of water.

According to the second general relation, the heat is equated to the electrical energy transformed in producing it. Thus

$$Q = \int I V \, dt \tag{4}$$

of which $I$ represents electric current and $V$ potential difference, or, considering rates,

$$\frac{dQ}{dt} = I V \tag{5}$$

Of the two relations, Eq. 5 is probably the more important. Frequently it is used to calibrate a piece of apparatus where ostensibly the first relation is being used.

Regardless of the method of calorimetry employed, there is always some uncertainty, some correction to be made. In certain instances the corrections are negligibly small. In other instances they have a considerable bearing on the final result. Generally the uncertainty relates to a temperature change. Naturally, it is important that, at all times during an experiment, the temperature of the calorimetric substance shall be as nearly the same throughout as possible. For liquids this means stirring, which itself requires additional corrections. Where solids are used for the calorimetric materials, this condition of approximate uniformity of temperature points toward the use of a material having a high thermal conductivity such as silver or copper.

There are various calorimetric procedures. The one to be selected for a particular task depends on the conditions that will be encountered. Must the measurement of heat transferred, evolved, or absorbed be made at high, moderate, or low temperatures? Is the rate uniform or variable? Is the process of long, moderate, or short duration? Is the amount of heat involved large, moderate, or minute?

Is a precise, a moderately accurate, or only a rough determination required? These are some of the questions that must be answered in advance of an actual determination. Here we shall consider a selection of certain widely used methods: (1) a standard compensated-loss method, (2) an adiabatic method, (3) a steady flow method, (4) a microcalorimetric method, (5) a bomb-calorimeter method.

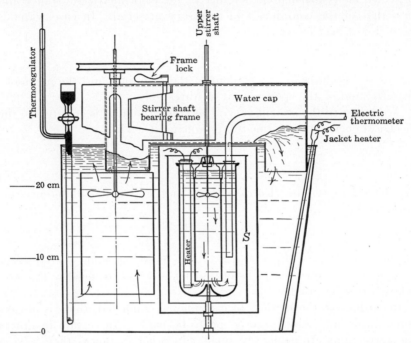

FIG. 1.  A modern precision calorimeter as used at the Geophysical Laboratory in Washington (by permission, W. P. White, *The Modern Calorimeter*, Chemical Catalog Co., 1928).

## 4. A Standard Compensated-Loss Method.

As the name implies, this method requires the application of a correction to compensate for the loss of heat to or from the chamber where heating effects are measured. For this purpose, temperature-time readings are taken. The method is particularly suitable for precision measurements which can be carried out at moderate temperatures, where the quantity of heat is of moderate amount and the time involved is rather brief.

A modern precision calorimeter, used at the Geophysical Laboratory of the Carnegie Institution of Washington, D. C., as described by W. P. White (1867–   ), is shown in Fig. 1. It embodies the following features: (1) an inner metal chamber containing the calorimetric fluid, continuously stirred, within which an electric heater, a temperature-measuring device, and a device for cooling the fluid are immersed; (2) a jacket of continuously stirred water, with heater, completely surrounding but separated from the metal chamber containing the calorimetric fluid, thus providing an environment of uniform temperature; (3) a convection and radiation shield $S$, which serves to reduce convection and radiation heat losses and thus to decrease thermal leakage; (4) a tight, water-cooled cover which practically eliminates evapora-

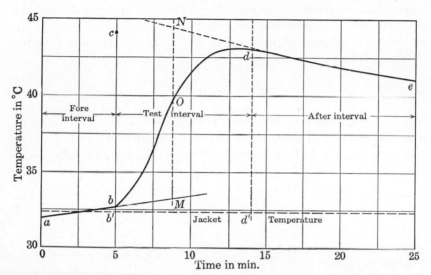

FIG. 2.  A time-temperature plot for a calorimeter such as that shown in Fig. 1.  The specific heat of a sugar is being determined.

tion; (5) platinum resistance thermometers for measuring the calorimetric substance and the water-jacket temperatures.

A temperature-time plot for an actual test using a calorimeter of this type is shown in Fig. 2.  Three intervals are shown during all of which temperature-time readings were taken and plotted.  During the *fore interval*, the temperature variation shown by *ab* is due to the differential effects of stirrer action and thermal leakage to the jacket, with the former predominating greatly.  During the *test interval*, the heat to be measured is transferred to the calorimetric fluid.  The course of the temperature-time curve is then largely determined by this fact. The effects of stirring and thermal leakage are greatly outweighed. During the *after interval*, the temperature variation is once more determined by the differential effects of stirrer action and of thermal leakage.  This time the latter predominates.  From data such as these, the experimenter has the task of computing the rise in temperature $T_c - T_b$ (Fig. 2) of the calorimetric fluid had there been no heat developed by stirring and no thermal leakage from the calorimeter chamber to the water jacket.

Granted that one has determined the $\Delta T(= T_c - T_b)$ for the addition of an unknown amount of heat, $Q$, more information is needed before $Q$ may be expressed quantitatively. One must effectively have the water equivalent of the calorimetric fluid, container, and accessory apparatus in order to apply Eqs. 2 or 3 directly, or he must calibrate the calorimeter to determine its constant, $A$, that is its temperature rise per unit amount of heat added, and then to determine $Q$ by the evident relation

$$Q = \frac{\Delta T}{A} \tag{6}$$

The latter of these two procedures is generally employed. Ordinarily, a known amount of heat, $Q_0$, is developed electrically (Eq. 4) in the same calorimeter and the corresponding $(\Delta T)_0$ for this condition is determined as was $\Delta T$. One obtains at once, on replacing $Q$ and $\Delta T$ of Eq. 6 by $Q_0$ and $(\Delta T)_0$,

$$A = \frac{(\Delta T)_0}{Q_0} \tag{7}$$

and then, with the aid of Eq. 6, the sought-for $Q$.

With the general plan for measuring an unknown quantity of heat in mind, we may now return to the details of procedure which are mostly concerned with corrections but finally lead to the determination of a desired $T_c$.

**5. Newtonian Leakage and Stirring Corrections.** Although in Fig. 2 the temperature of the calorimetric substance is shown as generally higher than that of its surroundings, it actually may be about the same or lower. Many workers prefer to start a test with the temperature of the calorimetric substance initially below that of the surroundings by an amount approximately equal to that by which it shall be above when the test is over. Whatever the condition as to these temperatures, account must be taken of the thermal leakage through the space between the inner calorimeter chamber and the jacket.

The simplest accounting for the leakage between a body and its surroundings assumes the Newtonian law for thermal leakage (often referred to as Newton's law of cooling. This states that the rate of transfer of heat to the body, due to this leakage only, $(dQ/dt)_N$, at any instant, varies strictly as the difference in temperature between that of the body, in this instance, the calorimetric fluid, and that of the surroundings, in this instance, the jacket, which is ordinarily kept constant. Thus, with $T$ as the fluid temperature and $T_j$ as the jacket temperature,

$$\left(\frac{dQ}{dt}\right)_N = -k(T - T_j) \tag{8}$$

The quantity $k$ depends upon the nature of the surfaces concerned, their areas, their separation, the atmosphere, and the structures in the intervening space.

Dividing both sides of Eq. 8 by $mc$, the thermal capacitance of the calorimeter chamber and its contents, we obtain

$$\frac{1}{mc}\left(\frac{dQ}{dT}\right)_N = \left(\frac{dT}{dt}\right)_N = -\frac{1}{mc}k(T - T_j) = -K(T - T_j) \tag{9}$$

$K$ is a characteristic of the calorimeter known as its *leakage modulus*. Units for its expression are reciprocal seconds, minutes, etc. Given that the temperature of a calorimetric fluid is different from that of the surroundings and that no source of heat is present, this modulus describes the rate of return of the temperature of the fluid to that of the surrounding jacket. Of two calorimeters, which initially deviate from equilibrium conditions as to temperature by the same amount, the one possessing the higher modulus returns the more quickly to equilibrium conditions. Without other cause for a change of temperature such as stirring, the reciprocal of a leakage modulus would equal the time required for the temperature difference $T - T_j$ to disappear completely were the initial rate for $(dT/dt)_N$ to remain constant. Thus with an initial leakage modulus for a calorimeter of 0.01 min$^{-1}$, and an initial 5 C° temperature difference, the initial rate of cooling is 0.05 C°/min, and the time that would be required for the temperature difference to disappear, could that initial rate of cooling be maintained, would be 5 C°/(0.05 C°/min) or 100 min. More with regard to its physical significance will appear shortly.

For a constant $T_j$ and a condition of heat development in the calorimeter chamber due only to stirring, as during the "after interval" (Fig. 2), an observed change of $T - T_j$ is determined by two factors. (1) the Newtonian leakage, and (2) the heating due to stirrer action. Thus, for the specified conditions, the observed rate of change of temperature $dT/dt$ is given by

$$\frac{dT}{dt} = \left(\frac{dT}{dt}\right)_N + \left(\frac{dT}{dt}\right)_S \tag{10}$$

of which $(dT/dt)_N$ is the rate due to Newtonian leakage and $\left(\dfrac{dT}{dt}\right)_S$ that due to stirring. Rearrangement, taking account of Eq. 9, yields

$$\left(\frac{dT}{dt}\right)_N = \frac{dT}{dt} - \left(\frac{dT}{dt}\right)_S = -K(T - T_j) \qquad (11)$$

Solving for $K$, we obtain

$$K = \frac{(dT/dt)_S - (dT/dt)}{T - T_j} \qquad (12)$$

In practice $K$ is determined from observations during the fore and after intervals. For ease and preciseness of determination of $dT/dt$, one should regraph the data for these intervals to yield geometric slopes of about unity.

During the fore interval for the case of Fig. 2, for which the Newtonian leakage is negligible ($T_a$, $T_b$, and $T_j$ are nearly the same), the rate at which the temperature rises is due almost entirely to stirring and therefore equals $(dT/dt)_S$. Measurement of the slope of the line $ab$ shows this rate to be about $+0.15$ C°/min. During the after interval, as may be seen, $dT/dt$ is about $-\dfrac{43.0°C - 41.0°C)}{10 \text{ min}}$ or $-0.20$ C°/min. With 9.5 C° as the average value of $(T - T_j)$ for this interval, $K$, the leakage modulus for the calorimeter, is found by Eq. 12 to be 0.0368/min. This means that, when the temperature of the calorimetric substance exceeds that of the jacket by 5.0 C°, say, its rate of cooling, were stirring absent, would be 5.0 C° $\times$ 0.0368/min. or 0.18 C°/min.

Obviously, the leakage and the stirring considerations apply to the "test interval" as well as to the other intervals. Also, during this interval, there occurs the rate of rise of temperature $(dT/dt)_P$ which is due to the phenomenon being measured. The observed rate of temperature rise includes all three effects,

$$\frac{dT}{dt} = \left(\frac{dT}{dt}\right)_S + \left(\frac{dT}{dt}\right)_N + \left(\frac{dT}{dt}\right)_P \qquad (13)$$

Rearranging and making use of Eq. 9 gives

$$(dT)_P = dT - \left(\frac{dT}{dt}\right)_S dt + K(T - T_j)\, dt \qquad (14)$$

We may now calculate the desired temperature rise $T_c - T_b$, that which would have occurred in the calorimeter had there been no temperature changes due to stirring or Newtonian leakage.

$$T_c - T_b = \int_{T_b}^{T_c} (dT)_P$$

$$= \int_{T_b}^{T_d} dT - \int_{t_b}^{t_d} \left(\frac{dT}{dt}\right)_S dt + \int_{t_b}^{t_d} K(T - T_j)\, dt \tag{15}$$

$$= (T_d - T_b) - \left(\frac{dT}{dt}\right)_S (t_d - t_b) + K \int_{t_b}^{t_d} (T - T_j)\, dt$$

Thus the correct temperature rise, suitable for use as $\Delta T$ in Eq. 2, is equal to the uncorrected temperature rise $T_d - T_b$ plus a stirring correction plus a Newtonian leakage correction.

The quantities $(dT/dt)_S$ and $K$ may be determined as earlier described; $T_d - T_b$ can be read from the graph of Fig. 2; the integral of Eq. 15 is most easily obtained by determining in appropriate physical units the quantity represented by the area $b'bOdd'b'$ of Fig. 2. For this purpose a planimeter may be used or one may use a trapezoidal summation procedure. With the integration done by either method the data of this figure yield approximately 64.8 C° min. This multiplied by $K$, 0.0368 min$^{-1}$, gives $+2.37$ C° as the Newtonian leakage correction. The stirring correction is given by the product of the constant rate $-0.15$ C°/min and the length of the test interval $t_d - t_b$, or 9.0 min, and is $-1.35$ C°. The combined correction is $+1.02$ C° and when applied to the observed rise $T_d - T_b$, or 10.30 C°, yields the desired rise $T_c - T_b$, or 11.32 C°. The further procedure for determining $Q$ has already been described above in connection with Eqs. 6 and 7.

It is to be emphasized that the test interval is ended, not when the maximum temperature is attained, but some time afterwards, when a uniform rate of return of the calorimeter temperature to that of the surroundings has been established. At the maximum, where the temperature is momentarily stationary, heat is being supplied to the calorimeter at just the rate that it is being dissipated by thermal leakage, and, hence, not all the heat to be transferred has been so transferred. The exact stopping point is not important because any decrease in the observed $T_d$ caused by extending the time limit will be balanced by changes in the time interval $t_d - t_b$ occurring in the stirring correction and by changes in the integral forming part of the leakage correction.

Though the above procedure yields precise results, it is sometimes found possible to eliminate some of the labor of integration involved in applying Eq. 15. For instance, at the Bureau of Standards, it has been found possible, in making certain types of determinations, to project line $ab$ of Fig. 2 forward and line $de$ backward and to select the points $M$ and $N$ in such a way that the vertical line connecting them is cut by the test-interval curve at a point $O$ such that $MO$ is 62% of $MN$. The temperature interval represented by $MN$ is then taken as the $\Delta T$ of Eq. 3. This procedure when theoretically applicable requires a careful determination of $T = f(t)$ for the test interval. For data plotted in Fig. 2, this method fails by an appreciable amount.

It was originally proposed by Count Rumford (1753–1814) to eliminate the thermal loss by conducting the experiment so that the jacket temperature is equal to the average of the initial and final calorimeter temperatures. Thus, although heat would be lost to the surroundings during the latter part of the run, this would be largely compensated for by the heat gained from the surroundings during the first part of the run. Such compensation usually would not be complete because the initial rate of increase of temperature of the calorimeter fluid usually would be more rapid than the final rate; hence more time would be spent by the calorimeter fluid above the temperature of the surroundings than below it. It is possible, however, to choose such a temperature for the surroundings that the net heat loss will be nearly zero. Errors are involved, however; and the method, satisfactory for a first approximation, is rarely employed where precision is sought.

**6. A Copper Block Calorimeter Method.** The principle of operation for this method is the same as that described for the standard compensated-loss method except that the calorimetric substance being a solid cannot be stirred. Its high thermal conductivity is relied on to maintain a nearly constant temperature at all times. A design by White of the Geophysical Laboratory in Washington is shown in Fig. 3. Interesting features are the stopcock key with a large tubular passage, an automatic device, not shown, for closing the calorimeter on entrace of a charge, and the opening to the copper block at the bottom for the insertion of a releasing rod for loosening the small receptacle $B$ when necessary.

**7. The Adiabatic Method.** In 1906, Theodore Richards (1868–1928) of Harvard University, winner of the Nobel prize in chemistry in 1914, suggested that thermal leakage might be eliminated by maintaining the jacket temperature at all times equal to that of the calorimetric fluid. The real advantage of the method consists of the minimizing or the eliminating of the uncertain convection, conduction, and radiation losses. Obviously, where the changes in temperature are rapid, the condition of no temperature difference between jacket and calorimetric fluid is difficult if not impossible to maintain. For runs of short duration, the adiabatic method seems to offer no advantage over the standard compensated-loss method with a well-designed calorimeter. For long runs, the adiabatic method is undoubtedly superior.

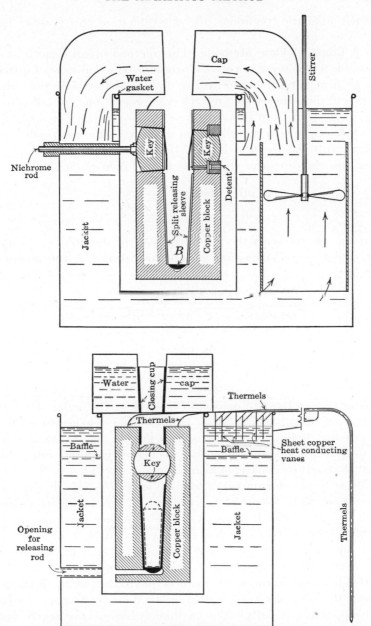

FIG. 3.  A copper block calorimeter designed by White and used at the Geophysical Laboratory in Washington.  The two sections shown are at right angles to each other.  (By permission, W. P. White, *The Modern Calorimeter*, Chemical Catalog Co., 1928.)

Granted adiabatic conditions, the determination of a $Q$ using Eqs. 6 and 7 is obvious.

**8. A Constant-Flow Method.**  This method of calorimetry is only applicable where there is a steady rate of production in or of introduction of heat into the calorimetric fluid which passes through the calorimeter in a steady stream.  In case precautions are taken to prevent loss of heat from this stream or to render such losses negligible, the whole of the heat input is taken up by the calorimetric fluid when a steady state has been attained.  If there are no losses to accessory apparatus, the rate of production of heat is then given by

$$\frac{dQ}{dt} = \frac{dm}{dt} \cdot c_p(T_2 - T_1) \tag{16}$$

where $dm/dt$ represents the rate of passage of the fluid, $c_p$ its specific heat, and $(T_2 - T_1)$ its change of temperature.  A continuous-flow

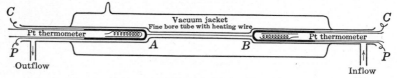

FIG. 4.  The continuous-flow calorimeter used by Callendar and Barnes (*Phys. Rev.*, **10,** 202, 1900).

calorimeter used by the English physicist H. L. Callendar (1863–1930) and the Canadian physicist H. T. Barnes (1873–   ), in which the heat was developed electrically, is shown in Fig. 4.  As stated in Chapter IV, this method of calorimetry has been used in determining the so-called electrical equivalent of heat.

Ordinarily the elimination of leakage losses requires that two similar tests be made, for which $c_p$, $T_2$, and $T_1$ will be identical but for which $dQ/dt$ and $dm/dt$ will vary.  The difference equation, obtained by subtracting one observation equation based on Eq. 16 from the other, will obviously be free from any leakage loss, and Eq. 16 is then more nearly strictly applicable.  There still remains, as unaccounted for, the difference in the heating effects due to the forcing of the liquid through the calorimeter.  A correction for this may be made, however.

An apparatus based on this method, which seems nearly perfect from the standpoint of leakage losses, has been used by the Polish physical chemist W. Swietoslawski (1881–   ), in certain microcalorimetric studies.  As shown in Fig. 5, the calorimetric fluid is caused to flow back and forth through a maze of spherical concentric shells.

Entering at the bottom of the maze at the temperature of the surrounding bath, the liquid first passes through the outermost shell, and then gradually inward until it passes around chamber $A$, from which there is leakage of heat outward at a rate dependent on the process under study. Thereafter the calorimetric fluid passes by the thermocouple junction $t$ (appears as a thermometer bulb in the figure), which is used to measure the temperature to which the calorimetric fluid has been raised. Even here, as can be seen, loss of temperature by the fluid is guarded against until it is well past the thermojunction. Of the thermal processes studied, the metabolism of a mouse is an example.

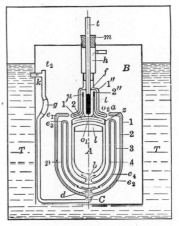

It is obvious that, with sufficient shielding, leakage losses may be reduced to zero or as near zero as is necessary. The only correction that need be made is for the work done and consequent heating produced by the forcing of the liquid through the maze. This can be determined by a check run during which there is no source of heat at the center. This rise of temperature taken from that observed with the active substance in place gives the desired $T_2 - T_1$ of Eq. 16 for its strict application.

FIG. 5.   A Swietoslawski flow microcalorimeter with negligible leakage loss (courtesy of W. Swietoslawski).

Obviously this device and method are applicable only for cases where the rate of evolution of heat is constant or nearly so. It would seem to be an improvement on the Barnes device.

**9. Swietoslawski's Microcalorimeter Method Employing Newtonian Leakage.** This method, first used by W. Swietoslawski in 1927, was designed particularly for the measurement of the rates of heat production and the heats produced in cases where the processes are prolonged and the rate of production is very small. Illustrations are the evolutions of heat in connection with (1) radioactive changes, (2) germination of grain, (3) metabolism of small animals, (4) setting of cements, (5) aging of alloys, and (6) gradual mechanical distortion of metallic solids, as lead, when a bar of it is supported by strings. In use as will be seen later it has been operated as an adiabatic calorimeter and as a "Newtonian cooling" calorimeter.

For such work as the above, Swietoslawski and his co-workers found it necessary not only to control the temperature of the so-called constant-temperature jacket of the calorimeter which he was able to keep at fixed values to within 0.001 C° or 0.002 C° or to vary gradually, but also to control the temperature of the room in which the calorimeter was placed, which he was able to keep at fixed values to within 0.1 C°. Fig. 6 shows diagrammatically the construction of the calorimeter which they used. The substance under study was placed in the center of a sphere, E, of glass or of copper which was suspended by three silk threads at the center of a large glass bulb capped with a

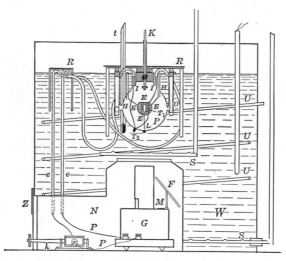

FIG. 6. Swietoslawski's microcalorimeter, employing Newtonian leakage (courtesy of W. Swietoslawski).

collar and plate. The water jacket, W, contained a stirrer, a thermometer, a large thermoregulator filled with toluol, and an electric heater, not shown. In space N, also protected from temperature variations by the water jacket, a galvanometer and a commutator connected to terminals of thermocouples were located. One couple of prime importance is that one whose warm and cold junctions are connected separately to the surfaces of spheres E and P and whose indications were directly dependent on the rate of production of heat in E. Light for the galvanometer entered through the window Z. The temperature of W could be varied at will.

In operation as an adiabatic calorimeter, it was necessary, with a heat-producing material within E, to increase the temperature of the jacket gradually so that the temperature difference indicated by the couple with junctions on the surfaces of E and P was continually zero. Where $dT/dt$ is the rate of increase of temperature of the jacket, and

$mc$ is the thermal capacitance of the sphere $E$ and its contents, the rate of production of heat $dQ/dt$, as may be derived from Eq. 3, is given by

$$\frac{dQ}{dt} = mc\,\frac{dT}{dt} \tag{17}$$

With the apparatus in operation as a "Newtonian leakage" calorimeter, one adjusts $T$, the temperature of sphere $E$, first to a few tenths of a degree more than and then some time later to about the same amount

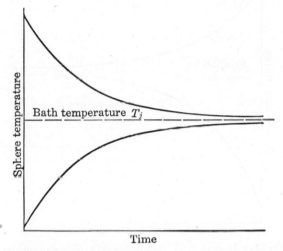

Fɪɢ. 7.    Time-temperature plot for Swietoslawski's microcalorimeter with sphere contents thermally inactive.

less than that of the water jacket.    With the jacket temperature $T_j$ maintained constant, the temperature differences between it and the outer surface of sphere $E$ as given by thermocouple readings are determined as functions of time.    If the contents of sphere $E$ are inactive thermally, the temperature variations with time for the two cases, first with $T_j$ initially less than and then greater than $T$, will be those shown in Fig. 7.    In accord with Newton's law of leakage, their equations are given by

$$\frac{dT}{dt} = -K(T - T_j) \tag{18}$$

which differs from Eq. 11 only in that no term due to stirring is present. If, however, the contents of sphere $E$ are active thermally, the situation is that described by Fig. 8, where Newton's law is again applicable. In this instance the two curves become asymptotic to $T_a$ and not to

$T_j$. For the precise determining of the rate of heat production, one may then use any one of three methods. The one which seems to be the most precise makes use of the tangent to the heating curve at the instant—point $O$ on the plot—when the temperature of the outer surface of $E$ is the same as that of the water in the jacket. Here Eq. 17 is strictly applicable, since at this instant no heat is transferred between $E$ and $P$ and the calorimeter is for a short time operating

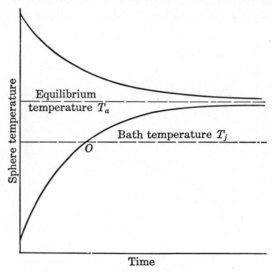

FIG. 8. Time-temperature plot for Swietoslawski's microcalorimeter with sphere contents thermally active.

adiabatically or very nearly so. The other methods employ the difference $T_a - T_j$ and the decay constant for the two exponential curves.

As illustrative of the delicacy of the calorimeter and his methods, Swietoslawski gave the following rates of increase of temperature $dT/dt$ for a sample of radioactive uranium ore within sphere $E$ for each of the four possible methods including the two described above.

| METHOD | $dT/dt$ |
|---|---|
| Adiabatic | 0.00207 C°/hr ± 10% |
| Shape of exponential curve | 207 C°/hr ± 4% |
| Difference $T_a - T_j$ | 207 C°/hr ± 3% |
| Tangent at point $O$ | 210 C°/hr ± 2½% |

The close agreement indicates a high order of achievement.

Following a process of heat evolution involving many days, using the tangent at point $O$, is simple. Following a determination of $dT/dt$ on some one day, one simply raises the temperature of the water jacket until it is again slightly above that of the outer surface of sphere $E$ and then makes a new determination of $dT/dt$ as before. This process may be repeated as often as one desires. In a test of the effect of the mechanical strain due to gravity on a lead block suspended at three points, the following data were obtained:

| TIME FOLLOWING SUSPENSION OF BLOCK | $dT/dt$ | $(1/m)(dQ/dt)$ |
|---|---|---|
| 12 days | 0.00141 C°/hr | $0.43 \times 10^{-4}$ cal/(hr gm) |
| 18 | 078 | .24 |
| 19 | 071 | .22 |
| 24 | 065 | .20 |
| 25 | 060 | .18 |

Given a plot of $(1/m)(dQ/dt)$ as a function of time, as may be obtained from such data, it is a simple matter to obtain by integration the heat evolved up to any given time.

**10. A Bomb-Calorimeter Method.** Another much-used type of calorimeter is that known as the bomb calorimeter. In Fig. 9, the bomb portion of such a calorimeter is shown. In use this bomb is immersed in a calorimetric fluid such as water. The complete calorimeter is largely used by chemists and engineers in determining heats evolved in combustion processes, where sudden high temperatures and/or pressures are produced. Provisions for withstanding high pressures include a needle-valve shut-off for the gas that may be introduced. Frequently it is necessary to start the process of combustion in such a calorimeter by supply-ing an initial local high temperature. For this pur-pose, one provides a short length of platinum wire which, dipping into the crucible containing the sub-stance to be burned, may be electrically heated to incandescence.

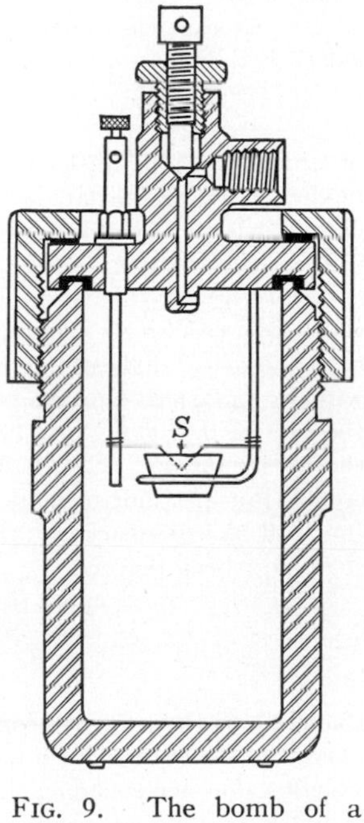

The heat evolved in the bomb of a bomb calori-meter is transmitted to the calorimetric fluid and is measured in the usual way. At the end, the products of combustion are still in the bomb under rather high pressure. To obtain results at normal pressure and temperature, certain corrections must be made.

FIG. 9. The bomb of a bomb calorimeter (by per-mission, J. M. Cork, *Heat*, 2nd ed., p. 182, New York, John Wiley & Sons, 1942).

Other types of calorimeters mostly used for special purposes, such as the R. Bunsen (1811–1899) ice calorimeter, the John Joly (1857–1933) differential steam calorimeter, and the A. Eucken (1884–    ) vacuum calorimeter, will be described in succeeding chapters.

## PROBLEMS

**1.** Assume a time-temperature graph obtained with a standard compensated-loss calorimeter which differs from that shown in Fig. 2 only in having a straight line connecting points $b$ and $d$ in place of the curve there shown, and determine the corrected temperature change for the heat supplied during the test interval.

**2.** Show that the equilibrium temperature $T_a$ for a standard compensated-loss calorimeter in operation is given by

$$T_a = T_j + \frac{(dT/dt)_S}{K}$$

**3.** Given a leakage modulus for a calorimeter of 0.040 1/min, a rate of heating due to stirring of 0.12 C°/min, and a constant jacket temperature of 25.0°C, determine the final equilibrium temperature for the calorimetric fluid.

**4.** Derive and plot the equation of the cooling curve for the after interval for a calorimeter without stirrer whose leakage modulus is 0.0050 1/min, whose jacket temperature is 27°C, and whose initial calorimetric fluid temperature is 30°C.

**5.** Show that the equation for the after interval for a standard compensated-loss calorimeter in operation is

$$T - T_a = (T_0 - T_a)\, e^{-Kt}$$

of which $T_0$ is the initial value of $T$, $T_a$ the equilibrium value, and $K$ the leakage modulus. Using the data of problem 3, determine the equations for the after-interval curves that correspond to initial temperatures that are 1.00 C° and 6.00 C° in excess of the jacket temperature $Tj$.

**6.** Given that the constant for the Newtonian cooling of a lead sphere of 1.0-cm radius in a certain Swietoslawski calorimeter at 300°K is 0.432 1/hr, that its thermal capacitance is 1.200 cal/C°, that the sphere contains 0.60 mg of radium in equilibrium with its radioactive products, and that the temperature of the sphere increases at the rate of 0.0700 C°/hr when the temperature of its outer surface is the same as that of its surroundings, determine (a) the rate of production of heat by radium in equilibrium per unit of mass and (b) the temperature excess over the surroundings that will be experienced by the outer surface of the lead sphere when a steady state shall have been reached.

**7.** Heats of reaction are frequently represented in reaction equations thus

$$C_{\text{graphite}} + O_2 = CO_2 + \Delta H$$

where $\Delta H$ is the heat developed with the burning of solid carbon to form a mole of $CO_2$. (a) Given that a charge of 0.200 gm of pulverized graphite is introduced into a bomb calorimeter whose volume when closed is 300 cm³, determine what air pressure at 300°K should be present initially if double the amount of air for complete combustion to $CO_2$ is needed to insure such complete combustion. (b) Given further that the heat set free with return of the bomb and contents to their original pressure and temperature is 1.568 kcal, determine the $\Delta H$ for the above equation.

# CHAPTER VI

## SPECIFIC HEATS OF SOLIDS AND LIQUIDS

**1. Introduction.** It is the common experience that the rate of temperature rise of a heated body depends, among other things, upon the material of which it is made. This fact is of importance in industry and in our daily lives, whenever one is concerned with bodies whose temperatures are changing because of the addition or removal of heat. During the setting of certain cements, for example, heat is slowly evolved. In huge concrete structures such as that at Boulder Dam, this has required the installation of a brine cooling system to remove the heat, which otherwise would produce a dangerous rise in temperature throughout the structure. In the designing of heating systems, it is important to know how rapidly the temperature of a certain mass of air will rise, for a given net rate of heat supply. Similarly, in the design of certain types of industrial furnaces where a rapid initial heating rate is desired, it is important to select the furnace material with this requirement in mind. In determining the efficiency of a steam-generating plant, it is necessary to be able to compute how much of the heat produced by the burning coal actually is utilized in heating and vaporizing water and in superheating the steam and how much is lost in other processes.

More homely examples are not hard to find. Everyone is familiar with the slow cooling rate of a hot potato or a hot bowl of soup whereas metal objects which have been brought in contact with them cool relatively rapidly, even considering differences in mass. In most of these examples, the property known as specific heat is not the only one involved, but in all cases it is an important one. Our most common experience in this connection is undoubtedly the daily heating and cooling of our earth and the temperature variation thereby produced. If one seeks the warmest and coldest spots on the earth, he will find the former in Death Valley, where a temperature of 130°F has been recorded, and the latter, not at either pole, but in north central Siberia, where a temperature of −90°F has been attained. Both places are located in huge land masses. Such locations are further characterized by large differences between the summer and winter temperatures, as is common in central United States.  These facts, which so profoundly affect our civilization, are explained to a certain extent at least by the fact that earth heats up more rapidly than water.  Expressed differently, the heat-storage capacity of earth material is small compared with that for water, or, in more scientific language, the specific heat of earth material is relatively small compared with that of water.  The fact that seasonal temperature variations are measurable to a much greater depth in water than in earth material is also a very important feature in the complete explanation of the effect described.

An illustration of the great importance of this heat-storage feature in nature is furnished by the Gulf Stream.  In the torrid Gulf of Mexico, the upper surface layers of water are heated by radiation from the sun.  The energy thus stored is carried through the strait between Florida and Cuba and, except for what is given up to the atmosphere and the adjoining cold ocean water, across the ocean to western Europe, whose temperatures and climate generally are affected greatly thereby.  Without the Gulf Stream, the climate of England would be more like that of Labrador, which has the same latitude, rather than that of Virginia, whose climate it matches more closely.

### THEORETICAL CONSIDERATIONS

**2. Definitions.**  Unfortunately the term specific heat is used in two different senses.  As used here and by many others, it is that characteristic of a substance which indicates the amount of heat that must be transmitted to a body composed of that substance in order to change its temperature, but not its state, per unit of mass and unit of temperature difference produced.  It is represented by $\bar{c}$ in the following equation,

$$Q = \bar{c}m \, \Delta T \tag{1}$$

of which $Q$ represents the quantity of heat which, added to a substance whose mass is $m$, will cause an increase of temperature $\Delta T$.

For the most part, a specific heat represents a storage capacity characteristic for energy supplied as heat.  More precisely, however, it represents a combined characteristic of storage for energy and of performance of work accompanying an increase of temperature resulting from the addition of heat.  To illustrate, when a quantity of water is heated from 0°C to 100°C, most of the energy supplied as heat is stored as internal energy in the water.  A small portion of the supply, however, is used to perform work in pushing back the atmosphere as

the water expands. This is quite in accord with the first law of thermodynamics as expressed in Eq. 7 of Chapter IV, namely,

$$Q = \Delta U + W \tag{2}$$

of which $Q$ represents energy transferred to a body as heat, $\Delta U$ the
body's increase in internal energy, and $W$ the work performed by the
body receiving the heat $Q$. Actually, the work done, when heat is
added to water while heating it from 0°C to 100°C, accounts for only
about 0.001% of the heat supplied and is usually quite negligible.
Often the percentages are much less. For gases, on the contrary, the
work done is usually far from being negligible. Referring to solids and
liquids, in what follows, we shall frequently speak of a certain process
as a heat-storage process, ignoring the fact that strictly a certain work
factor of negligible amount is also involved.

In Eq. 1, $\bar{c}$ stands for an average for a temperature interval. Often,
however, the value for the characteristic at a particular temperature
is desired. This is obtained by proceding to the limiting case, in which
both the heat involved and the temperature change produced become
infinitesimal and are represented by $dQ$ and $dT$. Thus with rearrangement we obtain

$$c = \frac{1}{m} \frac{dQ}{dT} \tag{3}$$

Normal units for specific heat are the cal/(gm C°), the btu/(pd F°),
the joule/(gm C°), etc. Speaking of water and of copper, we may
describe them in part by saying that they are characterized by specific
heats of about 1.00 cal/(gm C°) and 0.092 cal/(gm C°).

Some use the term "thermal capacitance of a substance" to represent
that which we have designated as its specific heat, and use the term
specific heat for the ratio of the "thermal capacitance of a substance"
to that of some standard substance. Usually but not always water is
taken as such standard substance. According to this usage specific
heat is a numeric, and those who follow it say that the specific heat of
silver, for instance, under ordinary conditions is about 0.0337 rather
than 0.0337 cal/(gm C°).

The confusion as to terms just mentioned is unfortunate. There
are logical objections to both. The prefix specific as in specific gravity
suggests ratio to many while the other term is easily confused with
"thermal capacitance of a body" not "of a substance" which will be
defined soon. It would be desirable if general agreement could be
obtained for some such a term as "thermivity" which, by its construction, would indicate a thermal property of a substance.

The "thermal capacitance of a body" is its combined heat-storage and work-performance capacitance per unit of temperature difference. It is equal to $mc$. Its unit is the cal/C°, etc., and we say, for instance, that the water in a certain tank has a thermal capacitance of 100,000 kcal/C°.

The "water equivalent of a body" or of a system of bodies is another, frequently used term. For a given body, it is the mass of water under standard conditions which has the same thermal capacitance. Its unit is the gram, and we say, for instance, that the water equivalent of 500 gm of silver under ordinary conditions is 16.85 ($= 500 \times 0.0337$) gm. It is obtained by dividing the thermal capacitance of 500 gm of silver by the specific heat of water. Use of the term water equivalent eliminates largely the need for the term thermal capacitance of a body.

The limitation of the term specific heat to a characteristic which does not involve a change of phase is necessary, if infinite values are not to occur. For instance, under normal conditions 540 cal of heat for each gram are supplied without change of temperature when water is boiled.

Often, in speaking of the specific heat of a substance, it is necessary to refer to the conditions under which heat is added. For gases there are three common conditions, those of constant pressure, constant volume, and saturation as a vapor. Their values vary greatly, and, in the case of water vapor that is kept saturated, the specific heat is actually negative. Because of this variation, it is desirable, where a possibility of doubt may arise, to specify the condition which accompanies any given value for a specific heat.

In the case of solids at ordinary temperatures or below, due to their relatively small expansivities, the work done when heat is added is usually very small in comparison with the heat used to increase the internal energy. Hence the specific heat of a solid under other experimentally realizable conditions usually differs but little from that at constant pressure, and the differences that exist are frequently ignored. Exactly similar statements may be made regarding liquids. However, because of their greater expansivities somewhat greater differences are to be expected.

Often, particularly in theoretical discussions, specific heats are referred to as molar heats and atomic heats, the former more often in the case of a gas or a liquid, the latter more often in the case of a solid, especially if one element only is involved. Specific heats as ordinarily expressed in cal/(gm C°) may be readily converted with the aid of the appropriate molecular weight or atomic weight as a conversion factor. Thus, for the specific heat of copper at constant volume, generally called its atomic heat at constant volume, we have

$$c_v = 0.0913 \frac{\text{cal}}{\text{gm K}°} \times 63.57 \frac{\text{gm}}{\text{gm-atom}} = 5.80 \frac{\text{cal}}{\text{gm-atom K}°} \qquad (4)$$

The 0.0913 cal/(gm K°) and the 5.80 cal/(gm-atom K°) describe the same property of copper and are the same quantity as truly as are 60 sec and 1 min.

As already noted, the specific heat of water at 15°C is *just* 1 cal/(gm C°) by definition. For other temperatures, variations have been found by the physicists H. A. Rowland (1848–1901) of Johns Hopkins University, H. T. Barnes (1873–   ) of McGill University, and others as is shown in Fig. 5 of Chapter IV. This variation led to the definition of the *mean* calory, referred to in Chapter IV, as $\frac{1}{100}$ of the heat required to raise the temperature of 1 gm of pure water from 0°C to 100°C, under a pressure of 1 A. The heat unit so defined is used in much work where great precision is not required.

**3. Simple Kinetic Theory.** A solid, particularly a metallic solid, may be thought of as a regular three-dimensional array of atoms, each vibrating about an equilibrium point. Each such vibratory motion may be resolved into three independent component vibrations, parallel to each of three coordinate axes. To each component the kinetic theory of solids assigns the energy $kT$ (not $\frac{1}{2}kT$ as is the case for gases where translatory motion only is involved), where $k$ is the Boltzmann atomic constant (see p. 204) $1.3805 \times 10^{-16}$ erg/(atom K°) and $T$ is the absolute temperature. The constant $k$, which is visualized as the gas constant for a single molecule, is of great importance and occurs in many theoretical expressions. The reason for the assignment of $kT$ rather than $\frac{1}{2}kT$ as the average energy of an atom is based on the fact that a vibrating particle of a solid has two independent modes of storing energy, kinetic and potential, rather than the single kinetic mode of an ordinary gas molecule. Basic kinetic-theory considerations will be discussed further in the chapter devoted to gases.

In accord with the foregoing, a solid containing $N$ atoms might be expected to have an internal energy content $U$ given by

$$U = N(3kT) = 3mRT \qquad (5)$$

where $m$ is the mass of the solid and $R$ the universal (molar) gas constant (see p. 200). If heat $Q$ is added to a solid in a container which does not permit of expansion, all the added heat will be used in producing an internal energy increase $\Delta U$, and a temperature rise $\Delta T$ will result. The expected specific heat at constant volume, in accord with Eqs. 3 and 5, is

$$c_v = \left[\frac{Q}{m \, \Delta T}\right]_v = \left[\frac{\Delta U}{m \, \Delta T}\right]_v = \left[\frac{3mR \, \Delta T}{m \, \Delta T}\right]_v = 3R$$

$$= 5.959 \, \frac{\text{cal}}{\text{gm-atom K}°} \tag{6}$$

Simple kinetic theory predicts that the atomic heats at constant volume of all solids shall be identical and show no temperature variation. Though the prediction fails rather badly in some respects, in other respects it is found highly useful.

It is interesting that Eq. 6 is obtained as an upper limiting value, as will appear later, when one assumes in accord with quantum considerations that the internal energy of a solid is associated with elastic standing waves instead of the vibratory energies of its constituent atoms.

**4. Dulong and Petit Law.** In 1819, the French scientists P. L. Dulong (1785–1838) and A. T. Petit (1791–1820) discovered that the molecular heats of many solids were about the same. An average value of 6.4 cal/(mol K°) for $c_p$, specific heat at constant pressure, was obtained. This is somewhat in excess of the 5.959 cal/(gm-atom K°) prediction of the simple kinetic theory for $c_v$.

Column 3 of Table I shows several experimental values of $c_p$. Since these were measured at constant pressure, while the value predicted above by the kinetic theory is for the condition of constant volume, some adjustments must be made before a satisfactory comparison is possible. This is a consequence of the fact that a direct experimental determination of a $c_v$ for a solid is very difficult. To obtain the desired values for $c_v$, recourse is made to thermodynamic theory. It shows that, given $c_p$ and certain other measurable data, $c_v$ may be computed with the aid of the relation

$$c_v = c_p - \frac{v\beta^2 T}{\kappa} \tag{7}$$

where $\beta$ is the volume expansivity of the substance, $v$ its specific volume, and $\kappa$ its compressibility. To illustrate, Zemansky * gives for copper at 300°K, 5.87 cal/(gm-atom K°) for $c_p$, 7.062 cm³/gm-atom for $v$, 49.2 × 10⁻⁶ 1/K° for $\beta$, and 0.776 × 10⁻¹² cm²/dyne for $\kappa$.

* M. Zemansky, *Heat and Thermodynamics*, p. 236, New York, McGraw-Hill Book Co., 1937.

Substitution of these values in Eq. 7 yields 5.71 cal/(gm-atom K°) for $c_v$, which is about 2.8% less than the value given for $c_p$. Values for $c_v$ given in Table I have been thus determined.

TABLE I

COMPARISON OF SPECIFIC HEAT (ATOMIC HEAT) VALUES WITH KINETIC THEORY

Values are means between 0°C and 100°C.

| Substance | Atomic Weight $\frac{gm}{gm\text{-atom}}$ | $c_p$ cal (gm K°) | $c_p$ cal (gm-atom K°) | $c_v$ cal (gm-atom K°) | Percentage Variation of $c_v$ from Kinetic-Theory Value |
|---|---|---|---|---|---|
| Aluminum | 26.97 | 0.217 | 5.83 | 5.44 | −10% |
| Boron | 10.82 | 0.287 | 3.10 | 3.10 | −50 |
| Cadmium | 112.41 | 0.557 | 6.26 | 5.85 | −1.7 |
| Carbon | 12.00 | 0.112 | 1.34 | 1.34 | −79 |
| Copper | 63.57 | 0.0930 | 5.92 | 5.65 | −5.0 |
| Gold | 197.2 | 0.0309 | 6.10 | 5.93 | −1.7 |
| Iron | 55.84 | 0.110 | 6.14 | 5.92 | −1.7 |
| Lead | 207.22 | 0.0310 | 6.43 | 5.97 | 0.0 |
| Molybdenum | 96.0 | 0.072 | 6.92 | 6.01 | 0.0 |
| Platinum | 195.23 | 0.0318 | 6.21 | 6.08 | 1.7 |
| Silicon | 28.06 | 0.168 | 4.71 | 4.71 | −22 |
| Silver | 107.880 | 0.0559 | 6.03 | 5.77 | −3.3 |
| Sodium | 22.997 | 0.307 | 7.06 | 6.20 | 3.3 |
| Tungsten | 184.0 | 0.034 | 6.26 | 6.15 | 3.3 |
| Zinc | 65.38 | 0.0939 | 6.14 | 5.73 | −5.0 |

Though the Dulong and Petit law and Eq. 6 seem to hold for most solids at room temperatures, there are several substances whose atomic heats or molecular heats at constant volume at room temperatures deviate considerably from the expected values. Boron, carbon, and silicon are among them. They are, however, only seeming exceptions to the general law. Research has shown that the specific heats of substances vary greatly with temperatures (Figs. 1 and 2). Starting with zero or near zero values near the absolute zero of temperature, the specific heats of all solids increase with increase of temperature first slowly then rapidly and then gradually to a more or less constant value. This constant value, as predicted by Eq. 6, is reached by many substances but not all at temperatures below room temperatures. Boron, carbon, and silicon are among the substances for which the constant value is obtained only at temperatures appreciably above room temperatures. Evidently the prediction of kinetic theory represents only one aspect of a much more general relation.

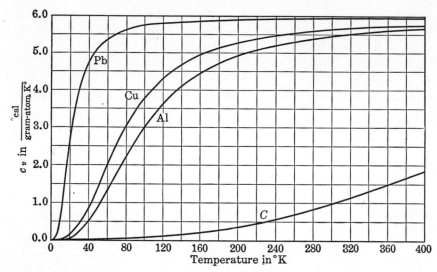

Fig. 1. The atomic heats at constant volume of lead, copper, aluminum, and carbon in solid form as functions of temperature for the range $0°K < T < 400°K$ (computed from data given by A. Euken in Wien-Harm, *Handbuch der experimental Physik*, **8**, 1929, and by M. Zemansky, *Heat and Thermodynamics*, 2nd ed., p. 240, New York, McGraw-Hill Book Co., 1943).

**5. Einstein's Theory.** The first theory to account even partially for the variations shown in Fig. 2 was offered by Albert Einstein (1879–   ), the great German physicist and Nobel prize winner of 1922, later associated with the Institute for Advanced Study located in Princeton, N. J. Basing his considerations on the quantum theory of another great German physicist and Nobel prize winner of 1918, Max Planck (1858–   ), Einstein assumed that the internal energy possessed by a solid, both potential and kinetic, which is associated with a vibratory degree of freedom of an atom, is not $kT$, but $h\nu/(e^{h\nu/kT} - 1)$, where $e$ is the base of the natural logarithm system, $h$ is Planck's constant $6.624 \times 10^{-27}$ erg sec, and $\nu$ an assumed characteristic frequency of vibration of the atoms of the solid. The internal energy per gram-atom was then obtained by multiplying the expression containing $h\nu$ by the number of degrees of freedom per gram-atom $3N_0$. $N_0$ is Avogadro's number (see p. 204). Differentiating with respect to temperature, in accord with Eq. 3, keeping the volume constant, leads to Einstein's specific-heat expression,

$$c_v = 3R \frac{e^{h\nu/kT}}{(e^{h\nu/kT} - 1)^2} \left(\frac{h\nu}{kT}\right)^2 \qquad (8)$$

The Einstein theory gave a good agreement with experiment at high temperatures, but at low temperatures its predictions were uniformly too low, the discrepancy increasing with decrease of temperature. Einstein's assumption of a single, common, vibratory frequency for the atoms of a body was open to objection.

**6. Debye's Theory.** Debye's*(1884–　) theory of specific heats published in 1912 has proved extremely successful in predicting specific heats and their variations with temperature. Debye assumed the internal energies of bodies to be associated with stationary, elastic sound waves, both longitudinal and transverse, which were thought to be present at all times. He used an expression developed by the English physicist and Nobel prize winner of 1904, Lord Rayleigh (1842–1919), in connection with a proposed classical theory of black-body radiation (see p. 444), which gives, for a vibrating solid, the possible number of different standing elastic wave trains per unit volume to be found within a given small frequency range. Each such standing wave train, constituting an independent mode of vibration, was treated by Debye as a degree of freedom and was assigned the quantum-theory value for its associated vibratory energy, namely, $hv/(e^{hv/kT} - 1)$. By summing up such associated energies for frequencies, $v$, ranging from the smallest possible frequency to a theoretically determined maximum value, $v_m$, an expression for the internal energy of a solid was obtained. The upper frequency limit $v_m$ was so chosen that the total number of degrees of freedom per gram-atom in the system equaled the classical number of $3N_0$ where $N_0$ is the Avogadro number. After differentiating to secure the variation of the internal energy with temperature, Debye obtained,

$$c_v = 3R \left[ 12 \left( \frac{T}{\Theta} \right)^3 \int_0^{v_m} \frac{(\Theta/T)^2}{e^{\Theta/T} - 1} \frac{dv}{v} - \frac{3\Theta/T}{e^{\Theta/T} - 1} \right] \tag{9}$$

$\Theta( = hv_m/k)$ is referred to as a characteristic temperature, often called the Debye temperature, a constant differing from substance to substance. There are several ways of determining $v_m$ and hence $\Theta$. Values for these constants may be obtained: (1) by substituting known values of $c_v$ in the Debye formula and solving for $\Theta$ directly; (2) by direct computation from the elastic properties of the substance; (3) by use of a formula due to the British physicist F. A. Lindemann which involves the melting point of the substance; or (4) by the residual-ray

---

* Debye, a Hollander by birth, a physicist associated with German and Swiss institutions for many years and winner of the Nobel prize for chemistry in 1936, is now at Cornell University, Ithaca, N. Y., as a physical chemist.

method in the case of non-metals.  If a beam of radiation containing all wavelengths is reflected many times successively from polished surfaces of the solid in question, one obtains finally a beam which is rather homogeneous in frequency.  The rays which comprise it form the residual rays.  Its predominant frequency, called the residual-ray frequency, is assumed, according to the last-mentioned method,

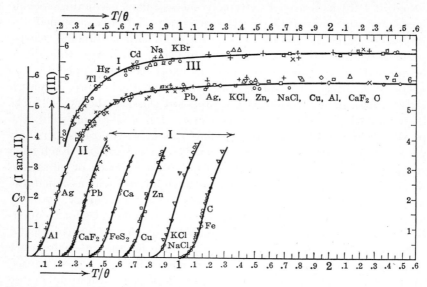

FIG. 2.  The atomic and molecular heats of several elements and compounds in solid form as functions of their characteristic temperatures.  Curve II is in its normal position with respect to the indicated coordinate axis.  Curves I have been shifted horizontally by varying amounts; Curve III has been shifted vertically.  The solid lines represent the prediction of Debye's theory.  (E. Schrödinger, *Physik. Z.*, **20**, 452, 1919.)

to be the $\nu_m$ of Debye's theory.  The values of $\nu_m$ and of $\Theta$ obtained by these four methods are of the same order of magnitude.

It is important to recognize that the Debye equation applies to all solids.  How well measured values of $c_v$ for various substances agree with theory is shown in Fig. 2.

An examination of Debye's expression shows that, at low temperatures, the value of $c_v$ is proportional to the cube of the absolute temperature.  This is known as the $T^3$ law and is useful in extending specific-heat measurements made at moderately low temperatures, say those of liquid air, to near the absolute zero.  For some time, Debye's expression was believed to be generally valid.  However, later measurements revealed significant differences from the predicted values for some substances at very low temperatures as well as at very high temperatures. This is typical of the new realms of exploration opened up by the methods of maintaining low temperatures and making accurate measurements under those conditions.

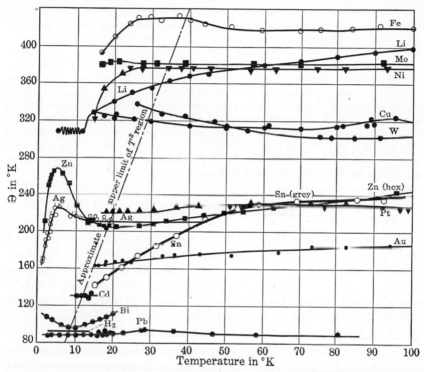

FIG. 3. Variation with temperature of computed characteristic temperatures, Θ, using Debye's theory. So far as there is deviation from constancy for any one substance, there is disagreement between theory and experiment. (By permission, M. and B. Ruhemann, *Low Temperature Physics*, p. 144, Cambridge, England, University Press, 1937.)

**7. Critique of Specific-Heat Theory.** One of the simplest ways of determining how closely the theory of Debye represents the actual facts for any given substance is to compute, from the experimentally obtained specific heats, the Debye characteristic temperature, Θ, at various temperatures throughout the experimental range. If the theory is strictly valid, a single value of Θ should suffice for the whole temperature range. How nearly this is true is shown in Fig. 3. It will be noted that, for many substances, Θ is rather constant over considerable ranges but that at low temperatures appreciable variations are observed, indicating the failure of the Debye expression. In the case of lithium and gray tin, the Debye expression does not appear to be valid at all.

Any method whatever by which a substance increases its store of internal energy as the temperature increases will affect its specific heat; and it is not surprising that, unless all such methods are included, some discrepancies between Debye's theory and experiment should occur. Actually this theory considers only the most important way of absorbing energy, that connected with the elastic wave motions within a body, a method which may be associated theoretically with the vibrations of its atoms about their equilibrium points in the solid lattice. Other considerations involving theories of energy absorption, which have been successful in particular cases in accounting for specific-heat anomalies and departures from Debye theory, are: (1) the molecules of a solid may be rotating; (2) discrete energy states may exist, and a definite amount of energy may be required to raise an atom from one state to another; (3) energy may be stored in the motions of electrons; (4) in alloys, energy is required to change the distribution of atoms throughout the solid from an orderly one, at low temperatures, to a random one at higher temperatures—this is one phase of a class known as *order-disorder phenomena;* (5) certain energy redistributions occur when the external magnetic properties of a substance change.

In general it may be said that the Debye theory, in conjunction with considerations based on the above factors advanced for explaining anomalies and low temperature effects, has been very successful in accounting for experimental results.

## EXPERIMENTAL METHODS

**8. General Considerations.** In all experimental determinations of specific heats, energy added to or taken from a body must be measured. Methods for carrying out these measurements are various. Where the energy is added or removed in the form of heat, a calorimetric measurement, something of the order of the measurements described in Chapter V, is involved. For precise work the precautions and procedures there set forth must be observed.

There are various ways in which procedures for determining specific heats may be grouped. As carried out here, the group assignment has depended on which of the following classifications fits best with the procedure involved: (1) an exchange of thermal energy without change of phase, (2) an exchange of thermal energy with change of phase of the calorimetric substance, (3) a differential rate of cooling or of heating due to thermal leakage, (4) the supplying of heat electrically.

**9. Methods Involving Exchange of Thermal Energy without Change of Phase.** (a) *Method of Mixtures.* The student who has studied elementary physics will be familiar with the method of mixtures. Using it, one places in thermal contact two bodies of known masses at different temperatures and notes the initial temperatures and the common final temperature. The process is carried out in a calorimeter, and the procedure outlined in Chapter V on calorimetry must be followed if precision is sought. Thus, a mass $m_1$ of aluminum at initial temperature $T_1$ may be *mixed* with a mass $m_2$ of water contained in a calorimeter of water equivalent $m_2'$, both being initially at temperature $T_2$. Since the heat lost by the aluminum must equal that gained by the calorimeter and contents plus that transferred to the surroundings, we have

$$m_1 \bar{c}_1 (T_1 - T_0) = (m_2 + m_2') \bar{c}_2 (T_0 - T_2) \tag{10}$$

where $T_0$ is the observed final temperature corrected for leakage losses due to radiation, conduction, and convection. From this $\bar{c}_1$, the mean specific heat of aluminum at constant pressure between $T_0$ and $T_1$, may be found, if $\bar{c}_2$, the mean specific heat of water at constant pressure between $T_2$ and $T_0$, is known.

It is obviously possible to use two liquids in the experiment provided they do not react chemically with each other. If this condition is not fulfilled, the liquids must be kept apart by placing one in a metallic or other vessel immersed in the calorimeter when the mixture method is used.

Often one desires the specific heat at a definite temperature, say $T'$, rather than the mean between two temperatures. The procedure for this, using the mixture method, consists of (1) making several determinations of the quantity of heat $Q$, as represented chiefly by the right-hand member of Eq. 10, corresponding to transfers of heat from the body at various initial high temperatures $T_1$ to a common final low temperature, or the reverse, (2) plotting $Q$ as a function of the initial temperature $T_1$ (Fig. 4), (3) obtaining the derivative $dQ/dT_1$ for the condition that $T_1 = T'$, and (4) substituting in Eq. 3. In carrying through the process, it is usually advisable to obtain $Q = f(T_1)$ in equation form and to seek the derivative $dQ/dT_1$ with its aid. Usually the equation will take the form of a power series, such as

$$Q = k_1 (T_1 - T_0) + k_2 (T_1 - T_0)^2 + k_3 (T_1 - T_0)^3 + \cdots \tag{11}$$

For the specific heat, $c$, at $T_1 = T'$, we then have

$$c = \frac{1}{M} \frac{dQ}{dT_1} = \frac{1}{M} [k_1 + 2k_2 (T_1 - T_0) + 3k_3 (T_1 - T_0)^2 + \cdots]_{T_1 = T'} \tag{12}$$

Thus, from an equation of the type of Eq. 11, representing data on platinum by Jaeger [*] (1877– ) with $M$, $T_0$, $k_1$, $k_2$, $k_3$, and $k_4$ having the values 1.000 gm-atom, 0°C, 6.735 cal/C°, $0.288 \times 10^{-3}$ cal/C°², $-0.092 \times 10^{-6}$ cal/C°³, $0.029 \times 10^{-9}$ cal/C°⁴, one is able to compute

[*] F. M. Jaeger, *Optical Activity and High Temperature Measurements*, p. 371, New York, McGraw-Hill Book Co., 1930.

a specific heat for platinum for any desired temperature within the prescribed range. Thus for 500°C one obtains 7.106 cal/(gm-atom K°).

(b) *Copper Block Calorimeter Method.* The second method of this group is, in one sense, also a method of mixtures. A copper block properly hollowed out and modified serves both as the calorimetric substance and its container. In one type of instrument, Fig. 3 of Chapter V developed by W. P. White (1867– ) at the Geophysical

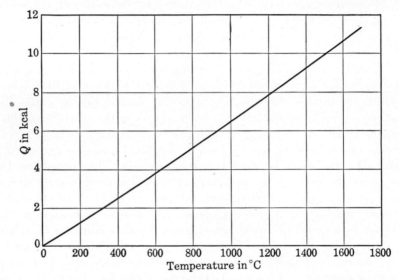

FIG. 4. A graph showing heat evolved, $Q$, by a platinum slug whose mass is 1 mole on cooling from various high temperatures, $T$, to the common low temperature, 0°C (by permission, F. M. Jaeger, *Optical Activity and High Temperature Measurements*, p. 371, New York, McGraw-Hill Book Co., 1930).

Laboratory in Washington, the substance studied, usually a solid, is enclosed initially in a thin-walled metallic container shaped to fit snugly and with good thermal contact in the copper block. After being heated together with the container in a furnace to a uniform high temperature, it is dropped quickly into the calorimeter, and, except for the stirring, the procedure of the standard compensated-loss method described on p. 114 is followed. The chief advantages of the method are its applicability over a wide temperature range, the elimination of stirring and evaporation errors, and a certain saving in time since less labor is involved than in a fluid calorimeter of corresponding precision.

For low temperatures, W. Nernst (1864–1941), German chemist and winner of the Nobel prize in chemistry in 1920, and his associates devised a somewhat similar arrangement with the calorimeter block enclosed in a vacuum-walled jacket to minimize thermal leakage.

**10. Methods Involving Exchange of Thermal Energy with a Change of Phase for the Calorimetric Substance.** (*a*) *Black's Ice Cavity Method.* This simple method, developed in Scotland by Joseph Black (1728–1799), consists of placing a heated solid of mass $m_1$ in a dry cavity in a block of ice, closing the cavity with another slab of ice, and collecting and determining the mass $m_2$ of water which has melted when thermal equilibrium has been reached. If $L$ is the heat of fusion of ice, and $T_1$ the initial temperature of the solid, we may determine the mean specific heat $\bar{c}$ of the solid between 0°C and $T_1$ from

$$m_1\bar{c}(T_1 - 0°C) = m_2L \tag{13}$$

No thermal-leakage correction is required. The chief difficulties involve obtaining large masses of ice of sufficient purity and, most significant of all, determining accurately the amount of ice melted. Usually, as much of the melted ice as possible is drawn from the cavity by a pipette, the rest being removed by means of a carefully massed piece of absorbent cotton. Even with these precautions, great accuracy is generally not obtained.

(*b*) *Bunsen's Ice Calorimeter Method.* R. Bunsen (1811–1899), a famous German chemist, circumvented the last-mentioned difficulty by an ingenious arrangement (Fig. 5). The vessel surrounding test tube $A$ is filled with boiled, air-free water at 0°C, as shown at $C$, and boiled mercury $D$, the latter extending into capillary $F$ through $E$, an adjustable connection. The whole apparatus, with the exception of the capillary tube and the mouth of tube $A$, is immersed in an ice bath to minimize heat flow to or from the surroundings. In use, a mantle of ice, $G$, is formed on the walls of tube $A$ at its lower end, either by bubbling ether inside the tube or by some other method. Next the capillary tube is adjusted in the sliding connection $E$ until the mercury stands near the extreme right of the scale. The body whose specific heat is to be measured, heated to any desired temperature, is then dropped into tube $A$. If convenient and possible, a small amount of oil with a low freezing point is placed in tube $A$ to insure good thermal contact. When equilibrium has been attained, some of the ice will have been melted, with a consequent decrease in volume. The mercury meniscus at the right in $F$ will have moved to the left until it has opened a volume of the capillary equal to the difference in volume of the ice which melted and the water to which it melted. Knowing the bore of the capillary, the distance the mercury meniscus recedes, and the density of the ice, one may then determine the mass of ice that has melted and the heat given up by the body being studied.

A more usual method of calibration of a Bunsen colorimeter results from heating to temperature $T_1$ a body of mass $m_1$ of a substance of known specific heat $\bar{c}_1$ and placing it in the calorimeter. Granted a capillary of uniform bore, suppose that, during such a calibration, the mercury thread traversed $n_1$ scale divisions. Then, if $m_2$ is the mass of ice melted, $L$ its heat of fusion, and $K$ a proportionality constant,

$$m_1\bar{c}_1(T_1 - T_0) = m_2L = Kn_1 \tag{14}$$

From this preliminary experiment, $K$ may be determined, thus

$$K = \frac{m_1 \bar{c}_1 (T_1 - T_0)}{n_1} \qquad (15)$$

Now if a mass $m$ of the substance being studied is heated to temperature $T$ and $n$ scale divisions are passed over by the mercury when the body is dropped into tube $A$, its specific heat $\bar{c}$ may be found from

$$\bar{c} = \frac{Kn}{m(T - T_0)} \qquad (16)$$

One difficulty encountered in practice is the fact that the ice encrusted on tube $A$ and the ice surrounding the entire apparatus usually have slightly different freezing

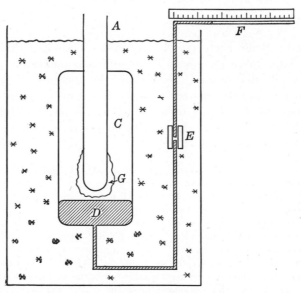

FIG. 5.  Bunsen's ice calorimeter.

points.  This results in a slow transfer of heat from the region where the freezing point is high to where it is low, and hence a slow drift of the mercury in the capillary, due either to the melting or the freezing of the ice $A$.  This effect may be greatly minimized by placing the calorimeter in a glass vessel before putting it in the ice bath.  The air space thus introduced greatly reduces the rate of heat flow.  A vacuum-walled jacket serves the purpose even better.

Another difficulty with Bunsen's method results from the fact that the ice mantles that form on $A$ vary slightly in density due, perhaps, to different methods or rates of freezing.  If the ice densities during the calibration and during the actual experiment differ, the resulting specific heat will obviously be in error.

This method, used by Bunsen with good success to determine the specific heats of rare metals available only in small quantities, has more recently been used by D. C. Ginnings and R. J. Corruccini of the National Bureau of Standards.  *See J. Chem. Eng. News*, **25**, 1757, 1947.

(c) *Joly's Differential Steam Calorimeter Method.* This method developed by the Irish mineralogist, geologist, and physicist John Joly (1857–1933) makes use of the heat set free by condensing steam. By determining the mass of steam which must be condensed on a body to raise its temperature by a known amount, it is possible to compute the specific heat of the body. This mass determination is accomplished with the aid of a sensitive balance and a double-walled, insu-

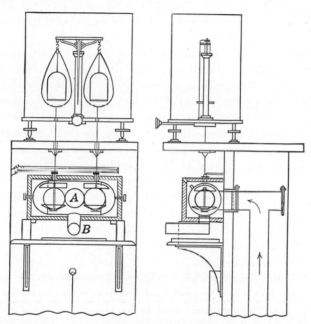

FIG. 6.   Cross-sectional views from the front and the side of Joly's steam calorimeter as set up for the study of gases. A indicates the place where steam enters the calorimeter; B, where it leaves. (*Proc. Roy. Soc. London,* **A47,** 218, 1889–1890.)

lated chamber, with an inlet and an outlet for steam as shown in Fig. 6. Within the chamber, two auxiliary pans attached to the bottoms of the regular balance pans are suspended by means of fine platinum wires. The solid of mass $m$, whose mean specific heat $\bar{c}$ is required, is placed in one of the pans, say the left-hand pan, inside the steam chamber. The balance is then adjusted by placing bodies of known masses on the right-hand pan outside. The temperature $T_1$ of the chamber is noted, and steam at temperature $T_2$ is admitted through inlet $A$. $B$ is an opening to the atmosphere to assure that the pressure in the steam chamber is atmospheric. Steam condenses on both pans and their contents, thus imparting heat to them until they are raised to the temperature of the incoming steam. In order to keep the balance in adjustment, one must add to the right-hand pan a mass $m'$ equal to the mass of the steam condensed on the left-hand auxiliary pan and its contents less that which condensed on the auxiliary right-hand pan. If the two auxiliary pans have equal masses and consequently equal thermal capacitances, we may write

$$m\bar{c}(T_2 - T_1) = m'L \qquad (17)$$

of which $L$ is the heat of condensation or of vaporization of steam. Eq. 17 may be solved for $\bar{c}$.

Steam condensing on the supporting wires near the chamber entrances interfered with massing. This difficulty was prevented by means of small heating coils as shown. Since it is impossible to make both auxiliary pans exactly alike, the careful performance of an experiment calls for a repetition of the work with the solid of unknown specific heat shifted to the other pan. The mean of the two specific heat values thus obtained is taken to be the true value. To such values, if the work is carried through carefully, great confidence may be given.

When the study involves a liquid or a gas, a thin-walled copper sphere is placed in each pan, one of the spheres containing the fluid under investigation, the other being evacuated. In the case of a gas, the specific heat so measured is that at constant volume. This was the first method devised for the satisfactory determination of this quantity directly. For precise work, two factors must be taken into consideration. (1) The expansion of the copper spheres, as a result of both increased temperature and pressure. Because of this factor, the work done by the expanding gas must be considered before $c_v$ can be obtained. (2) The reduction of all massings to a vacuum. This is necessary because of the different buoyant effects of the steam and the dry air in which the massings are conducted.

For this method no auxiliary experiment is required, except perhaps as a check on the equality of the pans. It is due chiefly to this fact that the determination of $c_v$ for gases is possible. In previous methods, the necessity for determining the thermal capacitance of the apparatus, a quantity which is very large in comparison with that of any usable amount of gas, rendered satisfactory measurements of $c_v$ for gases practically impossible.

**11. Method Involving Differential Rates of Cooling or of Heating Due to Thermal Leakage.** The rate of loss of heat by a body on cooling, $-mc_p \, dT/dt$, depends on its surface area $A$, the nature of its surface, its temperature $T$, and its surroundings which we usually assume to be at a uniform temperature $T_0$.  If Newton's law for leakage holds, the relationship is given by

$$\frac{dQ}{dt} = -mc_p \frac{dT}{dt} = kA(T - T_0) \tag{18}$$

where $k$ is a constant which depends on various characteristics including the temperature of the body and its surroundings.  If Newton's law does not hold, Eq. 18 is replaced by

$$mc_p \frac{dT}{dt} = A F(T, T_0) \tag{19}$$

where $F(T, T_0)$ signifies that $dT/dt$ depends in some consistent manner upon the temperatures $T$ and $T_0$.

Applying the method to cooling, let a mass $m$ of the substance whose specific heat $c_p$ is desired be heated and placed in a container of thermal capacitance $C$, whose surface is polished and preferably highly reflecting.  Note the time $\Delta_1 t$ required for the substance and container to cool through a small temperature range $\Delta T$.  Next, using the container only, note the time $\Delta_2 t$ required for it to cool through the same small temperature range with the same surrounding temperature.  Since heat is lost to the surroundings in the two cases under identical conditions, there is necessarily the same average rate of heat loss.  Hence, we have for a given temperature

$$A F(T, T_0) = (mc_p + C)\frac{\Delta T}{\Delta_1 t} = C\frac{\Delta T}{\Delta_2 t} \tag{20}$$

It follows that

$$c_p = \frac{C}{m}\left(\frac{\Delta_1 t}{\Delta_2 t} - 1\right) \tag{21}$$

Since all quantities entering the right-hand member are directly measurable, this equation serves for determining the desired specific heat.  If $C$ is not known initially, it may be determined by performing the experiment as outlined above, using a substance of known specific heat and arriving at an equation similar to Eq. 21 in which all quantities but $C$ are known.  Regnault used this method with some success for liquids but did not deem it satisfactory for solids mainly because the contact between the solid (even if finely divided) and the container wall cannot be made as definite as in the case of liquids.  Experimental refinements employed by Regnault included the use of a polished thin-walled silver tube to hold the liquid under investigation.  This was placed in an evacuated chamber with inner walls coated with lamp black, the whole being immersed in an ice bath. Perhaps the greatest difficulty with the method results from one's inability to insure that only a negligible drop in temperature occurs in the film of liquid in contact with the container, which remains more or less stationary

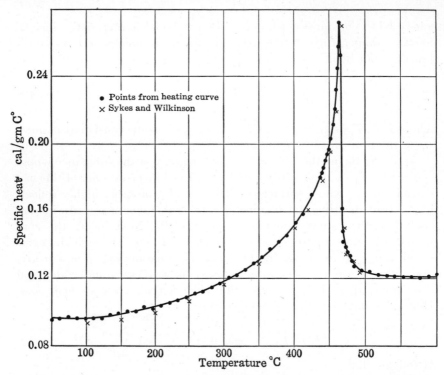

FIG. 7. The specific heat of beta brass as a function of temperature, showing variations accompanying the gradual change with increase of temperature from the ordered atomic crystal lattice of the $\beta'$ state to the disordered atomic crystal lattice of the $\beta$ state for a brass containing 48.10% zinc and 51.90% copper as reported by metallurgist C. S. Smith (1903–   ) of the American Brass Co. of Waterbury, Conn. The xxx points represent data by Sykes and Wilkinson for a beta brass of slightly different composition. (By permission, C. S. Smith in *The Symposium on Temperature—Its Measurement and Control in Science and Industry*, p. 978, New York, Reinhold Publishing Corp., 1941.)

even when the liquid is stirred. In the case of metallic solids, with identical plating of the surfaces of the bodies to be compared, this method would seem to be highly satisfactory.

This differential thermal-leakage method has been used considerably of late in the study of the variations of the specific heats of substances in the temperature regions where order-disorder transitions occur.   Fig. 7 shows such results for beta brass which were based on a comparison of the cooling rates of selected amounts of brass and of copper, for which latter substance the specific-heat variations with temperature were already known.   Since new steady states for order-disorder transitions (from a separate systematic or ordered arrangement for the zinc and the copper atoms of a crystal in the case of beta brass to a non-systematic or disordered arrangement for those atoms, but the same arrangement if the differences in the kinds of atoms are ignored) with change of temperature are established but slowly, this method seems to be more or less ideal.   By keeping the temperature difference between a specimen and its surroundings small, one can readily satisfy the requirement of passage on cooling from one steady state condition through a succession of near equilibrium states to another steady state condition.

The case for heating in place of cooling is obviously exactly similar.

**12. Methods Involving the Supply of Heat Electrically.**   (a) *Differential Continuous Flow Method.*   A continuous-flow method for the determination of $J$ has already been described.   As there, so also here, a steady stream of a liquid or a gas, whose specific heat is desired, is caused to flow at a constant known rate $m/t$ through apparatus in which heat is supplied electrically at the rate $IV$.   With continued flow, a steady state is reached, with a constant difference in temperature $\Delta T$ between the inlet and the outlet points.   For this condition we have

$$IV = \frac{m}{t} c_p \, \Delta T + AF(T, T_0) \qquad (22)$$

where $AF(T, T_0)$ as in Eq. 19 is the rate of loss of heat by thermal leakage.

The apparatus, which Barnes used in 1889 in measuring the specific heat of water by the differential continuous-flow method, is shown in Fig. 4 of Chapter V.   Heat was supplied electrically by a current through the spiraled central wire.   An accurate potentiometer was used to measure (a) the difference in potential $V$ between the copper end pieces and (b) the difference in potential across a standard 1-ohm resistor included in the circuit.   From this second measurement, the current $I$ was found using Ohm's law.   The product of the two gave the input power $IV$.   Differences in temperature were measured by means of resistance thermometers.   The copper end pieces served to equalize the stream temperatures in the neighborhood of the thermocouple junctions.   The central conductor of platinum was made spiral in shape so as to affect a complete mixing of the stream.  A vacuum jacket minimized leakage losses.

The rate of loss of heat by thermal leakage $A F(T, T_0)$, for constant-flow methods, depends upon the mean difference in temperature between the stream and its surroundings.   If, then, a second test be conducted with the same difference in temperature, but with a different supply rate of electrical energy and a different rate of flow of water, the same leakage loss rate $A F(T, T_0)$ will occur and may be eliminated from consideration by taking differences between the two equations of the form of Eq. 22, representing the two sets of observations.   Denoting, by subscripts 1 and 2, two such tests using Barnes's procedure, it follows that

$$\overset{\bullet}{c_p} = \frac{(IV)_1 - (IV)_2}{(m/t)_1 - (m/t)_2} \frac{1}{\Delta T} \tag{23}$$

The relatively high accuracy of the method is due to the fact that no correction for the thermal capacitance of the apparatus is required, a circumstance resulting from the maintained constancy of temperature for the various parts of apparatus.   Since thermal lag in the temperature-measuring instrument is not present, it is possible to use a pair of differential thermometers in place of the resistance thermometers with small sacrifice in precision.

(b) *Differential Equated Thermal-Leakage Method.*  This method is similar to the continuous-flow method.  It differs in that the liquid is heated as a whole rather than as a stream.  Here by taking differences, one equates the difference between two electrical supply rates to the net rate of heat supply without thermal leakage to a differential but known mass of the substance under study.  It is suited for liquids where the amount of liquid on hand does not permit of the continuous-flow method.

Apparatus suitable for such a method is shown in Fig. 8.  $H$ represents an open framework carrying a heating coil (leads not shown in the figure) which may be a part of a coil commonly used in radiant heaters.  $C$ is a cooling coil through which, when lowered into the liquid whose upper boundary is $L$, ice water or a cooled brine may be passed to bring the liquid once heated back to the starting temperature.  $B_1$ and $B_2$ are metallic objects whose use will be explained later; $S$ is a motor-driven stirrer, and $T$ is a thermometer.  All are inside a Dewar flask, $D$, immersed in water that may be stirred if necessary.  Fine wire strung out so as to be in contact with the walls or nearly so on all sides where the leakage losses occur and connected as one arm of a Wheatstone bridge will serve in a preferred method for measuring temperature changes.

At least two, but generally three, sets of readings must be taken, one with block $B_1$ installed, the other two with block $B_2$, which is of the same material and the same mass (strictly same thermal capacitance) as block $B_1$.  Block $B_1$ with inner boundary at $b_1$ differs from block $B_2$ whose inner boundary is $b_2$.  The inner shell of block $B_1$ should not be in contact with the outer shell.  This arrangement makes it possible, with the same upper liquid level $L$, to heat up different amounts of liquid at the same rate $(dT/dt)$ with identical thermal leakages.  Then, with identical values for $dT/dt$, one may equate the difference in energy supply rates $(IV)_1 - (IV)_2$ to the rate of storage of heat in that amount of liquid $m$ which represents the difference between the two amounts used, depending on whether block $B_1$ or block $B_2$ is in place. Thus

$$(IV)_1 - (IV)_2 = mc_p \frac{dT}{dt} \tag{24}$$

A satisfactory procedure follows. (1) With $B_1$ in place, the liquid at the $L$ level, and the whole at temperature $T_0$, heat is supplied electrically at a convenient rate

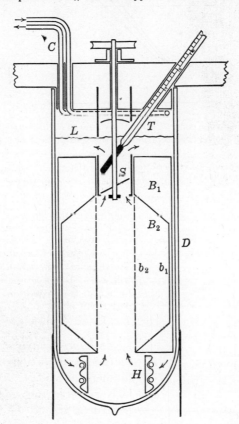

F_IG. 8. Apparatus for a differential, equated thermal-leakage method.

$(IV)_1$ and values for a temperature-time curve, $T = f_1(t)$, are recorded for the chosen temperature range and plotted (Fig. 9). (2) By means of a cooling liquid passed through $C$, the temperature of the whole is brought back to $T_0$. (3) $B_1$ is replaced by $B_2$, and liquid of measured mass $m$ is removed to bring the upper level back to $L$. (4) At a decreased supply rate $(IV)_2'$, estimated to give a temperature-time curve somewhere near that given by the observed $T = f_1(t)$, a $T = f_2'(t)$ is obtained for the same range as before. (5) The temperature of the calorimeter and contents is brought back to $T_0$ as before. (6) At a new supply rate $(IV)_2''$, which should yield a temperature-time curve very close to that given by $T = f_1(t)$, a $T = f_2''(t)$ is obtained for the same range as before. (7) Values for $(IV)_2$ for various sets of values

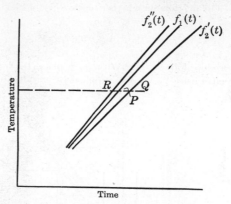

FIG. 9. Temperature-time curves for the three runs of a differential, equated thermal-leakage method for determining the specific heat of a liquid.

of $T$ are computed using corresponding sets of values of $dT/dt$, as at $P$, $Q$, and $R$, taken from the three distribution curves of Fig. 9. For this we use the approximation

$$\frac{(IV)_2 - (IV)_2''}{(IV)_2 - (IV)_2'} = \frac{(dT/dt)_P - (dT/dt)_R}{(dT/dt)_P - (dT/dt)_Q} \tag{25}$$

which becomes the more exact as $T = f_2''(t)$ approaches $T = f_1(t)$. (8) Finally, using values for $(IV)_2$ thus computed, values for $c_p$ are obtained by substitution in Eq. 24.

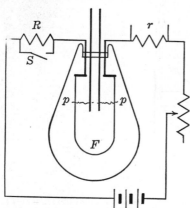

FIG. 10. A simplified arrangement for a lamp-filament method of measuring specific heats.

To eliminate uncertainties of readings it will generally be desirable to obtain values for $dT/dt$ from equations which have been derived to fit the observed curves showing $T = f(t)$.

(c) *Lamp-Filament Method.* This method is applicable only to metallic filaments in vacuo. Though particularly suitable for incandescent temperatures, it may be used for lower temperatures also. A simplified arrangement of apparatus which may be used is diagrammed in part in Fig. 10. It shows a lamp filament $F$ mounted in a glass lamp bulb or other chamber which may be evacuated. To prevent appreciable departures from a constant temperature along the portion of a filament being studied, fine potential leads are joined to the filament at $p$, $p$

and to heavy leads, which extend outside the bulb or chamber.   The
part of the filament under consideration is limited to that portion
between the contacts at $p$, $p$.   The current from the storage battery,
as shown, passes through a variable control resistor, a standard resistance $r$ (for use in measuring the current), the lamp filament, and
a resistor $R$ which may be thrown in or thrown out of the circuit at
will.   The leads from $r$ and from $p$, $p$, connected in turn to a potentiometer or other suitable device, permit of determinations of electrical
currents and potential differences.

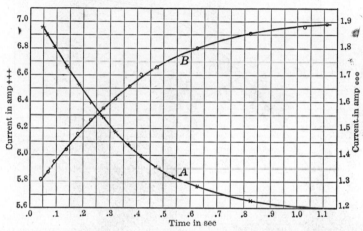

FIG. 11.   For a particular test, the variation, with time, for the current used during
($A$) the heating, and ($B$) the cooling, of a portion of a lamp filament in an evacuated
bulb from one condition of uniform temperature to another (A. G. Worthing, *Phys.
Rev.*, **12**, 199, 1918).

Starting with a stationary state of operation with resistor $R$ in the
circuit, a current $I_1$ passing, and a potential drop $V_1$ between the
contacts $p$, $p$, closing of switch $S$ results in a gradual but quick change
to a second stationary state with a current $I_2$ and a potential drop $V_2$.
Throughout this period, however, there is the following equality with
regard to energy rates

$$IV = mc_p \frac{dT}{dt} + \mathcal{R}A \qquad (26)$$

of which $\mathcal{R}$ represents radiancy, that is the rate of emission or radiant
energy per unit of radiating area, and $A$ the radiating area of the
filament.   The three terms of the equation in order represent the rate
of supply of energy to the filament electrically, the rate of storage of
energy in the filament, and its rate of emission of energy by radiation.

Given $I$ and $V$ as a function of time, the dimensions of the filament and its resistivity $\rho$ and radiancy $\mathcal{R}$ as functions of the temperature $T$ as obtained from other work, one is able to compute a series of values for $c_p$. Opening switch $S$ leads to a similar series which is associated with a cooling of the filament.

A curve showing $I = f_1(t)$ (Fig. 11) may be obtained (1) with an oscillograph to one of whose two pairs of condenser plates the current

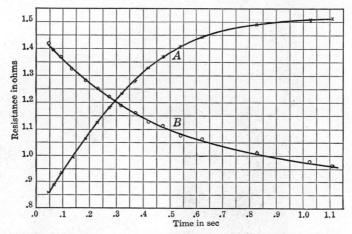

FIG. 12.   The resistance of a uniformly heated portion of a lamp filament in an evacuated bulb as a function of time $(A)$ on heating, $(B)$ on cooling, from one temperature to another (A. G. Worthing, *Phys. Rev.*, **12**, 199, 1918).

leads of Fig. 10 are attached, or (2) from repeated trials for instantaneous balances with a potentiometer to which those same terminals are attached. Obviously a curve showing $V = f_2(t)$ may be determined similarly. The actual details of operation need not be discussed here.

The curves of Fig. 12, obtained from $I$ and $V$ measurements employing a potentiometer, represent data obtained for a circular tungsten filament of 0.1148 gm mass, a length of 10.05 cm, a radius of 0.01387 cm, and a surface area of 0.870 cm². Given that a resistance of 1.100 ohms corresponds to a temperature of 1810°K and a radiancy, $\mathcal{R}$, of 14.62 watts/cm², and that throughout its range of incandescence the value of $(T/R)(dR/dT)$ for tungsten is 1.200, one may compute the specific heat for tungsten for this temperature using Eq. 26 and data obtainable from Figs. 11 and 12. Thus, for 1810°K, we may obtain as the needed additional data: $t = 0.212$ sec, $I = 6.46$ amp, $V = 7.11$ volts, $dR/dt = 1.45$ ohm/sec. There follow

$$\frac{dT}{dt} = \frac{dR}{dt} \times \frac{1}{(T/R)(dR/dT)} \times \frac{T}{R}$$

$$= 1.45 \frac{\text{ohm}}{\text{sec}} \times \frac{1}{1.200} \times \frac{1810°\text{K}}{1.100 \text{ ohm}} = 1990 \frac{\text{K}°}{\text{sec}} \quad (27)$$

$$c_p = \frac{IV - \mathcal{R}A}{M \, dT/dt} = \frac{45.9 \text{ watts} - 12.7 \text{ watts}}{0.1148 \text{ gm} \times 1990 \text{ K}°/\text{sec}}$$

$$= 0.1450 \frac{\text{joules}}{\text{gm K}°} = 0.0346 \frac{\text{cal}}{\text{gm K}°} = 6.38 \frac{\text{cal}}{\text{gm-atom K}°} \quad (28)$$

(d) *Corbino's Wheatstone Bridge Method.* An ingenious method, applicable likewise to metallic lamp filaments, was brought out in 1912 by the Italian physicist O. M. Corbino (1876–   ). It makes use of a Wheatstone bridge and is capable of considerable accuracy. The method is rather involved and will not be considered further.

(e) *Nernst's Low-Leakage-Loss Method.* This method for determining specific heats of solids was developed in Germany by Nernst and his collaborators. It has been of great value in checking theoretical predictions. As planned by A. Eucken (1884–   ), the solid, if a metal, served as its own calorimeter. As shown in Fig. 13A, a cylindrical block of the metal to be tested was drilled to receive a cylindrical plug of slightly lesser diameter. In the space between the two was wound a pure platinum wire which served both as a heating coil and as a resistance thermometer. The top of the plug was shaped to insure good thermal contact. The whole calorimeter thus formed was suspended in an evacuated glass vessel which in turn was immersed in a constant-temperature bath (Fig. 13B) of ice, solid carbon dioxide, liquid air, or liquid hydrogen, depending on the temperature region under investigation.

In operation, hydrogen was first admitted to the interior of the glass vessel, in order that the calorimeter might assume the temperature of the bath as quickly as possible. Next, this vessel was evacuated in order to minimize thermal leakage. In one experiment cited by Nernst, the calorimeter block was composed of 396.3 gm of lead. It was suspended in an evacuated glass vessel which in turn was immersed in liquid air at a reduced pressure to yield 61°K. After a run of 4 min, the resistance of the coil increased by 0.407 ohm and the temperature rose 1.219 K°. During this time the potential drop across the heating coil was 1.586 volts, and the current through it was 0.1444 amp. The heat developed in the calorimeter was

$$Q = 1.586 \text{ v} \times 0.1444 \text{ amp} \times 240 \text{ sec} \times \frac{1.000 \text{ cal}}{4.179 \text{ joule}} = 13.13 \text{ cal} \quad (29)$$

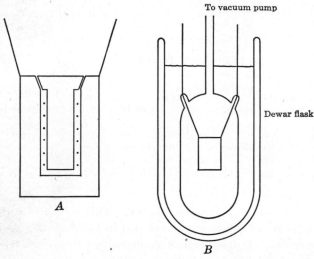

FIG. 13. A vacuum calorimeter as planned by Euken for the application of Nernst's low-leakage-loss method for measuring specific heats at low temperatures. At $A$ some details of calorimeter construction are shown; at $B$, its method of mounting in surroundings which could be maintained at various low temperatures.

A correction for the amount of heat lost by conduction along the leads left 12.99 cal as the net supply. Hence the heat capacitance of the calorimeter block was

$$C = \frac{12.99 \text{ cal}}{1.219 \text{ K}°} = 10.65 \frac{\text{cal}}{\text{K}°} \quad (30)$$

Subtracting the heat capacitance of the platinum and other non-lead material, which was determined to be 0.13 cal/K°, left 10.52 cal/K°. Finally, as the atomic heat of lead at 61°K, Nernst obtained

$$c_p = \frac{10.52 \text{ cal/K}°}{396.3 \text{ gm}} \times \frac{206.4 \text{ gm}}{1 \text{ gm-atom}} = 5.48 \frac{\text{cal}}{\text{gm-atom K}°} \quad (31)$$

Nernst and Lindemann investigated the variations of the specific heats of a number of pure substances over a temperature range extending from the ice point to 16°K. The results were used as a check on theoretical predictions.

(f) *The Adiabatic Method.* Adiabatic calorimetry as noted in Chapter V seems to have been first employed by Prof. Theodore Richards (1868–1928) at Harvard University, winner of a Nobel prize in chemistry in 1914. It represents a definite improvement over the low-leakage-loss method. It involves an additive procedure, that of maintaining the jacket at the temperature of the calorimetric fluid. How this has been done with high precision by Swietoslawski is shown in Chapter V under microcalorimetry. Otherwise, the procedure is exactly that of the low-leakage-loss method. This method was much used by Simon and Lang in Germany.

## PROBLEMS

**1.** Two hundred grams of flint glass at 200°C is dropped into 100 gm of water at 20.0°C. If, without loss of heat to the outside, a temperature of 24.0°C results, what is the average specific heat of the glass for the temperature range given?

**2.** The specific heats of water, ice, and iron as ordinarily expressed are 1.00 cal/(gm C°), 0.46 cal/(gm C°), and 0.109 cal/(gm C°). Express these in btu/(pd F°) and (gmv $\Lambda$)/(gm K°).

**3.** Given that the specific gravities of iron and ice are 7.8 and 0.92, determine the amounts of heat in btu required to heat 1.0 ft$^3$ each of water, ice, and iron 1 F°. (See problem 2.)

**4.** Given that, between 0°C and 100°C, the average volume expansivity of mercury is $182 \times 10^{-6}$ 1/C°, and that its average specific heat is 0.0334 cal/(gm C°), determine the fractional part of its specific heat which is represented by work done against atmospheric pressure on heating.

**5.** Given that at 0°C mercury has a constant-pressure specific heat of 0.0334 cal/(gm C°), a specific volume of 0.07355 cm$^3$/gm, a volume expansivity of $182 \times 10^{-6}$ 1/C°, and a compressibility of $3.80 \times 10^{-6}$ cm$^2$/kgwt, compute for mercury at 0°C the atomic heats at constant pressure and constant volume.

**6.** The amounts of heat necessarily added to a gram-atom of aluminum continuously at a pressure of 1 A, in order to raise its temperature without loss of heat in succession from 50°K in each case to 100°K, 150°K, 200°K, 250°K, and 300°K are 103 cal, 293 cal, 530 cal, 794 cal, and 1077 cal. Plot a curve showing the heat added to the aluminum as a function of the temperature to which it was raised. From the plot, determine graphically the atomic heats of aluminum at 100°K and 200°K.

**7.** Using the experimental data of Fig. 1, compute the amounts of heat required to heat 1 kg each of lead and of copper from 0°K to 200°K. Compare the ratio of these amounts with the ratio of their specific heats at 0°C.

**8.** In an experiment to determine the average specific heat of a 230-gm slab of glass between 350°C and room temperature, the slab at 350°C is dropped suddenly into a calorimeter containing transformer oil at a room temperature of 12.00°C, the oil is stirred vigorously, and a thermocouple record of the oil temperature is taken. Given that the water equivalent of the oil, its container, and the stirrer is 400 gm, that the rate of increase of temperature due to stirring alone when at 12.00°C and with the glass specimen in the liquid is 0.70 C°/min, and that the temperature readings (except for the first seven which were taken 15 sec apart), for successive 30-sec intervals, are

| 12.00°C | 37.95°C | 38.86°C | 37.23°C | 35.80°C |
|---------|---------|---------|---------|---------|
| 20.80   | 39.04   | 38.43   | 36.85   | 35.48   |
| 29.60   | 39.37   | 38.02   | 36.49   |         |
| 35.30   | 39.30   | 37.62   | 36.14   |         |

determine the average specific heat of the glass. (See standard compensated-loss calorimetry method of Chapter V.)

**9.** A small truncated cone of graphite, having a mass of 20.0 gm, heated in succession to 500°C, 1000°C, and 1500°C in a furnace, is dropped into a well-shielded, copper-block calorimeter having a water equivalent of 400 gm in surroundings at 0.00°C. The resulting temperatures corrected for thermal leakages are 5.75°C, 15.65°C, and 29.80°C. What are the mean specific heats between 0°C and the stated temperatures which are to be computed?

**10.** Using Eq. 11 and the values for the constants $k_1$, $k_2$, etc., given in the text for platinum, compute the specific heats of platinum at 500°C, 1000°C, and 1500°C.

**11.** A Bunsen ice calorimeter is used to determine the specific heat of a lead-tin alloy. A 1.75-gm slug of the alloy initially at 100°C was used. The movement of the mercury thread corresponded to a volume change of 8.44 mm³. Compute the specific heat of the alloy and the composition on the basis that the alloy is one of mixed crystals, that is, that, on freezing, the crystals which form are of pure lead and of pure tin. [$L_{H_2O} = 79.2$ cal/gm, $d_{ice\ at\ 0°C} = 0.9160$ gm/cm³, $d_{H_2O\ at\ 0°C} = 0.9998$ gm/cm³, $\bar{c}_{Pb} = 0.031$ cal/(gm C°), $\bar{c}_{Sn} = 0.054$ cal/(gm C°).]

**12.** Using the Joly differential steam calorimeter with one of the two equal containers containing 1.0 kg of glycerol, an antifreeze component, it is found that, on heating from 20°C to 100°C, it is necessary to add 94.0 gm to the pan from which the empty container is suspended. What is the specific heat which results from the given data?

**13.** Using C. S. Smith's data for the specific heat of the copper-zinc alloy beta brass as shown in Fig. 7, compute roughly the energy per unit of mass which is required to change merely the ordered arrangement of atoms below about 465°C to the disordered arrangement above. Assuming that the shift starts at about 200°C and is completed at about 550°C, determine the approximate percentage of the heat added during this temperature interval which is associated with the order-disorder transition.

**14.** Using the equated thermal-leakage method for determining the specific heat of ethyl alcohol, one finds that at 20°C with the larger amount of liquid 500.0 watts yield a value of 15.00 C°/min for $dT/dt$, that with the smaller amount of liquid, less by 460.0 gm, 240.0 watts yield 14.00 C°/min while 290.0 watts yield 15.20 C°/min. What is the specific heat for ethyl alcohol that results?

**15.** In two succeeding runs using the continuous-flow method for the measurement of the specific heat of turpentine, the temperatures at the inlet and the outlet were maintained at 20.15°C and 30.50°C with the rates of passage of the liquid 4.00 kg/min and 2.50 kg/min. The corresponding currents and potential drops were 11.6 amp and 116 volts for the first run and 9.45 amp and 94.5 volts for the second. What is the specific heat of turpentine for the specified temperature range?

**16.** A 10-gm piece of aluminum wire, wound as a helix and suspended in an evacuated adiabatic calorimeter whose walls with the aid of thermocouples are constantly kept at the same temperature as the helix itself, was heated electrically at a constant rate of just 0.22 watt. The following temperature time data were obtained.

| TEMPERATURE | TIME |
|---|---|
| °K | sec |
| 40 | 0. |
| 60 | 124 |
| 80 | 375 |
| 100 | 744 |
| 120 | 1212 |
| 140 | 1762 |

From the data given, determine the specific heats of aluminum at 60°K and 100°K.

17. A tungsten wire 1.00 mm in diameter heated in a vacuum to 2400°K is allowed to cool by radiation under conditions such that the rate of absorption of radiation from the surroundings is negligible, and the following data are obtained:

| $T$ | $\Re$ | $t$ |
|---|---|---|
| °K | watts/cm² | sec |
| 2400 | 55.8 | 0.00 |
| 2200 | 37.2 | 0.39 |
| 2000 | 23.7 | 0.90 |
| 1800 | 14.20 | 1.84 |
| 1600 | 7.77 | 3.33 |
| 1400 | 3.82 | 6.11 |

Determine the specific heats of tungsten at 2200°K and at 1600°K.

18. Given that the filament to which Figs. 11 and 12 refer has a temperature of 2014°K and a radiancy of 24.5 watts/cm² when its resistance is 1.230 ohms, compute the specific heat of tungsten at constant pressure at 2014°K.

19. A 525-hp aircraft engine has a specific fuel consumption of 0.60 pd/(bhp-hr) (bhp signifies brake horsepower) when using 20,000 btu/pd fuel. If 30% of the heat developed by the combustion, assumed complete, is dissipated by a radiation system using Prestone, for how many gallons per minute must the pump be designed when the Prestone operates between 240°F and 300°F? Assume the specific gravity of Prestone to be 1.125 and that its specific heat varies linearly from 0.675 btu/(pd F°) at 212°F to 0.735 btu/(pd F°) at 300°F.

20. A 150-pd patient, whose normal rate of developing heat under normal resting conditions is 1800 kcal/day, develops a fever temperature at the rate of 0.6 F°/hr while resting under conditions that would result normally in a maintenance of his normal temperature. At about what rate is heat being developed within his body? What is the ratio of this rate to his normal resting rate? If, as in the early stages of certain fevers, there is principally a practical cessation of flow of heat to the skin, at about what rate would his temperature rise?

# CHAPTER VII

## THERMAL CONDUCTION OF SOLIDS AND LIQUIDS

**1. Introduction.** In discussions of the temperature concept, it is frequently stated that temperature is that characteristic of a body which determines the direction of transfer, if transfer occurs, of heat or of internal energy from one body to another when they are brought into contact. Further, we may say that the process of transfer involved at the point or area of contact is thermal conduction. More particularly, it is the process by which equilibrium of temperature is established in a solid body, initially not at the same temperature throughout, if left to itself.

Transfer of heat from one region to another may be accomplished in various ways, of which thermal conduction is but one. Other common methods are convection and radiation. More uncommon are the electrical methods associated with the terms Thomson effect and Peltier effect as well as certain electromagnetic methods which are much less well known. Ordinarily no one process occurs to the exclusion of all the others, though frequently one predominates greatly. Illustrations of exclusive transfers occur in that by radiation from the sun to the earth, in that by convection from the furnace in the basement to the register or radiator on a floor above, and in that by conduction from the fire-pot side of a furnace wall to the exterior.

Classically the point of view with regard to thermal conduction was that the internal energy or heat was transferred mechanically from one part of the body to another by molecular or atomic impacts. This point of view still holds reasonably well for poor conductors; but, for good conductors, that is, for metals generally, the movements of the valence electrons represent by far the predominant factor. More with regard to this will appear later.

Like density, rigidity, thermal expansivity, etc., for their fields, thermal conductivity is a describing characteristic for its field of heat conduction. Because it enters in the explanation and the correlation of physical phenomena, it is of interest to the physicist and the chemist. Further, the process of thermal conduction occurs repeatedly in nearly all living and inanimate processes, sometimes as one to be combatted, more often as one to be viewed favorably and aided. It is the usual thing for the engineer to give it consideration in his design of a machine, a structure, or a product. The importance of this subdivision of heat is quite evident.

**2. Theory.** An important concept relating to thermal conduction is temperature gradient. It is defined for a point in space as the maximum rate of change of temperature with change of position at that point. It is represented by $(dT/dl)_n$, often without the subscript $n$. A common unit is the C°/cm. Fig. 1 shows the temperature distribution occurring in an electrically heated metal rod near a cold terminal to which it is firmly attached. The isothermal surfaces, obtained by

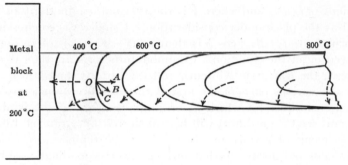

Fig. 1. Traces of isothermal surfaces in a metal bar, heated electrically.

rotation of the figure about an axial line, are seen to vary gradually from an approximately plane surface near that terminal to an approximate cylindrical form with rounded end in the region free or nearly free from the cooling effect of the cold terminal. To the 500°C isothermal at $O$, line $OA$ has been drawn perpendicularly and lines $OB$ and $OC$ in other directions. For the case diagrammed, assume that at $O$ an infinitesimal change in position along $OA$ is accompanied by an infinitesimal change in temperature, such that $dT/dl$ for that direction is, say, 120 C°/cm. This rate of change is greater than that for any other direction as $OB$ or $OC$. In fact, the rate of change for any other direction may be obtained by multiplying the value along the normal $OA$ by the cosine of the angle the new direction makes with $OA$. Thus the value of $dT/dl$ along $OB$ would be (120 C°/cm) × cos 30° or 104 C°/cm. The term temperature gradient is reserved for the value directed along the normal. It is a vector quantity. At all points normal to the isothermal surfaces passing through those points, they are directed from low to high temperatures. Of the arrows with tails at $O$ in Fig. 1, arrow $OA$ only represents the temperature gradient. The dashed arrows directed generally oppositely show, however, the directions of heat flow, at the various points through which they pass.

The defining equation for heat conduction assumes that the rate of transfer of heat by conduction in a body across an element of surface is proportional to the area of that element, the temperature gradient at that point, and the cosine of the angle between the normal to that element of surface and the temperature gradient. The equation is

$$\frac{dQ}{dt} = -ks \left(\frac{dT}{dl}\right)_n \cos \varphi \tag{1}$$

where $dQ/dt$, a heat current, is the transfer rate of heat across an element of area $s$ whose normal makes an angle $\varphi$ with the temperature gradient $(dT/dl)_n$ and where $k$ is the thermal conductivity of the material at the place under consideration. Usually $s$ is so chosen that it is normal to $(dT/dl)_n$; $\cos \varphi$ is then unity. Cos $\varphi$ is often omitted in the writing of the equation. Common units for $k$ are the cal/(cm$^2$ sec C°/cm), the watt/(cm$^2$ C°/cm), and the btu/(ft$^2$ hr F°/in.). Visualizing the various parts of the first of these units, we may say that, in the case of silver for which at ordinary temperatures $k$ is about 1.0 cal/(cm$^2$ sec C°/cm), heat will be transferred at a rate of 1.0 cal/sec across a cm$^2$ of surface in silver, where the temperature gradient is 1.0 C°/cm and normal to that surface. Correspondingly, we may say that, for the case of window glass for which at ordinary temperatures $k$ is about 5.5 btu/(ft$^2$ hr F°/in.), heat will be transferred at a rate of 5.5 btu/hr across 1 ft$^2$ of window-glass surface when the temperature gradient in the glass directed normal to that surface amounts to 1 F°/in.

The equation which underlies thermal conduction and temperature distribution is based on the conservation of energy. Usually referred to as Poisson's equation, in honor of the great French mathematician Siméon Poisson (1781–1840), it is

$$k\left(\frac{\partial^2 T}{\partial x^2} + \frac{\partial^2 T}{\partial y^2} + \frac{\partial^2 T}{\partial z^2}\right) + \frac{1}{V}\frac{dQ}{dt} = \frac{1}{V}\frac{dU}{dt} \tag{2}$$

The first member on the left involving the three partial derivatives may be shown to represent, per unit of volume, the rate of heat conduction into an element of volume, $V$, at the point $(x, y, z)$. Similarly $1/V \, dQ/dt$ and $1/V \, dU/dt$ represent, for that element of volume, the rate of production of heat, electrically or otherwise, and the rate of storage of heat both per unit of volume. Exactly similar equations are found in the fields of gravitation, electricity, magnetism, sound, and radiation with, of course, appropriate changes of interpretation for the different symbols. For a problem and its solution in one field, there is commonly a corresponding problem and solution in each of the other fields.

In this book there will be occasion for the application of the foregoing only to simple conditions such as we shall be interested in experimentally. It should be kept in mind, however, that Poisson's equation is perfectly general and that, when proper boundary conditions for a portion of a body are given, the equation serves together with those boundary conditions for the determination of the heat flow and the temperature distribution in that portion of the body. For such more general procedure, physics and industry generally are greatly indebted to the French mathematician Jean Fourier (1768–1830), who, in 1822 in his *Théorie analytique de la chaleur*, indicated a method of solution which has been generally followed since.

It is interesting that Fourier, while serving as an appointed chief magistrate of Isére, France, and while engaged in the preparation of his monumental work on heat conduction, was interested in the practical problem of reducing heat losses through the walls of buildings. It is also interesting that Eq. 1 may be rearranged for linear conductors, to yield what is sometimes called Fourier's law, viz.

$$\frac{dQ}{dt} = \frac{\Delta T}{\varphi} \tag{3}$$

where $dQ/dt$ and $\varphi$ are referred to as thermal current and thermal resistance respectively. This relation antedated by several years the much more familiar, similar electrical law known as Ohm's law.

There are three convenient, idealized, steady-state conditions for the precise measurement of the characteristic $k$. In the first arrangement, the temperature gradients at all points in the body have the same direction. This corresponds to the uniform, unidirectional flow of heat along a rod whose sides are thermally insulated. In the second arrangement, the flow of heat is radially outward from the axis of a cylindrical rod of circular cross section. Here, in general, temperature gradients differ from point to point both in magnitude and direction. According to the third arrangement, the flow of heat is radially out from the center of a sphere. Here also temperature gradients differ in magnitude and direction from point to point. How these arrangements have been realized or approximated in actual methods for the measurement of $k$ follows. For the solution of the more general cases involving other types of flow of heat and the period during which steady states are being established, the procedure developed by Fourier, already referred to, is very important.

### THERMAL CONDUCTIVITY METHODS FOR GOOD CONDUCTORS

**3. Some General Considerations.** Substances which may be classed as good thermal conductors are usually metals. As may be expected, the conditions under which thermal conduction takes place and the methods of measurement are varied. The factors that enter to distinguish one method from another are: (1) direction of flow of heat, whether unidirectional (parallel to the axis of a rod), radially cylindrical, or radially spherical; (2) lateral leakage or no lateral leakage of heat in unidirectional flow; (3) steadiness or variableness in the supply

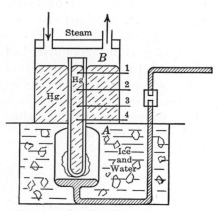

of heat; (4) production of heat throughout the specimen electrically or production of heat at some one region as at an end or along an axis. Corresponding to many combinations of these factors, acceptable methods of measurement of $k$ are recognized.

**4. Methods Involving Unidirectional Conduction in Rods without Lateral Leakage.** (a) *Berget's and Searle's Methods Employing Guard Cylinders.* A. Berget in France in 1888, in determining the thermal conductivity of mercury and later of solid metals, used the arrange-

Fig. 2. Apparatus with a guard cylinder as used by Berget to determine the thermal conductivities of mercury and other liquid substances.

ment shown in Fig. 2. The actual material under test is that contained in the central cylindrical glass tube between levels $A$ and $B$. Outside is a guard cylinder of the same material as that under test, whose purpose is to reduce the lateral flow of heat in the test specimen and consequently to produce a more nearly constant temperature gradient throughout the material under test. At 1, 2, 3, and 4, small iron wires, insulated except at their inner ends, are inserted for temperature-measuring purposes. Two such wires together with the intervening mercury in the column form a thermocouple which can be used to obtain directly the temperature difference between the two mercury-iron junctions. Given in addition their linear separation, the desired temperature gradient along the column is easily obtained.

In Berget's test with mercury the diameter of the central tube was 1.3 cm, its length from $A$ to $B$, 20 cm. In chamber $B$ at the top, heat was supplied by condensing steam or otherwise. Of this heat only a small portion was conducted down the rod and later received by the R. W. Bunsen (1811–1899) ice calorimeter (see p. 143) below, where it was measured in accord with the standard procedure described in Chapter VI. A larger portion of the heat was conducted downward through the surrounding guard cylinder where it served to keep the flow in the central column constant and unidirectional. By means of the thermocouples, average temperature gradients were readily obtained. Given in addition the cross section of the central column, average values of $k$ follow from Eq. 1. For the mercury column with

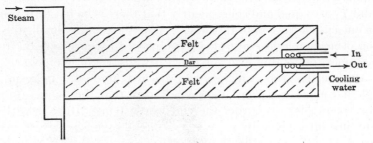

FIG. 3. Apparatus designed by Searle for the measurement of thermal conductivities of metals. It involves unidirectional conduction with negligible lateral leakage.

ends at 0°C and 100°C, Berget obtained 0.02015 cal/(cm$^2$ sec C°/cm). He also concluded that $k$ varied with temperature in accord with

$$k = k_0[1 + c(T - T_0)] \tag{4}$$

In his work, G. F. C. Searle (1864–     ) in England modified Berget's procedure by making his guard cylinder of very poorly conducting material such as felt (Fig. 3). In so far as there is leakage through this thermal insulation, his method fails.

(b) *Ångström's Method Employing Sinusoidal Temperature Waves.* This method developed by the Swedish physicist Anders Ångström (1814–1874) was first used in a study of the thermal conductivities of metals. For such a study, the metal should be in the form of a long rod. Strictly unidirectional flow is assumed, without lateral leakage and without the production or the absorption of heat within the region concerned. The underlying relation, based on Eq. 2, is

$$\frac{d^2 T}{dx^2} = \frac{1}{kV}\frac{dU}{dt} = \frac{cm}{kV}\frac{dT}{dt} = \frac{c\delta}{k}\frac{dT}{dt} = \frac{1}{\kappa}\frac{dT}{dt} \tag{5}$$

The combination $k/c\delta$, or $\kappa$, an approximately constant term occurring frequently in thermal conduction problems, describes a certain characteristic of the material to which the equation is applied and is known as its diffusivity.  One end of the rod is kept at a constant temperature $T_1$, while that of the other end is varied in a simple harmonic manner about its mean temperature, $T_0$, in accord with

$$\Delta T_0 = (\Delta T_0)_m \sin \frac{2\pi}{P} t \tag{6}$$

$\Delta T_0$ is the instantaneous value of the variation whose maximum value, the amplitude, is $(\Delta T_0)_m$.  $P$ is the period of the harmonic variation.

$T_0$ may differ from $T_1$.  However, for what follows, we assume that $T_0$ and $T_1$ are equal and consequently that there is no net heat transfer from one end of the rod to the other.  Where $(\Delta T_0)_m$ is small, the condition of negligible lateral leakage is obtained by enclosing the rod in a container, preferably evacuated, with walls at the temperature $T_1$. For the steady state which is approached gradually following the simple harmonic variation, it may be shown that the temperature, $T$, at any point distant $x$ from the end whose temperature is varied is, at any instant $t$, given by

$$\Delta T = T - T_0 = (\Delta T_0)_m e^{-\alpha x} \sin \left( \frac{2\pi}{P} t - \frac{2\pi}{L} x \right) \tag{7}$$

As is apparent from Fig. 4, which shows the temperature variations in the rod at two instants differing in time by about $P/8$, a very highly damped, sinusoidal temperature wave traverses the rod in the positive $x$-direction.  The damping constant $\alpha$, and the wavelength $L$, are both functions of $P$, as may be shown by combining Eqs. 5 and 7.  Replacing $\alpha$ and $L$ of Eq. 7 by these functions, we have

$$\Delta T = (\Delta T_0)_m \, e^{-\sqrt{\pi/P\kappa} \, x} \sin \left( \frac{2\pi}{P} t - \sqrt{\frac{\pi}{P\kappa}} x \right) \tag{7a}$$

Comparing two maximum values of $\Delta T$, namely $\Delta_1 T$ and $\Delta_2 T$ at positions $x_1$ and $x_2$, without regard to their times of occurrence, one obtains

$$\ln \frac{\Delta_1 T}{\Delta_2 T} = \sqrt{\frac{\pi}{P\kappa}} \, (x_2 - x_1) \tag{7b}$$

Solving for $k$ we obtain finally

$$k = c \delta \kappa = \frac{\pi c \delta}{P} \left( \frac{x_2 - x_1}{\ln \Delta_1 T / \Delta_2 T} \right)^2 \tag{7c}$$

In a rod of copper for which $\kappa$ at room temperatures is about 1.15 cm$^2$/sec, a period $P$ of 5 min and a separation $x_2 - x_1$ of 5 cm leads to a ratio of about 8.2 for $\Delta_1 T / \Delta_2 T$. The corresponding value for the wavelength $L$ obtained from Eqs. 7 and 7$a$ is about 65 cm. For such a value for $x_2 - x_1$, the ratio of the $\Delta T$'s is about 500, so tremendously is the temperature wave damped. From $L/P$, one may obtain about

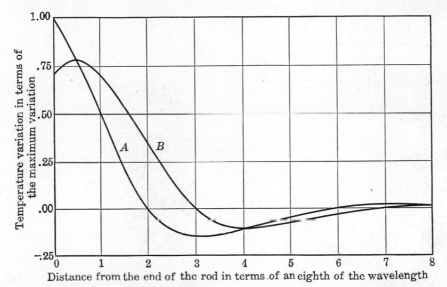

FIG. 4. Temperature distribution in an end portion of a long rod, protected from lateral, thermal leakage, resulting from an externally produced periodic sinusoidal variation of temperature at that end. $A$, distribution with the temperature variation at the end a maximum. $B$, distribution one-eighth of a period later. For the case shown, the damping results in a reduction of amplitude to $\frac{1}{90}$ of the original amplitude at a distance of one wavelength from the end.

2.2 mm/sec as the velocity of the temperature wave along the rod. This is not to be confused with the speed of transfer of heat along the rod.

Other methods for measuring thermal conductivities are more satisfactory than this. It is of most interest now because of the application which may be made to the conduction of heat occurring in rock and soil just beneath the surface of the earth's crust where the periodic variations are produced by diurnal and seasonal changes of temperature. A problem relating to such variations is to be found at the close of the chapter.

(*c*) *Kohlrausch's Method Employing Uniform Electrical Production of Heat Throughout the Rod Tested.* Developed in Germany in 1898–

1899 by F. Kohlrausch (1840–1910), this method is of special interest because it leads to a direct determination of the ratio of the electrical to the thermal conductivity of the substance studied, a ratio of much importance. It is susceptible of high accuracy. The metal studied, in the form of a rod and protected from loss of heat laterally, is heated by a direct current (Fig. 5.) Because of the lateral insulation, the heat developed can be conducted only lengthwise toward the ends M and N which are maintained at some desired temperature. For an element of the bar between $l$ and $l + dl$, when a steady state has been reached, the rate of conduction of heat toward $M$ at $l$ less that at $l + dl$ is equal to the rate of production of heat electrically between $l$ and $l + dl$.

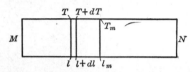

Fig. 5. Diagram to illustrate Kohl-rausch's method of measuring $k$.

For the case where the temperature difference involved is so small that variations in $k$ and the electrical resistivity $\rho$ are negligible, this means

$$ks \frac{dT}{dl} - ks \left( \frac{dT}{dl} + \frac{d^2T}{dl^2} dl \right) = I^2 R = (i\pi r^2)^2 \times \frac{\rho \, dl}{\pi r^2}$$

$$= i^2 \rho s \, dl \qquad (8)$$

where $i$ represents the electrical current density in the bar, $\rho$ its resistivity and $s$ its cross section. Eq. 8 reduces to

$$\frac{d^2T}{dl^2} = \frac{-i^2 \rho}{k} \qquad (9)$$

By two successive integrations, one obtains

$$T = -\frac{i^2 \rho}{2k} l^2 + c_1 l + c_2 \qquad (10)$$

With $T_m$ representing the maximum temperature which occurs at $l_m$, midway of the length of the rod, the integration constant $c_2$ is eliminated by forming the difference

$$T_m - T = \frac{i^2 \rho}{2k} (l^2 - l_m{}^2) + c_1(l_m - l) \qquad (10a)$$

Then by differentiating Eq. 10a to obtain an expression for $dT/dl$ and noting that necessarily $dT/dl = 0$ where $l = l_m$, one obtains for $c_1$

$$c_1 = 2 \frac{i^2 \rho}{2k} l_m \qquad (10b)$$

Elimination of $c_1$ from Eq. 10$a$ by means of Eq. 10$b$ gives, in terms of measurable quantities, except for $k$,

$$T_m - T = \frac{i^2 \rho}{2k} (l_m - l)^2 \tag{11}$$

where $l$ is the distance from one end of the rod to an arbitrarily chosen position having the temperature $T$. Since $i\rho(l_m - l)$ represents the potential difference $V_m - V$ between $l_m$ and $l$, Eq. 11 may be rewritten to yield

$$k = \frac{1}{2\rho} \frac{(V_m - V)^2}{T_m - T} \tag{12}$$

$V_m - V$ is most accurately determined by taking one-half of the potential difference between the two positions on opposite sides of $l_m$ which possess the same temperature $T$. This procedure fortunately eliminates errors that would arise otherwise on account of Thomson emf's which are present. Since all quantities on the right-hand side of Eq. 12 may be measured with high accuracy, this method permits of high accuracy.

W. Jaeger (1862– ) and H. Diesselhorst (1870– ) in Germany used Kohlrausch's method in an extended study of the relation between electrical and thermal conductivities, $1/\rho$ and $k$, of several metals.

**5. Methods Involving Unidirectional Conduction in Rods with Lateral Leakage.** (a) *Biot, Despretz, and Forbes' Rod Leakage Method.* This method was proposed by the French physicist J. B. Biot (1774–1862) in 1816 and tested by C. M. Despretz (1789–1863) in 1821. Later, in 1854 it was considerably used by the German physicist G. H. Wiedemann (1826–1899) and R. Franz in a study with rather highly refined apparatus which resulted in the publication of the Wiedemann-Franz law. (See p. 189.) All such work, however, concerned only comparisons of $k$ for different metals. Only in 1862 did the Scotch physicist James Forbes (1809–1868) introduce the feature (step 2 in what follows) which made it possible to determine $k$ for any one metal in terms of absolute units.

There are two separate experimental steps in the making of a determination by the Biot, Despretz, and Forbes method. For the first, a uniform rod with a uniform surface is used. One end (Fig. 6) is kept in contact with a constant source at a temperature higher (or lower) than that of the surroundings, whose temperature should be uniform. If the source is hot, there will be a thermal current along the rod with a gradual leakage of heat from the lateral surface. When a steady state has been reached, the rate of conduction of heat across any chosen cross section of the rod where the surface is at temperature $T_1$ is equal to the rate of conduction across a section, farther from the

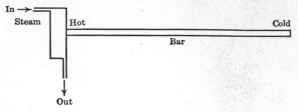

FIG. 6. Apparatus suggested by Biot and used by others to determine the thermal conductivity of a substance in the form of a metal bar. It involves unidirectional conduction with lateral leakage.

high-temperature source, where the surface is at temperature $T_2$, plus the rate of leakage laterally, £, from the surface between the two chosen cross sections. Thus

$$k\pi r^2 \left(\frac{dT}{dl}\right)_1 = k\pi r^2 \left(\frac{dT}{dl}\right)_2 + £ \tag{13}$$

Values for the temperature gradients $(dT/dl)_1$ and $(dT/dl)_2$ are obtained directly from a graph of $T = f(l)$ for the rod (Fig. 7A).

The lateral leakage rate is obtained by the second experimental step which employs a second rod that, except in length, must be identical

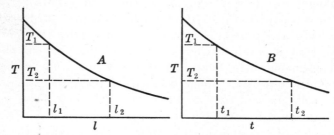

FIG. 7. Graphs showing, for the rods used in the Biot-Depretz-Forbes method of measuring $k$, (A) the surface temperature as a function of distance from the hot source in contact with one end, (B) the surface temperature as a function of time for the uniformly heated rod cooling as a whole.

with the first. This second rod is heated to a temperature higher than $T_1$. Then, with the surroundings the same as for the first step, the bar is allowed to cool by thermal leakage and a curve showing $T = f(t)$ (Fig. 7B) is obtained. Given the specific heat $c$, the density $\delta$, and the radius, $r$, of this second rod, one readily sees that, for any particular $T$, its thermal leakage rate per unit of length $d\mathcal{L}/dl$ is given by

$$\frac{d\mathcal{L}}{dl} = -c\pi r^2 \delta \frac{dT}{dt} \tag{14}$$

The assumption is now made that the leakage rate $d\mathcal{L}$ for an element of the first rod of length $dl$ at the temperature $T$ is identically the $d\mathcal{L}$ of Eq. 14. For a vacuum, this assumption is justified. Outside a vacuum, the differences in temperature distribution may vary convection leakages, and some uncertainty may result. Granted the assumption, a value for the leakage rate $\mathcal{L}$ of Eq. 13 follows. It is

$$\mathcal{L} = -\int_{l_1}^{l_2} \frac{d\mathcal{L}}{dl} dl \tag{15}$$

In the integration, care must be taken to insure that associated values of $dT/dl$ and $dl$ always have the same temperature $T$.

With $\mathcal{L}$ of Eq. 13 determined, a solution for $k$ follows, which is based on the two distributions $T = f(l)$ and $T = f(t)$.

It has been tacitly assumed that the $dT/dl$ values obtained from $T - f(l)$ are average values for the chosen cross sections. As Fig. **1** shows, this assumption may not be even approximately true. Factors which favor its justification are low convection loss, low thermal emissivity of the metal surface, large cross section of the rods, and high temperature gradients. If the method is to be used this feature should be carefully examined. Except where measurements are to be made in a vacuum, this method would seem to be inferior to the methods already described which involve unidirectional conduction without lateral leakage.

(b) *Worthing's Lamp-Filament Method.* This method, which was first used successfully in 1914 at the General Electric Laboratories in Cleveland, Ohio, has been applied thus far only to materials in the form of lamp filaments at incandescence in evacuated lamp bulbs. Thus far this method, or something closely related, is the only one that has been found possible for such extremely high temperatures. It may, of course, be applied to non-incandescent materials as well. The underlying principles in part are those employed by Biot, Despretz, and Forbes and in part those employed by Kohlrausch.

This method requires a cooled portion of filament such as may be produced by clamping a metal block to the wire under investigation. The lead-in supports at the ends of a mounted filament may be so used, though a block that may be clamped to and freed from the filament part way along its length is preferable. Further, the filament should be of such length that, when clamped, the temperatures of portions midway between the clamp and lead-in support shall not be appreciably affected by the clamping. Essentially two sets of data are necessary. In the first set, one

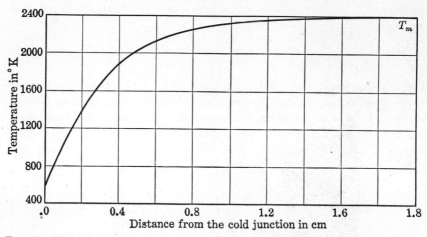

FIG. 8. The temperature distribution near a cooling junction in an incandescent tungsten lamp filament for the case where $r = 0.10$ mm and $T_m = 2400°$K (A. G. Worthing, *J. Franklin Inst.*, **194**, 597, 1922).

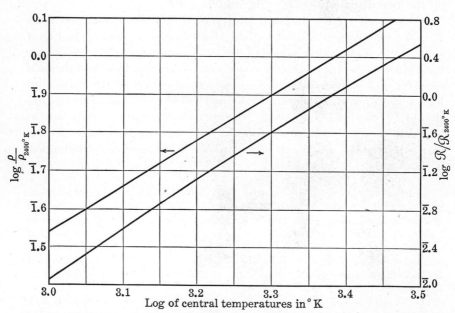

FIG. 9. The resistivity and the radiancy of tungsten in terms of values at 2400°K as functions of temperature (W. E. Forsythe and A. G. Worthing, *Astrophys. J.*, **61**, 152, 1925).

obtains, with an optical pyrometer or some other device, the temperature distribution (Fig. 8) along the filament or a segment of it for a steady-state condition of operation at some particular filament current, or, what is the same, some particular central temperature, $T_m$. For the second set of data, the filament is operated at various central temperatures to yield both the radiancy, $\mathcal{R}$, and the resistivity, $\rho$, of the material as functions of temperatures of operation, as in Fig. 9. In making these determinations, it is desirable to eliminate the effects of the non-uniform temperatures resulting from the presence of cooled portions, effects usually referred to as end losses. This may be done by taking difference readings on two filaments that differ only in length as has been described on pp. 73 and 74, or by employing a single filament with very fine potential leads attached at some distances from the cool supports, or by applying corrections to the measurements made on a single filament with end losses present.

In what follows, the subscript $m$ refers only to the condition occurring when the temperature is the $T_m$ of the first set of data. As in Fig. 9, it is generally desirable to plot $\log \rho/\rho_m$ and $\log \mathcal{R}/\mathcal{R}_m$ as functions of $\log T$ since then a straight line is obtained for the former and a nearly straight line for the latter relation.

Given Figs. 8 and 9 and the radius of the filament, assumed of uniform, circular cross section, we next construct the input and output curves of Fig. 10. Near the center of the long filament, for the condition of steady-state operation, the rate of supply of energy per unit length of filament or the input per unit of length, $\mathcal{I}_m$, is given by $IV/l$. This is the same as the rate of loss of energy per unit length by radiation in the same region, or the output per unit of length, $\mathcal{O}_m$, since radiation represents the sole method of disposing of energy at that place. Near a support, however, the input rate per unit length for the energy which is supplied electrically, $\mathcal{I}$, varies with the distance from the clamping block or end support. Obviously, since the input $\mathcal{I}\Delta l$ for a length $\Delta l$ is $I^2 \Delta R$, such variation is strictly proportional to the resistivity, $\rho$. It follows that $\mathcal{I} = f_1(l)$ may be obtained from Figs. 8 and 9. In so doing, one selects various values of $l$ from Fig. 8 and notes the corresponding $T$'s and, with the aid of Fig. 9, the corresponding $\rho/\rho_m$'s. Then, on the basis of the proportionality between $\mathcal{I}$ and $\rho$, values of $\mathcal{I}[= (\rho/\rho_m)\mathcal{I}_m]$ may be computed and plotted and the curve $\mathcal{I} = f_1(l)$ drawn. Similarly the curve showing the radiation output per unit of length, $\mathcal{O} = f_2(l)$, is obtained by plotting appropriate values of $\mathcal{O}[= (\mathcal{R}/\mathcal{R}_m)\mathcal{I}_m]$. Actually, in Fig. 10, $\mathcal{I}/\mathcal{I}_m$ and $\mathcal{O}/\mathcal{O}_m$ have been plotted as functions of $l$.

Consider next the thermal situation at $l_1$ of Fig. 10. As is shown in Fig. 8, there is here a temperature gradient $(dT/dl)_1$ directed along the filament and therefore conduction of heat toward the cooling junction; accordingly, we have

$$k = \frac{(dQ/dt)_1}{s(dT/dl)_1} \tag{15a}$$

of which $s$ represents the cross-sectional area of the filament. With the evaluation of $(dQ/dt)_1$ a value for $k$ follows. The integral $\int_{l_1}^{l_m} \mathcal{I}/\mathcal{I}_m \, dl$, represented by the area $l_1 q r l_m l_1$, multiplied by $\mathcal{I}_m$, gives the rate of supply of energy to the length $l_1 l_m$. Likewise the integral $\int_{l_1}^{l_m} \mathcal{O}/\mathcal{O}_m \, dl$, represented by the area $l_1 p r l_m l_1$, multiplied by $\mathcal{I}_m$ gives the rate of loss of energy from the same length $l_1 l_m$ by radiation. The difference between these two rates, represented by the cross-hatched area $pqrp$, multiplied by $\mathcal{I}_m$ is the rate of loss of energy by other methods than by radiation, namely, by heat conduction. $(dQ/dt)_1$ may be obtained, therefore, by evaluating the cross-hatched area $pqrp$ and multiplying by $\mathcal{S}_m$. Eq. 15a may evidently be rewritten as

$$k = \frac{\mathcal{S}_m}{s(dT/dl_1)} \int_{l_1}^{l_m} \frac{(\mathcal{S} - \Theta)}{\mathcal{S}_m} \, dl = \frac{IV/l_m}{s(dT/dl_1)} \int_{l_1}^{l_m} \left( \frac{\rho}{\rho_m} - \frac{\mathcal{R}}{\mathcal{R}_m} \right) dl \qquad (15b)$$

With the latter term of Eq. 15b in mind, the reason why $\rho/\rho_m$ and $\mathcal{R}/\mathcal{R}_m$, rather than $\mathcal{S}$ and $\Theta$, have been graphed in Fig. 10 as functions of $l$ becomes evident.

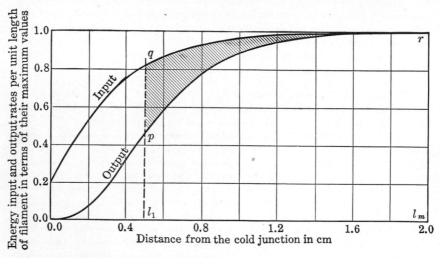

FIG. 10. The input rate per unit of length, and the radiation output rate per unit of length, expressed in terms of their maximum values, as functions of the distance from a cooling junction for a tungsten lamp filament in a vacuum, for the case where $r = 0.10$ mm and $T_m = 2400\,°$K (A. G. Worthing, *J. Franklin Inst.*, **194**, 597, 1922).

In deriving Eq. 15b, it was assumed that the average temperature gradient in the filament at $l_1$ was equal to $(dT/dl)_1$, as measured along the surface. For the filaments at the maximum temperatures at which they have been studied, theory shows that, except near $T_m$, this assumption is nearly true and that the resulting error is quite negligible. From one complete set of data, values of $k$ for a great range of $T$ are obtainable.

**6. Method Involving Cylindrically Radial Conduction in Tubes.** (a) *Mendenhall and Angell's Method Employing Uniform Electrical Heating Throughout.* This method, developed at the University of Wisconsin, was first described in 1911 by C. E. Mendenhall (1872–1935) and M. F. Angell (1878–1930) in a study of the thermal conductivities of nickel and aluminum. They used long, thick-walled tubes (Fig. 11A) mounted in a water-jacketed, evacuated enclosure and heated electrically. Centrally along the length of each tube, a region was found where the flow of heat was radial or very nearly so. The rate of heat supply was measured electrically, the necessary temperatures by means of platinum to platinum-rhodium thermocouples. For the temperature of the inner surface, a junction protected by quartz tubing was used; for that of the outer surface, a junction held in contact by a quartz fiber and weights. For the latter, springs, $SS$, insured that contact was at one point only.

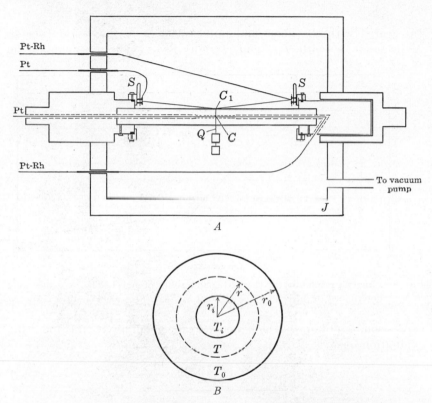

FIG. 11. Mendenhall and Angell's apparatus, employing tubes of nickel and aluminum. Thermal conduction is radial. ($A$) a longitudinal section (*Phys. Rev.*, **33**, 425, 1911); ($B$) a magnified cross section showing the relation between $T$ and $r$ for the tube under test.

In the region where the axial component of the temperature gradient was zero, the rate of flow of heat across a cylindrical surface of radius $r$ and length $l$, for the condition of a steady state, was exactly equal to the rate of production of heat within that part of the tube wall which was bounded radially by that surface (Fig. 11$B$). Accordingly

$$-k2\pi rl\frac{dT}{dr} = i^2\rho l\pi(r^2 - r_i^2)\tag{16}$$

where, as before, $i$ and $\rho$ represent current density and resistivity, and $r_i$ the inside radius. Separation of the variables $T$ and $r$, preparatory to integration, yields

$$dT = -\frac{i^2\rho}{2k} \frac{r^2 - r_i^2}{r} \, dr \qquad (16X)$$

Integrated with the inner and outer surfaces of the metal tube as limits, that is, with $T_i r_i$ and $T_o r_o$ as lower and upper limits, an

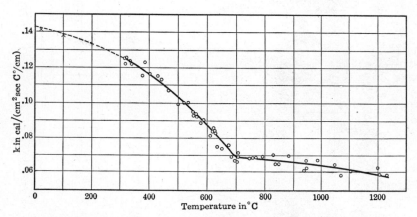

FIG. 12. Angell's results for the thermal conductivity of nickel. The xx values were determined by Jäger and Diesselhorst. (*Phys. Rev.*, **33**, 421, 1911.)

expression is obtained which on rearrangement gives the following evaluation for $k$

$$k = \frac{i^2\rho}{4} \frac{r_o^2 - r_i^2 + 2r_i^2 \ln \dfrac{r_i}{r_o}}{T_i - T_o}$$

$$= \frac{IV}{4\pi(r_o^2 - r_i^2)l} \frac{r_o^2 - r_i^2 + 2r_i^2 \ln \dfrac{r_i}{r_o}}{T_i - T_o} \qquad (17)$$

of which $I$ and $V$ represent current and potential difference. The method is simple and direct, requires no guard ring or thermally insulating sheath, and is capable of yielding precise results. Fig. 12 shows Angell's results for nickel. The break at 700°C suggests a change of phase, which, since nickel is both solid and crystalline above and below 700°C, is probably one of rearrangement of atoms within the crystals.

**7. Methods Suitable for Very Low Temperatures.** (a) *Lees' Method Employing a Bar in an Enclosing Cylindrical Shell.* C. H. Lees (1864– ) in England in 1908 described a method suitable for measuring thermal conductivities at low temperatures. Essentially it is an established method with means provided for maintaining the surroundings at desired low temperatures. The surroundings in this case (Fig. 13) consisted of the interior surface of a hollow, closed, cylindrical shell of copper mounted in a stoppered Dewar * flask. To obtain the desired temperature for the surroundings, the whole was first cooled by liquid air or other material and then, after removal of the cooling agent, heated electrically with the aid of a surrounding coil to the desired temperature. The metal specimen, *R*, in rod form, 0.5 cm by about 7 cm, was mounted centrally in a cylindrical shell with one end firmly attached to an end wall. A coil for heating the test sample is shown at the opposite end at *C*, while two coils of platinum wire for the measurement of its temperature gradient are shown at *A* and *B*. Outside the copper shell is coil *P* whose resistance is the same as that of coil *C*.

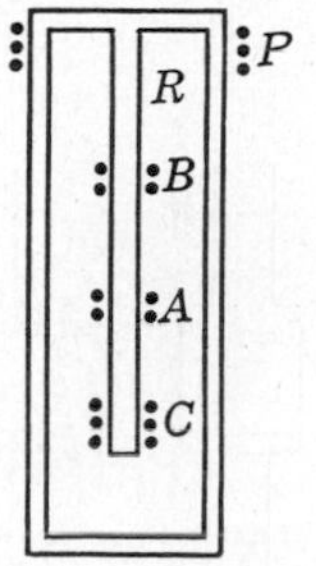

In operation, with the surroundings at the desired temperature, heat was supplied electrically at a measured rate, $IV$, in coil *C* until the temperature difference $T_A - T_B$ indicated by coils *A* and *B* became constant. Except for certain corrections to be discussed presently,

$$VI = ks \frac{T_A - T_B}{L} \qquad (18)$$

where $s$ represents the cross-sectional area of the rod and $L$ the separation between *A* and *B*.

Two causes for deviation from Eq. 18 need to be considered. Some of the heat developed in *C* was lost by radiation and by convection from both the coil and the surface of the bar. This loss may be kept relatively low by evacuating the shell (this seems not to have been done by Lees) and by giving to the rod a surface with poor radiating qualities. Most of all, the relative loss due to radiation decreases rapidly with decrease of temperature. Corrections on this account were not found necessary.

Fig. 13. Diagram of Lees' apparatus employing a bar in an enclosing cylindrical shell. The shell itself was enclosed in a stoppered Dewar flask.

The second cause for deviation from Eq. 18 required correction. A steady difference in temperature between *A* and *B* during heating by means of coil *C* meant a constant, steady rate of increase of temperature of all parts of both the rod and the shell. Because of this the measured difference $T_A - T_B$ was too small for the direct application of Eq. 18. It may be shown, however, that, if the first above-mentioned loss is negligible, a precise correction may be made for the second. It is exactly the steady temperature difference $T_B' - T_A'$ between *B* and *A* when the heating current without change of magnitude passes through *P* instead of through *C* and the direction of the thermal conduction current in *R* is reversed. The magnitude of this correction depends on the relative thermal capacitances of the rod and the shell. Where, for instance, the thermal capacitance of the rod is $\frac{1}{20}$ of that for both rod and shell, $T_B' - T_A'$ is equal to only $\frac{1}{40}$ of the corrected $T_A - T_B$.

In his experimental work, Lees made determinations of $T_B' - T_A'$ just before and just after his $T_A - T_B$ determinations. The average of the two differences

* Sir James Dewar (1842–1923), physical chemist, inventor of the widely used Dewar flask.

was taken as the correction and was added to the measured $T_A - T_B$. With the correction applied, Eq. 18 may be rewritten as

$$k = \frac{VIL/s}{(T_A - T_B) + (T_B' - T_A')} \tag{19}$$

Lees made an extensive study of many metals throughout the temperature range −170°C to 18°C.

(b) *DeHaas' Method for Liquid-Helium Temperatures.* Thermal conduction in the region of 25°K and lower has been studied with special zeal only since about 1930. Some experimental work had been carried on in this region previously, but little of interest had been expected from thermal-conductivity studies and this field was neglected. However, in the systematic study of properties of materials at very low temperatures conducted at the H. Kamerlingh Onnes (1853–1926), winner of the Nobel prize in physics in 1913, cryogenic institute at Leyden, Holland, thermal conduction was eventually included. The study of lead at liquid-air and at near liquid-hydrogen temperatures showed its thermal resistivity (reciprocal of the thermal conductivity, a term which seems preferred at these low temperatures) to decrease, at first as expected, with increasing rapidity with lowering of the temperature. However, when the study was continued to liquid-helium temperatures, a really surprising result was found at about 9°K.

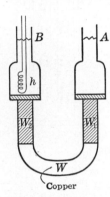

FIG. 14. A simplified diagram of De Haas' apparatus for studying thermal conductivities at liquid helium temperatures.

A much-simplified diagram, giving certain essential features of apparatus used by W. J. DeHaas (1878– ) and his co-workers is shown in Fig. 14. The material was studied in the form of two short rods, $W_1$ and $W_2$. They were mounted between a copper yoke and two glass-tube reservoirs containing liquid hydrogen or liquid helium. In one of these tubes at $h$ a heating coil was located. Both tubes formed parts of vapor thermometers. The part diagrammed was enclosed in a low-temperature chamber, and the space surrounding it was evacuated so that the transfer of heat from one of the glass-tube reservoirs to the other was almost wholly by thermal conduction through the specimen rods and the copper yoke. The transfer by radiation was negligibly small. The temperature of reservoir $A$ was maintained constant by pumping off vapor formed in the bulb of the vapor thermometer, and causing the liquid to boil at a desired rate.

The temperature of reservoir $B$ was maintained constant by means of the current through heating coil $h$.

From the known rate of supply of heat in $B$, the temperature difference $T_B - T_A$, the dimensions of the rods $W_1$ and $W_2$, and a previous study of the yoke $W$, the thermal resistivity or conductivity of the rods was obtained by applying Eq. 1 with cos $\varphi$ equal to unity, namely

$$\frac{dQ}{dl} = IV = -ks\frac{dT}{dt} \quad (20)$$

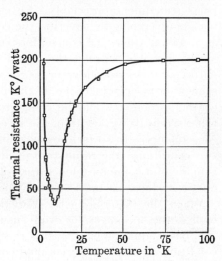

The results DeHaas obtained for a certain specimen of lead are shown in Fig. 15. With decrease in temperature starting at 50° K, there is first a slow decrease in thermal resistance, then a gradually increasing rate of decrease, then a minimum at about 9°K followed by a rise to the 50°K value at 2.2°K, the lowest temperature at which measurements were made. This same variation with temperature seems to

FIG. 15. De Haas' results for the thermal resistance of a lead specimen (W. J. De Haas and H. Bremmer, p. 45 of *Communication* 214 *of the Physical Laboratory of the University of Leyden*, 1931).

be a more or less general characteristic. The significance of this behavior is not known.

## THERMAL-CONDUCTIVITY METHODS FOR POOR CONDUCTORS

**8. General Considerations.** In this section we discuss solids only, including therein granular and powder forms. In principle, any method applicable to a good conductor may be used with poor conductors. Usually, however, the dimension of the poor conductor chosen for the direction of flow of heat is small, and the measurement of the temperature gradient is often made difficult thereby because of uncertainties as to temperatures at the points of measurement. Ordinarily the chosen sources and sinks (bodies from or to which the heat is transferred) for thermal currents are good conducting metallic solids. The attempt is made by their use to insure that at least two chosen surfaces of the poor conductor in any one case shall be at known, constant temperatures. Unfortunately, these surfaces are not always in good direct contact with the metallic sources and sinks.  If a minute film, whether or not it contains air is immaterial, separates the specimen being studied from the source or the sink for an appreciable part of the assumed contact area, the average temperatures of the separated parts will differ appreciably.  Often, but not always, this difficulty may be overcome by covering the contact surfaces with a liquid such as an oil or water.  Of course, for paper and asbestos this procedure is hardly possible.  Could the liquid chosen be without effect on the nature of the poor conductor, as for oil or water on glass, and have the same thermal conductivity as the poor conductor being studied, the contact problem would be completely eliminated.  Since the film is usually relatively very thin, the second condition is ordinarily of little consequence.  In so far, however, as there is failure to achieve these two conditions, the results obtained, for cases where the assumption is made of a common temperature of source or sink and adjacent conductor surface, are open to some question.

When the material to be studied is obtainable in single coherent bodies, the specimens for study usually take the form of thin slabs. The basic equation employed is that which results from Eq. 1 for the condition of simple unidirectional conduction, namely,

$$k = -\frac{dQ/dt}{s\,dT/dl} = -\frac{Q/t}{s\,\Delta T/l} \qquad (21)$$

Where surface film difficulties are absent, the data obtained with a single specimen suffice for a determination of $k$.  However, where surface-film difficulties are present, at least two tests with slabs of different thicknesses must be used.  Generally more will be required for reliable results.  Here we shall assume that two suffice, a procedure that tacitly assumes that the surface films are equivalent for the two cases.  The mathematical treatment is similar to that for a simple electrical circuit containing two resistances in series.  Representing the thermal resistance of the films at the source and the sink taken together by $\varphi_a$ and those of the two specimens being studied by $\varphi_1$ ($= l_1/ks$) and $\varphi_2(=l_2/ks)$, we may write for the condition that the thermal currents are the same and presumably also the thermal resistances for the two films, in accord with Eq. 3

$$\frac{Q}{t} = \frac{\Delta T_1}{\varphi_a + \varphi_1} \qquad (22)$$

$$\frac{Q}{t} = \frac{\Delta T_2}{\varphi_a + \varphi_2} \qquad (23)$$

Combining the two equations to eliminate $\varphi_a$ and replacing $\varphi_1$ and $\varphi_2$ by their equals by definition, we obtain

$$k = \frac{1}{s} \frac{l_2 - l_1}{\Delta T_2 - \Delta T_1} \frac{Q}{t} \qquad (24)$$

Consistent values of $k$ obtained from several pairs of specimens of different thicknesses $l$ would seem to justify results obtained by this process.

When the material to be studied is in the form of granules or of powder, the specimens may additionally take the form of a cylindrical shell or a spherical shell. When dealing with one of these two types, the $k$ measured is strictly not that of the granular or powdered material, but instead that of the combination of material, air film and minute air pockets, that actually occurs. Obviously, where such air films occur throughout the material, the remarks above regarding the eliminating of air films next to the source and sink are without much significance.

**9. Methods Employing Thin Disks or Slabs.** (*a*) *Lees and Poensgen Two-Disk Method.* The work reported by Lees in England in 1898 was among the earliest studies of the thermal conductivities of poor conductors. Material in the form of two equal thin circular disks was clamped between three circular plates of copper to form a flattened cylindrical unit with a plate of copper at the center and another at each end. Heat produced electrically in the central copper plate was conducted through the disks parallel to their axes to the outer copper plates. The plane surfaces of the disks were assumed to have the temperatures of the adjacent copper plates, for whose determinations thermocouples were used. Given the rate or rates of

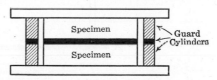

FIG. 16. Lees' disk method, as improved by Poensgen, for measuring the thermal conductivities of poor conductors in the form of thin disks.

production of heat, the cross-sectional area of the disks, the temperature difference attained for a steady state, and the slab thickness or thicknesses, Eq. 21 or Eq. 24 may be applied at once to determine $k$.

An improvement on Lees' arrangement, developed in Germany by R. Poensgen in 1911, is shown in Fig. 16. The main difference is found in the guard rings which were provided for the central plate and for the test plates. That for the central plate was maintained electrically at the same temperature as the central plate. Guard rings for the test plates were made of cork dust, magnesia, alumina, or other very poor conductors.    The improvement over Lees' design consists largely in the greater certainty of unidirectional flow, particularly for test specimens of such thickness that the loss laterally might not be disregarded.

(*b*) *Jakob's Single-Disk Method.*  M. Jakob (1879–    ) in Germany in 1924 (since 1937 at the Illinois Institute of Technology) modified Lees and Poensgen's design to make determinations possible by using a single disk.  It differed essentially in that loss of heat from the heater in one direction was prevented by having a guard plate which was maintained electrically at the same temperature as the heater.

That apparatus such as Jakob's can also be used for liquids is evident.  For such work, uncertainties regarding contacts between the liquid and the metal plates will disappear entirely.  By having the heater at the top and the liquid disk thin, no trouble is experienced because of convection currents.

(*c*) *Fitch's Single-Thin-Disk Method.*  This method differs mainly from those listed above in that the thermal current $dQ/dt$ is determined by the rate of heating of a block of known thermal capacitance.

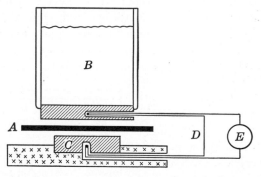

Fig. 17.  Fitch's thin-disk apparatus for the measurement of thermal conductivities of poor conductors.

Particularly intended for temperatures ranging from 0°C to 100°C, it may well be extended to other temperatures.  The poorly conducting test specimen in the form of a thin disk, *A*, of thickness *l*, Fig. 17, is shown between a source of heat, *B*, and a heat receiver, *C*.  Water in *B*, maintained at a constant temperature by means of steam entering through a brass tube (not shown), closed except for many small holes, serves admirably as a heat source.  *C* consists of a large cylinder of copper with its upper surface plane and polished.  It is largely surrounded by granulated cork.  The bottom of *B* is a thick copper plate with its lower surface likewise plane and polished. It has been drilled, as has $C$, to receive thermocouple wires $D$ which may be connected to the galvanometer or potentiometer $E$. Means are thus provided for measuring temperature differences, which are assumed to be those occurring between the flat surfaces of the test specimen.

Normal procedure, in which a "temperature-difference" calibration for the thermocouple system is assumed known, follows. One first establishes a steady state in the test specimen by placing it temporarily between the heat source, $B$, and a copper block similar to that of $C$ and at the same temperature. Then with the copper block of $C$ of mass $m$ and specific heat $c$ in equilibrium with its insulating guard at room temperature $T_0$, the test specimen, $A$, and the heat source, $B$, at $T_B$ are quickly placed in position and temperature-difference readings $T_B - T_C$ are taken at regular time intervals. With the data plotted logarithmically as in Fig. 18, an approximate straight line is obtained

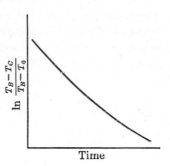

whose initial slope, $\dfrac{1}{T_B - T_0}\dfrac{d(T_B - T_0)}{dt}$,

or $\dfrac{1}{(\Delta T)_0}\left(\dfrac{dT_B}{dt}\right)_0$ at $t = 0$, multiplied by

the temperature difference $(\Delta T)_0$ yields the desired rate of increase of temperature. The governing equation is again that for unidirectional flow where for $dQ/dt$ we use the initial rate

$$k = \frac{dQ/dT}{s(dT/dl)} = \frac{mcl[d(\Delta T)/dt]_0}{s(\Delta T)_0} \tag{25}$$

The method is simple and convenient.

**10. Methods Employing Radial Conduction.** (a) *Nusselt's Spherical-Shell Method.* This method reported in 1908 by W. Nusselt (1882–   ) is found useful for powdered, granulated, and threadlike materials such as powdered diatomaceous earth, cork, and asbestos. The outer, spherical shell of Nusselt's apparatus was of copper with internal radius of 15 cm. Concentric with it there was an internal shell of aluminum of 7.5-cm external radius. At the center an electric heater was located. Between the two metal shells was the material to be studied in the form of a third shell. Thermocouple junctions were located at various places on its inner and outer surfaces.

For the condition of a steady state, the rates of transfer of heat are the same across all spherical surfaces within the test shell, which are concentric with its inner and outer surfaces of radii $r_i$ and $r_o$, and we have the basic relation

$$\frac{dQ}{dt} = IV = -4\pi k r^2 \frac{dT}{dr} \tag{26}$$

and by integration the equation applicable; namely,

$$k = \frac{IV(r_o - r_i)}{4\pi r_o r_i} \frac{1}{T_i - T_o} \tag{27}$$

(*b*) *Niven's Cylindrical-Shell Method.* In principle this method is much the same as Mendenhall and Angell's for metallic conductors. The equations that apply are derived similarly. The differences that occur arise from the fact that in Mendenhall and Angell's method the origin of the heat was throughout the shell whereas here the origin is in a core about which the shell is located. Corresponding to Eqs. 16 and 17, we have

$$-k 2\pi r l \frac{dT}{dr} = \frac{dQ}{dt} \tag{28}$$

and

$$k = \frac{[dQ/dt \ln (r_o/r_i)]}{2\pi l (T_i - T_o)} \tag{29}$$

where $r_o$ and $r_i$ represent outside and inside radii, $l$ the shell length, and $T_i$ and $T_o$ inside and outside temperatures. Niven's shells were obtained by filling the space between two concentric metal tubes with the material. Heat was supplied electrically along the axis of the inner tube at measured rates. With temperatures for steady-state conditions obtained from thermocouple readings, and thermal currents equated to $IV$, one obtains the desired thermal conductivity at once with the aid of Eq. 29.

## THERMAL CONDUCTIVITIES OF CRYSTALS

**11. General Considerations.** That anisotropic bodies possess different thermal conductivities for different directions of propagation of heat through them was first determined in 1829 by the Swiss physicist A. A. de la Rive (1801–1873) and de Candolla in a study involving wood.

For a single crystal, mathematical theory predicts and experiment verifies that the isothermal surfaces surrounding a point source of heat within the crystal shall be ellipsoidal. If the crystal is isotropic, these surfaces are spherical. If the crystal is uniaxial, the surfaces are ellipsoids of rotation symmetrical with respect to the crystal axis.

If the crystal is biaxial, all three axes of the ellipsoidal isothermal surfaces differ in magnitude. As may be deduced, the thermal conductivities of the crystal along the three main axes vary directly as the squares of the lengths of those main axes.

**12. De Senarmont's Method Employing a Point Source in a Crystal Plate.** For his work, De Senarmont cut thin parallel-sided plates of the crystal and covered them with a light film of wax. A point at the center was heated by a small metal tube, carrying hot air, which passed through the crystal plate at that point. When a steady state was reached with the heat supplied at a certain rate, a portion of the wax film was melted and the definite boundary between the melted and the unmelted wax was clearly visible (Fig. 19). It is clear that the thermal conductivity of quartz does not vary with directions perpendicular to the axis, though, parallel to the axis, it is about twice, as 0.030 to 0.016, that perpendicular to it. De Senarmont's method yields only relative results.

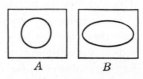

A            B

Fig. 19. Isothermal surfaces in quartz for the case of a point source of heat in a crystal in planes (A) perpendicular and (B) parallel to the principal axis.

### 13. Eucken's and Nernst's Results for Quartz and for Diamond.

A. Eucken (1884– ) in Germany was not the first to make a determination of the actual thermal conductivity of quartz. His work, however, has been the most thorough and the most comprehensive for this material. Using a modification of Lees' method for poor conductors (see p. 181), he determined conductivities at about 100°C and −190°C (boiling liquid air). Using other materials as well as quartz, Eucken found that the thermal conductivities of amorphous forms increased with temperature and that those for crystals decreased. Additional studies have shown that the thermal conductivity of an amorphous body is always less than that of the crystal of identical chemical composition. At room temperature, the conductivity of a quartz crystal perpendicular to its axis is about five times that for amorphous quartz; at the temperature of liquid hydrogen the ratio is of the order of 500.

In his study of diamond, the German chemist and winner of the Nobel prize in chemistry in 1920, W. Nernst (1864–1941), following Jakob's single-disk method, used a small slab with faces about 2 mm by 5 mm and 1.3 mm thick. Good thermal contact between the specimen and the electrically heated and the cooled copper plates was obtained by applying zinc amalgam to the contact surfaces. Rather surprisingly there was found a thermal conductivity of 0.4 cal/(cm$^2$/sec C°/cm), which varied but little between 21°K and 345°K. This is exceedingly high for a substance electrically nonconducting. In fact, it is even rather high for electrical conductors.

The value quoted is about 40 per cent of that for silver, which is our best thermal conductor as well as our best electrical conductor.

Eucken has pointed out that the above results are very interesting theoretically.   The study of specific heats at very low temperatures shows a general conformity of specific heat with Debye's prediction of a variation proportional to the third power of the temperature and consequently approximately near zero values for specific heats at those very low temperatures.   This leads to the expectation that most of the atoms would then be no longer in thermal motion and unable to participate in the process of thermal conduction.   Granted also that there are no free electrons in the non-conducting diamond, one finds it very difficult to give an explanation for the high thermal conductivity observed for the low temperature.

Observations on window glass between 0°C and 21°K showed a decrease in conductivity with decrease in temperature to about a half of the value at the higher temperature.   The thermal conductivity of ice with a value of 0.005 cal/(cm² sec C°/cm) at 0°C similarly decreases slowly.

### THERMAL CONDUCTIVITIES OF LIQUIDS

**14. General Considerations.**   Methods for determining $k$ for liquids are complicated by the possibility of convection currents.   On this account, the forms which the material being investigated may take seem to be limited to three.   One form is a vertical column in which the density, varying with the temperature, decreases gradually in going from the bottom to the top, with a guard cylinder if necessary to prevent temperature and hence also density variations laterally.   The second form is that of a thin film, the third that of a fine, tubular thread.   Variations of method for each form are possible, depending, for instance, on whether or not there is a steady state, a periodic change of the temperature of the heat source or the heat sink, a condition of a gradual departure from or of a return to an equilibrium state. Compared with poorly conducting solids, however, liquids possess one favorable feature.   They yield good contacts with the metallic sources and sinks for heat which are used in the thermal-conductivity determinations.

**15. Berget and Jakob's Vertical-Column Method.**   This method has been described above in conjunction with determinations of $k$ for good conductors such as mercury.   In principle it is a uniflow method with lateral insulation.

**16. Lees' Flat-Film Method.**   This is a modification of Lees' method for poorly conducting solids.   The apparatus is shown in Fig. 20.

$C$, $C_1$, $C_2$, and $C_3$ are copper plates. $G$ is a glass plate; $L$ is the liquid confined by an ebonite ring $E$. $W$ is the heating coil. From the measured temperatures of $C_2$ and $C_3$, the known dimensions, and the thermal conductivity of the glass plate, it is possible to determine the rate of supply of heat to the liquid. Given this, the dimensions of the film, and the temperature difference between its surfaces, a value for $k$ follows simply. Corrections must be made for the presence of the ebonite ring. Jakob's single-disk modification (p. 182) would seem to be an improvement.

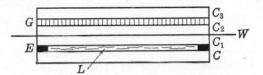

FIG. 20. Lees' disk apparatus for use with liquids.

**17. Stefan Winkelmann Concentric-Cylinders Method.** A German physicist A. Winkelmann (1848– ), using a method employed by the Austrian physicist Josef Stefan (1835–1893) in studying gases, enclosed the liquid under investigation between two long coaxial brass cylinders with walls slightly separated, immersed the whole in a vertical position in ice water, and noted the change with time of the pressure of the air in the inner cylinder which served as the bulb of a gas thermometer. Two difficulties appeared. One was the slight convection currents in the thin liquid layer. It seems that this might have been eliminated by making the layer sufficiently thin. The other difficulty, much more serious, was due to the non-uniformity of temperature within the inner cylinder. With the cooling of the gas in the cylinder by conduction outward, there was a more or less stagnant layer of gas next to the cylinder walls whose temperature at the wall boundary was necessarily lower than that of the gas near the center. In consequence of this, the temperatures computed for the inner cylinder walls using measured pressures were in error. Had the inner cylinder been evacuated and its wall temperatures measured by means of fine wire thermocouples, it seems that reasonably accurate results might have been obtained.

P. W. Bridgman (1882– ), physicist at Harvard University, modified this method in a study of liquids under pressure. He supplied heat electrically inside the inner cylinder and measured the temperatures of the cylinder walls. His method seems to be free from the objections raised above.

**18. Goldschmidt's Differential-Capillary Method.** This method, carried out for liquids by R. Goldschmidt in Germany in 1911, employed two silver capillary tubes of 2-mm internal diameter. One was 100 mm long, the other 10 mm. Both were provided with 0.05-mm platinum wires mounted axially. The capillary tubes were attached to large brass blocks and immersed vertically in the liquid to be tested. The same electric current was passed through the two platinum wires. Because of the smallness of the capillary, no convection troubles were experienced. As was to be expected, near the ends, there was longitudinal conduction of heat in addition to the normal radial conduction, much as in a lamp filament near a cooling support. The same end effect was expected in the short tube. On the assumption that the end effects were equivalent, differences (1) in supplied wattages, (2) in measured filament resistances, and (3) in tube lengths were used to obtain, for the computed central length of the longer liquid filament, a corrected rate of supply of heat to the metal filament and a corrected temperature. The formula given in connection with Niven's method for good conductors (see above) is applicable; namely,

$$k = \frac{IV}{2\pi l} \frac{\ln r_2/r_1}{T_1 - T_2} \tag{30}$$

This method seems to be reasonably free from errors.

## EXPERIMENTAL RESULTS

**19. The Thermal Conductivities of Metals.** Whether metals are in solid or in liquid form, their thermal conductivities are relatively very high. Further, metals when solid are generally better conductors than when liquid. Also, a metallic alloy is generally a poorer conductor

## TABLE I

SOME VALUES OF THE RATIO $k/\sigma T$, IN UNITS OF $10^{-8}$ CAL/(SEC OHM CM$^2$ K$^{\circ 2}$)

Taken from data by Lees (*Phil. Trans.*, **208**, p. 381).

|          | −170°C | −100°C | 0.0°C | 18.0°C |
|----------|--------|--------|-------|--------|
| Aluminum | 1.50   | 1.81   | 2.09  | 2.13   |
| Copper   | 1.85   | 2.17   | 2.30  | 2.32   |
| Silver   | 2.04   | 2.29   | 2.33  | 2.33   |
| Zinc     | 2.20   | 2.39   | 2.45  | 2.43   |
| Cadmium  | 2.39   | 2.43   | 2.40  | 2.39   |
| Tin      | 2.48   | 2.51   | 2.49  | 2.47   |
| Lead     | 2.55   | 2.54   | 2.53  | 2.51   |
| Iron     | 3.10   | 2.98   | 2.97  | 2.99   |

than its component metals are.  On the whole, the thermal conductivities of metals and alloys vary in the same order as their electrical conductivities, a law first enunciated in Germany in 1853 by Wiedemann and Franz.  Later, in 1881, the Danish physicist Ludwig Lorenz

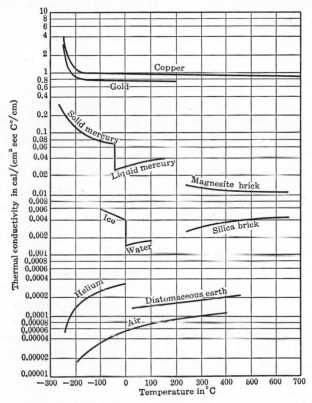

FIG. 21.  The thermal conductivities of various substances as functions of temperature.  The vertical scale is logarithmic.  (By permission, Zemansky, *Heat and Thermodynamics*, 2nd ed., p. 78, New York, McGraw-Hill Book Co., 1943.)

(1829–1891) added a condition relating to temperature variation.  In its complete form, with $\sigma$ representing electrical conductivity, the law is

$$\frac{k}{\sigma T} = \text{constant} \tag{31}$$

How well this relation is fulfilled may be seen in Table I.  Eq. 31 suggests by its form that the free electrons of metals and alloys, as for electrical conduction, are the main carriers of heat in thermal conduction.  Such is believed to be the case.

Fig. 21, taken from *Heat and Thermodynamics* by M. W. Zemansky (1900–   ), of the College of the City of New York, shows how the thermal conductivities of several substances vary with temperature. The $k$'s for the metals, though about constant for a great range of temperature, generally tend toward very high values as $0°K$ is approached. An exception seems to occur for lead (Fig. 14). Though their thermal conductivities may be very high near $0°K$, there is nothing yet to indicate superconduction in this region for heat similar to super electrical conduction.

**20. The Thermal Conductivities of Non-Metals.** Due to the absence of free electrons in electrical insulators, the transfer of heat energy in them must be due to the passing on of energy from one molecule to another by the impact method or by radiation within the body. These methods seem to be much less effective than the free-electron methods, and consequently electrical insulators, with a few exceptions (see below), are very generally heat insulators.

Thermal conductivities of non-metallic liquids seem to range from about 0.0003 cal/(cm$^2$ sec C°/cm) to about 0.0020 cal/(cm$^2$ sec C°/cm). The thermal conductivity of a substance in the liquid state is less than in the solid state; $k$ for ice at $0°C$ is about 0.005 cal/(cm$^2$ sec C°/cm), that for liquid water at $0°C$ is about one-third of this value. In many solutions of salts in water, it is found that $k$ decreases with increase of salt concentration. In other instances no change is found. Judged by experiments using small amounts of gelatin in water, the viscosity of a liquid is without effect on its thermal conductivity. Lastly many non-metallic liquids fit rather well the theoretical relation

$$\frac{k}{\delta c} = a \tag{31a}$$

where $\delta$ is the density, $c$ the specific heat, and $a$ a constant.

### INDUSTRIAL APPLICATIONS

**21. General Considerations.** Industry depends both on the transfer of heat by metals and on the insulation of heat by poor conductors. Uses of the first type occur in the transfer of heat from an open flame or the gases in a firebox to the water in a kettle or steam boiler above, in the transfer from the condensing steam in the radiator to the outer surface, in the transfer through fins from the explosion chambers of air-cooled internal-combustion engines, and in the transfer of heat from refrigerated chambers through the walls of tubes through which the refrigerating brine is pumped. Uses of the second type occur in the steam locomotive, where the escape of heat from the steam boiler and cylinders to the outside is greatly hindered by the introduction of insulating material between the bounding double steel walls, in the heat conservation of the double windows and the insulated walls of the cars of a train, and in the heat conservation of the building walls of homes and factories.

Where heat is to be transferred, most available metals including many alloys will usually serve, since, in the rapid transfer of heat from the source to the place of utilization, other processes than heat conduction by the metal limit the rate of utilization. Consequently a specification of thermal conductivity for metals in designs is usually unnecessary.

Where heat is to be conserved, however, there is need of considering carefully the thermal conductivities of the insulating materials to be used since they are fundamental factors in the conservation processes. In what way this is true and the method of carrying out the study for the case of "heat transfer [failure to conserve] through building walls," is shown by a National Bureau of Standards report * by the physicists M. S. Van Dusen (1892–   ) and J. L. Finck (1893–   ).

**22. Heat Transfer by Building Walls.** In their study, Van Dusen and Finck used 22 types of wall. The apparatus used is sketched diagrammatically in Fig. 22. The test wall or panel as shown separates two chambers in both of which the air temperatures are maintained constant to within about 0.5 F° with temperature differences ranging from about 50 F° to about 80 F°. The air speeds in the spaces between the shields and the test panel corresponded to winds of about 5 mi/hr.

The high-temperature side of the test panel was covered with a ¼-in. flexible sheet of cork composition which was pressed tightly against the panel. Each of 8-in. square sections of the flexible sheet were provided with five copper-constantan thermocouples connected in series with alternate junctions varnished to opposite surfaces. During any test, they gave the temperature drop through the cork composition. From the temperature gradient which occurred, the area of the sheet, and its previously measured thermal conductivity, the thermal current through the sheet and the wall was determined. Analogous to the ammeter in electrical measurements, this cork sheet was called a conductimeter. For a given temperature difference between the air of the two chambers, it enabled the investigators to determine the thermal current that would pass through the test panel with the conductimeter removed, provided the air temperature difference were reduced by the temperature drop occurring in the conductimeter. To illustrate, in one instance with an air temperature difference of 51.0 F° the temperature drop of the conductimeter was 11.1 F° and the thermal current measured was that expected for a 39.9 F° temperature difference without the conductimeter.

The insulation of a house wall depends not only on the insulating properties of the material of the wall but also on that of air films that may exist between outside and inside. Air is a very poor conductor. In case of no wind, these films are relatively thick; in case of winds, they are less thick, with the thickness generally decreasing with an increase in wind velocity. (See p. 385.) Ordinary brick house walls have at least four of these films, one on each side of the brick and one on each side of the plaster.

It is convenient to speak about the thermal current density, $I_a$, the conductance per unit area, $C_a$, and the resistance per unit area, $R_a$, of the specified thickness of a layer of material as well as the transmittance per unit area, $C_a^+$, of two or more layers in series. One or more of these layers may be air films. (Sometimes merely conductance, resistance, and transmittance are erroneously used for these terms.)

* Van Dusen and Finck, *Bur. Standards J. Research*, **6**, 452, 1939.

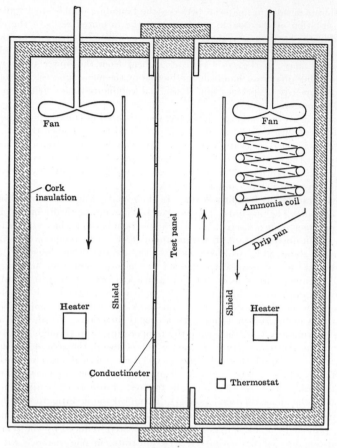

FIG. 22. Diagrammatic sketch of apparatus used by Van Dusen and Finck in a study of heat transfer through building walls (M. S. Van Dusen and J. L. Finck, *J. Research, Natl. Bur. Standards*, **6**, 452, 1939).

We shall find them necessary in the further discussion. Their defining equations, analogous to certain corresponding, defining, electrical equations, are

$$I_a = \frac{1}{A}\frac{dQ}{dt} = k\frac{\Delta T}{\Delta l} \tag{32}$$

$$C_a = \frac{I_a}{\Delta T} = \frac{k}{\Delta l} \tag{33}$$

$$R_a = \frac{\Delta T}{I_a} = \frac{\Delta l}{k} \tag{34}$$

$$C_a^+ = \frac{1}{R_a + R_b + \cdots} = \frac{I_a}{\Delta T_1 + \Delta T_2 + \cdots} \tag{35}$$

## TABLE II

DATA OBTAINED BY VAN DUSEN AND FINCK FOR AN 8-IN. HOLLOW, DOUBLE-SHELL TILE WALL TOGETHER WITH SOME RESULTS THAT MAY BE COMPUTED

There was a forced air motion on both sides of the shell corresponding to a 5-mi/hr wind. The high-temperature surface was covered with a cork conductimeter. The sensitivity of the conductimeter was 12.6 btu/(hr ft$^2$ mv); that of its thermocouple, 10.9 F°/mv.

| Temperature of Warm Air | Temperature of Cold Air | Temperature of Warm Surface of Wall | Temperature of Cold Surface of Wall | Emf of Conductimeter | Mean Wall Temperature | Temperature Drop in Conductimeter |
|---|---|---|---|---|---|---|
| °F | °F | °F | °F | mv | °F | F° |
| 73.0 | 22.0 | 58.4 | 27.8 | 1.02 | 43.1 | 11.1 |
| 92.6 | 44.2 | 77.9 | 49.0 | 1.06 | 63.4 | 11.5 |
| 122.9 | 63.4 | 104.6 | 69.6 | 1.41 | 87.1 | 15.4 |

| Temperature Drop in Wall | $\Delta T$ of Cold Air Film | $\Delta T$ of Warm Air Film | Thermal Current Density | Tile Conductance per Unit Area | Tile Resistance per Unit Area |
|---|---|---|---|---|---|
| F° | F° | F° | $\dfrac{btu}{ft^2\ hr}$ | $\dfrac{btu}{(ft^2\ hr\ F°)}$ | $\dfrac{F°}{Btu/ft^2\ hr}$ |
| 30.6 | 5.8 | 3.5 | 12.9 | 0.42 | 2.38 |
| 28.9 | 4.8 | 3.2 | 13.4 | .46 | 2.16 |
| 35.0 | 6.2 | 2.9 | 17.7 | .51 | 1.97 |

| Resistance per Unit Area of Cold Air Film with Wind | Resistance per Unit Area of Warm Air Film with Wind | Corrected Temperature Range for Wall without Conductimeter | Transmittance of Wall (without Conductimeter) and of Air Films per Unit Area |
|---|---|---|---|
| F°/(btu/ft$^2$ hr) | F°/(btu/ft$^2$ hr) | F° | Btu/(ft$^2$ hr F°) |
| 0.45 | 0.27 | 39.9 | 0.32 |
| 0.36 | 0.24 | 36.9 | 0.36 |
| 0.35 | 0.16 | 44.1 | 0.40 |

Common units used by the heating and ventilating engineer for $k$, $I_a$, $C_a$, $R_a$, and $C_a{}^+$ are: the $btu/(ft^2\ hr\ F°/in.)$; the $btu/(ft^2\ hr)$; the $btu/(ft^2\ hr\ F°)$, sometimes called "moht"; the $F°/(btu/ft^2\ hr)$, sometimes called "thom," an abbreviation for thermal ohm; and the $btu/(ft^2\ hr\ F°)$.   A conductance of 0.42 $btu/(ft^2\ hr\ F°)$ for the tile of a tile wall 8 in. thick means that, through each sq ft of such a wall when the temperature difference between its tile surfaces is 1 F°, heat will be conducted at a rate of 0.42 btu/hr.   A transmittance of 0.32 $btu/(ft^2\ hr\ F°)$ or of 0.32 moht for an 8-in. tile wall including its two air films means that, through each sq ft of such a wall when the temperature difference between the two adjacent atmospheres is 1 F°, heat will be conducted at a rate of 0.32 btu/hr.

Data obtained by Van Dusen and Finck for a particular wall and some of the results that follow are given in Table II.   The first five columns represent the observed data.   Given that the sensitivity of the conductimeter is 12.6 $btu/(hr\ ft^2\ mv)$, that an emf of 1 mv corresponds to a temperature difference of 10.9 F°, and Eqs. 32 to 35, one easily obtains the remaining columns of the table, which show that the air films on both the inside and the outside of the tile are only less important than the tile itself in determining the loss of energy through the wall; that to these air films for the condition of a 5 mi/hr wind, at least for the cold air film, one may ascribe, as for the tile itself, certain thermal resistances per unit area; and that a certain resistance per unit area and a certain transmittance per unit area may be ascribed to the wall as a whole.   Generally as shown building materials are better insulators at low temperatures than at high temperatures.

**23. Computing in Advance the Requirements of a Heating System.**   In the planning of a heating system for a home or other building, one does not have quite the simple condition discussed above.   There may be many layers including extra air films between the air outside and that inside.   One such is described as an 8-in., two-cell, hollow tile, stucco, inside furring, wood-lath-and-plaster wall.   Making use of tables of thermal resistances per unit area to be found in the literature, we obtain for the resistance per unit of area, including one still-air film as the equivalent of an outside film with a strong wind and an inside film with normal air convection, $(1.67 + 0.06 + 0.91 + 0.40 + 0.61)$ or 3.65 $F°/(btu/ft^2\ hr)$.   The corresponding conductance per unit area is 0.274 $btu/(ft^2\ hr\ F°)$.   If one is concerned with a heating system in a building with such walls and wishes to prepare for a condition of an internal temperature of 65°F and a simultaneous external temperature of $-25°F$ with wind, he must plan for a thermal current density through the wall of about 0.274 $btu/(ft^2\ hr\ F°)$ × 80 F° or 22 $btu/(ft^2\ hr)$.   It is evident that the current density for the window areas, which must be treated separately in the same manner, will be much larger unless something of the nature of storm-window protection with its layer of still air is provided.   Various workers differ considerably in the values for thermal resistance per unit area obtained for the same materials.

## PROBLEMS

**1.** Commonly used units for thermal conductivity are the $cal/(cm^2\ sec\ C°/cm)$, the $watt/(cm^2\ K°/cm)$, the $btu/(ft^2\ hr\ F°/in.)$, and the $btu/(ft^2\ hr\ F°/ft)$.   What are the factors for conversion from each set of units to the others?

**2.** The thermal conductivity of silver at 0°C is given as 1.01 $cal/(cm^2\ sec\ C°/cm)$; that of hairfelt at 86°F as used for insulation, 0.022 $btu/(ft^2\ hr\ F°/ft)$.   What is the ratio of the two conductivities?

**3.** The thermal conductivity of a tungsten lamp filament at 350°C, the approximate temperature of the copper lead wires at the places where the filament ends are clamped, is about 0.8 watt/(cm² K°/cm). Given that the diameter of the wire of a 25-watt, 115-volt vacuum tungsten lamp, with a normal maximum operating temperature of 2535°K, is about 0.0287 mm and that the temperature gradient in the filament just at the contact of the filament with a copper lead is about 25,000 K°/cm, compute the rate of conduction of heat from the tungsten to one of the copper leads and the percentage of the energy supplied to the filament at normal operation which is lost by conduction to the two lead wires.

**4.** In a test to determine the thermal conductivity of a 25% NaCl brine, Berget's method is used. The diameter of the central cylindrical core is 1.00 in. The upper surface of the brine, in contact with a non-corrosive metal, is heated by steam. At the lower boundary the heat is received through similar metal by a Bunsen ice calorimeter. Two thermojunctions projecting into the central core and separated vertically by 4 in. show temperatures of 60°F and 40°F. The rate of reception of heat by the ice calorimeter is 0.094 btu/hr. What is the thermal conductivity of the brine?

**5.** In a test using Searle's method for determining the thermal conductivity of red brass, a 50-cm circular cylinder of 5.00-cm diameter is used with steam at one end and circulating water at the other. A thermocouple with junctions 30.0 cm apart registers a temperature difference of 48.0 C°, and the circulating water entering at a temperature of 18.00°C and leaving at 20.50°C flows through at a rate of 185 cm³/min. What is the thermal conductivity of the brass?

**6.** Calendar at McGill University, Montreal, investigating the thermal conductivity of undisturbed sandy soil found during early May in 1895 that the daily variation between the successive maxima and minima 4.0 in. below the surface amounted to 5.4 F° and 10.0 in. below to 1.8 F°, and that the maxima at the lower level lagged about 8 hr with respect to the upper level. Using data by Ingersoll and Zobel for slightly damp clay or sandy soil, namely a specific heat of 0.45 cal/gm C° and a density of 1.65 gm/cm³, compute the expected thermal conductivity for the soil studied by Calendar.

**7.** Given that, in the crystal rock of the earth below the region where the temperature variations occurring at the earth's surface are appreciable, there is an average increase of temperature of 1.0 C° for each 40 m of depth (measurements in oil wells have shown variations from 19 m/C° to 130 m/C°) and that the average thermal conductivity for crystal rock is 0.0045 cal/(cm² sec C°/cm), determine the time required to melt a cm layer of ice at 0°C by heat thus received (δ of ice at 0°C = 0.92 gm/cm³).

**8.** In applying Kohlrausch's method for determining the thermal conductivity of nickel, a 20.0-cm-long circular rod just 2 mm in diameter is used. It is found that, with ends maintained at 0.00°C, the maximum temperature is 2.00°C. Given further that the average electrical resistivity for the nickel is 6.93 μohm cm, and that the potential difference between the terminals is 4.06 mv, determine what electric current is required and the thermal conductivity of the nickel. Plot a curve showing how the temperature varies along the length of the rod.

**9.** For a long, round-wire tungsten filament ($r = 0.0100$ cm) mounted in a vacuum and operated at 3.90 amp a maximum temperature of 2400°K is obtained. Given that the resistivity and the radiancy of tungsten at 2400°K are $73.6 \times 10^{-6}$ ohm cm and 55.8 watts/cm² and that for the region near a lead-in wire the distributions of Figs. 8 and 10 apply, determine the temperature and the rate of heat conduction along the filament occurring 0.50 cm from the junction.

**10.** Given that, in applying the Mendenhall and Angell radial-flow method to the nickel tube used by them, a current of 995 amp was used with a potential drop of 53.8 mv over 1.00 cm of the central portion (0.168 cm I.D., 1.20 cm O.D.) and that 14.5 C° was obtained as the temperature difference between the inner and external surfaces, determine the thermal conductivity of the nickel.

**11.** Frozen water pipes are sometimes thawed out by means of electric currents. Assuming a frozen water pipe, 1.00 in. I.D., 1.25 in. O.D. and given that the resistivity of the steel pipe at 0°C is $12 \times 10^{-6}$ ohm in., that its thermal conductivity is 0.89 btu/(ft² sec F°/in.), and that the loss of heat from the outer surface of the pipe on heating is negligible, determine how long it will take to just thaw the ice (δ of ice is 57.5 pd/ft³) and what the temperature of the outer surface of the pipe during melting will be if a current of 1000 amp is used.

**12.** In a determination of the thermal conductivity of lead at about 10°K using the DeHaas low-temperature method, two round lead bars, each 2.0 cm long and 0.60 cm² in cross section, were used. With a 0.40 K° temperature difference between the hot and cold terminals, the transfer of heat to the cooler terminal took place at the rate of 0.126 watt. Assuming the thermal resistance of the copper yoke to be negligible, determine the combined thermal resistance of the two rods and the thermal resistivity and the thermal conductivity of the lead at the given temperature.

**13.** Two Pyrex glass disks with diameters of 10.0 cm and thicknesses of 4.00 mm are tested in accord with Lees' parallel-disk method as modified by Poensgen. With the outer metal plates maintained at 0.0°C, the inner plate containing the heating coil is maintained at 5.0°C by means of a 2.0-amp current and a potential drop of 10.7 volts. What is the thermal conductivity of the Pyrex glass?

**14.** On a cold day, it is found that the inner and the outer surfaces of a window glass area 4.0 ft × 5.0 ft differ by 3.0 F°. Given that the glass is just 3/16 in. thick, and that its thermal conductivity is 0.40 btu/(ft² hr F°/ft), determine the amount of heat that is lost through the window in 1 day. With a heat of combustion of 15,000 btu/pd and an 80% efficiency for the heating system, what is the day's consumption of coal that results on account of the window?

**15.** While using a 12-mm layer of water in a Jakob's single-disk device, it is found that a temperature difference of 5.0 C° is maintained between the upper plate and the lower plate when energy is supplied at a rate of 0.024 watt/cm² and the lower plate is kept at 25°C. What is the thermal conductivity of water at 25°C?

**16.** At what rate will pond ice increase in thickness when the upper surface is kept at 10.0°F and the thickness is 8.0 in., if the thermal conductivity of ice is 1.27 btu/(ft² hr F°/ft)? (Density of ice = 57.5 pd/ft³.)

**17.** In a determination of the thermal conductivity of cork using Fitch's single-thin-disk method the following data were obtained:

| | |
|---|---|
| Thickness of cork board | 2.0 mm |
| Mass of copper block | 800 gm |
| Area of contact with block | 12.0 cm² |
| Initial temperature of block and surroundings | 25.0°C |
| Maintained temperature of hot bath | 95.0°C |

Successive temperature readings of block taken at 5.0-min intervals:

25.0,   26.8,   28.5,   30.2,   31.8,   33.4°C

Given further that the specific heat of copper is 0.090 cal/(gm C°), plot the log temperature difference-time curve and determine with its aid the thermal conductivity of the cork at 25°C

**18.** In a study of the thermal conductivity of wool, by Nusselt's spherical-shell method, a central metal sphere 5.00 in. in diameter and a hollow metal shell 6.00 in. I.D. and 7.00 in. O.D. are used. When a steady state has been reached with an input rate of energy of 4.95 watts, the temperatures of the inner sphere and outer shell are 100°F and 60°F respectively. What is the thermal conductivity of the wool for the condition occurring in the test? Express the result in both British engineering and metric units?

**19.** An asbestos sleeve 2.0 in. I.D. and 4.0 in. O.D. is fitted to a rod which is maintained at 250°F, heat being supplied electrically at the rate of 29.2 watts per ft of length. The outer surface of the sleeve for the condition of a steady state is 150°F. What is the thermal resistance of a ft length of sleeve?

**20.** A steel pipe with an I.D. of 3.0 in. and an O.D. of 4.0 in., which is used to carry steam at 1100°F, has an asbestos sleeve 3.0 in. thick. Given that the temperature of the outer surface of the asbestos is 400°F, that the thermal conductivity of the asbestos is 0.060 btu/(ft$^2$ hr F°/in.), and that that of steel at 1100°F is 18 btu/(ft$^2$ hr F°/ft), compute the temperature drops expected in both the steel and the asbestos covering. Also determine the rate at which energy is lost from the pipe per foot of length.

**21.** Using the method and apparatus described under Goldschmidt's differential-capillary-filament method in a study of kerosene, values of 0.476 watt and 0.035 watt for the supply rates were obtained for a central temperature difference of 20.0 C°. What is the thermal conductivity of the kerosene?

**22.** Given that the shell of a certain 8 cu ft electric refrigerator has an average thermal resistance per unit of area of its inside wall of 4.0 F°/(btu/ft$^2$ hr), that the inside wall area is 30 ft$^2$, that the inside and outside temperatures are 42°F and 80°F, and that the rate of supply of energy to the motor is 80% of the rate of the removal of heat from the cold chamber, determine at what rate heat will be delivered to the room by the refrigerator.

**23.** The windows of many railroad cars consist of two thicknesses of glass separated by an air space. With ⅛ in. as the glass thickness, $\frac{3}{16}$ in. as their separation, and 7.2 btu/(ft$^2$ hr F°/in.) and 0.17 btu/(ft$^2$ hr F°/in.) as the thermal conductivities of glass and air, determine the rate of loss of heat through such a double window, which is 2 ft square, when the train is in motion and the temperatures inside and out are 60°F and 20°F. For the air film on the inside, assume a thermal resistance per unit area of 0.27 F°/(btu/ft$^2$ hr). Compare this loss rate with that which occurs when a single thickness of glass is used.

**24.** What would be the transmittance per unit area and the rate of transmission of heat per unit area for a 22°F outside temperature and a 73°F inside temperature were the 8-in. tile of the wall of Table II replaced by 4-in. tile and there were included a 4-in. thick layer of rock wool whose thermal conductivity is 0.28 btu/-(ft$^2$ hr F°/in.)? What percent reduction of the heat loss is brought about by the introduction of the rock wool?

# CHAPTER VIII

## THERMAL PROPERTIES OF GASES

**1. Introduction.** The important role played by gases in our civilization scarcely needs emphasis. From a biological point of view, one may list oxygen, nitrogen, and carbon dioxide as essential. Each is intimately connected with the life processes of plants and animals. Commercially, oxygen, being essential to all processes involving combustion, heads a list which includes hydrogen, helium, nitrogen, illuminating gas, acetylene, nitrous oxide, argon, neon, chlorine, and many others, all having certain well-known uses. If one includes the poisonous gases, one can extend the list considerably. Omitting them, however, one finds listed, in the catalogue of a certain chemical manufacturer, some 35 gases which are commercially available. Presumably all have found some application in industry or in pure science research.

Although the tenuity of gases is an obvious and familiar property, it is not commonly realized how great is the molecular density associated with this tenuity even in extremely rarefied gases. In certain radio tubes, for example, where pressures of $10^{-7}$ mm-Hg (one-ten-billionth of an atmosphere) are maintained, one still finds that each $cm^3$ within the "evacuated" space contains approximately three billion molecules. Ordinary vacuum incandescent lamps contain ten times this number of molecules per $cm^3$. Pressures as low as $10^{-10}$ mm-Hg have been reached. This represents man's best efforts in the direction of a perfect vacuum.

In spite of the high molecular density ($3.5 \times 10^6$ molecules/$cm^3$) occurring in our very best vacuums, the average distance traversed by any particular molecule, say, a molecule of nitrogen in nitrogen, between collisions with other molecules is of the order of 700 km. This testifies to the extreme smallness of the molecules. Since a nitrogen molecule at room temperature has an average speed of about 500 m/sec, this means an average elapsed time of more than 2 min between collisions for any particular molecule. From another point of view, in a cubical vessel 10 cm on an edge, in which a pressure of $10^{-9}$ mm-Hg exists, any given nitrogen molecule would traverse the vessel on the average 700,000 times between collisions with other molecules. Nevertheless such a box would contain $3.5 \times 10^{10}$ molecules. To obtain a pressure such as this in our atmosphere, one would have to ascend at least 250 km, the general region of formation of the aurora. To obtain such "vacuums" as these in the laboratory, one requires a well-designed diffusion pump employing mercury vapor or some organic oil vapor, in series with a good mechanical pump. Also required is a cooling trap placed between the pumps and the vacuum chamber and filled with liquid air to condense relatively high-boiling-point materials from the interior of the chamber.

At the other end of the pressure scale, one notes as commonplace 2000 lb/in.$^2$ in commercial oxygen cylinders. Pressures attained momentarily in explosions greatly exceed these figures.

An interesting concept which has come to the front during the second quarter of the twentiety century as a result of the active interest in surface phenomena is that of a two-dimensional gas. It has been observed that, when monomolecular films of certain substances are deposited on the surfaces of certain solids or liquids, the equation governing the behavior of the film under different temperature and stress conditions is similar in form to the ideal gas law. Similarly, other films behave as liquids, and still others as solids. The future importance of these new twin sciences of surface physics and surface chemistry seems great.

It is not surprising that the study of the properties of gases has occupied the attention of physicists since the dawn of the experimental era. It might have been early suspected that a gas represents matter in its simplest form and is therefore a good starting point in the search for a fundamental understanding of the nature of matter. For many years, relatively much was known about the nature of gases and little about the nature of solids and liquids. Only since about 1930 has it become possible to account theoretically to some extent for observed properties of matter in these latter forms.

**2. Ideal Gas Laws.** There are seven well-recognized laws which taken together describe to a considerable extent the main properties of ideal gases. They are:

(a) *Boyle's Law.* Robert Boyle (1627–1691), Irish by birth but English by adoption, was among the first to describe quantitative experiments relating to gases. The law bearing his name states that, for a given mass of an ideal gas maintained at a constant temperature, the product of the pressure and the volume is constant.

(b) *Charles' Law.* Jacques Charles (1746–1823), a Frenchman of distinction, seems to have made the discovery of the law bearing his name in 1781, though, according to Allen and Maxwell,* the account of it was first presented to the world by Gay-Lussac (see below) in 1802. The law, often referred to as the law of Charles and Gay-Lussac, states that, with the pressure maintained constant, the volume of a given mass of an ideal gas varies in direct proportion with the temperature. Combined with Boyle's law it yields the very important ideal-gas relation

$$pv = RT \tag{1}$$

of which $p$, $v$, $T$, and $R$ stand in order for pressure, specific volume, temperature,† and the universal gas constant.‡ A third law deducible at once from the foregoing and embodied in them states that, with the volume maintained constant, the pressure experienced by a given mass of an ideal gas varies in direct proportion with the temperature.

(c) *Dalton's Law of Partial Pressures.* John Dalton (1766–1844), of Manchester, England, distinguished for his work in connection with atomic theory, was awarded the first Royal Medal of the Royal Society in 1826. The law of partial pressures states that the pressure experienced by a mixture of two chemically inactive, ideal gases in a given volume at a given temperature is equal to the sum of the two pressures that would be experienced were first one gas and then the other separately present.

(d) *Gay-Lussac's Law of Combining Volumes.* Joseph Louis Gay-Lussac (1778–1850) was a French chemist of great distinction. The

* H. S. Allen and R. S. Maxwell, *A Textbook of Heat*, p. 130, Macmillan and Co., London, 1939.

† Many use the term "absolute temperature" here because, in contrast to Centigrade temperatures, the quantity concerned is measured from the absolute zero, that is, 0°K. However, whenever *temperature*, rather than *difference in temperature*, is met in equations attempting to express natural phenomena, that temperature is always reckoned from the absolute zero. To illustrate, even though we may speak of a temperature of 0°C, we do not fail to recognize that $(0°C)^4$ is the same as $(273°K)^4$. To the authors, the qualifying term "absolute" seems quite useless and will not be used in this book.

‡ Frequently the ideal-gas equation is written as $pV = NRT$, of which $p$, $V$, and $T$ represent pressure, volume, and temperature; $R$ is then said to represent the gas constant *for a mole of the gas*, and $N$, a numeric, the number of moles of gas under consideration. If, as is customary, the mole as a unit of mass appears as a part of the unit of $R$, as in 1.986 cal/(mol K°), the equation fails to check from the standpoint of units. Checking occurs, however, if $N$ is interpreted as a mass. If the $v$ of Eq. 1 is multiplied by $M$ to obtain $V$, so also $RT$ must be multiplied by $M$ to obtain $MRT$, and we may write, in place of Eq. 1,

$$pV = MRT \tag{1a}$$

a form preferable to that in which the $M$ is replaced by $N$.

law bearing his name states that, when measured under standard conditions as to temperature and pressure, the volumes of chemically reacting, ideal gases bear simple whole-number ratios to one another and to the volumes of the resulting products.

(e) *Avogadro's Law of Numbers of Molecules.*  Amedeo Avogadro (1776–1856), an Italian physicist of great ability, is chiefly remembered for his great contribution to atomic theory made in 1811.  The law states that equal volumes of ideal gases measured at the same temperature and pressure contain equal numbers of molecules.

(f) *Joule's Law of Energy Content.*  James P. Joule (1818–1889) was an English physicist whose work has already been noted in connection with the first law of thermodynamics.  The basis for this law was Joule's failure to detect any change of temperature in air initially under 22 A pressure on freely expanding without doing external work to 11 A.  The law states that the energy content of a given mass of an ideal gas is a function of temperature only.

(g) *Maxwell's Law of Distribution of Molecular Speeds.*  James Clerk Maxwell (1831–1879), of Scottish birth and education, was a British physicist of the first order whose work has been fundamental in many fields.  His law, published in 1859, was based on probability considerations and states that the distribution of molecular speeds of an ideal gas in equilibrium at any given temperature is given by

$$N_c dc = \frac{4N}{\sqrt{\pi}} \left( \frac{m}{2kT} \right)^{3/2} c^2 e^{-\frac{mc^2}{2kT}} dc \qquad (2)$$

of which $N$ is the total number of molecules of mass $m$ under consideration, $T$ is the temperature, $k$ is the Boltzmann constant whose significance will be discussed later, and $N_c dc$ is the number of molecules with speeds between $c$ and $c + dc$.  See Appendix I for a derivation of Eq. 2.

For ideal gases the laws as stated are exact by definition.  But there are no ideal gases, and not even one of the laws is obeyed strictly by any real gas.  However, as close approximations under conditions of ordinary pressure and not too low a temperature, they are all extremely valuable.  Avogadro's law, however, becomes exact for even real gases when modified to state that the number of molecules of a substance required to form a mole of a substance is the same for all substances.  Boyle realized that his law was an approximation only and failed to give true results at small volumes or great pressures.

It was noted in Chapter II that, in gas thermometry, it is necessary to regard Eq. 1 as an approximation and to apply suitable corrections

to the readings of gas thermometers on that account. The approximation, however, is sufficiently good for many purposes. For example,
the volume occupied by a given mass of nitrogen at standard temperature and pressure conditions is smaller than that predicted by the
ideal-gas law by about only 1 part in 2500. As the pressure is reduced,
better agreement is to be expected. There are gases, however, particularly those with large molecules, for which the agreement is not
good even for conditions that are originally favorable.

The general validity of the various laws presented is so good that it
is desirable to consider in some detail an *ideal gas* whose properties
are exactly those described by them.

### KINETIC THEORY OF GASES

**3. A General Outline.** The kinetic theory assumes a gas to consist
of small elastic "billiard ball" molecules which, except at times of collision, neither attract nor repel one another. They are assumed to
move to and fro with various speeds, colliding occasionally and exchanging momenta with each other and with the walls of the containing vessel. A consequence of the last-named process is the observed
pressure, or, as it is sometimes called, the external pressure. With rise
in temperature, the molecular motion is assumed to be more rapid and
the frequency of collision of molecules with walls and the momentum
transferred during each collision are assumed to increase, and likewise
the pressure.

Consider some of the predictions of the theory. Assume a cubical
box of edge $l$ and volume $V$, containing a large number $N$ of molecules
in motion. Obviously, any given rate of trans-
fer of momentum to the walls by the molecules
with their widely varying speeds can be brought
about as well by molecules all of which have a
common speed, $\tilde{c}$. Let such an assumption of
constant speed be made. Also let it be assumed
that the molecules may be divided into three
equal groups, with those in one group traveling
back and forth without collision with other
molecules in paths parallel to the $x$-axis while
those in the other groups travel similarly in
paths parallel to the $y$- and the $z$-axes. Consider one such molecule
(Fig. 1). With mass $m$, the momentum it transfers to face $A$ on
rebounding elastically from it is $2m\tilde{c}$. Since, between collisions at
that face, the particle travels a distance $2l$, the number of collisions

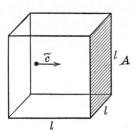

Fig. 1.   A molecule in
a box.

at that face per unit time is $\tilde{c}/2l$ and the momentum transferred per unit time by the single molecule is $m\tilde{c}^2/l$. The total of such rates of transfer of momentum to face $A$ by the $N/3$ molecules moving back and forth perpendicular to it is identical with the force which the gas exerts on $A$, according to Newton's second law; and we have

$$F_A = \frac{N}{3}\frac{m\tilde{c}^2}{l} \qquad (3)$$

From the definition of pressure, $p$, it follows that

$$p = \frac{1}{3}\frac{Nm}{l^3}\tilde{c}^2 = \frac{1}{3}\frac{Nm}{V}\tilde{c}^2 = \frac{mn}{3}\tilde{c}^2 = \frac{1}{3}\delta\tilde{c}^2 \qquad (4)$$

where $n$ is the number of molecules per unit volume and $\delta$ is the density of the gas. On the basis of the assumptions made, $p$ is directly proportional to both $\delta$ and $n$. Solving for $\tilde{c}$, we obtain

$$\tilde{c} = \sqrt{\frac{3p}{\delta}} \qquad (5)$$

Eqs. 3 and 4 are identically those obtained when one does not make the assumption of a common speed $\tilde{c}$ but accepts instead the well-established Maxwellian speed distribution (see below). The interpretation assigned $\tilde{c}$ in this more rigorous deduction is given by

$$\tilde{c}^2 = \frac{1}{N}(c_1{}^2 + c_2{}^2 + c_3{}^2 + \cdots c_N{}^2) \qquad (6)$$

of which $c_1$, $c_2$, etc., represent the speeds of the various $N$ molecules. The speed $\tilde{c}$ is often called the root-mean-square speed or more simply the rms speed.

Rearranging Eq. 4, we may write

$$pV = \tfrac{1}{3}Nm\tilde{c}^2 = \tfrac{2}{3}N\tfrac{1}{2}m\tilde{c}^2 = \tfrac{2}{3}NE \qquad (7)$$

wherein $E$ is obviously the average translational kinetic energy of a molecule. It does not include rotational, vibrational, or other energy.

Since $N$ and $E$ are constant for a given mass of a specified gas at a given temperature, Eq. 7 is in fact a statement of Boyle's law with $\tfrac{2}{3}NE$ as the value of the constant. This relation will appear later in a discussion of specific heats.

Combining Eqs. 1 and 7, we obtain

$$pV = Mpv = MRT = \tfrac{2}{3}NE \qquad (8)$$

Since $R$ is a universal constant and since $M$ and $N$ are necessarily constant for a given mass of gas, it follows that $E$ is directly proportional to $T$, which, as always in Mother Nature's scheme of things, is measured from the absolute zero.

Making use of the law of Avogadro, which, originally set forth as a postulate but in the first quarter of the twentieth century definitely established as a fact by radioactivity studies, states that equal volumes of ideal gases under the same conditions as to pressure and temperature contain equal numbers of molecules, and introducing the Avogadro number, $N_0$, the number of molecules of a gas per mole, we may now write, with the aid of Eqs. 7 and 8,

$$E = \frac{1}{2}m\tilde{c}^2 = \frac{3}{2}\frac{MRT}{N} = \frac{3}{2}\frac{MRT}{MN_0} = \frac{3}{2}kT \qquad (9)$$

of which $k$ like $N_0$ is a highly important constant. It is known as the Boltzmann molecular constant after the great Austrian physicist Ludwig Boltzmann (1844–1906). (To one accustomed to thinking of the mole as a unit of mass, the equating of $N$ to $MN_0$ will not appear strange, for $N_0M$ represents the product of a number of molecules per unit mass, the mole, by the mass of a group of molecules and accordingly yields the number of molecules forming the group.)

From Eq. 9, we obtain at once the very important relation

$$k = \frac{R}{N_0} \qquad (9a)$$

$R$ and $N_0$, along with other basic physical-chemical constants, have been the subjects of much careful research. From a careful analysis of the results, R. T. Birge (1887–    ), physicist at the University of California, has derived certain most probable values. $R$, Birge's $R_0$, was evaluated in accord with Eq. 1 as applied to an ideal gas under standard conditions. With $(1.013246 \pm 0.00004) \times 10^6 \, dy/cm^2$ as the standard atmosphere, $(22,414.6 \pm 0.6) \, cm^3/mole$ as the specific volume of the ideal gas under standard conditions, and $(273.16 \pm 0.01)$ °K as the standard ice-point temperature, there follows

$$R = \frac{1 \, A \, 1 \dfrac{gmv}{mole}}{273.16°K} = (8.3143 \pm 0.0003) \times 10^7 \, \frac{ergs}{mole \, K°} \qquad (9b)$$

of which gmv is the volume unit known as the gram-molecular volume. The value for $N_0$, however, was based on measured characteristics of calcite, namely, its molecular weight, $M$, its density at 20°C, $\delta$, its grating space at 20°C, $d_{20}$, and its geometrical constant, $\varphi$. With $M$ equal to $(100.091_4 \pm 0.005)$ gm/mole, $\delta$ equal to $(2.71029 \pm 0.00003)$ gm/cm$^3$, $d_{20}$ equal to $(3.03567_4 \pm 0.00018) \times 10^{-8}$ cm, and $\varphi$ equal to $1.09594 \pm 0.00001$, there follows

$$N_0 = \frac{M}{2\delta(d_{20})^3 \varphi}$$

$$= (6.02283 \pm 0.0011) \times 10^{23} \frac{\text{molecules}}{\text{mole}} \qquad (9c)$$

This value for $N_0$ is believed to have greater certainty than that obtained, as previously, from the ratio of the faraday to the electronic charge. In accord with Eq. 9a there follows

$$k = (1.38047 \pm 0.00026) \times 10^{-16} \frac{\text{erg}}{\text{molecule K°}} \qquad (9d)$$

Eq. 9 indicates that the $E$ is a function of temperature only and does not change from gas to gas. Thus, in so far as hydrogen or any other gas at 0°C approximates an ideal gas, we have, for that gas,

$$E_{0°C} = \frac{3}{2} \times 1.38047 \times 10^{-16} \frac{\text{erg}}{\text{molecule K°}} \times 273.16°\text{K}$$

$$= 5.6564 \times 10^{-14} \frac{\text{erg}}{\text{molecule}} \qquad (10)$$

Correspondingly the translational kinetic energy per mole of ideal gas at 0°C is given by

$$N_0 E_{0°C} = 6.0228 \times 10^{23} \frac{\text{molecules}}{\text{mole}} \times 5.6564 \times 10^{-14} \frac{\text{erg}}{\text{molecule}}$$

$$= 3.4067 \times 10^{10} \frac{\text{ergs}}{\text{mole}} = 3406.7 \frac{\text{joules}}{\text{mole}} \qquad (11)$$

**4. Maxwell Speed Distribution.** The formal statement of this law in mathematical form is given above in Eq. 2. A graph of the equation for molecules of oxygen at two different temperatures is shown in Fig. 2. Since the areas under the curves represent the same number of molecules, they must be the same although $T$ is different for the two curves. With increase of $T$, however, there is naturally a general broadening of the distribution and a shift to higher speeds. The maximum of the curve obviously corresponds to a *most probable speed*, $\alpha$. For a given temperature, it is the speed possessed by more molecules than is any other speed. The *root-mean-square speed* $\tilde{c}$ is higher than this as shown in Fig. 2 not only because, in forming $\tilde{c}$, the higher speeds have more effect than do the lower speeds, but also because molecules having speeds in excess of the most probable speed are more numerous than those having less speeds. A speed known as the *average speed*, $\bar{c}$, also

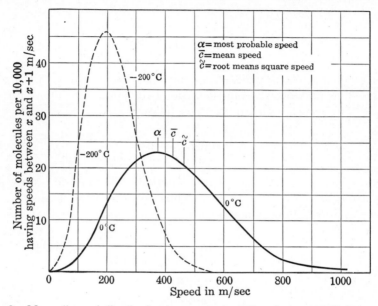

FIG. 2. Maxwell speed distribution for oxygen at 0°C and at −200°C (by permission, Physics Staff, University of Pittsburgh, *An Outline of Atomic Physics*, 2nd ed., p. 10, New York, John Wiley & Sons, 1937).

shown in Fig. 2 lies between the two. Of the three, the *root-mean-square speed* is by far the most important theoretically for translational energies and pressures depend on the squares of speeds.

Given Maxwell's distribution curve for a specified gas at a specified temperature, one may construct the ideal-gas distribution curve for any gas at any temperature by making use of a principle of similarity. Introduction of the root-mean-square speed, $\tilde{c}$, into Eq. 2 leads to

$$N_c = \frac{1}{\tilde{c}} \frac{4N}{\sqrt{\pi}} \left(\frac{m\tilde{c}^2}{2kT}\right)^{3/2} \left(\frac{c}{\tilde{c}}\right)^2 e^{-\frac{m\tilde{c}^2}{2kT}\left(\frac{c}{\tilde{c}}\right)^2} \tag{12}$$

and this, in view of Eq. 9 which shows that $m\tilde{c}^2/2kT$ equals $\frac{2}{3}$, may be rewritten as

$$N_c = \frac{1}{\tilde{c}} \frac{4N}{\sqrt{\pi}} \left(\frac{2}{3}\right)^{3/2} \left(\frac{c}{\tilde{c}}\right)^2 e^{-\frac{2}{3}\left(\frac{c}{\tilde{c}}\right)^2} = \frac{1}{\tilde{c}} f\left(\frac{c}{\tilde{c}}\right) \tag{13}$$

Further, since, for a given total number of molecules, $N$, there are necessarily equal numbers of molecules in *corresponding* speed intervals,

$$N_c dc = N_{c/\bar{c}} d\left(\frac{c}{\bar{c}}\right) \tag{13a}$$

and consequently

$$N_c = N_{c/\bar{c}} \frac{d\left(\frac{c}{\bar{c}}\right)}{dc} = \frac{1}{\bar{c}} N_{c/\bar{c}} \tag{13b}$$

Finally there results from Eqs. 13 and 13$b$

$$N_{c/\bar{c}} = f\left(\frac{c}{\bar{c}}\right) \tag{13c}$$

Eq. 13$c$ shows that, when speeds, $c$, and frequencies of occurrence per unit speed interval, $N_c$, are expressed in terms of $\bar{c}$, and $N_{c/\bar{c}}$, a single graphed curve serves to give the speed distribution for all gases at all temperatures, and the principle that all ideal-gas distributions are similar is established. How the principle may be applied to determine the distribution of speeds for another gas at another temperature using the graph of Fig. 2 is the subject of a problem at the close of the chapter.

The checking of the Maxwell distribution experimentally has been realized. Of the methods employed, that carried out by I. F. Zartman (1899– ) at the University of California is perhaps the simplest. He heated some bismuth in furnace $A$ (Fig. 3), which together with the space outside had been highly evacuated. Of the molecules of bismuth vapor escaping through slit $B$, some passed through parallel slit $C$ toward rotating drum $E$ of diameter $d$ containing a third slit, $D$, which was parallel to both slits $B$ and $C$. At the instant $B$, $C$, and $D$ were in line, a number of bismuth molecules would enter the chamber of $E$, moving toward $P$ on the opposite cylinder wall. Consider such a molecule whose speed was $c$. It required the time $t(= d/c)$ to reach the far side. Consider also a point $N$ on the drum, which, at the instant of entrance of the molecule into the drum rotating with angular speed $\omega$, was on a line making an angle $\theta(= \omega t = \omega d/c)$ as shown with respect to $OP$. Let the point $N$ be so chosen that, as the molecule under consideration traversed the drum, the point itself moved into the position to receive the molecule as it reached the far side of

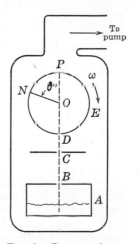

Fig. 3. Zartmann's apparatus for testing the Maxwell distribution law. $A$ is a furnace containing bismuth. The space outside was highly evacuated. Some bismuth atoms leaving $A$ by the way of the small openings $B$ and $C$ entered the rotating drum $E$ and were spread out in a "velocity spectrum" along $NP$.

the drum wall, and condensed. For faster molecules, the points of condensation were obviously nearer $P$; for slower molecules, farther away. Thus there was deposited on the drum wall a bismuth film of varying thickness from which a molecular speed distribution could be determined. The results (Fig. 4) showed agreement with Maxwell's predictions within the limits of experimental error.

In order to bring Zartman's experimental curves into agreement with theory, it was necessary to take account of two facts. First,

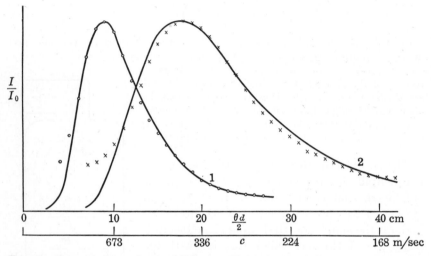

FIG. 4.   Zartmann's results for bismuth. Theoretical and experimental intensity distributions assuming a vapor composition of 40% $Bi_1$ and 60% $Bi_2$. $T$ equals 851°C. Curve 1, $n = 120.7$ rps; curve 2, $n = 241.4$ rps. Bottom line gives the molecular velocity corresponding to several displacements at a cylinder speed of 241.4 rps. (*Phys. Rev.*, **37**, 390, 1931.)

ordinary bismuth vapor is a mixture of single bismuth atoms and diatomic molecules, each having a separate speed distribution. Second, the molecules in the beam do not have the same speed distribution as do the molecules in the furnace. This is because the more speedy molecules are the more likely to escape and the Maxwell distribution (Eq. 13), though not the theory, must be modified to take this into account.

**5. The Quantum Distributions.**   Though the Maxwell speed distribution for gases agrees remarkably well with observation ordinarily, discrepancies are found at extremely low temperatures and high densities, where the basic assumptions underlying the classical kinetic theory are known to fail. There are, however, two distributions founded on quantum-mechanical principles which at ordinary temperatures differ but slightly from the Maxwell distribution, but which, under conditions where the latter fails, still show agreement with experiment. They are the Fermi *-Dirac † and the Einstein ‡-Bose distributions. All particles in nature seem to be governed by one or the other. Helium and in fact all gases composed of electrically neutral molecules are examples of "Einstein-Bose" gases. At temperatures near the absolute zero, its molecular speed distribution seems to be in accord with the Einstein-Bose predictions rather than with the classical Maxwell theory. Fermi-Dirac distributions, however, apply to gases whose molecules are not electrically neutral.

The failures just noted do not detract from the practical usefulness of the classical kinetic theory but merely serve to define more closely the limits of its applicability. The Maxwell, Einstein-Bose, and Fermi-Dirac distributions are each founded on a certain set of definite assumptions, and it is an interesting fact that the latter two theories, each for its own field, seem to agree with observation over wider ranges of conditions than does the simple Maxwell theory.

**6. Mean Free Path.** In the random motions with varying speeds occurring within a gas, the distances traversed by a molecule between successive collisions are not constant.

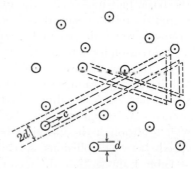

FIG. 5. Illustrating mean free path.

The mean, however, of a great number of such distances is an important characteristic known as the *mean free path*. Except for a single molecule, assume that all the molecules of a gas in a box are at rest in random positions and that that one is moving with a speed $c$ among the others. When in such motion it comes "in contact" with another molecule and a collision occurs, their centers will be separated by the distance $d$, the diameter of a molecule (Fig. 5). Obviously, the frequency of collision and the distances traversed between collisions are the same as those that would occur were the stationary molecules strictly point molecules and the moving molecule had the diameter $2d$. With this in mind, follow the motion of the hypothetical molecule moving with speed $c$ for a time $t$. The space swept out will have a jaggedly cylindrical shape. Its volume will be $\pi d^2 ct$, and the stationary point molecules falling within its boundaries will have suffered collisions. If the number of molecules per unit volume is $n$, their total number will be

* Enrico Fermi (1901– ), an Italian physicist, was awarded the Nobel prize in physics in 1938. He is now at the University of Chicago.

† P. A. M. Dirac (1902– ), an English physicist, was awarded a Nobel prize in physics in 1933.

‡ See p. 136.

$n\pi d^2 ct$, and the mean free path, $\lambda$, will be

$$\lambda = \frac{\text{distance traveled}}{\text{number of collisions}} = \frac{ct}{\pi d^2 ctn} = \frac{1}{\pi n d^2} \tag{14}$$

The above derivation has been oversimplified. By assuming a strict Maxwellian speed distribution, a more correct formula may be shown to be

$$\lambda = \frac{1}{\sqrt{2}\pi n d^2} \tag{15}$$

Since, as shown by Eq. 4, $n$ varies as the pressure, the mean free path varies inversely with the pressure. It is possible to determine the mean free path and the molecular diameter experimentally by independent methods and thus to check Eq. 15.

That molecules possess finite diameters or spheres of influence is the basic fact underlying the explanation of why a gas, released from a container in a room, does not immediately disperse throughout the atmosphere of the room but remains where released in appreciable concentration for some time. If the particles had effectively zero diameters, they would never collide (the mean free path would become infinitely great), and, in view of the great speeds possessed by the individual molecules, an almost instantaneous dispersion of the gas would occur. An actual gas may be likened to a milling crowd of people which, although the individuals may be moving with relatively large speeds between collisions, spreads out but slowly.

Table I shows that the mean free path for a gas may become very great at reduced pressures. In experimental work, it is often the cri-

TABLE I

MEAN FREE PATH OF $N_2$ MOLECULES (MOLECULAR DIAMETER $3.50 \times 10^{-8}$ CM) AT $0°$C.

John D. Strong (1905–  ), *Procedures in Experimental Physics*, New York, Prentice-Hall, 1938.

| Pressure mm-Hg | Mean Free Path cm |
| --- | --- |
| 760 | $8.5 \times 10^{-6}$ |
| 1 | 0.0065 |
| $10^{-3}$ | 6.5 |
| $10^{-4}$ | 65 |
| $10^{-5}$ | 650 |
| $10^{-6}$ | 6500 |
| $10^{-9}$ | 65,000,000 (65 km) |

terion for determining the extent to which important apparatus must be evacuated. Thus, for the Zartman experiment described above, it was necessary to have the gas pressure so low that the disturbing effects of occasional collisions in the rotating cylinder were negligible. Mean free paths of the order of 100 times the diameter of the cylinder would obviously suffice. The relative frequency of such occasional collisions with the residual gas in an evacuated space which an experimenter is willing to accept sets the upper limit to the pressure that will be tolerated in this experiment.

**7. Molecular Sizes.** The quantity $d$ occurring in Eq. 15 has been determined in several ways, all yielding effective diameters of molecules which were assumed spherical, regardless of their actual shapes. As methods, to be found in more specialized textbooks, one may list those based on (1) viscosity, (2) diffusion, (3) conduction of heat, (4) deviations from the ideal-gas law and (5) smallest molar volume. Certain other methods are less obvious. The theory associated with each permits one to compute an effective molecular diameter $d$. As shown in Table II, the diameters of many of the simpler, monatomic, diatomic, and even triatomic molecules seem to be of the order of 3 Å.

TABLE II

SOME MEASURED DIAMETERS OF MOLECULES, ASSUMED SPHERICAL, OBTAINED BY VARIOUS METHODS

Diameters are given in Å ($= 10^{-8}$ cm).

| Gas | Viscosity | Diffusion | Thermal Conduction | Van der Waals Equation | Onnes' Virial Coefficient | Smallest Volume | Radiometer Effect | Slow Cathode Rays | Molecular Refraction |
|---|---|---|---|---|---|---|---|---|---|
| He | 1.9, 2.2 | 2.2 | 2.2 | 2.3, 2.6 | | 3.5 | | 2.6, 2.8, 2.9 | 1.5 |
| A | 2.5, 2.7, 2.9, 3.0 | | | 2.9 | | 3.5 | | 3.1 | 3.0 |
| Hg | 3.6 | | | 2.4 | | 2.9 | | | |
| $H_2$ | 2.2, 2.3, 2.4 | 2.7 | 2.7 | 2.3, 2.4, 2.8 | 2.3 | 3.7 | 2.9 | 3.9, 4.1 | 1.9 |
| $N_2$ | 3.0, 3.1, 3.2, 3.8 | 3.8 | 3.8 | 3.1, 3.5 | 3.0 | 3.6 | | 3.3, 3.5 | 2.4 |
| $O_2$ | 2.7, 2.9, 3.0, 3.6 | 3.6 | 3.6 | 2.9 | 2.6 | 3.4 | 3.9 | 2.6 | 2.3 |
| $H_2O$ | 2.6, 2.7 | | | 2.9 | | 3.1 | | | 2.3 |
| $CO_2$ | 2.9, 3.0, 3.2, 4.6 | 4.6 | 4.8 | 3.2, 3.4 | | 3.8 | | 3.4 | |
| $C_2H_6O$ | 3.6 | | | | | | | | |
| $C_2H_{10}O$ | 4.8 | | | | | | | | |
| $CHCl_3$ | 4.8 | | | | | | | | |

## *PVT* RELATIONS FOR REAL GASES

**8. Departure Coefficients.** The ideal-gas concept, as already noted, is a convenient fiction. No actual gas obeys the ideal-gas law exactly. The degree of departure from being ideal for any one gas at any one temperature, however, is important and may be obtained from a plot of $pv/RT$, or $K$, as a function of $p$. $K$ is known as a *departure coeffi-*

*cient* since its variation from unity is a measure of the departure of the gas at any particular pressure and temperature from the ideal state. However, in order to separate the curves corresponding to different temperatures on a single plot, it is customary to plot, in place of $K$, the quantity $pv/RT_0[= pv/(pv)_0]$ as a function of $p$. The subscript 0 of $(pv)_0$ indicates a standard condition, usually 1 A and 0°C. Such curves are called isotherms. For an ideal gas, they consist of a set of straight lines, parallel to the pressure axis.

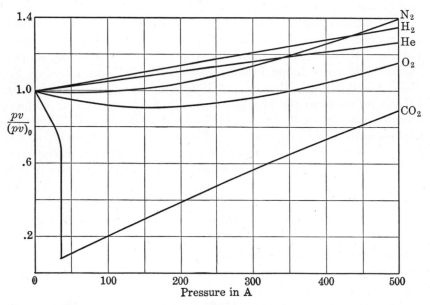

FIG. 6.   Isotherms for several gases at 0°C showing departures from Boyle's law.

Departure coefficient data were obtained by the French physicist Émile Amagat (1840–1915) in 1893 for several gases at pressures as high as 3000 A (Fig. 6). Later some of the same and other gases were studied by other workers. For temperatures and pressures commonly occurring, there seem to be three types of behavior. The curves showing departure coefficients for gases of the first type, represented by hydrogen, starting with unity at low pressures, seem to rise immediately from the horizontal with increase of pressure. Those of the second type, represented by nitrogen, drop for a certain moderate pressure range before rising; those of the third type, represented by carbon dioxide, drop similarly, but remain below the horizontal, for a very large pressure range. The carbon dioxide curve is further complicated by the fact that, for the temperature shown, liquefaction occurs. This accounts for the vertical section of the curve, where the volume changes though the temperature and pressure remain constant. A complete set of curves for any one gas may show in one plot the characteristics ascribed to the three types of gases separately.

We desire general laws describing the characteristics of real gases, and a question arises as to the bases on which gases may be compared. That of equal temperatures does not lead to comparable results. It is, however, reasonable to expect that the

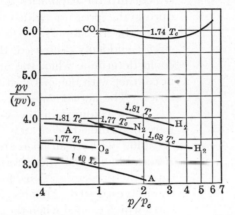

FIG. 7. Some isotherms plotted in a reduced-scale system. A logarithmic plot has been used for the horizontal scale.

three gases hydrogen, nitrogen, and carbon dioxide, so different at room temperature, might show more nearly similar characteristics if compared at temperatures which are similarly related to their critical temperatures. The critical temperature (to be discussed in some detail on p. 292) for a substance is the maximum limiting temperature, whatever the pressure, at which its liquid and its gas phases can jointly exist in equilibrium. This suggests a "reduced temperature scale" in which the critical temperature for a given gas is taken as a temperature unit for that gas. Similarly, one may employ for each gas reduced pressure and reduced volume scales which are based on its critical pressure and its critical volume as units. As an example, isotherms similar to those of Fig. 6 are shown in Fig. 7 where reduced pressure and volume scales are employed and comparisons are made between gases at approximately the same reduced temperature. The differences in behavior are far from being as apparent as before.

## 9. Michels' Experiments.

In 1935, A. Michels (1889– ) and his co-workers in the Netherlands redetermined and extended the isothermal data of Amagat, using in part the apparatus of Fig. 8. The carbon dioxide investigated was contained in the glass portion $A$ of the piezometer (pressure vessel), which consisted of a number of small chambers connected by capillaries. The lower section of the piezometer $C$ was composed of steel and was filled with oil. The space above the mer-

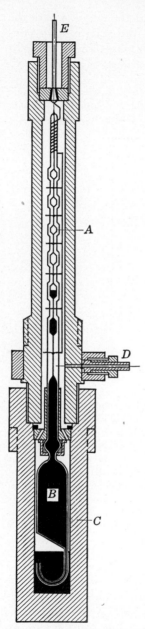

cury and surrounding the piezometer chambers was also filled with oil. The whole was immersed in a thermostated bath. In operation, pressure was applied to the oil through inlet $D$, thus compressing the gas in the piezometer. Volume determinations were carried out with the aid of platinum wires sealed into the capillaries as shown. Thus, during the pressure adjustment, by noting when the resistance of the platinum wire circuit suddenly decreased, the experimenter could determine when the mercury was just in contact with one of the wires in the capillaries. The actual volumes occupied by the gas when confined in the various chambers were determined separately by the method of filling with clean mercury and massing. A suitable gage in the external oil line indicated the pressure. Thus, for each temperature investigated, Michels noted the pressures which existed when the gas was confined to a series of known volumes. From these data, plots of $(pv)/(pv)_0$ against $p$ for various temperatures have been made.

The apparatus shown was useful from 16 to 250 A. An essentially similar apparatus was designed for the range 70 to 3000 A. Still a third apparatus was made for operation near the critical point. The data for Fig. 9 are those obtained by Amagat. The area enclosed by the dashed line in the lower left corner of the figure represents states in which the liquid and the gas phase exist in equilibrium. The other dashed line is the locus of a minimum for $pv/(pv)_0$.

**10. Burnett's Experiments with Helium.** Isothermal data for helium were determined in 1936 in an ingenious manner by E. S. Burnett (1880- ), at the U.S. Helium Production Plant at Amarillo, Texas. Measurements of pressure and temperature only were required; no volume determination was necessary. The apparatus, shown in Fig. 10, consists of two, nearly equal, double-walled metal tanks, of volumes

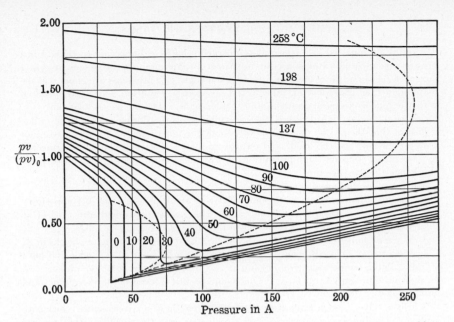

FIG. 9. Isotherms of carbon dioxide. Obtained by Amagat. (Amagat, *Ann. chim. phys.*, **29**, 117, 1893.)

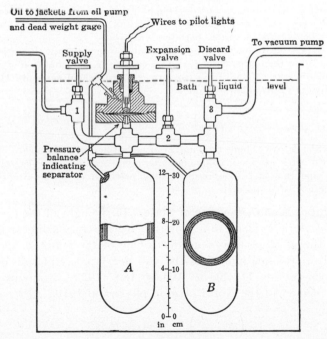

FIG. 10. Apparatus used by E. S. Burnett in a study of helium (*J. Applied Mechanics*, **58**, A-136, 1936).

215

$V_A$ and $V_B$, immersed in a constant-temperature bath. Connecting to tank $A$ is a pressure balance indicator consisting of a metal diaphragm in contact on its lower face with oil at the same pressure. Only when these two pressures are equal will the diaphragm take up a neutral, undeflected position, a condition delicately indicated with the aid of electrical contacts and a pilot light. The oil serves two purposes. First, by filling, at high pressure, the cavity between the double walls of the tanks, it insures that there is no increase in volume of the inner, gas-filled tanks because of a difference between the inside and outside pressures. Second, the oil is connected to a sensitive, compact, high-pressure gage which serves to measure the oil pressure and hence the gas pressure.

The procedure followed was:

1. Evacuate both containers to some relatively small pressure, say 0.1 mm-Hg.

2. Close valve 2, open valve 1, and admit the gas being studied into tank $A$ at some high initial pressure which, in Burnett's study of helium, was 130 A.

3. When a temperature equilibrium is reached, read the pressure $p_0$ of the gas in $A$.

4. With valve 3 closed, open valve 2 and allow the helium to expand to fill both vessels. After temperature equilibrium is restored, read the common pressure $p_1$. Evaluate the pressure ratio $p_0/p_1$. This would be just 2 for equal tank volumes and an ideal gas.

5. Close valve 2, open tank $B$ to the atmosphere or to a reservoir, then evacuate tank $B$. The initial conditions are now duplicated with the exception that the gas in tank $A$ is now at pressure $p_1$ instead of $p_0$.

6. Repeat the whole cycle many times until the pressure has become so small that it cannot be accurately measured. One has, then, for some one temperature, a series of pressure ratios corresponding to a series of initial pressures. The whole process may be repeated at various bath temperatures.

Given the pressure ratios described, one evidently needs only the ratio $V_a/V_b$ in order to express the isothermal departure coefficient, $K$, as a function of pressure. By extrapolating the pressure ratios to zero pressure, where gases are known to conform closely to Boyle's law, one obtains

$$\frac{p_0}{p_1} = \left[\frac{V_a + V_b}{V_a}\right]_{p=0} \tag{16}$$

and from it the desired volume ratio and eventually the isotherm sought.

Though Burnett's method is unique in requiring no actual volume determinations and at the same time in yielding results of high precision, as yet no extensive data using his method have appeared.

**11. Van der Waals' Equation of State.** In the light of the preceding paragraphs, it is evident that a better $p$-$v$-$T$ relationship than that given by the ideal-gas law is needed. One of the simplest and most successful relations is known as the van der Waals equation of state after its proposer, J. D. van der Waals (1837–1923), a famous Dutch physicist, winner of the Nobel prize in physics in 1910.

$$\left(p + \frac{a}{v^2}\right)(v - b) = RT \tag{17}$$

of which $a$ and $b$ are constants which may be determined experimentally, and $v$ is the molal volume of the gas, a quantity commonly expressed in volume units per mole. As $a$ and $b$ approach zero, the equation reduces to that for the ideal gas. Actually, the ideal-gas law is also approached as $v$ becomes very large.

There is a theoretical basis for the van der Waals relation. Consider first the constant $b$. That the ideal-gas law should break down at small specific volumes, where the volumes occupied by the molecules become appreciable, is to be expected. With the pressure of the gas increased indefinitely, the specific volume does not approach zero but instead a finite limit which, it would seem, might be identified with the $b$ of the equation. However, for larger specific volumes, other interpretations have been given to $b$ which vary from two to four times the aggregate volume occupied by the molecules per unit mass. That such a term as $(v - b)$, representing a "free volume," should appear in this gas law seems quite reasonable.

Another unreality of the ideal-gas concept is the assumption of no intermolecular forces. The phenomenon of condensation into a liquid phase, for example, makes it evident that such forces do exist. They are, in fact, responsible for what is called the *internal pressure* of a gas, a concept which will receive added significance with the discussion of the porous-plug experiment.

Imagine a plane passed through a gas, and consider, at any instant, the intermolecular forces which act across it. Each molecule on the left, say, will attract and be attracted by some small number $n$ of those on the right. Compare this situation with a second situation similar in all respects save that the total number of molecules per unit volume is doubled, i.e., the specific volume is halved. Now for this second case any given molecule on the left will interact on the average with $2n$ of its *neighbors across the plane*, and, since there are also twice as many molecules as before on the left which form such bonds, it is clear that the number of force bonds crossing the plane has increased fourfold, that is as $(1/v)^2$. A natural consequence of such intermolecular-force bonds would be that, for a given externally applied pressure, the gas should occupy a volume less than that which it would occupy as an ideal gas. Or, what is the same, the gas acts as though subject to a pressure in excess of such externally applied pressure. Since this excess appears in consequence of internal forces, it is naturally referred to as an internal pressure. As shown, this pressure, which in its effects is additive to the normal external pressure, is proportional to $1/v^2$ or equal to $a/v^2$, where $a$ is a constant. In equation form this is expressed by

$$p_i = \frac{a}{v^2} \tag{18}$$

It is important to realize that these corrections to the ideal gas law are first-order corrections only, and that the failure of the van der Waals equation in any particular case is evidence that second-order differences are important. One obvious departure from reality is the assumption of hard elastic spherical "billiard ball" molecules. It is easily seen, for example, that a collision between two carbon dioxide molecules cannot be accurately described using this assumption.

Van der Waals constants $a$ and $b$, applying to limited regions, have been determined for many gases. For them it is a simple matter to determine the internal pressure $a/v^2$ when $v$ is known. It is possible, however, to determine the internal pressure directly from $p$-$v$-$T$ data; the expression for it may be shown from thermodynamic considerations to be $T(dp/dT)_v - p$. Some values for air are of interest. For a temperature of 0°C and pressures of 1 A, 60 A, and 100 A, the internal pressures are 0.0028 A, 9.99 A, and 26.0 A. For −75°C, the corresponding values are 0.0056 A, 26.1 A, and 84.5 A. For conditions of reduced temperatures and high pressures, the internal pressures may exceed the ordinary external pressure many times.

When a gas expands under pressure and does work against outside compressing forces, it also must do work against these internal forces. For example, for air at −79.0°C and 100 A, the work done against internal forces is nearly as great as that done against external forces. There is, however, an important distinction in effect between internal and external work. In case of external work, energy is transferred from the body to an outside body; in case of internal work, there is merely a transfer from one kind of energy to another within the body, as from kinetic to potential.

For substances in the liquid state, internal pressures may be hundreds or thousands of times as great as the external pressures to which they are subjected.

**12. Other Equations of State.** Other equations besides van der Waals' have been advanced, some theoretically deduced, others arrived at largely by experiment. We mention that by C. Dieterici (1858–1929)

$$p(v - b)e^{a/RTv} = RT \qquad (19)$$

as an example of the first class, and, as examples of the second class, those by R. Clausius, the German physicist (1822–1888),

$$\left[ p + \frac{a}{T(v + c)^2} \right] (v - b) = RT \qquad (20)$$

the French physicist Daniel Berthelot (1865–1927),

$$\left[ p + \frac{a}{Tv^2} \right] (v - b) = RT \qquad (21)$$

where $\Delta T$ is the decrease in temperature that occurs when the gas expands freely from some pressure $p$ to a lower pressure $p - \Delta p$. The subscript $u$ signifies that the internal energy of the gas remains constant throughout the process.   To insure this it is only necessary that no energy, either in the form of heat transferred or in consequence of work performed, leaves or enters the system during the expansion. Table III shows some values of $\eta$ for air, for which a cooling is noted under the conditions shown.

TABLE III

VALUES OF $\eta$ FOR AIR IN (C°/A), ACCORDING TO ROEBUCK

| $p$ in A | −100°C | 0°C | 150°C |
|---|---|---|---|
| 1 | 0.445 | 0.311 | 0.172 |
| 100 | . . . . . | 0.244 | 0.146 |

In accord with the table, we should expect that Joule, with an initial temperature of, say, 5°C, could he have corrected for the great thermal capacitance of his tanks and the surrounding water, would have obtained a cooling of about 3.4 C°.   On the other hand, working at the University of Wisconsin, J. R. Roebuck (1876–   ) has found that with helium heating occurs normally with free expansion.

In seeking explanations for changes of temperature produced by free expansions in gases, where changes of molecular structure are not involved, one looks for possibilities of internal transfers of kinetic energy into potential energy and the reverse.   Actually there are two possibilities for each type of transfer.   That from kinetic into potential normally occurs as a consequence of work done (a) against the van der Waals attractive forces when molecules not in contact are separated still further and (b) against the mutual exclusion forces that occur when molecules at impact are distorted in the process of deflecting each other.   Transfers from potential into kinetic occur, of course, whenever these processes are reversed.   Actually there may possibly be long-range repulsive or negative attractive forces between molecules in certain cases, but the net effect of such long-range forces seems generally, if not always, to be attractive.   For this discussion such net effect is assumed.

For a given mass of gas and the case of no change of molecular structure such as occurs with change of phase, dissociation, and certain other processes, the potential energy possessed because of van der Waals forces would seem to depend solely on the volume.   In contrast, the potential energy possessed because of exclusion forces would seem to depend on the frequency of molecular impacts, their intensity, and their duration. For a given temperature the potential energy thus possessed obviously decreases with increase of the volume occupied.

On the assumption that our temperature-measuring instruments respond chiefly to the average translational kinetic energy per molecule, a cooling on free expansion is expected if the increase of the stored potential energy associated with the attractive forces *exceeds* the decrease of the stored potential energy associated with the exclusion forces. On the other hand, heating is to be expected on free expansion if the increase of potential energy associated with the attractive forces is *exceeded by* the decrease associated with the exclusion forces.

Granted that both heating and cooling effects occur with free expansion, one expects, in accord with the foregoing, that heating effects will be found in gases where the attractive forces are relatively weak as in the inert gas helium, and that cooling effects may be found in gases where the attractive forces are relatively strong as in oxygen, nitrogen, and many other gases. Qualitatively, so far as experimental results are available, these expectations are realized.

The theoretical ideal gas is sometimes defined as a gas composed of molecules of negligible volume for which the Joule effect is zero. For such a gas, it is obvious that not only must the van der Waals forces be zero but also that the stored potential energy associated with the exclusion forces must be zero, a condition that can result only if the duration of molecular impacts is also negligible.

**14. Joule-Thomson Experiment—Porous-Plug Expansion.** Unconvinced by the outcome of his free-expansion test, Joule, in collaboration with the great English physicist William Thomson (1824–1907), later to become generally known as Lord Kelvin, devised a more successful experiment for obtaining information concerning intermolecular forces. It is known as the porous-plug experiment. As originally performed, the porous plug was a wooden tube packed rather tightly with silk or cotton wool. Much of the porous-plug work done in more recent years, however, has been done with test-tube-shaped pieces of porous porcelain as the plugs. Nevertheless, the method of operation has been essentially the same. As carried out, gas is supplied at a constant high pressure $p_1$ at one side of the plug and, after expansion on passing through the plug, is removed at a lower constant pressure $p_2$ from the other side. Further, the incoming gas is passed through copper coils immersed in a temperature-controlled bath so that the initial temperature of the gas is constant. Thermocouples on either side of the plug indicate any change in temperature that may occur. Great care is taken to prevent energy transfer in the form of heat, that is, an exchange which is dependent on a temperature difference. The great advantage of the Joule-Thomson over the Joule experiment, both of which seek information regarding intermolecular forces, arises from the fact that, in the former, a steady-state condition is reached and that the only energy changes occurring thereafter relate to the maintaining of that condition.

Most processes that we meet in the study of heat and thermodynamics are characterized by some one quantity being maintained constant. In a free expansion, there is constancy of the internal energy $U$. What it is in the case of a porous-plug expansion may be derived easily. Referring to Fig. 13, consider a portion of gas on the high-pressure side of the plug which is about to undergo a porous-plug

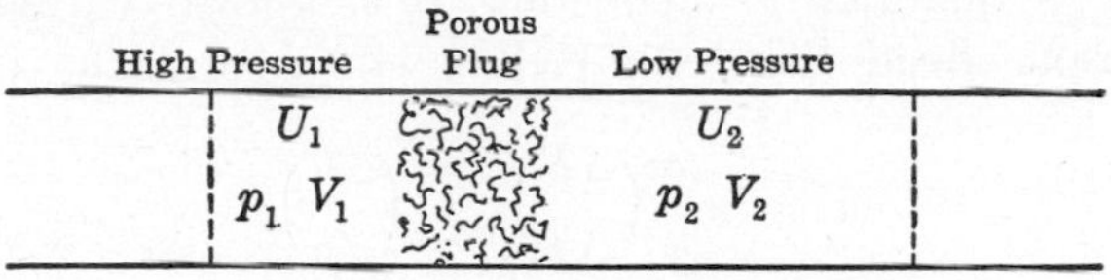

|  | Porous |  |
| High Pressure | Plug | Low Pressure |
| $U_1$ | | $U_2$ |
| $p_1$  $V_1$ | | $p_2$  $V_2$ |

FIG. 13. Illustrating the nature of the porous-plug process. In the theory of the process, account must be taken of the change in stream velocity, if any, of the gas on passage through the plug.

expansion. Let $U_1$ be its internal energy, $p_1$ its pressure, and $V_1$ its volume. Let $U_2$, $p_2$, and $V_2$ be corresponding values occurring just after passage through the plug. With such passage, work $W_1$, equal to $p_1V_1$, is done on the chosen portion of gas by the gas back of it on the high-pressure side. As the gas passes through the plug, it similarly does work on the gas ahead of it to the extent of $p_2V_2$. Assume the stream velocities on the two sides of the plug to be either negligible or the same. Applying next the first law of thermodynamics, we have, as shown in Chapter V, Eq. 7,

$$Q = \Delta U + W \qquad (26)$$

Since no energy exchange in the form of heat is permitted, the only changes of energy which occur involve $\Delta U$ and $W$. For the process as described above,

$$W = p_2V_2 - p_1V_1 \qquad (27)$$

and

$$\Delta U = U_2 - U_1 \qquad (28)$$

Substitution in Eq. 26 yields

$$U_1 + p_1V_1 = U_2 + p_2V_2 = \text{constant} \qquad (29)$$

On dividing through by the mass, we have

$$\frac{U + pV}{m} = u + pv = h = \text{constant} \tag{30}$$

The quantity $h(= u + pv)$, known as *enthalpy per unit mass* or *specific enthalpy*, is the quantity which is maintained constant for the porous-plug expansion. Such expansions which are of importance in steam engineering are often referred to by engineers as "isenthalpic" or "throttling" expansions. Like free expansions, isenthalpic expansions are irreversible. In the foregoing discussion, it has been assumed that the change in kinetic energy with change of velocity of passage along the tube is negligible.

We define a quantity $\mu$, analogous to $\eta$, known variously as the Joule-Thomson effect, the Joule-Kelvin effect, and the porous-plug effect.

$$\mu = \lim_{\Delta p \to 0} \left(\frac{\Delta T}{\Delta p}\right)_h = \left(\frac{dT}{dp}\right)_h \tag{31}$$

where the subscript $h$ signifies an expansion at constant enthalpy. Thermodynamics shows that $\mu$ and $\eta$ are not independent but are related by an equation which allows one to be computed in terms of the other.

Using the apparatus of Fig. 14, Roebuck and his students at the University of Wisconsin determined $\mu$ for several gases. The apparatus consists essentially of an unglazed porcelain thimble, the porous plug, surrounded by a steel cylinder. The path of the gas through the apparatus is indicated in the legend to the figure. From the low pressure side of the plug the gas passes to a compressor where it is raised once more to the higher pressure and repeats the cycle. For temperature measurements, a set of sensitive mercury thermometers, compared regularly with a standardized platinum resistance thermometer, is used.

Some porous-plug results for nitrogen obtained by J. R. Roebuck and co-workers are given in Table IV. One observes that not all values for $\mu$ are positive, thus corresponding to a cooling on porous-plug expansion, and that not all negative values correspond to the nitrogen's being in a liquid state. For 0°C and 180 A a value of $+0.1015$ C°/A is given. This means that, if nitrogen at 0°C and 185 A is expanded through a porous plug to a pressure of 175 A, we may expect a cooling of about 10 A $\times$ 0.1015 C°/A or 1.02 C°. For $-150$°C and 180 A, a value of $-0.0211$ C°/A is given. Correspondingly, at $-150$°C and 185 A expanded to 175 A, we expect a heating of approximately 0.21 C°.

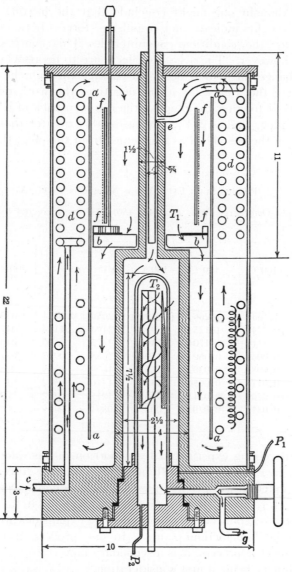

Fig. 14. Porous-plug apparatus used by J. R. Roebuck and his co-workers. The gas under investigation enters at $c$, passes to and through the twin coils $d$, through vent $e$ into the space surrounding the platinum resistance thermometer $T_1$, to the space surrounding the test tube of porous porcelain, the porous plug proper, through the porous porcelain to the space surrounding the platinum resistance thermometer $T_2$, and to the exit $g$. Pressures were obtained by connecting tubes $P_1$ and $P_2$ to a "dead weight" manometer. Other apparatus not described here was generally used in maintaining constant bath temperatures. (*Proc. Am. Acad. Arts and Sciences*, **60**, 537, 1925.)

On first thought one might conclude that the heating effect just mentioned might indicate net repulsive forces between nitrogen molecules for the condition encountered. This conclusion is not justifiable, however. The negative effects are to be associated largely with the changes in $pv$ that occur on passage through the plug. Actually, where the values for $\mu$ are negative, the work done on the nitrogen about to enter the plug by the nitrogen back of it in pushing it into the plug, that is $p_1 V_1$, is considerably greater than the work done by it on the gas ahead as it emerges from the plug, that is $p_2 V_2$.

TABLE IV

Porous-Plug Effect for Nitrogen in C°/A

Roebuck and Osterberg, *Phys. Rev.*, **48,** 450, 1935, as corrected by the original authors.

| $p$ \ $T$ | −160°C | −150°C | −100°C | 0°C | 100°C | 200°C | 300°C |
|---|---|---|---|---|---|---|---|
| 1 A | 1.633 | 1.266 | 0.6490 | 0.2656 | 0.1292 | 0.0558 | 0.0140 |
| 20 | 0.724 | 1.125 | .5958 | .2494 | .1173 | .0472 | .0096 |
| 33.5 | 0.311 | 0.1704 | .5494 | .2377 | .1100 | .0430 | .0050 |
| 60 | 0.0068 | 0.0601 | .4506 | .2088 | .0975 | .0372 | − .0013 |
| 100 | −0.0088 | 0.0202 | .2754 | .1679 | .0768 | .0262 | − .0075 |
| 140 | −0.0175 | −0.0056 | .1373 | .1316 | .0582 | .0168 | − .0129 |
| 180 | −0.0263 | −0.0211 | .0765 | .1015 | .0462 | .0094 | − .0160 |
| 200 | −0.0315 | −0.0284 | .0087 | .0891 | .0419 | .0070 | − .0171 |

The normal cooling experienced by a portion of gas due to internal work done in expanding against internal attractive forces plus that due to the external work represented by $p_2 V_2$ is here exceeded by the external work represented by $p_1 V_1$ which is done on it.

Cooling effects connected with porous-plug expansions are important in commercial liquefaction plants. In one process, it is the main factor; in another process, it is a secondary factor, work done in operating machinery being a first consideration.

## THERMAL CONDUCTION IN GASES

**15. Kundt and Warburg Differential, Cooling Thermometer Method.** The chief difficulty attending a determination of the thermal conductivity, $k$, for a gas is the elimination of simultaneous heat transfers due to convection and to radiation. These effects seem first to have been taken into account in Germany in 1875 by

August Kundt (1838–1894) and E. Warburg (1846–1931). The gas under test was enclosed in a spherical bulb which was tightly stoppered. A mercury-in-glass thermometer with its stem passing through the stopper and with its bulb at the center of the spherical bulb was included. The gas-filled bulb was first heated to some convenient high temperature, such as 100°C, and then quickly placed in a bath of ice water. From the rate of lowering of the temperature and a knowledge of the thermal capacitance of the thermometer and of the gas in the large bulb, therma leakage rates could be determined. Normally these rates included all three of the known methods of heat transfer, namely convection, conduction, and radiation.

With regard to thermal leakages in gases, kinetic theory indicates, other things unchanged: (1) that leakage by convection, once it becomes appreciable, increases with increase of pressure; (2) that leakage by conduction, once the mean free path of the molecules has become small compared with the smallest dimensions of the container, does not change with change of pressure; (3) that leakage by conduction in the range of pressure where the mean free path is comparable with or greater than the smallest dimensions of the container, decreases with decrease of pressure; and (4) that leakage by radiation is wholly independent of pressure, being present alway to the fullest extent.

In agreement with the predictions just noted, Kundt and Warburg found for their apparatus increased leakage rates characteristic of convection above pressures of 150 mm-Hg, constant leakage rates between that pressure and a low pressure of about 1 mm-Hg, and decreasing leakage rates for still lower pressures. Between the two specified pressures it was assumed that leakage was due to conduction and radiation only. Experimentally, the leakage due to radiation only was obtained by noting leakage rates when the space was completely evacuated. These rates subtracted from the appropriate combined conduction and radiation leakage rate, yielded the necessary data. Application finally of thermal conduction theory similar to that underlying W. Nusselt's (1882–  ) spherical-shell method for poorly conducting solids as described in Chapter VII but taking account of the fact that the temperature of the source within the shell was constantly changing, yielded the desired results. Though correct in principle, this method is not as satisfactory as other methods to be described and is now chiefly of historical interest.

### 16. Hercus and Laby Parallel-Plate Method.

This method, employed originally in Australia in 1919 by E. O. Hercus (1891–  ) and T. H. Laby (1880–  ) is essentially M. Jakob's single-disk method for poorly conducting solids (Chapter VII) adapted for gases. The advantage of the method is that, since there is no horizontal temperature gradient in the gas being investigated, there are no convection currents and hence no convection losses. The radiation correction is minimized by silvering the lower surface of the central disk and the upper surface of the lower disk. The actual radiation correction may be made (1) by calculation, (2) by repeating the experiment with the apparatus evacuated as in the method of Kundt and Warburg, or (3) by repeating the experiment as closely as possible under the same temperature conditions, but with a different plate separation. Using the last procedure, and representing the power input to the central plate by $IV$, one has

$$(IV)_1 = \frac{kA\,\Delta T}{l_1} + \sigma A\,\Delta T \tag{32}$$

and

$$(IV)_2 = \frac{kA\,\Delta T}{l_2} + \sigma A\,\Delta T \tag{33}$$

where $A$ is the effective area of the central plate, $\Delta T$ the temperature difference between the plates, $l$ the plate separation, and $\sigma$ a leakage

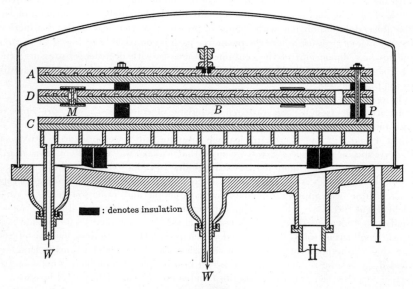

FIG. 15. Apparatus used by Hercus and Sutherland in a study of the thermal conductivity of air by the Hercus and Laby parallel-plate method. $A$, $B$, and $C$ are the copper plates. $D$ is a guard ring. $M$ is one of three buttons separating $B$ from $D$. $W$, $W$ are a water inlet and a water outlet. II is an outlet to a vacuum pump. I is one of 24 tubes through which thermocouple and heater wires were led into the apparatus. $A$, $B$, and $D$ were kept at the same temperature. (*Proc. Roy. Soc. London*, A145, 601, 1934.)

constant pertaining to radiation. The last term in each equation represents the common radiation loss. Elimination leads to

$$k = \frac{(IV)_1 - (IV)_2}{A\,\Delta T(1/l_1 - 1/l_2)} \tag{34}$$

All quantities on the right-hand side are readily measured. The method seems to be rather free from errors and should yield accurate

results.    Using this method with air at 0°C (Fig. 15), Hercus and
Sutherland obtained $k = 5.72 \times 10^{-5}$ cal/(cm$^2$ sec C°/cm).

**17. Schleiermacher's Hot-Wire Method.**    This method, which involves the leakage of energy from an electrically heated wire mounted
on the axis of a uniform long, straight tube to the walls of the tube,
seems to have been developed in Germany in 1888 by A. A. Schleiermacher (1857–    ).    It is similar in principle to the method of Kundt
and Warburg.    The hot wire, which replaced the thermometer of their
method, was operated to yield a steady state and permitted careful
direct measurements of leakage rates.    In this respect it was a great
improvement over the method of Kundt and Warburg.

A difficulty with Schleiermacher's procedure is its failure to account
properly for the cooled end portions of the hot wire.    How this may
be done satisfactorily was first shown by H. L. Callendar (1863–1930)
in England in 1897–1898 in the elimination of the end effects of the
lead-in wires of platinum resistance thermometers (Chapter II).    By
using two wires differing only in length end to end in the same tube
or in similar connecting tubes differing only in length, and taking differences, it is possible to obtain thermal leakage data for a portion of
wire whose temperature is uniform throughout.    This differential
principle has already been noted in connection with linear expansivity
and specific-heat measurements in which two wires or rods differing
only in length were used.

Given data involving thermal leakage by conduction only from a
wire of uniform temperature, values for thermal conductivity may be
obtained by employing Eq. 29 of Chapter VII which was derived for
thermal conduction in poorly conducting solids and liquids, namely,

$$k = \frac{dQ/dt}{2\pi l \, \Delta T} \ln \frac{r_2}{r_1} \tag{35}$$

Here $l$ represents the difference-length which is of uniform temperature, $\Delta T$ its temperature excess over that of the tube wall, and $r_1$ and
$r_2$ the radii of the wire and tube wall.    The wires in all tubes must be
of the same material and the same diameter.

The hot-wire method has been considerably used in determining
thermal conductivities of gases.    Here we may mention the work of
H. Gregory and T. Archer who, working in the laboratory of Professor H. L. Callendar (1863–1930) in England, reported an important
study of air and of hydrogen in 1925.    Their apparatus is shown in
Fig. 16.    As indicated in the inset at the lower right, two pairs of tubes
differing in radii (0.4592 cm and 1.714 cm) were used.    Those in each

pair differed only in length in accord with the difference principle. The wires in all tubes were of the same material and the same radius (0.007696 cm).   Their results are shown in part in Fig. 17, which contains, for air as the gas studied, an interesting proof of the three states

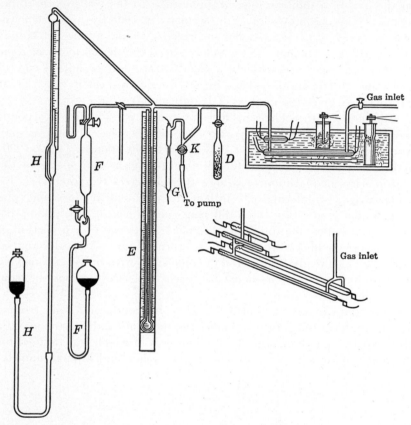

FIG. 16.   Diagram of apparatus used by Gregory and Archer in a study of thermal conductivities of air and hydrogen at temperatures near 0°C (*Proc. Roy. Soc. London,* **A110,** 108, 1926).

of leakage mentioned in connection with Kundt and Warburg's method, namely (1) one in which convection is present, (2) another in which convection is absent but conduction is constant with changing pressure, and (3) a third in which conduction decreases with pressure.   As a function of gas pressure, there is shown an *equivalent* thermal conductivity, a *computed* conductivity which assumed that the thermal leakage was due to thermal conduction only.   One sees from the figure that, for pressures ranging from about 7 cm-Hg to 15 cm-Hg, the equivalent conductivities are equal for the two pairs of tubes and do not vary with pressure. Obviously, for this pressure range, in accord with theory, thermal leakage for each of the two pairs of tubes is dependent only on radiation and conduction. Fig. 17 also shows that, for the pair of tubes of small diameter, convection played only an insignificant part for all pressures up to atmospheric pressure. The

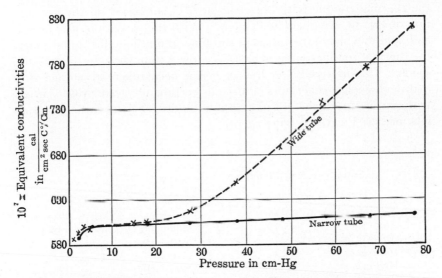

FIG. 17. Graph showing computed equivalent thermal conductivities for air at about 12°C, according to Gregory and Archer, using difference data obtained with wire of 0.007696-cm radius in two pairs of tubes having radii of 0.4592 cm and 1.1714 cm, on the assumption that the observed thermal leakage from the wire was entirely due to thermal conduction (*Proc. Roy. Soc. London*, **A110**, 113, 1926).

figure also shows the tendency, with decrease in pressure below 7 cm-Hg, toward a leakage at zero pressure which depended on radiation only, values for which were obtained by operation of the tubes with the gas removed to the greatest extent possible. Subtraction of these latter rates from the combined conduction and radiation leakages yielded the data to which Eq. 35 was applied.

In a particular test, using the apparatus described, Gregory and Archer, with a temperature of 14.862°C for the wire, a temperature of 0.017°C for the inside of the small tube wall, and a pressure of 15.67 cm-Hg, found 0.0013629 cal/(cm sec) for $1/l\ dQ/dt$ and 0.0000598 cal/ (cm² sec C°/cm) for $k$. For the same condition using the large tube, the value found for $k$ was smaller by only 1 part in 600. They found great consistency in their results throughout.  On the basis that the variation of $k$ with temperature is given by

$$k = k_0(1 + \epsilon \, \Delta T) \qquad (36)$$

values for $k$ at 0°C, $k_0$, were computed.

**18. Some Values of $k$ for Gases.**  Certain experimental values for the thermal conductivities of gases at 0°C, all based on the assumption of Eq. 36, are given in Table V.  With the exception of hydrogen and helium which have values in the general non-metallic liquid range, the thermal conductivities of gases are lower than those for liquids and solids.  The high value for hydrogen has been taken advantage of in hydrogen-cooled generators.  Also, in certain ultracentrifuges, where temperature gradients are undesirable, hydrogen jets, rather than air jets, are used as the driving agent.

TABLE V

SOME THERMAL CONDUCTIVITIES, $k$, FOR GASES AT 0°C

| Gas | $k$ in cal/(cm² sec C°/cm) | Author | Date |
|---|---|---|---|
| Air | $5.83 \times 10^{-5}$ | Gregory and Archer | 1925 |
| Air | 5.78 | Mann and Dickens | 1932 |
| Air | 5.77 | Nothdurft | 1936 |
| Hydrogen | 40.4 | Gregory and Archer | 1925 |
| Hydrogen | 42.45 | Nothdurft | 1936 |
| Oxygen | 5.88 | Nothdurft | 1936 |
| Methane ($CH_4$) | 7.21 | Mann and Dickens | 1932 |
| Ethane ($C_2H_6$) | 4.36 | Mann and Dickens | 1932 |
| Propane ($C_3H_8$) | 3.60 | Mann and Dickens | 1932 |

## SPECIFIC HEATS OF GASES—THEORY

**19. Simple Kinetic Theory.**  It was shown in Chapter VI that the specific heat of a substance at constant volume $c_v$, is given by

$$c_v = \frac{1}{m}\left(\frac{dU}{dT}\right)_v = \left(\frac{du}{dT}\right)_v \qquad (37)$$

To apply this to gases, one needs to know how the specific internal energy, $u$, varies with temperature for the condition of constant volume.  Here we present the classical theory.  Its predictions are generally fulfilled by most gases at ordinary temperatures.  Later, certain modifications resulting from quantum considerations will be introduced.

For the ideal monatomic gas composed of billiard-ball molecules, we may use Eq. 9, namely,

$$E = \tfrac{3}{2}kT \tag{37a}$$

where $E$ is the mean kinetic energy of a single molecule.  Provided we neglect submolecular energies, it is related to $u$, the internal energy density, or, as it is more frequently called, the molar internal energy density, as follows:

$$u = EN_0 = \tfrac{3}{2}kN_0T = \tfrac{3}{2}RT \tag{38}$$

where $N_0$ is the Avogadro number.  This gives, for the molar specific heat of an ideal monatomic gas at constant volume,

$$c_v = \left(\frac{du}{dT}\right)_v = \frac{3}{2}R \tag{39}$$

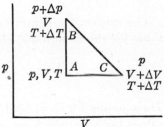

FIG. 18.  Illustrating a relation existing between the specific heats of a gas at constant pressure and at constant volume.

We may now derive a corresponding expression for $c_p$, the specific heat for the condition of no change in pressure. Consider Fig. 18, the origin for which is to be thought of as far to the left and far below the apparent origin of the figure. Let $A$ represent an initial state of the gas characterized by $p$, $V$, $T$.  Let $B$ and $C$ represent two slightly changed states produced by the addition of heat in one case at constant volume, in the other at constant pressure.  The temperature changes are to be the same.  The amount of heat added for the change $AB$ is obviously

$$Q_{AB} = c_v m\, \Delta T \tag{39a}$$

Similarly the heat that must be added for the change $AC$ is

$$Q_{AC} = c_p m\, \Delta T \tag{39b}$$

This latter change, however, may be brought about in another way, namely, by changes along the path $ABC$, and we have

$$Q_{ABC} = Q_{AB} + Q_{BC} \tag{39c}$$

of which $Q_{BC}$, since no change of temperature is involved, must be equivalent to the work performed with the passage of the gas state along the line $BC$.  As a first approximation, this is equal to $p\,\Delta V$, the variation from it being represented in the figure by the area of the triangle $ABC$.  As sufficiently small values for $\Delta T$ are assumed, this variation becomes ignorable, and, in the limit, it may be ignored without error. Replacing in the limit $Q_{ABC}$ by $Q_{AC}$ and $Q_{AB}$ and $Q_{BC}$ by their equals, we obtain,

$$[c_p m \, \Delta T = c_v m \, \Delta T + p \, \Delta V]_p \tag{40}$$

However, for the ideal gas at constant pressure, as follows from Eq. 1,

$$[p \, \Delta V = m R \, \Delta T]_p \tag{41}$$

and we have

$$c_p = c_v + R \tag{42}$$

With $c_v$ for the *monatomic* ideal gas equal to $\frac{3}{2}R$, we have for the corresponding $c_p$

$$c_p = \tfrac{5}{2}R \tag{43}$$

The ratio $c_p/c_v$, denoted by $\gamma$, is of much interest. Its theoretical value for the monatomic ideal gas as obtained from Eqs. 39 and 43 is

$$\gamma = \frac{c_p}{c_v} = \frac{\frac{5}{2}R}{\frac{3}{2}R} = \frac{5}{3} = 1.67 \tag{44}$$

These values for $c_p$, $c_v$, and $\gamma$ agree very closely with the experimental values for gases which are monatomic.

**20. Degrees of Freedom.** In dealing with gases whose molecules are more complex than those assumed in the previous discussion, the concept of a *degree of freedom* is useful. A molecule is said to have a number of degrees of freedom equal to the number of its *independent* methods of exchanging energy. Thus, if the spherical molecules of simple kinetic theory be assumed "frictionless" so that no energy of rotation can be transferred during impacts between them, it is clear that there remain but three *independent* modes of motion capable of entering into energy exchanges. They may be popularly described as translations up and down, side to side, and front to back. They constitute the three translational degrees of freedom which such billiard-ball molecules may possess. A diatomic molecule, however, imagined to be constructed of two ball masses connected by a rigid bond, dumb-bell fashion, has two rotational degrees of freedom in addition to three of translation, a total of five. Although energy exchanges, accompanied by changed rotational speeds about the long axis of such molecules, seem impossible as a result of molecular impacts, independent rotations about any two axes perpendicular to this can occur. There is still another method of transfer of energy which may be realized, particularly at high temperatures. The two atoms of the diatomic molecule may be set into vibration along the long axis, and an additional vibrational degree of freedom is thereby introduced. Similarly a triatomic molecule, imagined with atoms at the corners of a triangle, may have three translational, three rotational, and as many as three vibrational degrees of freedom. There is also the possibility, in any type of molecule, of energy being transferred by virtue of intra-atomic motions, thus introducing additional degrees of freedom. In the previous development, the relation $u = \frac{3}{2}RT$ would seem to be valid for a gas whose molecules possess three degrees of freedom only, and such seems to be the case.

The principle of the *equipartition of energy* was first advanced by James Clerk Maxwell, of whom we have spoken, and later extended by Ludwig Boltzmann. It assumes that the translational and the rotational degrees of freedom have associated with them the same average amount of energy per molecule. If this holds, it is clear that this energy per molecule and degree of freedom is $\frac{1}{3} \times \frac{3}{2}kT$ or $\frac{1}{2}kT$. For $d$ such degrees of freedom, $(d/2)RT$ should replace $\frac{3}{2}RT$ in the above development. Following through, one sees that

$$c_v = \frac{d}{2} R \qquad (45)$$

$$c_p = \left(\frac{d}{2} + 1\right) R \qquad (46)$$

$$\gamma = 1 + \frac{2}{d} \qquad (47)$$

How well the simple theory taking into account translational and rotational degrees of freedom only succeeds is shown in Table VI. For

TABLE VI

MOLECULAR HEATS OF GASES AT 15°C AND ATMOSPHERIC PRESSURE

Taken in large part from *An Outline of Atomic Physics*, by the Physics Staff of the University of Pittsburgh, 2nd ed., p. 15, New York, John Wiley & Sons, 1937.

| Character of Molecule | Molecule | $c_v$ in cal/ mol °C | Degrees of Freedom | Ratio of Molecular Heats, $c_p/c_v$ | |
|---|---|---|---|---|---|
| | | | | Observed | Expected |
| Monatomic | Helium | 2.98 | 3 | 1.66 | 1.667 |
| Monatomic | Argon | 3.01 | 3 | 1.67 | 1.667 |
| Monatomic | Mercury vapor | 2.98 | 3 | 1.67 | 1.667 |
| Diatomic | Hydrogen | 4.83 | 5 | 1.410 | 1.400 |
| Diatomic | Nitrogen | 4.94 | 5 | 1.404 | 1.400 |
| Diatomic | Oxygen | 4.97 | 5 | 1.401 | 1.400 |
| Diatomic | Hydrochloric acid | 4.99 | 5 | 1.41 | 1.400 |
| Diatomic | Carbon monoxide | 4.94 | 5 | 1.404 | 1.400 |
| Triatomic | Carbon dioxide | 6.71 | .. | 1.304 | 1.333 |
| Polyatomic | Ethyl ether (35°C) | 25.7 | .. | 1.08 | 1.333 |

all monatomic gases and many diatomic gases at room temperatures, the agreement is excellent. However, the agreement is not good for certain diatomic or for most, if not all, more complicated molecules. Without doubt, vibrational degrees of freedom explain the discrepancies.

Although the specific-heat predictions of classical theory are generally verified at ordinary temperatures, decided variations were found when tests were made at appreciably higher and lower temperatures. This was particularly so at the lower temperatures. Once found, these differences led to tests based on quantum considerations, and a shift from the accepted, classical, Maxwellian distribution for molecular velocities to the Bose-Einstein distribution of quantum mechanics, followed. So doing has led to new conceptions and new experiments, with results which have been generally in accord with the revised theory. Of these results only a few will be considered here in connection with a discussion of the specific heat of hydrogen. For further interesting discoveries and discussions, more advanced treatises must be consulted.

**21. Specific Heat of Hydrogen.** The specific heat of hydrogen has been studied particularly in Germany by the physicist A. Eucken (1884– ) and others. Some of their results for hydrogen in the state that it is found at ordinary temperatures are shown in Fig. 19. At least three stages may be differentiated, all of which are strictly in accord with quantum theory. Below about 60°K, the molecular heat of hydrogen, though diatomic, was found to be $\frac{3}{2}R$, a value which is classically associated with a monatomic gas. Between 60°K and room temperatures, the molecular heat increases gradually to the expected $\frac{5}{2}R$. Two new degrees of freedom are involved, those connected with rotations about two axes which are not only perpendicular to each other but also to a possible axis joining the centers of the two atoms. Energy exchanges connected with the degree of freedom associated with this last-mentioned axis cannot be realized to any observable extent at temperatures at which diatomic molecules can exist. At temperatures in excess of room temperature, Fig. 19 shows, as the third stage, a very slow gradual increase in the value of $c_v$ for hydrogen. A new degree of freedom is apparently being introduced, that connected with longitudinal vibratory motion of the two atoms with respect to each other.

The apparently anomalous behavior at low temperatures is explainable on the basis of quantum mechanics. It may be stated here, without demonstration, that, on the basis of this theory, the molecules are able to rotate only with certain angular velocities, or what is the same only with certain rotational energies, which are determined by quantum considerations. Since the first possible energy value is rather large compared with the average translational energy of the molecule at low temperatures, it follows that, in this region, only very rarely will molecules in collision possess the translational energy needed to increase the rotational energy of one of the colliding molecules, that the rotational degrees of freedom function but slightly in the energy interchanges, and that the gas behaves at the reduced temperatures like a monatomic gas. As the temperature is raised, more and more molecules attain translational energies large enough to enable them to excite rotational-energy changes at impact and the value of $c_v$ gradually rises to its classical value at room temperatures, after which the rotational degrees of freedom function in accord with classical theory. As indicated in Fig. 19 there are two types of hydrogen molecules, ortho and para. For one of these the specific heat in the region of transition attains a value greater than $\frac{5}{2}R$. For a discussion of these and related features, the reader is referred to other sources.

The decrease in molecular heat at low temperatures has not been observed in gases other than hydrogen. Compared with hydrogen, the lowest occurring values

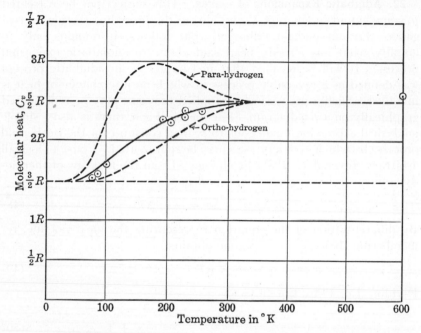

FIG. 19. The specific heats of hydrogen. Curve is based on quantum mechanics. The observed values were obtained by A. Eucken and his co-workers. (By permission, Physics Staff of the University of Pittsburgh, *An Outline of Atomic Physics*, 2nd ed., p. 210, New York, John Wiley & Sons, 1937.)

for rotational energy for other gases are much smaller in comparison to the translational energies, and for them the deviations from the classical value for $c_v$ are expected to occur only at much lower temperatures. Unfortunately, these temperatures are so low that the desired $c_v$ measurements have not yet been made with any degree of precision.

The increase of $c_v$ above $\frac{5}{2}R$, shown in Fig. 19, is ascribed to a sixth degree of freedom, that associated with the vibration of the two atoms of a hydrogen molecule back and forth along the line joining their centers. As for the two rotations responsible for the change between 60°K and room temperature, this degree of freedom is realized only gradually with increase in temperature. Its total contribution to the molecular heat, could the hydrogen molecule maintain its diatomic character at the necessary elevated temperatures, would be found, as indicated above, to be twice the $R/2$ contribution of the ordinary degree of freedom. The realization of the expected $c_v$ of $\frac{1}{2}R$ is prevented by the dissociation which occurs and results in the formation of monatomic molecules for which the classical value of $\frac{3}{2}R$ is expected.

Though not yet definitely verified experimentally, still another stage is probable for the curve of Fig. 19. This stage would cover a range extending from somewhere below the lowest temperature for which a $c_v$ is graphed to the absolute zero, where a value other than $\frac{3}{2}R$ is to be expected.

**22. Adiabatic Expansions of Gases.** This subject has been treated to some extent in Chapter V and also in the preceding section on real gases. For an understanding of what follows, it remains only to amplify what has already been said about the adiabatic expansion process. It will be recalled that in Chapter V an adiabatic process was defined as a reversible process in which no interchange of heat is involved. Such a process, when applied to a gas, may be represented graphically on a $p$-$v$ diagram. For the ideal gas, there is also a simple analytical expression (analogous to $pv$ = a constant for the isothermal process) by which such a process may be represented. Consider a small arbitrary, reversible, adiabatic change. From the first law of thermodynamics, we have, since $Q = 0$ and in view of Eq. 37,

$$p \, \Delta v = -\Delta u = -c_v \, \Delta T \tag{48}$$

By differentiation of the equation representing the ideal-gas law, remembering that $c_p - c_v = R$, one obtains

$$p \, \Delta v + v \, \Delta p = R \, \Delta T = (c_p - c_v) \, \Delta T \tag{49}$$

Dividing Eq. 49 by Eq. 48 yields

$$1 + \frac{v \, \Delta p}{p \, \Delta v} = -\frac{c_p - c_v}{c_v} = -\gamma + 1 \tag{50}$$

from which, on separating variables, one obtains

$$\frac{\Delta p}{p} = -\gamma \frac{\Delta v}{v} \tag{51}$$

If $\gamma$ is a constant, which is true for the ideal gas, one obtains, upon integration,

$$pv^\gamma = \text{constant} \tag{52}$$

the equation for the adiabatic of an ideal gas. Making use of the ideal gas law this may also be put in the equivalent forms

$$Tv^{\gamma-1} = \text{constant} \tag{53}$$

and

$$p^{1-\gamma} T^\gamma = \text{constant} \tag{54}$$

On the $p$-$v$ plot of Fig. 20, several adiabatics and several intersecting isothermals are shown drawn to scale for a diatomic, ideal gas. At points of intersection for the two sets of curves, the ratio of slopes $(dp/dv)_a/(dp/dv)_T$ is 1.40.

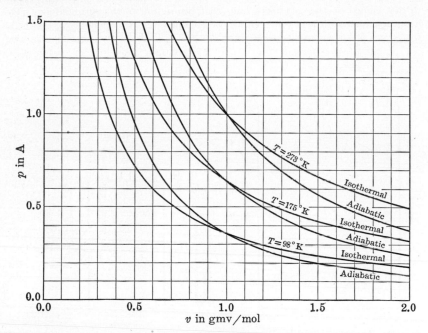

FIG. 20. A $p$-$v$ graph showing several adiabatics and interesting isothermals for an ideal gas whose $\gamma$ is 1.40.

## SPECIFIC HEATS OF GASES—EXPERIMENTAL METHODS

A knowledge of the temperature variations of $c_p$, $c_v$, and $\gamma$ for gases is of great importance both industrially and in checking certain aspects of the kinetic theory of gases. Unfortunately, all but a few of the methods for solids and liquids must be discarded because the thermal capacitance of the apparatus in any one instance is so large in comparison to that of any feasible amount of gas which may be employed. Only the Joly differential steam-calorimeter method, the vacuum-calorimeter method, the continuous-flow method, and the method of mixtures may be employed, all somewhat modified.

**23. Regnault's Mixture Method for Determining $c_p$.** This method was developed in France by Henri Regnault (1810–1878). Gas at high pressure (Fig. 21) is released from tank $A$ by means of valve $V$. It then flows through the coils in $H$, a heated oil bath, and enters the calorimeter $C$ at the temperature $T$ of the oil bath. The heated gas, in escaping to the atmosphere by a devious path through the calorimeter, raises the temperature of the calorimeter. To insure a constant rate of flow, the manometer reading $D$ is kept constant by adjusting valve $V$. Clearly, if the initial and final temperatures of the calorimeter be noted over any convenient time interval, we may equate the heat lost by the gas in falling from $T$ to the mean calorimeter temperature to that gained by the calorimeter plus that transferred to the surroundings. The heat capacitance of the calorimeter may be obtained by calculation or by experiment with a gas of known specific heat. The net heat transfer to the surroundings, that

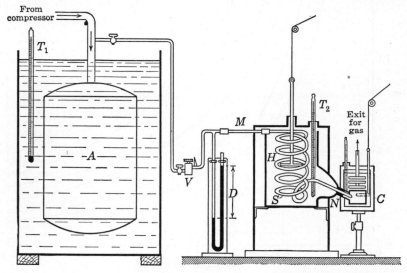

FIG. 21. Apparatus used by Regnault to determine $c_p$ for several gases (by permission, J. K. Roberts, *Heat and Thermodynamics*, p. 130, London, Blackie and Son, 1940).

is its leakage loss, may be determined directly by experiment with no gas flowing through the calorimeter. The mass $\Delta m$ of the gas employed is obtained from measurements of the temperature $T$, the initial pressure $p_1$, and final pressure $p_2$ of the gas in $A$. Given the volume of $A$ and assuming that the ideal gas law holds, we have

$$p_1 V = (m + \Delta m)RT \tag{55}$$

$$p_2 V = mRT \tag{56}$$

and on subtraction

$$\Delta m = \frac{V(p_1 - p_2)}{RT} \tag{57}$$

By increasing the duration of the experiment, $\Delta m$ and thus the heat transferred by the gas may be made relatively large.

A modification of this method by Holborn and Henning in Germany permits its use up to 1400°C.

**24. Callendar's Constant-Flow Method for Measuring $c_p$.** This method is feasible because, as was indicated in Chapter VI, no correction for the heat capacitance of the apparatus is required. An adaptation of the constant-flow method of Callendar and Barnes used in a determination of $J$ (Chapter IV), it seems to have been first employed in the study of gases in 1909 in England in a study of carbon dioxide by W. F. G. Swann (1884–   ), now of the Bartol Research Foundation, Swarthmore, Pa. The most accurate work by this method, however, seems to have been carried out by K. Scheel (1866–   ) and W. Heuse (1878–   ) in Germany. In the apparatus used by them (Fig. 22), the gas at the desired temperature enters the calorimeter at the bottom, flowing past a platinum resistance thermometer $P_1$. It is then conducted through a spiral and a series of shielded passages, as indicated by the arrows, past heater unit $H$ and resistance thermometer $P_2$, which registers its outgoing temperature. The purpose of the shields is to insure that, as far as possible, any heat from heater $H$ which would normally be lost to the surroundings is actually transferred to the gas. The path between heater $H$ and thermometer $P_2$ was packed with fine copper gauze to insure that all sections of the gas stream were at the same temperature. By enclosing the entire apparatus in a

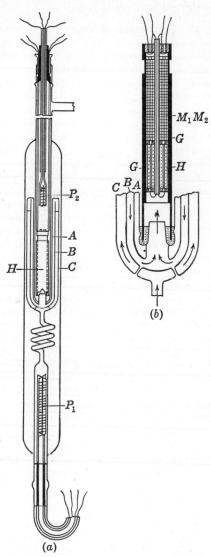

Fig. 22. Apparatus used by Sheel and Heuse to determine $c_p$ by a constant-flow method (*Ann. Physik*, **37**, 79, 1912).

vacuum-tight envelope, heat loss to the surroundings was minimized. The whole apparatus may be immersed in a constant-temperature bath.

**25. Joly's Differential Steam-Calorimeter Method for Measuring $c_v$.** This method was described in Chapter VI. No change of procedure whatever is required.

**26. Spectroscopic Method for Determining $c_v$.** When the spectrum of a diatomic or other polyatomic gas is studied it is found to consist of a great number of lines grouped together into "bands." The molecules in such a gas possess energy which may be stored in translational motion of the molecule as a whole, rotational motion of the molecule as a whole, vibratory motions of parts of a molecule with respect to the remaining parts, and motions of the external electrons associated with their atoms. According to the quantum theory, with each of these modes of storing energy there is associated a discrete set of possible energy values or levels. Those for translation are so close together that the distribution of possible energies is practically continuous, save at the very lowest temperatures, $T \ll 1°K$. This is not true, however, of the levels associated with rotation, vibration, and electronic configuration.

Each line in a molecular spectrum corresponds to a transition of molecules from one definite set of energy conditions as to rotation, vibration, and electronic motion to another. In the study of the "band spectrum" of a particular molecule, one may use the Einstein or the Debye expressions (Chapter VI, Eqs. 8 and 9) to compute, as a function of the temperature, that part of the total specific heat associated with vibrations of the particular frequency considered. A similar but more involved treatment allows one to compute the specific-heat contribution associated with electronic motions. For the rotational and translational contributions, one usually accepts the classical values of $n/2\,R$ and $\frac{3}{2}R$, respectively, where $n$ is the number of rotational degrees of freedom. By adding all these contributions, the total specific heat is obtained. This method is so sound theoretically, and its predictions are in such good accord with the best experimental results, that it has become a commonly accepted method for determining $c_v$ at high temperatures.

In Table VII the results of G. G. Sherratt and Ezer Griffiths (1888– ) for carbon dioxide, discussed in a following section, are compared with the spectroscopic values. The spectroscopic values, computed, as described above, using $2.019 \times 10^{13}$, $6.885 \times 10^{13}$, and $3.840 \times 10^{13}$ vib/sec for the three vibrational frequencies, do not include any electronic contributions. The deviations noticed may be due in part to these neglected contributions.

TABLE VII

COMPARISON OF VALUES OF $c_v$ FOR CARBON DIOXIDE BY THE SPEED OF SOUND AND THE SPECTROSCOPIC METHODS. VALUES CORRECTED TO 1 A PRESSURE

(*Proc. Roy. Soc. London*, **A147**, 294, 1934)

| Temperature °C | $c_v$ (Speed-of-Sound Method) cal/(mol K°) | $c_v$ (Spectroscopic Method) cal/(mol K°) |
|---|---|---|
| 0 | 6.62 | 6.67 |
| 200 | 8.65 | 8.49 |
| 400 | 10.06 | 9.80 |
| 600 | 10.81 | 10.64 |
| 800 | 11.30 | 11.21 |
| 1000 | 11.76 | 11.61 |

## MEASUREMENT OF γ—EXPERIMENTAL METHODS

**27. Clément and Desormes' Adiabatic Expansion Method.** The earliest determination of the ratio of the two specific heats of a gas was that made by the French physicists Clément (1779–1841) and C. B. Desormes (1777–1862) in 1819. The gas is initially in a large vessel which is provided with a manometer and a large stopcock or other easy means for producing a large opening to the outside which may be opened or closed quickly. Starting with an equilibrium condition in the vessel, with a pressure $p$, somewhat in excess of atmospheric pressure $p_0$, the vessel is opened to the atmosphere and then closed after a second or two. If all is well, the pressure in the vessel is then $p_0$ but the temperature is lower than that of the surroundings. Following this the vessel is allowed to come into equilibrium with its surroundings. The pressure within rises in the process to $p_2$. From these three pressures, the ratio of the two specific heats, $\gamma$, may be computed by

$$\gamma = \frac{\log p_1 - \log p_0}{\log p_1 - \log p_2} \tag{58}$$

Though the method is very simple, difficulty is often experienced because of oscillations occurring with the opening of the stopcock and a consequent pressure inside the vessel on closure which differs from $p_0$.

**28. Lummer and Pringsheim's Adiabatic Expansion Method.** This method was proposed by the German physicists O. Lummer (1860–1925) and E. Pringsheim (1859–1917) in 1894. Suppose, as for the Clément and Desormes method, a thermally insulated vessel containing gas at some pressure $p$ to be opened suddenly to the atmosphere so that the pressure falls to $p_0$. There will be a drop in temperature of the gas from $T_1$ to $T_2$. Since this process is closely adiabatic, we may, assuming the gas to be ideal, apply Eq. 54 in the form

$$p^{1-\gamma} T_1{}^{\gamma} = p_0{}^{1-\gamma} T_2{}^{\gamma} \tag{59}$$

Solving for $\gamma$, we obtain

$$\gamma = \frac{\log (p/p_0)}{\log (p/p_0) - \log (T_1/T_2)} \tag{60}$$

Experiments using this relation were reported in England in 1920–1921 by J. R. Partington (1886–    ). The gas studied was enclosed in a spherical, 120-l copper vessel immersed in a water bath. Pressures were measured by means of a paraffin oil manometer. Temperatures were obtained from the resistances of a single loop of a very fine wire which was suspended near the center of the sphere and formed one arm of a Wheatstone bridge. The instrument used to detect the balance point of the bridge was a sensitive string galvanometer of period 0.01 sec so that fairly rapid resistance and hence temperature changes could be followed. The initial temperature of the gas was assumed to be that of the bath and was read with a mercury thermometer. The final temperature of the gas was determined by adding ice to the bath until the resistance of the wire loop attained the same value noted in the experiment.  The bath temperature at this point was assumed to equal that of the gas after expansion.  Using this method Partington measured $\gamma$ for air, hydrogen, and carbon dioxide with good precision, considering the difficulties in making the temperature measurements and the numerous corrections involved.

**29. Ruckhardt's Vibrating-Ball Method.**  An ingenious method of not too great precision was described by E. Ruckhardt (1888– ) in 1929.  It employs the apparatus shown in Fig. 23.  It consists of a large gas-filled vessel of volume $V$ with

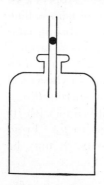

a tight-fitting cork containing a tube of uniform bore $s$.  Into this tube a close-fitting ball of mass $m$ is dropped and allowed to vibrate about its equilibrium position, its frequency of vibration $f$ being noted.  The compressions and expansions of the gas in the vessel produced by the ball vibrating in the tube are very closely adiabatic, and the variations in $p$ and $V$ that occur are subject to the condition expressed by Eq. 52.  As the ball moves from its position of equilibrium, a restoring force, $-s\,dp$, develops.  How it varies with the displacement, $dV/s$, may be determined by differentiating the governing relation (Eq. 52).  Thus

$$\frac{-s\,dp}{dV/s} = s^2\gamma\,\frac{p_0}{V_0} \tag{61}$$

FIG. 23.  Ruckhardt's apparatus for measuring $\gamma$.

of which $p_0$ and $V_0$ represent values for the equilibrium position.  The ratio of the restoring force to the displacement is a constant, and the motion of the ball is therefore simple harmonic motion.  Substitution of this constant, normally called the force constant, $k$, in the well-known equation for the frequency, $f$, of a simple harmonic motion, yields

$$f = \frac{1}{2\pi}\sqrt{\frac{k}{M}} = \frac{1}{2\pi}\sqrt{\frac{s^2\gamma}{m}\frac{p_0}{V_0}} \tag{62}$$

and by rearrangement

$$\gamma = \frac{4\pi^2 f^2 m V_0}{s^2 p_0} \tag{63}$$

Since all quantities on the right are directly measurable, Eq. 63 serves as a means for determining $\gamma$.  Ruckhardt used this method with success in studying air and carbon dioxide.  A difficulty arises in the obtaining of a ball-tube combination that is satisfactory.

As a possible experimental arrangement, consider a 3-mm steel bearing-ball vibrating in a close-fitting tubing leading to a liter flask filled with air at atmospheric pressure.  Using 7.85 gm/cm³ as the density of steel and 1.400 as the value of $\gamma$, one obtains with the aid of Eq. 63 a convenient frequency of 1.265 vib/sec.  An electric current through a solenoid surrounding the tube may be used for control purposes.

**30. Maneuvrier's Null Compression Method.**  This method developed in France by Georges Maneuvrier (1849– ) is similar to the adiabatic expansion method described above save that in this method no determination of temperature changes is required.  Consider the

$p$-$v$ diagram of Fig. 24, in which four separate states of a mass $m$ of gas are represented at the four points $O$, $A$, $B$, and $C$. Lines $OA$, $OB$, $OC$, and $AC$ represent respectively small constant pressure, isothermal, adiabatic, and constant-volume processes. If the changes in pressure, volume, and temperature are kept small with respect to their initial values, we may represent them with negligible error as short straight lines. Consider the cycle $OACO$. The heat given off during the process $OA$ is $mc_p \, \Delta_1 T$. For the process $AC$, heat is added to the extent of $mc_v(\Delta_1 T + \Delta_2 T)$. Since no heat is required for the adiabatic process $CO$, the net heat transfer per cycle, $Q$, is

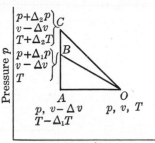

$$Q = -mc_p \, \Delta_1 T$$
$$+ \, mc_v(\Delta_1 T + \Delta_2 T) \quad (64)$$

Fig. 24. The theory of the null method of Maneuvrier.

The net work done per cycle is represented by the area of triangle $OAC$ and has the value $(m \, \Delta v \, \Delta_2 p)/2$. From the first law of thermodynamics, we may compute the net change in internal energy of the gas for the cycle as

$$\Delta U = -mc_p \, \Delta_1 T + mc_v(\Delta_1 T + \Delta_2 T) - \frac{m \, \Delta v \, \Delta_2 p}{2} \quad (65)$$

But, since the initial and final states of the gas are the same, we may equate $\Delta U$ to zero. Further, if the changes $\Delta v$ and $\Delta_2 p$ are sufficiently small in comparison with $v$ and $p$, we may neglect the work term of Eq. 65 as a higher-order infinitesimal, in comparison with the two preceding terms, leaving

$$mc_v(\Delta_1 T + \Delta_2 T) = mc_p \, \Delta_1 T \quad (66)$$

whence

$$\gamma = \frac{c_p}{c_v} = \frac{\Delta_1 T + \Delta_2 T}{\Delta_1 T} \quad (67)$$

If the gas may be considered ideal, we may, for the constant-volume processes $AC$ and $AB$, replace $\Delta_1 T$ and $\Delta_2 T$ by their equals as obtained from Eq. 1 for the condition of $v$ constant, namely, $v \, \Delta_1 p/R$ and $v(\Delta_2 p - \Delta_1 p)/R$. So doing, we obtain

$$\gamma = \frac{\Delta_2 p}{\Delta_1 p} \quad (68)$$

of which $\Delta_2 p$ and $\Delta_1 p$ are evidently the adiabatic and isothermal pressure changes corresponding to the volume change $-\Delta v$. If the last term in Eq. 65 be retained, we should obtain instead

$$\gamma = \frac{\Delta_2 p}{\Delta_1 p}\left(1 - \frac{R}{2c_v}\frac{\Delta_1 p}{p}\right) \tag{69}$$

of which the last term in the parentheses is a correction term and requires an approximate value of $c_v$ for its evaluation.

A laboratory form of apparatus minus certain details for use with Maneuvrier's method is shown in Fig. 25. It consists of a large vessel $A$ of known volume fitted

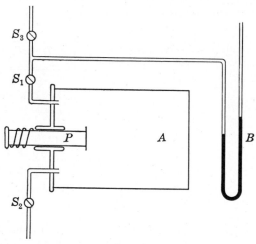

FIG. 25. Apparatus simplified for the measurement of $\gamma$ by the method of Maneuvrier. Not shown are a catch for retaining plunger $P$ in its innermost position and a device for a nearly instantaneous half turn of stopcock $S_1$ as soon as plunger $P$ reaches its innermost position.

with a gas-tight plunger $P$ so that the volume of the gas in $A$ may be changed by a measurable amount. A manometer for measuring gas pressures in excess of atmospheric is shown at $B$. Stopcock $S_3$ connects this manometer to a compressed-air line to allow various manometer settings to be made. Stopcock $S_1$ is so arranged that, when the plunger is operated, $S_1$ is opened briefly and the manometer is momentarily connected to vessel $A$.

A procedure for this method follows. (1) With $P$ in its outermost position, open $S_2$, thus connecting $A$ with the atmosphere. (2) Through stopcock $S_3$, force air into the space above the liquid in the left-hand column of the manometer until a pressure is obtained which is estimated to be equal to that which will occur later in $A$ when the plunger $P$ is thrust in. (3) Close valve $S_2$. (4) Thrust in the plunger as far as it is permitted to go. In this position it will be retained by a catch (not shown in the figure). Stopcock $S_1$ will then automatically and for a very brief time only connect $A$ with manometer $B$. Release the catch and withdraw the plunger at once.

(5) Note whether or not the manometer reading has changed. (6) Except possibly for step 2, repeat the foregoing processes until no change of manometer readings with repetition is observable. (7) Record the unchanging pressure difference indicated by the manometer as the adiabatic $\Delta_2 p$ of Eqs. 68 and 69. (8) Next, particularly if vessel $A$ is well jacketed, a similar but somewhat different total procedure is followed in order to determine the isothermal $\Delta_1 p$. The difference consists in letting the piston $P$ remain in the thrust-in position, opening valve $S_1$ by hand at one's leisure, keeping it open, and noting a possible change in manometer reading at equilibriums. The pressure difference, obtained after one or more trials, which is characterized by no change in pressure difference at equilibrium, is taken as the isothermal $\Delta_1 p$ of Eqs. 69 and 68. (9) Finally Eq. 68 or 69 is applied to determine $\gamma$. An alternative method of obtaining $\Delta_1 p$ consists in computing it on the basis of a known volume for $A$, a known change in volume accompanying the inthrust of the plunger $P$, and the atmospheric pressure. This method is a null or no-change method and shares in the general satisfactoriness of this feature. It has been used in the study of carbon dioxide under high pressures.

**31. Speed-of-Sound Method.** The basic equation for this method dates back to Sir Isaac Newton (1642–1727), one of the greatest of physicists of all time, who published in his *Principia* a theoretical equation for the velocity of sound, $S$, in any medium. His equation is

$$S = \sqrt{\frac{M}{\delta}} \qquad (70)$$

of which $M$ is the appropriate elastic modulus of the medium and $\delta$ its density. Applied to a gas, $M$ becomes a bulk modulus, and, if the isothermal modulus is chosen, it may be equated to the pressure. However, as applied to air by Newton, a velocity about 85% of the experimentally observed value was obtained. The failure to check was eventually explained a century later by the great French mathematician and astronomer Pierre Laplace (1749–1827). He showed that $M$ of Eq. 70 should be interpreted as the adiabatic bulk modulus. For a gas, Eq. 70 may accordingly be rewritten as

$$S = \sqrt{\frac{\gamma p}{\delta}} \qquad (71)$$

of which $\gamma$ is the ratio of the two specific heats that concerns us. For an ideal gas, Eq. 70 reduces to

$$S = \sqrt{\gamma R T} \qquad (72)$$

Applying Eq. 72 to a specific gas, one must introduce, as a conversion factor, the molecular weight of the gas, e.g., 32.00 gm/gm-mole for oxygen.

As a more fundamental relation, applicable to all gases, ideal and real, thermodynamic reasoning yields

$$S = v \sqrt{-\gamma \left(\frac{dp}{dv}\right)_T} \qquad (73)$$

That this reduces to Eq. 72 for the ideal gas is easily verified. Obviously Eqs. 72 and 73 may be used in reverse order for determining $\gamma$. Thus, from Eq. 73, we obtain

$$\gamma = -\frac{S^2}{v^2}\left(\frac{dv}{dp}\right)_T \qquad (74)$$

Among the methods of measuring the speed of sound in a gas which makes use of the above theory and which assumes a value for $\gamma$ is one described in 1865 by the German physicist August Kundt (1839–1894). He used a glass tube containing the gas under consideration and a small amount of cork dust. The tube ends were closed by movable stopper diaphragms. One diaphragm was adjustable by hand; the other was attached to the end of a metal rod which was clamped at its center and could be set in longitudinal vibration by stroking with a rosined cloth. Standing sound waves were produced in the gas, and the dust patterns produced at maximum resonance showed clearly the positions of nodes. With the wavelength thus determined and the pitch of the sound determined otherwise, the speed $S$ results. Using this procedure, Kundt and Warburg in 1876 reported 1.666 (1.675 as corrected) for the $\gamma$ of mercury vapor.

With the development of radio a great improvement of the method became possible. The diaphragm attached to one end of the rod to be stroked has been replaced by the diaphragm of a loud speaker. Simultaneously there has been a great improvement due to the replacing of the former intermittent sounds of short duration by a steady continuous sound of whatever frequency one may desire. Also the cork dust has been superseded by stethescope tubes.

Using the more refined apparatus, many workers have made determinations of $\gamma$ under various conditions. Among these we cite the work of the English physicists J. R. Partington and W. G. Shilling reported in 1923 in which values for $\gamma$ up to 1000°C were obtained. A somewhat more elegant method in so far as the measurements of frequency and the determination of a state of maximum resonance were concerned is that reported by the English physicists G. G. Sherratt and Ezer Griffiths in 1936. Their apparatus is shown in Fig. 26. The furnace tube $A$, and sound-generating chamber $B$, were combined into a continuous gas-tight unit. The sound was produced by causing a quartz crystal to vibrate by electrical means at its natural frequency. Any one of three such crystals could be brought at will under the furnace tube by means of a gas-tight cone joint. This

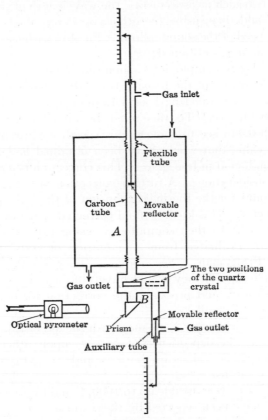

FIG. 26. Apparatus used by G. G. Sherratt and Ezer Griffiths in determining $\gamma$ by the speed of sound method, using high frequencies (*Proc. Roy. Soc. London*, **A147**, 294, 1934).

permitted, for any temperature, determinations of wavelength at three different frequencies. These frequencies, measured very accurately by electrical means, were about 7900, 14,000, and 19,000 vib/sec. With a crystal in position at the end of tube $A$ and emitting sound waves, the movable reflector was shifted along the tube to obtain two, or more, well-separated positions yielding resonance. These positions, characterized by separations of integral numbers of half wavelengths of the sound in the gas in the tube, were readily determinable from the increased rates of supply of energy electrically to the vibrating crystal which occurred at resonance. Further, the number of such maximum supply rates, encountered as the reflector was shifted from one position to another, gave the number of included half-wavelength intervals. From two such measurements, the wavelength of the sound may be obtained, and then, using the otherwise determined vibration frequency, the speed of the sound follows. Finally, with the aid of Eq. 72 or 74, the desired $\gamma$ is obtained.

In a particular run employing carbon dioxide with a 7911.2 vib/sec crystal at the bottom of the furnace tube, these workers obtained, at 200°C, an observed wavelength of 4.136 cm, leading to an observed speed of 330.5 m/sec. To this must be added a correction term amounting to 0.9 m/sec to convert this speed, measured in a narrow tube, to the value that would have been obtained had the measurement been conducted in free space. This correction is computed from theoretical considerations. A further correction of 0.2 m/sec must be added to account for the thermal expansion of the rod supporting the movable reflector. This leaves a final corrected speed of 331.6 m/sec. Sherratt and Griffiths then computed $\gamma$, using Eq. 74 with the coefficient $(dp/dv)_T$ evaluated from an equation of state developed by Beattie and Bridgeman. (See above.) They obtained $\gamma = 1.231$. Had they used Eq. 72, they would have obtained $\gamma = 1.230$. Thus, at this temperature and pressure, the correction for departure from ideal conditions is small.

Knowing $\gamma$ (which is $c_p/c_v$) one may with the aid of Eq. 7 of Chapter VI, which shows the dependence of $c_p - c_v$ upon other measurable quantities, determine values for both $c_p$ and $c_v$. This was done by Sherratt and Griffiths.

Values of $\gamma$ for carbon dioxide up to 1000°C and for carbon monoxide up to 1800°C have been reported by these workers.

## PROBLEMS

**1.** At what temperature will the monatomic molecules of mercury vapor and argon have the same average speeds that oxygen molecules have at 0°C?

**2.** What changes in the values assigned to the main coordinate lines of Fig. 2 are required in order that the full-line curve may represent a similar distribution for an equal number of molecules of hydrogen at 20.0°C and 1 A?

**3.** What are the root-mean-square speeds of molecules of helium, hydrogen, oxygen, and nitrogen at their boiling points under a pressure of 1 A?

**4.** Using the data of Table I, compute the mean free path for nitrogen molecules at 1 A and (a) 100°C, (b) 3000°K, (c) the boiling point of nitrogen.

**5.** The constant $a$ in van der Waals' equation is 0.00717 A(gmv/mol)$^2$ for carbon dioxide and 0.00042 A(gmv/mol)$^2$ for hydrogen. Compute the internal pressures for these gases and the ratio of internal to external pressures for values of $v/v_0$ ($v_0$ refers to standard conditions) of 1, 0.01, and 0.001.

**6.** The constant $b$ in van der Waals' equation is 0.00191 gmv/mol for carbon dioxide. Using in addition the value for $a$ given in problem 5, compute for 0°C the pressure and the "departure coefficient" for a specific volume of 0.025 gmv/mol, assuming van der Waals' equation to be strictly true.

**7.** Van der Walls' $b$ for oxygen is given as 0.00142 gmv/mole. Assume 4 as the "aggregate volume" factor and compute a diameter for the billiard ball $O_2$-molecule. Compare this with what is obtained, using a density of 1.25 gm/cm$^3$ for $O_2$ at $-205$°C. The space between close-packed spheres is 26% of the occupied volume.

**8.** Assuming that internal pressure is represented by the thermodynamic expression

$$p_i = \left[ T \left( \frac{dp}{dT} \right)_v - p \right]$$

evaluate this expression using (a) the ideal gas law and (b) van der Waal's equation. What are your conclusions?

**9.** Given that the pressure inside a tank containing carbon dioxide at 40°C is 100 A and that the safety valve operates at 200 A, compute with the aid of Fig. 9 the fractional part of the originally contained gas that escapes when the gas is accidentally heated to 100°C. At what temperature did the gas begin to escape?

**10.** In the work of Hercus and Sutherland referred to in the text, the following data were obtained. For a plate separation of 1.2499 cm and an effective cross-sectional area of 332.1 cm$^2$, an input of 1.1881 watts sufficed to maintain one plate at 12.48°C and the other at 27.28°C. To reproduce these same temperatures with a plate separation of 0.5898 cm and an effective cross-sectional area of 331.0 cm$^2$, it was found that an input of 2.3250 watts was required. It was also observed that then the temperature of the center plate (of thermal capacitance 256 cal/C°) was increasing slowly at the rate of $2.49 \times 10^{-5}$ C°/sec. Compute the rate of heat transfer by conduction through the gas and $k$ for air.

**11.** In the determination of $k$ for air by Gregory and Archer, using the method and apparatus described in the text, the following data were obtained for the larger pair of tubes. Temperature of wire, 24.105°C; temperature of inner surface of tube 0.010°C; resistance of wire per unit length, 0.058047 ohm/cm; rate of heat transfer per unit length due to radiation, 0.0000126 cal/(cm sec). As the pressure in the system was varied, the following rates of supply of energy per unit of length were required to maintain the temperature of the wire constant.

| PRESSURE cm-Hg | RATE OF SUPPLY OF ENERGY PER UNIT LENGTH cal/(cm sec) |
|---|---|
| 77.39 | 0.0024510 |
| 46.86 | .0020738 |
| 27.23 | .0018704 |
| 13.03 | .0018215 |
| 5.19 | .0018105 |
| 3.17 | .0018033 |
| 2.15 | .0017984 |
| 0.071 | .0009966 |

Compute, for each pressure, the rate of heat transfer due to conduction and convection and the thermal conductivity, assuming that the convection loss at 3.00 cm-Hg is negligibly small and that at that pressure the mean free path of the molecules is small with respect to the radius of the tube. What is the explanation for the sudden drop in going from the next to the lowest to the lowest pressure?

**12.** With the aid of Fig. 20, determine the expected temperatures when air at 0°C and 1.0 A is reversibly adiabatically (a) expanded to 1.50 of its initial volume, (b) compressed to a pressure of 1.50 A.

**13.** With the aid of Fig. 20 determine (a) the expected drop in temperature for dry air at the center of a cyclonic whirl which rises from a region where the pressure and the temperature are 1.00 A and 0°C to a region where the pressure is 0.70 A, and (b) the expected increase in temperature at the center of an anticyclonic whirl in which dry air falls from a region having a pressure of 0.70 A and the temperature just determined to a region where the pressure is just 1.05 A.

**14.** In an experiment employing apparatus such as was used by Scheel and Heuse, in carrying out the constant-flow method of measuring the specific heat of hydrogen at atmospheric pressure, 24.05°C and 39.80°C were obtained as the measured temperatures when hydrogen was passed through at a rate of 0.1100 gm/sec and the rate of supply of heat was 25.00 watts and again when the rates were 0.0300 gm/sec and 7.00 watts. What is the resulting $c_p$ for hydrogen?

**15.** Making use of the relations expressed by Eqs. 1 and 52, derive the Clément and Desormes relation of Eq. 58.

**16.** On expanding carbon dioxide gas ($\gamma = 1.300$) adiabatically from 800.00 mm-Hg and 27.0°C to a pressure of 750.0 mm-Hg, as in the Lummer and Pringsheim method of measuring $\gamma$, what is the expected lowering of the temperature?

**17.** In a determination of $\gamma$ by the method of Maneuvrier, the large vessel had a volume of 10,000 cm³. The piston diameter and stroke were respectively 4.00 cm and 6.18 cm. For carbon monoxide ($\gamma = 1.41$) at an initial pressure of 750.0 mm-Hg, what are the expected isothermal and adiabatic pressure changes accompanying an inward thrust of the piston?

**18.** Some data obtained by Sherratt and Griffiths in their determination of $\gamma$ for carbon dioxide for a crystal frequency of 13,828 vib/sec are

| TEMPERATURE °C | SPEED OF SOUND m/sec |
| --- | --- |
| 22.3 | 266.3 |
| 92.0 | 295.4 |
| 233 | 341.6 |
| 586 | 437.9 |
| 659 | 454.0 |
| 773 | 478.2 |
| 941 | 513.4 |
| 1032 | 532.1 |

Neglecting corrections for all disturbing effects mentioned in the text, compute $\gamma$ as a function of temperature, and plot your results. Assuming $c_p - c_v = R$, compute and plot $c_v$ and $c_p$ as functions of temperature. What conclusions can be drawn from the curves?

# CHAPTER IX

## ELEMENTARY THERMODYNAMICS

**1. Introduction.** In the field of elementary mechanics there are two great principles that stand out. Many, but not all, of the phenomena which that division of physics includes depend upon them for their mathematical treatment. They are Newton's second and third laws of motion (the first law is but a qualitative definition of the term force, which is more precisely defined by the second law.

Similarly, in the field of heat, there are four great principles that stand out. Similarly many, but not all, of the phenomena of this division of physics depend upon them for their mathematical treatment. The first principle, known as the zeroth law of thermodynamics, has been discussed on p. 21. As there noted in the form of an important corollary to the law, we have a great principle or axiom which states that bodies in equilibrium have a common temperature. The principle is not susceptible of proof. In both what precedes and what follows, this principle has been and will be tacitly assumed.

The second great principle in the field of heat is known as the first law of thermodynamics. It is in effect an extension of the conservation-of-energy principle to cover the whole of physics. It has been discussed already. The third great principle is known as the second law of thermodynamics, and it will form a basis for the treatment of much that follows. Like the first, these latter two principles are generalizations of experience. They cannot be deduced from more elementary considerations. They can be tested only by searching for exceptions. None has been found so far. The fourth great principle, known as the third law of thermodynamics, is beyond the scope of this text and will not be discussed further here.

Curiously, the first contribution leading to the enunciation of the second law was presented in France in 1824 by Sadi Carnot (1796–1832) from the standpoint that heat is an imponderable fluid, commonly called caloric, and antedated the first law. This contribution, the only one made by Carnot during his short life, was entitled "Reflections on the motive power of fire and on the proper machines for developing this power." He assumed that "motive power," mechanical work as we now call it, can accompany the transfer of heat from a

253

source at one temperature to a sink at another and that it was not connected with any transformation as energy. He said, "The production of the motive power in the steam engine is therefore not due to a real consumption of caloric, but due to its transfer from a hotter to a colder body." In his contribution, Carnot's main purpose seems to have been the development of the conditions of maximum efficiency of operation of a steam engine and a determination of what that maximum efficiency might be. Whether or not he was a real believer in the caloric theory in 1824, as the above quotation would suggest, Carnot's process of reasoning did not make use of the concept that caloric was an indestructible fluid. Certainly, before his death in 1832, he was a believer in the present-day dynamical theory. With regard to the topics he discussed, his method of reasoning and his conclusions were accurate, and little has been added since.

Subsequent contributions leading to enunciation of the second law of thermodynamics, as we now know it, were made by B. P. E. Clapeyron (1799–1864) in France, Ludwig Boltzmann (1844–1906) and R. Clausius (1822–1888) in Germany, and W. J. M. Rankine (1820–1872) and William Thomson (1824–1907), who later became Lord Kelvin, in England.

The second law of thermodynamics has been of immense value both theoretically and practically. Theoretically with its aid many phenomena of physics and chemistry have been discovered and many laws have been deduced; practically, without its aid, the engineer designing and testing engines would find his ideal of efficiency, that for which he would strive, far beyond that which Mother Nature recognizes as possible.

**2. The Carnot Cycle for an Ideal Gas.** There are two types of Carnot cycles, the direct and the reversed. Both consist of a certain set of four reversible processes which, performed on a body, leaves the body in just the condition that it was in initially. The direct cycle results in work performed *by* the body and transfer of heat from a source at one temperature to a sink at another, lower temperature. The reversed cycle has exactly opposite results. The processes are alternately isothermal and adiabatic, and it matters not at what place in a cycle one imagines the cycle to actually start. Consider the cycle diagram for an ideal gas shown in Fig. 1. Starting at $A$, the processes, taken in clockwise order, are reversibly isothermal to $B$, reversibly adiabatic to $C$, reversibly isothermal to $D$, and reversibly adiabatic back to $A$.

Given $\gamma$, the ratio of the two specific heats of the gas, and the coordinates of $A$ and $C$ or of $B$ and $D$, the coordinates of $B$ and $D$ or of

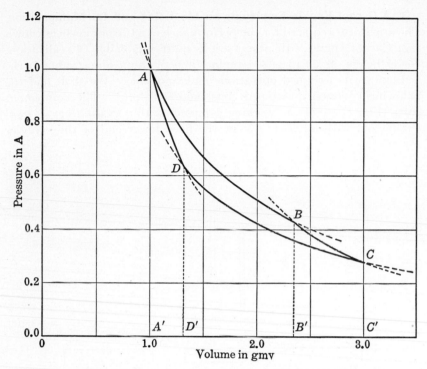

FIG. 1.   A Carnot cycle drawn to scale for an ideal gas whose $\gamma$ is $\frac{5}{3}$.

$A$ and $C$ may be determined.   To illustrate, for a gas whose $\gamma$ is $1\frac{2}{3}$, let the coordinates of $A$ be 1.000 A, 1.000 gmv (gram-molecular volume), and 360°K, and of $C$ be 0.278 A, 3.000 gmv, and 300°K in conformity with the equation

$$\left(\frac{pV}{T}\right)_A = \left(\frac{pV}{T}\right)_C \tag{1}$$

Then, to obtain those for $B$, we make use of the two relations

$$p_A V_A = p_B V_B \tag{2}$$

and (see Eq. 52, p. 238)

$$p_C V_C^{5/3} = p_B V_B^{5/3} \tag{3}$$

Solution yields

$$V_B = \left[\frac{p_C}{p_A} \frac{(V_C)^{5/3}}{V_A}\right]^{3/2} = 2.339 \text{ gmv} \tag{4}$$

$$p_B = 0.428 \text{ A} \tag{5}$$

and, of course, $T_B$ is 360°K.   Similarly for the coordinates of $D$ one obtains 0.634 A, 1.314 gmv, and 300°K.

**3. A Carnot Engine Employing an Ideal Gas and Its Manipulation.**
The apparatus required for the performance of a Carnot cycle is known
as a Carnot engine. In practice it is quite impossible of realization.
Nevertheless, as an idealized engine, it is of tremendous value in the
deductions its assumed operations make possible. We shall find the
following commonly assumed construction helpful. The component
parts (Fig. 2) are (1) a "working cylinder" with a *tight-fitting, frictionless* piston, with all parts except the fixed lower end of the cylinder

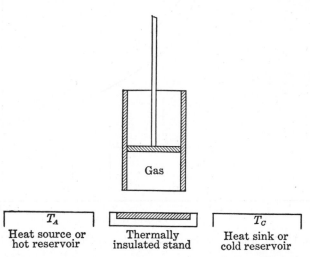

FIG. 2. Parts of a Carnot engine consisting of (1) an insulated cyclinder with freely
moving piston completely insulated thermally except for the bottom boundary, (2)
an insulated stand, (3) a hot reservoir, and (4) a cold reservoir.

completely insulated thermally; (2) a portion of ideal gas within the
cylinder; (3) a heat source or hot reservoir maintained at a constant
temperature $T_A$ with upper surface thermally conducting and fitted
to receive the "working cylinder"; (4) a heat sink or cold reservoir
differing from the heat source only in having a lower temperature $T_c$;
(5) a thermally insulated stand fitted to receive the working cylinder.
The upper surfaces of items (3), (4), and (5) should be at the same
level so that no work is involved in shifting the "working cylinder"
laterally from the top of one to the top of another.

Consider how this engine may be used in carrying the enclosed gas
through the cycle shown in Fig. 1. Let us start at point $A$. The
"working cylinder," with the gas compressed, is then on top and in
thermal contact with the hot source. The first stage of the cycle is
represented by process $AB$ and corresponds to an infinitely slow expan-

sion * of the gas under conditions that differ but infinitesimally from a uniform temperature throughout. This can occur only if the external force opposing the motion of the piston is very gradually reduced. Work is performed by the expanding gas, and a quantity of heat $Q_{AB}$ is taken in by the gas at the temperature $T_A$. When point $B$ of the cycle is reached, the cylinder is transferred to the insulated stand and the gas is permitted to expand adiabatically from $B$ to $C$, a point at which the contained gas has the temperature $T_C$ of the heat sink. Then, with the cylinder transferred to the heat sink, the gas is slowly compressed by an external force, until point $D$ is reached. During this process a quantity of heat $Q_{DC}$ is forced out of the "working cylinder" into the cold sink. Next the cylinder is transferred to the insulated stand and the gas is compressed adiabatically by an external force until its temperature is once more $T_A$, that of the heat source. The cylinder and its contents once more in their initial conditions are then shifted to their initial positions, completing the cycle. The amounts of heat transferred and of work done are considered below.

**4. Application of the First Law of Thermodynamics to a Carnot Cycle Employing an Ideal Gas.** This highly important procedure involves the application of Eq. 7 of Chapter IV, namely,

$$Q = \Delta U + W \tag{6}$$

to the separate processes of the cycle. Before doing so, however, we shall derive certain needed equations. Those with which we start apply only to ideal gases and have been derived elsewhere. They are

$$\frac{p_A V_A}{T_A} = \frac{p_B V_B}{T_A} = mR = \frac{p_C V_C}{T_C} = \frac{p_D V_D}{T_C} \tag{7}$$

and

$$\frac{p_A V_A^\gamma}{p_D V_D^\gamma} = 1 = \frac{p_B V_B^\gamma}{p_C V_C^\gamma} \tag{8}$$

Evidently $A$ and $B$ or $C$ and $D$ may represent any two points on an isothermal. Likewise $A$ and $D$ or $B$ and $C$ may represent any two points on an adiabat. Eq. 7 yields

$$\frac{p_A V_A}{p_D V_D} = \frac{T_A}{T_C} = \frac{p_B V_B}{p_C V_C} \tag{9}$$

* The provision of an infinitely slow expansion insures that nothing more than an infinitesimal temperature difference can occur in the gas under consideration at any time, a condition that is essential in order that a change may be isothermal.

Combined, Eqs. 8 and 9 yield

$$\frac{V_A}{V_D} = \left[\frac{T_C}{T_A}\right]^{\frac{1}{\gamma - 1}} = \frac{V_B}{V_C} \qquad (10)$$

and

$$\frac{V_A}{V_B} = \frac{V_D}{V_C} \qquad (11)$$

For the ideal gas, this shows that, if a number of isothermals are drawn to intersect two adiabatics, the ratio of the volumes at intersections for one isothermal is exactly the same as the corresponding ratio for any other isothermal.

Let us now apply the first law of thermodynamics to the separate processes of the cycle diagrammed in Fig. 1. Since no *internal work* is done by an ideal gas on expanding (see Chapter VIII), the heat added, $Q_{AB}$, during the isothermal process $AB$ is necessarily equal to the work done by the gas, $W_{AB}$. Equating such work to the $\int p\, dV$ between appropriate limits, we obtain

$$Q_{AB} = W_{AB} = \int_{V_A}^{V_B} p\, dV = mRT_A \ln\frac{V_B}{V_A} \qquad (12)$$

Both $Q_{AC}$ and $W_{AB}$ are represented in the graph by the area $ABB'A'A$

During the adiabatic process $BC$, no heat is added. However, work is done by the gas. The amount, $W_{BC}$, is given by (see comment following Eq. 8)

$$W_{BC} = \int_{V_B}^{V_C} p\, dV = p_C V_C{}^\gamma \int_{V_B}^{V_C} \frac{dV}{V^\gamma} = \frac{p_C V_C{}^\gamma}{1 - \gamma}(V_C{}^{1-\gamma} - V_B{}^{1-\gamma})$$

$$= \frac{1}{\gamma - 1}(p_B V_B - p_C V_C) = \frac{mR}{\gamma - 1}(T_A - T_C) \qquad (13)$$

$W_{BC}$ is represented in Fig. 1 by the area $BCC'B'B$. For the process $CD$, we have, as for the process $AB$,

$$Q_{CD} = W_{CD} = mRT_C \ln\frac{V_D}{V_C} = -mRT_C \ln\frac{V_B}{V_A} \qquad (14)$$

This is represented on the diagram by the area $CDD'C'C$. This area, through being described oppositely from the areas already named, represents a negative amount of work done *by* the gas or a positive amount done *on* the gas. Similar to Eq. 13, we have

$$W_{DA} = \frac{1}{\gamma - 1}(p_D V_D - p_A V_A) = -\frac{mR}{\gamma - 1}(T_A - T_C) \quad (15)$$

In Fig. 1, this is represented by the area $DAA'D'D$. The convention as to sign is the same as in Eq. 14.

Comparison of Eqs. 13 and 15 shows at once that the net result of the work done during the two adiabatic processes of a Carnot cycle is zero. Thus

$$W_{BC} + W_{DA} = 0 \quad\quad\quad (16)$$

For the cycle as a whole, however, the work performed does not equate to zero. Thus

$$\Sigma W = W_{AB} + W_{BC} + W_{CD} + W_{DA} = W_{AB} + W_{CD}$$
$$= Q_{AB} + Q_{CD} = mR(T_A - T_C) \ln \frac{V_B}{V_A} \quad (17)$$

On the graph, this is represented by the enclosed area $ABCDA$. Substitution of the values given above for the coordinates of $A$, $B$, $C$, and $D$ yields for the net amount of work done *by* the gas during the performance of the Carnot cycle described above

$$\Sigma W = \frac{273}{360} \text{ mol } \frac{1}{273} \frac{\text{gmv A}}{\text{mol K}°} 60 \text{ K}° \ln 2.34$$
$$= 0.142 \text{ gmv A} = 322 \text{ joules} \quad (18)$$

**5. The Efficiency of a Carnot Engine Employing an Ideal Gas.** A thermal engine is a machine that carries a portion of some suitable substance, capable of storing heat energy, repeatedly through a given cycle in which the substance is alternately brought in contact with a hot reservoir or source and a cold reservoir or sink. Depending on the cycle, a net amount of work is done *by* the substance or *on* the substance. Where a positive amount of work is done by the substance, we are interested in that characteristic of the machine and cycle known as efficiency. At present only cycle efficiency, or, what is the same, the efficiency of an idealized engine which carries the contained substance through the cycle, is of interest. In a later chapter the efficiencies of real machines will be considered.

The efficiency of a thermal engine, $\eta$, is defined as the ratio of the work done during a cycle to the heat supplied to the working substance during the cycle. Thus, for the Carnot cycle discussed above, we have

$$\eta = \frac{\Sigma W}{Q_{AB}} = \frac{Q_{AB} - Q_{DC}}{Q_{AB}} = \frac{mR(T_A - T_C)\ln (V_B/V_A)}{mRT_A \ln (V_B/V_A)}$$

$$= \frac{T_A - T_C}{T_A} = 1 - \frac{T_C}{T_A} \quad (19)$$

for the particular cycle specified above,

$$\eta = 1 - \frac{300°K}{360°K} = \frac{1}{6} \quad (20)$$

This means that, with a Carnot engine operating between a source at 360°K and a sink at 300°K, ⅚ of the heat taken in at 360°K will be rejected at 300°K, and that only ⅙ of the intake energy can possibly be used in performing mechanical work.

**6. Carnot's Theorem and Carnot's Principle.** Efficiency is one of civilization's watchwords. Naturally Carnot, studying basic efficiency considerations, was led to what is known as Carnot's theorem. One statement is, of all engines operating between two given temperatures, none can be more efficient than the Carnot engine. Actually its proof is based on a postulate sometimes referred to as Carnot's principle but more often as the Second Law of Thermodynamics.

The Carnot cycle, as described above, was assumed to have been traversed in the order $ABCDA$ (Fig. 1). However, since all four processes are reversible, it is obvious that the cycle might be traversed as readily in the reverse order, that is, via $ADCBA$, and that a Carnot engine is a reversible engine. Should the cycle be so traversed, the previous cold sink would become a heat source, where, during each cycle, an amount of heat $Q_2$ ($= Q_{DC}$) would be absorbed by the engine. Further, the previous hot source would become a sink to which, during each cycle, an amount of heat $Q_1$ ($= Q_{BA}$) would be transferred. Obviously, some outside agent would be required to do a net amount of work on the gas of the engine which would now be acting as a refrigerator. The amount of work $W$ ($= Q_1 - Q_2$) added in each cycle, in the form of internal energy in the gas, to $Q_2$ would yield the necessary $Q_1$ for transfer at the higher temperature.

Consider two identical Carnot engines operating at the same speed, the first forward in the normal manner, the second backward, between the same isothermals and adiabats. The work done *by* the first will be just equal to that which must be done *on* the second, and, as is evident, these two idealized engines might so continue indefinitely.

At the close of each cycle, not only these engines but also the outside universe would be in just the same state as at the beginning.

Consider next the accomplishment of two dissimilar engines, $A$, a Carnot engine, and $B$, an engine of any other chosen type, whether reversible or irreversible. Let the two operate at the same cyclical speed between the same hot and cold reservoirs at temperatures $T_1$ and $T_2$. Let engine $B$ operate in the normal forward direction, in each cycle absorbing an amount of heat $Q_1'$ from the hot reservoir, performing an amount of work $W$, and transferring an amount of heat $Q_2'$ ($= Q_1' - W$) to the low-temperature reservoir. Let engine $A$ operate backwards in a Carnot cycle, in each cycle absorbing an amount of heat $Q_2$, not necessarily the same as $Q_2'$, from the low-temperature reservoir, experiencing an amount of work $W$ performed on it, and transmitting to the high-temperature reservoir an amount of heat $Q_1$, not necessarily the same as $Q_1'$.

Assume temporarily that engine $B$ is more efficient than engine $A$, or, what is the same, that $W/Q_1' > W/Q_1$. Since then $Q_1$ would be greater than $Q_1'$ and $Q_2$ would be greater than $Q_2'$ by the same amount, the assumption made would lead to the expectation that the two engines could operate as a single unit without performing any external work whatever but still, during each cycle, transfer heat to the extent of $Q_2 - Q_2'$ ($= Q_1 - Q_1'$) from the low-temperature reservoir to the high-temperature reservoir. Such a transfer of heat without any change in the universe outside was declared to be contrary to all experience and impossible of accomplishment. Granted this postulate, it follows, in accord with Carnot's theorem, that, for given conditions of operation, no heat engine can exceed the Carnot engine in efficiency.

As the generalization of experience upon which the foregoing declaration was based, the German physicist R. Clausius (1822–1888) offered the following. "It is impossible to construct a device that, operating in a cycle, will produce no effect other than the transfer of heat from a cooler to a hotter body.* This is one form of what is known as Carnot's principle or the second law of thermodynamics.

As a variation of the proof of Carnot's important theorem, consider two other engines $A$ and $B$ acting as above as a single unit, between the same hot and cold temperatures. This time let engine $B$, operating as before in a forward direction, during each cycle absorb heat $Q_1''$, from the hot reservoir, perform a net amount of work $W''$, and deliver heat $Q_2''$ ($= Q_1'' - W''$) to the cold reservoir. Let engine $A$, a Carnot engine operating in a backward direction, as previously,

---

* Mark W. Zemansky, *Heat and Thermodynamics*, 2nd Ed., p. 127, McGraw-Hill Book Co., New York, 1943.

absorb heat $Q_2$ ( $= Q_2''$) from the cold reservoir, experience work $W$ performed on it, and deliver heat $Q_1$ to the hot reservoir.

As before, assume temporarily that engine $B$ is more efficient than engine $A$, or, what is the same, that $\dfrac{W''}{Q_2'' + W''} > \dfrac{W}{Q_2 + W}$. Since $Q_2$ and $Q_2''$ are equal, it follows that $W''$ is greater than $W$ and that, during each cycle, the compound engine in effect merely withdraws an amount of heat $Q_1'' - Q_1$ from the hot reservoir and performs work $W'' - W$ which is exactly equivalent to the heat thus withdrawn. Such complete utilization of heat in the performance of work was likewise declared to be contrary to all experience and impossible of accomplishment. The generalization of experience upon which this second declaration was based has been variously stated by the English physicist Lord Kelvin (1824–1907), the German physicist Max Planck (1858–    ), winner of the Nobel prize in physics in 1918, and others. As stated with slight modifications, by Buckingham* (1867–1940) of our Bureau of Standards, it is, "All experience shows . . . that no thermal engine will take in heat from a given body" and utilize the whole of that heat in performing work, "but that there must always be some colder body into which the engine may reject a part of the heat that it has taken from the hot body." This is a second form of Carnot's principle or the second law of thermodynamics.

It is obvious that the two statements of Carnot's principle are intimately related. Though we shall not do it here, it is possible to show that the postulation of either one implies the other.

One of the immediate results of the deduction that the efficiency of a Carnot engine cannot be exceeded was a denial of the possibility of what was called a "perpetual motion of the second kind" (see Chapter IV for the meaning of a "perpetual motion of the first kind"). This perpetual-motion principle presupposed that the tremendous, often called inexhaustible, supply of thermal energy possessed by earth, sea, and atmosphere was available for the performance of work. With this assumed principle as a guide, the conservation of natural resources would not have its present great appeal. The reasoning back of the denial follows. Since, in its normal operation, the Carnot engine uses only a portion of the heat taken from the hot source in the performance of work and transfers the remainder to a cold sink, Nature's tremendous and apparently inexhaustible supply of thermal energy, so far as it represents energy necessary to maintain temperatures equal to those of the cold sinks, is completely unavailable for the performance

---

* Edgar Buckingham, *An Outline of the Theory of Thermodynamics*, p. 97, The Macmillan Co., New York, 1900.

of work.  Further, as Carnot's work also showed, there is only partial
availability for the portion of that huge supply which is associated
with temperatures above those of the cold sinks.  Strictly, the principle denied did not claim perpetual motion as a possibility.  It merely
seemed to suggest a situation approaching that condition.

The above considerations regarding engine operation and the denials
connected therewith, which led to the two selected statements of
Carnot's principle, lead also to important conclusions regarding the
efficiencies of thermal engines.  One conclusion is that all reversible
engines operating between the same two temperatures have the same
efficiency, that of the reversible Carnot engine.  Another conclusion
is that engines having less efficiencies than those for Carnot engines
are irreversible engines, and vice versa.

Still another conclusion, this time comparing the efficiency of a
reversible engine with that of any real engine, may be reached by in-
voking another generalization of experience.  The operations assumed
for the reversible engines, in the discussion above, are such that we
might have a "perpetual motion of the third kind," a type of motion
that does not contradict the law of conservation of energy, nor, in
fact, the second law of thermodynamics, which as yet has not been
stated in its most general form.  Were real engines reversible engines,
it should be possible, with the aid of backward-running as well as
forward-running real engines, always to have the same constant
amount of energy at our disposal.  Such a possibility, however, is contrary to our experience, and the assumed "perpetual motion of the
third kind" is in consequence declared impossible.  This generalization
of experience, nevertheless, carries with it the important implication
that all real engines are irreversible engines and consequently less
efficient than reversible engines.

Thus far we have tacitly assumed an ideal gas as the working substance for our Carnot engine.  That is not necessary, however.  The
discussion above, which indicated that all reversible engines necessarily have the same efficiency, carried no assumptions as to the nature
of the working substances.  It follows that real gases, liquids, and
solids, which also can be subjected to isothermal and adiabatic processes, may also be used as working substances for idealized Carnot
engines.  That it would be much more difficult to produce the Carnot
cycle with a solid or liquid in place of a gas is not important here.

Summarizing the foregoing, we have Carnot's theorem, as stated by
the Indian physicists M. Saha (1893–   ) and B. N. Srivastava, *"The
efficiency is the same for all reversible engines, and this efficiency is the
highest limit for the efficiency of any engine that can be constructed or*

*imagined.*" For the efficiency $\eta$ of a real engine, one can never hope to exceed $(1 - T_2/T_1)$, or, in fact, even to equal that value.

**7. The Second Law of Thermodynamics.** This law is a generalization of certain experiences of mankind relating to thermal engines. It has been variously expressed. One statement due to Buckingham which has been quoted above is Carnot's principle (not Carnot's theorem). Another according to Clausius is, "Heat cannot, of itself, pass from a colder to a hotter body." According to Kelvin, "It is impossible by means of an inanimate material agency to derive mechanical effect from any portion of matter by cooling it below the temperature of the coldest surrounding objects," or, as restated by Buckingham, "It is impossible to obtain work by using up the heat in the coldest bodies present." According to the English physicist J. K. Roberts (1897–1944), "It is not possible for a self-acting machine working in a cyclical process, unaided by any external energy, to make heat pass from one body to another at a higher temperature." Other authors have presented somewhat altered statements.

Though differently expressed, the statements for the second law that have been given are essentially equivalent. Since they are generalizations of experience, their truth or falsity must rest on the correctness of the many deductions which are based on them and are capable of verification. Thus far, if we except comparisons of instantaneous states in minute systems, out of the huge number of applications attempted, no failures have been found. Actually, if the law is looked upon as a statement which applies only to a system for which the average instantaneous condition for its parts may be equated to the infinite-time average for those parts, even these apparent failures are not to be counted. Physicists, chemists, engineers, and scientific workers generally accept the second law of thermodynamics without reservation.

The statements given above for the second law of thermodynamics are generally negative in nature and not all-inclusive. An affirmative form of statement which is all-inclusive, but which lacks much in concreteness and in ease of comprehensibility, may be given, however. It depends on the concept of entropy which is to be developed later. Its origin is somewhat uncertain to the authors of this book, but in thought it is, "In isolated systems, changes of condition are accompanied by either no change in entropy or by an increase in entropy depending on whether all processes involved are reversible or include one or more that is irreversible." That each of the above negative statements is covered by this positive statement may be easily demonstrated and forms the basis for a problem at the close of this chapter.

**8. Absolute Temperature Scales.** Thus far, we have tacitly accepted as our temperature scale that which is based on a constant-volume gas thermometer employing an assumed ideal gas. Had we used a real gas such as hydrogen or helium instead, the formulas and the general relations already developed for *real substances* would have been about equally simple or complex and would have contained about an equal number of arbitrary constants. Whether a real gas or an assumed ideal gas is used as a basis in thermometry has not been vital thus far. But now with the introduction of the Carnot cycle, and of relations derived with its aid, such is no longer the case. Wherever thermodynamic reasoning is involved, the question of the temperature scale is important.

The fact that *the efficiencies of all reversible Carnot engines, whatever the working substance, working between the same two temperatures, are the same* suggests the possibility of temperature scales which would be independent of the thermometric substances. That such is the case was first recognized in England in 1848 by the brilliant young physicist William Thomson who later became Lord Kelvin. The bases for such procedure as described by him have been universally accepted since, and the individual temperature scales founded upon them are recognized as the scales to which all others must be reduced in the final analyses.

In discussing the development of a particular thermodynamic scale, we start with the Carnot-cycle concept and the arbitrarily defined steam and ice points as the temperatures of a source and a sink. Let 100 idealized Carnot engines be set to work, all using the same working substance and all working between the same two adiabatics, with engine 100 operating between the steam point, $T_{100}$, as we shall call it, and a somewhat lower temperature, $T_{99}$, which will be defined later. Let engine 99 operate between $T_{99}$ and a somewhat lower temperature, $T_{98}$, which will likewise be defined later. Similarly let the other engines, 97, etc., down to 1, operate between similar pairs of temperatures with engine 1 operating between temperatures $T_1$ and $T_0$, the ice point. Further, let each succeeding machine between 100 and 1 have, as its intake supply of heat, the outgo rejection of heat from the machine just above it in number; e.g., for engine 99 the intake $Q_{99}$ would be the exhaust from engine 100. Also let the amount of work performed per cycle by each machine be identically the same. The temperatures $T_{99}, T_{98}, T_{97} \cdots T_1$ will then be uniquely defined, and, what is most interesting, the temperatures so determined will be the same regardless of what working substance is being used, including therein the ideal gas. Let us describe these temperatures

as 99, 98, 97, etc., thermodynamic degrees above the ice point.  Referring to Eq. 17, one sees, in the light of Eq. 11, that the condition of
equal amounts of work per cycle for a given pair of adiabats for the
various engines, if an ideal gas is used, is also that of equal differences
between the temperatures of the sources and the sinks as measured with
an ideal-gas thermometer.  Hence the two temperature scales, the
thermodynamic and the ideal-gas, are identical.  $T_{99}$, $T_{98}$, etc., are
the same as 99°C, 98°C, etc., on the ideal-gas scale.

Starting with the ice point as a top source of heat, one may make use
of a similar set of ideal Carnot engines, each succeeding one using as
its input source of heat that which was rejected by the engine just one
step above.  Doing so, one comes eventually to an engine, if the steps
are just right, which will use up all the heat taken in at its upper
operating temperature.  Its lower temperature will be 0°K, whose
value with respect to the ice point may be obtained by taking the
product of the number of engines by the temperature interval for each
machine.  Throughout, the scale will be identical with the ideal-gas
scale.

There is a more direct way of determining the interval between the
ice point and the absolute zero.  To a Carnot engine operating between the steam and the ice points, the efficiency relations of Eq. 19
may be used.  Once $\eta$ or $W/Q_1$ is known, one may, recognizing that
$T_{100} - T_0$ is 100 thermodynamic degrees by definition, solve for $T_0$
to obtain

$$T_0 = \frac{1 - \eta}{\eta} (T_{100} - T_0) \tag{21}$$

The thermodynamic scale just described is generally known as the
Kelvin scale after its discoverer.  Another thermodynamic scale much
used in engineering with its temperature unit equal to $\frac{1}{180}$ of the
steam point-ice point interval is known as the Rankine scale after
William John Rankine, an outstanding Scottish physicist and engineer
early interested in engineering thermodynamics.  The best present
value for $T_0$ is 273.16°K or 491.67°R.

**9. Changes in $Q$ and $W$ Vary with the Path.**  Up to the present we
have used the first law of thermodynamics only in the integral form, as

$$Q = \Delta U + W \tag{22}$$

It is now desired in a differential form; and, as such, it is sometimes
written

$$đQ = dU + đW \tag{23}$$

Note that the đ's preceding the $Q$ and the $W$ bear cross bars.  These
are intended to indicate, what will be shown later, that $đQ$ and $đW$

are not exact differentials although $dU$ is.  Mathematically this means that we cannot integrate in the general case with respect to $đQ$ and $đW$.  Physically this means that the amount of heat that is added to or taken away in changing a body from some one specified state to some other specified state depends on how the change is made.  Exactly the same thing is to be said regarding the work that is done by the body.  In contrast, the change in internal energy $dU$ is definite and does not depend on how the change is made.

Compare, with the aid of Fig. 1, the quantities of heat that must be supplied and the amounts of work that must be done when a mass $m$ of an ideal gas is transferred from the state indicated at $A$ to that indicated at $C$ first via $ABC$ and then via $ADC$.  Eqs. 12 and 14 yield

$$Q_{ABC} = Q_{AB} + Q_{BC} = mRT_A \ln \frac{V_B}{V_A} + 0 \qquad (24)$$

$$Q_{ADC} = Q_{AD} + Q_{DC} = 0 + mRT_C \ln \frac{V_B}{V_A} \qquad (25)$$

A comparison of these equations shows that the heat that must be supplied depends on the path on the $pV$-diagram or, what is the same, on how the change is made.  Similarly, with the aid of Eqs. 12 to 15, we obtain

$$W_{ABC} = W_{AB} + W_{BC} = mR \left[ T_A \ln \frac{V_B}{V_A} + \frac{1}{\gamma - 1} (T_A - T_C) \right] \qquad (26)$$

$$W_{ADC} = W_{AD} + W_{DC} = mR \left[ \frac{1}{\gamma - 1} (T_A - T_C) + T_C \ln \frac{V_B}{V_A} \right] \qquad (27)$$

A comparison of these last two equations shows likewise that the work done depends on the path.  Now compare $\Delta U_{ABC}$ with $\Delta U_{ADC}$.  Using Eq. 6, we obtain

$$\Delta U_{ABC} = Q_{ABC} - W_{ABC} = -\frac{m}{\gamma - 1} R(T_A - T_C) \qquad (28)$$

$$\Delta U_{ADC} = Q_{ADC} - W_{ADC} = -\frac{m}{\gamma - 1} R(T_A - T_C) \qquad (29)$$

For the two paths considered, the changes in internal energy are the same.  That such changes should be dependent only on the initial and the final states and not on the path of transfer is what one would expect a priori, and may be verified by repeated trials using various paths.  What the various values are for a particular $m$ and certain paths of transfer leading to a particular pair of states as $A$ and $C$ is left for a problem.

**10. Entropy.** The mathematical treatment of problems involving the transfer of heat in accord with Eq. 23 becomes well-nigh impossible unless an integrating factor can be found which when applied to đQ will make integration possible. What this means will appear later.

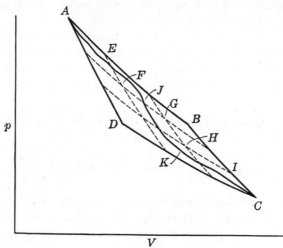

FIG. 3. A subdivided Carnot cycle diagram for showing that $\Sigma đQ/T$ is a function of the initial and the final states only. This diagram is not drawn to scale.

The expressions for $Q_{ABC}$ and $Q_{ADC}$ for an ideal gas given by Eqs. 24 and 25 differ only in that $T_A$, the temperature of the isothermal process $AB$, appears in the former, while $T_C$, that of the isothermal process $DC$, appears in the latter. It follows that

$$\frac{Q_{ABC}}{T_A} = \frac{Q_{ADC}}{T_C} \tag{30}$$

Obviously, for the two paths leading in Fig. 1 from $A$ to $C$, we may write

$$\left[\sum \frac{đQ}{T}\right]_{ABC} = \left[\sum \frac{đQ}{T}\right]_{ADC} \tag{31}$$

Eq. 31 suggests that the values of the summations shown depend only on the starting and the ending points of the path transversed. Consider Fig. 3, which shows the Carnot cycle of Fig. 1 subdivided into several smaller Carnot cycles each bounded by isothermals and adiabatics. Obviously, Eq. 31 applies to each subcycle, and it follows that the summation $\Sigma đQ/T$ for the path $AEFGHIC$, or for any other path as $AJKC$ from $A$ to $C$ which may be thought of as approximated as closely as desired by a succession of infinitesimal isothermal and adiabatic processes, must equal that for the path $ABC$. In the limiting case the summation becomes the integral $\int dQ/T$.

Since the value of this integral is dependent solely on its limits, the quantity $(dQ/T)$ is an exact differential and $1/T$ is the integrating factor needed for the mathematical treatment mentioned above. This exact differential is usually represented by $dS$,

$$dS = \frac{dQ}{T} = \frac{dU}{T} + \frac{dW}{T} \tag{32}$$

of which $S$ stands for a new function called entropy. The concept of entropy is much used in theoretical discussions in physics and chemistry. As a word of caution, it should be noted that Eq. 32 has been shown thus far to be applicable only to *reversible processes* involving ideal gases. Later the limitation to ideal gases will be removed.

Next consider the possibility that $dW/T$ may be likewise an exact differential. Here for an ideal gas

$$\frac{dW}{T} = \frac{p\, dV}{T} = \frac{R\, dV}{V} = R\, d(\ln V) \tag{33}$$

That $\int d(\ln V)$ is a function of its limits indicates that, as far as ideal gases are concerned, though $dW$ is not an exact differential $dW/T$ is. Finally, considering $dU/T$, we may write again for the ideal gas, using Eq. 37 of Chapter VIII,

$$\frac{dU}{T} = \frac{mc_v\, dT}{T} = mc_v\, d(\ln T) \tag{34}$$

as for $dW/T$, the integral of $dU/T$ for an ideal gas is a function of its limits. Both $dU$ and $dU/T$ are exact for an ideal-gas problem.

Consider next the possibility of $1/T$ as an integrating factor for $dQ$ for other materials than an ideal gas. For this discussion we use Eqs. 19 which show how the efficiency of a Carnot engine employing an ideal gas depends on the intake and exhaust temperatures and Carnot's theorem developed later which states that the efficiencies of all reversible engines operating between the same intake and exhaust temperatures are equal. We write Eqs. 19, somewhat abbreviated, as

$$\eta = \frac{\Sigma W}{Q_{AB}} = \frac{Q_{AB} - Q_{DC}}{Q_{AB}} = \frac{T_A - T_C}{T_A} \tag{19}$$

By virtue of the theorem, it is now possible to state that, in their entirety, Eqs. 19 apply to all substances. In particular, it becomes possible to write

$$1 - \frac{Q_{DC}}{Q_{AB}} = 1 - \frac{T_C}{T_A} \tag{35}$$

and

$$\frac{Q_{AB}}{T_A} = \frac{Q_{DC}}{T_C} \tag{36}$$

of which $Q_{AB}$ and $Q_{DC}$ may be identified with $Q_{ABC}$ and $Q_{ADC}$ above. Eq. 36 is thus identified to be the same as Eq. 30, and the reasoning

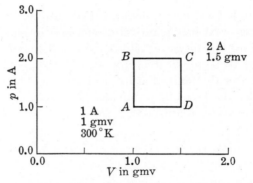

FIG. 4. A $p$-$V$ diagram illustrating entropy computations.

that led to the development of Eq. 32 for ideal gases may now be modified to include all materials, whether gaseous, liquid, or solid. It follows that $dQ/T$, that is $dS$, is an exact differential for all reversible processes. It is not possible, however, to say that $dU/T$ and $dW/T$ of Eq. 32 are separately exact differentials for all reversible processes. The most that can be said is that their sum $(dU + dW)/T$, through being equal to $dS$, is an exact differential.

To illustrate how entropy changes may be computed and that the change in entropy for a body depends only on the initial and final states, consider heating a portion of ideal gas whose $\gamma$ is $\frac{4}{3}$, from state $A$, Fig. 4, described by 1 A, 1 gmv, and 300°K to state $C$ described by 2 A and 1.5 gmv. Evidently there are an infinite number of ways of making the change. Consider first the path $ABC$ and then the path $ADC$. Since the gas is an ideal gas with $\gamma$ equal to $\frac{4}{3}$, it follows at once (1) that the mass of the gas is $^{273}\!/_{300}$ moles, (2) that its specific heat at constant pressure is $4R$, (3) that its specific heat at constant volume is $3R$, and (4) that the temperatures corresponding to points

$B$, $C$, and $D$ are 600°K, 900°K, and 450°K. For the path $ABC$, we have, as a result of applying Eq. 32,

$$S_C - S_A = m \left[ \int_{300°K}^{600°K} \frac{c_v \, dT}{T} + \int_{600°K}^{900°K} \frac{c_p \, dT}{T} \right]$$

$$= 3Rm \int_{300°K}^{600°K} \frac{dT}{T} + 4Rm \int_{600°K}^{900°K} \frac{dT}{T} \tag{37}$$

$$= Rm \left( 3 \ln 2 + 4 \ln \frac{3}{2} \right) = 6.68 \, \frac{cal}{K°}$$

For the path $ADC$, we have similarly

$$S_C - S_A = m \left[ \int_{300°K}^{450°K} \frac{c_p \, dT}{T} + \int_{450°K}^{900°K} \frac{c_v \, dT}{T} \right]$$

$$= 4Rm \int_{300°K}^{450°K} \frac{dT}{T} + 3Rm \int_{450°K}^{900°K} \frac{dT}{T} \tag{38}$$

$$= Rm \left( 4 \ln \frac{3}{2} + 3 \ln 2 \right) = 6.68 \, \frac{cal}{K°}$$

The changes in entropy via $ABC$ and via $ADC$ are the same. In computing entropy changes where heat is added at continuously varying temperatures, one must, as above, employ integration.

There are two additional functions involving entropy which are much used in physics and chemistry. They are the Helmholtz function $A$ and the Gibbs function $G$ which are defined as follows

$$A = U - TS \tag{39}$$

$$G = U + pV - TS = H - TS \tag{40}$$

of which $H$, representing enthalpy, has been discussed in Chapter VIII. Unfortunately, both $A$ and $G$ have often been referred to as free-energy functions. We shall not have occasion to use them in this book. We shall, however, show in a few instances the value of entropy considerations.

**11. Computation of Changes of Entropy.** How to determine the actual value of the entropies of certain simple systems is beyond the scope of this book. We may, however, consider how to compute certain changes of entropy. The case of an ideal gas experiencing reversible constant-volume and constant-pressure changes has already been discussed in the preceding section. Let us here consider two special cases.

1. What is the change in entropy experienced by a mass $M$ of water in the form of ice at some temperature $T_1$, below 0°C, on having its temperature raised at constant pressure to $T_2$, where $0°C < T_2 < 100°C$? The process is reversible. Let $c_i$ and $c_w$ be the specific heats of ice and of liquid water. Let $L$ be the heat of fusion of ice. Then, from the definition of entropy, since all processes are reversible and $dQ$ is exact and equal to $cm\, dT$, we have

$$\Delta S = \int dS = \sum \frac{dQ}{T} = m \left[ c_i \int_{T_1}^{0°C} \frac{dT}{T} + \frac{L}{T_0} + c_w \int_{0°C}^{T_2} \frac{dT}{T} \right]$$

$$= m \left[ c_i \ln \frac{T_0}{T_1} + \frac{L}{T_0} + c_w \ln \frac{T_2}{T_0} \right] \tag{40a}$$

Substitution of given values will lead to the desired result.

2. What change in entropy is experienced by a mass $m$ of an ideal gas, characterized by $p_1$, $V_1$, and $T_1$, on expanding freely to a volume $V_2$? The process is irreversible. $\Delta S$ may be computed only by considering reversible changes that will bring about the same change. Since the gas is an ideal gas, the final temperature will also be $T_1$, and the gas may be carried from the initial state to the final state by letting it expand isothermally. The heat added then will be equal to the work done on expanding. The change in entropy for this case follows simply with the aid of Eq. 24, and we have

$$\Delta S = \frac{Q}{T_1} = \frac{mRT_1}{T_1} \ln \frac{V_2}{V_1} = mR \ln \frac{V_2}{V_1} \tag{40b}$$

**12. The Clapeyron Equation.** One of the most useful relations which has been obtained with the aid of entropy considerations is the Clapeyron equation, which describes conditions governing changes of state, as in the vaporization of a liquid. In our derivation of the equation, we shall consider the series of processes (Fig. 5) making up cycle $ABCDA$, at whose corners there occur the combinations of $p$, $v$, $T$ values shown. Starting at point $A$ with the material in liquid form at temperature $T$ and a pressure $p$ just equal to its vapor tension, cause the liquid to pass along the path $AB$ of the cycle by adding heat until the temperature $T + \Delta T$ is reached, under the condition that the external pressure equals the vapor tension of the liquid. Then, by means of additional heat, but without change of pressure or temperature, vaporize the liquid completely. Point $C$ of the cycle is then reached. Next, with the vapor kept just saturated, the necessary heat is added or withdrawn until the temperature is reduced to $T$ and point

$D$ of the cycle is reached. Finally, with the pressure and temperature maintained constant, withdraw heat until the vapor is just completely liquefied. Once more the condition of the material is represented by point $A$ on the diagram, and the cycle has been completed. Although the $BC$ and $DA$ processes are isothermal, the other two are not adiabatic; and this cycle is therefore not a Carnot cycle.

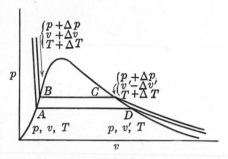

We shall consider first the changes in internal energy per unit mass that occur as the material is carried around the cycle. Second, we shall consider similar changes in the entropy of the material per unit mass.

FIG. 5. A $p$-$v$ diagram used in deriving Clapeyron's equation.

Both of these sums must separately equate to zero. Finally, from a combination of the results, we shall seek the expected relation.

Let $L$ = the heat of vaporization at temperature $T$.
$L + \Delta L$ = the heat of vaporization at temperature $T + \Delta T$.
$\quad c_{AB}$ = the specific heat of the liquid for a change along $AB$.
$\quad c_{DC}$ = the specific heat of the vapor for a change along $DC$.

From considerations of internal energy changes (see Eq. 22), we have for the cycle

$$\Sigma\, \Delta u = [c_{AB}\, \Delta T - p\, \Delta v] + [(L + \Delta L) - (p + \Delta p)(v' - \Delta v' - v -$$
$$\Delta v)] + [-c_{DC}\, \Delta T - p\, \Delta v'] + [-L + p(v' - \Delta v' - v)] = 0 \quad (41)$$

Neglecting differentials of the second order, this may be reduced to

$$\sum \frac{\Delta u}{\Delta T} = (c_{AB} - c_{DC}) + \frac{\Delta L}{\Delta T} - \frac{\Delta p}{\Delta T}(v' - v) = 0 \quad (42)$$

A summation of the changes of entropy per unit mass for the cycle, summed up in the manner just described for internal energy changes per unit mass, yields

$$\Sigma\, \Delta S = \left[\frac{c_{AB}\, \Delta T}{T + \Delta T/2}\right] + \left[\frac{L + \Delta L}{T + \Delta T}\right]$$
$$+ \left[\frac{-c_{DC}\, \Delta T}{T + \Delta T/2}\right] + \left[\frac{-L}{T}\right] = 0 \quad (43)$$

Taking account of the fact that to the first approximation $1/(T + \Delta T)$ may be replaced by $(1/T)(1 - \Delta T/T)$ and neglecting all second- and higher-order terms, we obtain

$$\Sigma \, \Delta S = c_{AB} \frac{\Delta T}{T}\left(1 - \frac{\Delta T}{2T}\right) + \frac{L}{T}\left(1 + \frac{\Delta L}{L} - \frac{\Delta T}{T}\right)$$

$$- c_{DC} \frac{\Delta T}{T}\left(1 - \frac{\Delta T}{2T}\right) - \frac{L}{T} = 0 \quad (44)$$

Further simplification yields

$$(c_{AB} - c_{DC}) + \frac{\Delta L}{\Delta T} - \frac{L}{T} = 0 \quad (45)$$

Finally, by combining Eqs. 42 and 45, and passing to the limit, we obtain,

$$L = T\frac{dp}{dT}(v' - v) \quad (46)$$

which is Clapeyron's equation.

It is of interest to apply this equation to water at its normal boiling point. Inserting measured values for $T$, $dp/dT$, $v'$, and $v$ we have

$$L = 373.16°\text{K} \times 0.035699 \frac{\text{A}}{\text{K}°}(1.3448 - 0.0008)\frac{\text{gmv}}{\text{mole}}$$

$$= 17.904 \frac{\text{gmv A}}{\text{mol}} \quad (47)$$

$$= 539.21 \frac{\text{cal}}{\text{gm}}$$

This value checks exceedingly well with the experimental value, 539.14 cal/gm, obtained at the Bureau of Standards in Washington.

Clapeyron's equation may also be obtained by applying the basic efficiency relation, Eq. 19, for a Carnot engine to a Carnot cycle whose intake of energy is furnished by condensing a saturated vapor at temperature $T$ and which delivers its unused heat to a sink at the temperature $T - dT$. This procedure leads to

$$\eta = \frac{W}{Q_1} = \frac{m\,dp(v' - v)}{mL} = \frac{T - (T - dT)}{T} = \frac{dT}{T} \quad (48)$$

and at once to Eq. 46. Though much longer, the first-described procedure is given here first because of the better conception regarding the universality of the two basic laws of thermodynamics to which it leads.

It is interesting to consider what interpretation may be given to the right-hand member of Eq. 46. For this purpose, we rewrite it as

$$L = p(v' - v) + \left(T \frac{dp}{dT} - p\right)(v' - v) \tag{49}$$

Of this, the first member on the right represents work per unit mass done against outside forces due to the external pressure. On the other hand, since $\left(T \frac{dp}{dT} - p\right)$ represents an internal pressure (see the discussion of van der Waals' equation in Chapter VIII), the product $\left(T \frac{dp}{dT} - p\right)(v' - v)$ represents work per unit mass done against internal forces. The two together represent, thus, the combined external and internal work done per unit of mass on vaporizing a substance, and that is the heat of vaporization of the material.

**13. The Boltzmann Fourth-Power Law for Blackbody Radiation.** For the derivation of this law relating to blackbody radiation, it is convenient to use a Carnot cycle. It is necessary also to make use of a fact first deduced theoretically by the great Scottish mathematical physicist J. Clerk Maxwell (1831–1879) in 1871 and discovered experimentally and independently by the Russian physicist P. Lebedew (1866–1912) in 1900 and by the American physicists E. F. Nichols (1869–1924) and G. F. Hull (1870–  ) at Dartmouth College shortly thereafter, in 1901. It is that radiant energy exerts a force on a body that absorbs or reflects it. In a cavity surrounded by opaque walls at a uniform temperature, or, as it is ordinarily called, a blackbody cavity, theory indicates that a radiant energy pressure exists which is equal to one-third of the radiant-energy density in the cavity. The fourth-power law itself was first derived theoretically by the German physicist Ludwig Boltzmann in 1884. A previous experimental discovery is often ascribed to another German physicist, Josef Stefan (1831–1897), as of 1879. A consideration of conditions indicates, however, that discovery was assumed but not actually verified.

For the derivation of the law, we assume an engine much like the Carnot engine described above, which was designed to work with an ideal gas. This engine will differ from it, in that the space within the cylinder is to be completely evacuated and in that the surfaces of the cylinder and piston, which were described before as being completely insulated thermally, are now to be perfectly reflecting, or, what is the same, insulated radiationally.

Fig. 6 shows on a $p$-$V$ diagram the particular Carnot cycle which will be used. We start, as indicated by position $A$, with the cylinder in contact with the hot source at temperature $T$ and with the piston pushed completely in so that the volume of the working space is zero. The piston is then drawn back until the working space possesses the volume $V$, as indicated by position $B$. The process is isothermal, and the working space is now filled with radiation characterized by temperature $T$ and pressure $p$. The cylinder is now shifted to the thermally insulating stand, and the working space is expanded adiabatically to the condition indicated at $C$, characterized by a pressure $p - \Delta p$ and a temperature $T - \Delta T$. Next the cylinder is shifted to the cold reservoir whose temperature is $T - \Delta T$. The piston is then moved in until the working space, as indicated at $D$, is reduced to zero. During this process, which is isothermal, both the pressure and the temperature

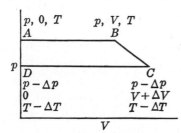

FIG. 6.   A Carnot cycle for black-body radiation.

remain constant. The final process consists in shifting the cylinder from the cold reservoir to the hot reservoir, and the cycle is then complete. This last process may be carried through instead as a regular adiabatic compression in which only negligibly small volumes are involved. The results will be identical.

As for the derivation of the Clapeyron equation, consider first the changes in internal energy in the working space for the complete cycle $ABCDA$, second the corresponding changes in entropy. For both cases, the summations must yield zero for the cycle. For the internal energy, we thus obtain

$$\Sigma U = [uV] + \left[ -\left( p - \frac{\Delta p}{2} \right) \Delta V \right]$$

$$+ \left[ -(u - \Delta u)(V + \Delta V) \right] + [0] = 0 \quad (50)$$

Neglecting differentials of the second order, we obtain

$$-p \, \Delta V - u \, \Delta V + V \, \Delta u = 0 \quad (51)$$

Taking into account the connection between $u$ and $p$ referred to above, Eq. 51 further reduces to

$$\frac{\Delta V}{V} = \frac{3}{4} \frac{\Delta u}{u} \quad (52)$$

Similarly, from entropy considerations, we obtain

$$\Sigma \, \Delta S = \left[ \frac{uV + pV}{T} \right] + [0]$$

$$+ \left[ \frac{-(u - \Delta u)(V + \Delta V) - (p - \Delta p)(V + \Delta V)}{T - \Delta T} \right]$$

$$+ [0] = 0 \quad (53)$$

Replacing $1/(T - \Delta T)$ by $(1/T)(1 + \Delta T/T)$ and $p$ and $\Delta p$ by $u/3$ and $\Delta u/3$ leads to

$$-\frac{\Delta T}{T} + \frac{\Delta u}{u} - \frac{\Delta V}{V} = 0 \quad (54)$$

Combined, Eqs. 52 and 54 lead to

$$\frac{\Delta u}{u} = 4 \frac{\Delta T}{T} \quad (55)$$

and on integration to

$$u = aT^4 \quad (56)$$

one form of the fourth-power law.

Though not shown here, it is possible to demonstrate that the radiant energy density in a blackbody cavity is related to the radiancy $\mathcal{R}$ of a blackbody at the same temperature by

$$\mathcal{R} = \frac{c}{4} u \quad (57)$$

where $c$ is the velocity of light. It follows therefore that

$$\mathcal{R} = \frac{ac}{4} T^4 = \sigma T^4 \quad (58)$$

The constant $\sigma$ is referred to often as the fourth-power radiation constant. Its value, as evaluated by R. T. Birge (1887– ) of the University of California, is $5.672 \times 10^{-12} \dfrac{\text{watts}}{\text{cm}^2 \, \text{K}^{o4}}$. Eqs. 56 and/or 58 represent the Boltzmann fourth-power law for blackbody radiation. It is one of the basic laws in the field of radiation. Without the concept of entropy, its derivation theoretically must have been greatly delayed.

As for the Clapeyron equation, there is a much simpler derivation for the fourth-power law which makes use of the efficiency relation for a Carnot engine. This derivation is left as an exercise for the student.

**14. The Entropy of an Isolated System Tends toward a Maximum.**
Important as is the concept of entropy in the derivation of relations
such as are expressed by Eqs. 46 and 58, it is perhaps of more value
in enabling an experimenter to foretell, with the aid of a small amount
of data, general conditions of equilibrium in systems where more than
one component or more than one phase of one component are present.
The general basis for such predictions is the second law of thermodynamics as stated in the affirmative form on p. 264, or in the abbreviated common form, "The entropy of an isolated system tends toward
a maximum."

It is difficult, on the basis of the foregoing discussion, to obtain a
satisfying physical concept of entropy similar to those that we have
for mass, energy or momentum. Perhaps, because there is not conservation of entropy, it is impossible or at least not to be expected.
The relations on which we must build our entropy concepts are (1) the
most fundamental of all thermodynamic laws, the zeroth law of thermodynamics (see p. 21) a corollary of which states, "An isolated, inextensible system tends with time toward an equilibrium condition with
a constant temperature throughout"; (2) the first law of thermodynamics, which, as expressed by Eq. 6,

$$Q = \Delta U + W \tag{6}$$

states that the energy added to a system in the form of heat is equal
to the sum of the increase in internal energy of the system and the
work done externally by the system; (3) Eq. 32,

$$dS = \frac{dQ}{T} \tag{32}$$

which, applying only to reversible processes, gives a quantitative
expression for changes of entropy that occur; and (4) the statement
of the second law of thermodynamics in its positive form, namely,
"In isolated systems, changes of condition are accompanied by either
no change in entropy or by an increase in entropy depending on
whether all processes involved are reversible or include one or more
that are irreversible."

In accord with the foregoing a metal bar with its temperature varying gradually from one end to the other will shift, if isolated, to an
equilibrium with a constant temperature throughout. In so doing,
the irreversible process of heat conduction is involved and the entropy
of the system will increase. Given the initial conditions and certain
characteristics of the metal, the amount of the increase may be com-

puted.  Similarly, an isolated system, composed of an evacuated, opaque enclosure and several bodies at different temperatures suspended within it by fine fibers, will experience an increase in entropy that may be computed, as they shift to an equilibrium.  The irreversible process of transfer of energy by radiation is here responsible.  Other illustrations of actions involving irreversible processes and increases of entropy are (a) the free expansion of air through a leaky stopper into an evacuated chamber, (b) the throttling of the liquid in an electrically operated refrigerator from a region of high pressure to a region of low pressure, (c) the oxidation of carbon in a flame, (d) the diffusion of alcohol in water, (e) the drawing of a wire, (f) the Joulean heating of an electric conductor by an electric current, (g) the magnetic hysteresis heating of iron by the reversal of its magnetism, (h) the coagulation of the white of an egg, (i) the slowing down by friction of the whirling motion of a stirred cup of coffee, etc.

An outstanding fact is that, wherever an irreversible process occurs, an increase of entropy of the involved system takes place.  It is also true, of course, that, where heat is added to a body reversibly, an increase in the entropy of that body takes place in accord with Eq. 32. However, at the same time, some other body or bodies in a system including the first body has lost an equal amount of entropy.  For the system, there is no change involved for a reversible process.

Despite the fact that in theory we very frequently deal with idealized reversible processes, processes that are strictly reversible are actually rare.  It is by far the common thing that "The entropy of an isolated system" which is not in equilibrium should tend "toward a maximum."

A brief discussion of the nature of entropy from a very different standpoint follows.

**15. The Statistical Nature of Entropy.**  Starting with the fundamental laws of mechanics, as presented by Newton's laws of motion and more particularly the laws of quantum mechanics, and a certain postulate, certain interesting parallels are obtained which lead to an interpretation for entropy.  The postulate is that a system of particles forming an isolated system, with a given total amount of energy and of momentum, whatever their initial distribution as to position and momentum, will tend toward an equilibrium distribution which on the basis of pure chance represents that one which occurs most frequently or, as is often said, is the most probable.  Strictly speaking, however, this equilibrium distribution is never maintained exactly even if ever exactly attained.  As has been shown experimentally for small systems involving a limited number of particles, appreciable deviations are constantly occurring with always a general tendency, however, to return to the distribution that is most probable. With systems involving huge numbers of particles, with some exceptions that may be specified, these deviations are undoubtedly present though generally undetectable. Two conclusions that may be drawn are: (1) The most probable distribution of a system of particles is the one that yields a maximum of entropy for the system. (2) When there are two possible states for a substance, containing the same amount of internal energy, as, for example, an ice-water mixture on the one hand and undercooled water on the other, the more stable state not only possesses the greater entropy but also the greater probability of occurrence on the basis of chance. The conclusion to which the foregoing seems to lead is that the entropy of a system in any particular condition is a measure of the probability of occurrence of that condition. On the other hand, as has been pointed out, the entropy principle, though a direct consequence of the great second law of thermodynamics, has certain limitations. Despite its great value, its predictions fail when applied to Brownian movements and to the spontaneous minute density fluctuations that occur in gases when the systems under consideration are sufficiently small. Even in these cases, however, the second law predicts an average around which observed states of matter center.

## PROBLEMS

1. Given an ideal gas with $\gamma$ equal to 1.40 and $p$, $V$, $T$ values of 1.000 A, 1.000 gmv, 300°K for point $A$ of Fig. 1 and 0.840 A and 288°K for point $C$ (the volume may be computed) of a Carnot cycle, compute $p$, $V$, $T$ values for points $B$ and $D$, and determine the $Q_{AB}$, $Q_{CD}$, $\Sigma W$, and the efficiency that characterizes the cycle.

2. Draw to scale graphs for the data given in problem 1.

3. Compute, for the data given in problem 1: (1) the heat required, the work done, and the changes in internal energy produced in heating the gas from point $C$ to point $A$ via $B$ and via $D$; (2) the corresponding changes in entropy for the gas.

4. Compute the change in entropy experienced by a kg of ice at 0°C on being heated to 100°C under a pressure of 1 A and then completely vaporized. Graph the change in entropy as a function of the temperature to which the ice has been heated.

5. One gram of water at a pressure of just 1 A on boiling changes from a specific volume of about 1.0 cm³/gm to about 1673 cm³/gm. On the basis that the heat of vaporization of water is 539.2 cal/gm, what are the changes that take place in $U$, $S$, and $H$?

6. If the gas used in the discussion of Fig. 4 had a $\gamma$ of 5/3, what would have been the entropy change in going from position $A$ to position $C$? in going from $B$ to $D$?

7. Given that a mole of ideal gas whose $\gamma$ is 1.40 expands from 30 A and 300°K to 5 A without change of temperature on passing through a porous plug, what is the change in entropy on such expansion?

**8.** From water under atmospheric pressure and at 0°C, heat may be removed, if done quietly, without causing the water to freeze. If heat has been removed to the extent of cooling water to −5°C before ice begins to form, what change in entropy per unit mass occurs during the sudden freezing that then takes place?

**9.** In a specific-heat experiment 100 gm of lead ($c_p = 0.0345$ cal/(gm C°)) at 100°C is mixed with 200 gm of water at 20°C. How different is the entropy of the system at the end from what it was just before the mixing?

**10.** Osborne and co-workers at the National Bureau of Standards report, for water at 0.00°C, specific volumes of 1.00021 cm³/gm for the liquid and of $2.06288 \times 10^5$ cm³/gm for the saturated vapor, a vapor tension of 0.006027 A, and a $dp/dT$ for the saturated vapor of 0.0004373 A/K°. What is the heat of vaporization of water at 0°C that may be derived?

**11.** Making use of the efficiency relation for a Carnot engine, derive Boltzmann's fourth-power radiation law. Use temperatures $T$ and $T + dT$.

**12.** Show that Buckingham's statement of Carnot's principle is included in the affirmative form of the second law of thermodynamics.

# CHAPTER X

## CHANGE OF PHASE *

**1. Introduction.** Among the effects on matter due to a change of temperature, the most striking is change of phase. Everyone is familiar with the relatively large changes in density, refractive index, etc., that usually accompany a transformation from, say, the liquid to the solid phase. The initial and final phases are so different in nearly all such readily apparent properties that it is not surprising to discover the equally appreciable changes in less readily observable properties, such as electrical resistivity, thermal conductivity, and specific heat. When matter is subject to large changes in pressure and temperature, even more striking phenomena appear. In the work of P. W. Bridgman (1882–   ), Nobel prize winner in physics for 1946, at Harvard University on water, for example, where pressures up to 45,000 A were applied, five new forms of ice were found, each having properties differing somewhat from those of the ice with which we are familiar.

In industry, direct application of change of phase is made in distillation processes. Refrigeration cycles offer another example, steam engines a third. In gasoline engines, change of phase is combined with chemical action. The subject is highly important economically. On the other hand, in mountainous regions, where there is difficulty in cooking food due to the lower boiling temperatures of water, change of phase becomes at least a temporary inconvenience.

Most changes of phase that occur may be grouped into two classes. Those accompanied by the transfer of heat at fixed temperatures, such as the boiling of water or any liquid-solid, solid-vapor, or liquid-vapor transition, are changes of the first kind. Also included are changes from one solid phase to another, involving a rearrangement of atoms, such as the transformation that occurs in iron at 920°C when, on

---

* Change of state is frequently used where, in this book, change of phase is used. In agreement with thermodynamic treatments, change of state is recognized as a broader term. To be specific, a change of state is understood to have taken place when there has occurred a change of pressure, or of temperature, or of some other state-determining factor, though the change may be trifling. A change of phase, however, signifies a more fundamental change, as from a vapor to a liquid, or a change from one crystalline structure to another. The number of states possible for a sample of material is infinite; the number of phases, however, is finite and few.

being heated, its atomic arrangement changes from body-centered cubic to face-centered cubic. These latter transformations involving drastic rearrangements are, like the former, usually accompanied by abrupt changes in volume, entropy, etc.

Among changes of phase of the second kind, those in which isothermal heats of transformations are absent, the most common is the Curie* transition for magnetic materials involving loss of magnetism on heating. For iron the temperature is about 770°C. Although in such changes there are heat effects, the heat transfer is not an isothermal transfer but occurs gradually over a temperature range. There are other examples, notably the order-disorder transformation, already referred to, that occurs in certain alloys. These changes show discontinuities in specific heat and in certain other properties. Phase changes of the second kind have received much theoretical and experimental attention during recent years.

**2. Graphical Representation of Phases.** When matter is homogeneous throughout in all its large-scale properties, it is said to be in a single phase. If, however, two or more divisions of matter with differing large-scale properties exist in a portion of space, two or more phases are said to exist there. Often, but not always, more than one such phase will be associated with a single substance. Ordinarily, substances possess at least three phases, solid, liquid, and gaseous. Frequently a substance has more than one solid phase. Thus, the substance water has three common phases, ordinary ice, liquid, and gas, and certain other, much less common ice phases as noted above. Which phases may be present in any instance will generally, though not always, depend largely on the existing pressure and temperature.

In representing phases and phase phenomena on two-dimensional plots, the $p$-$v$ and $p$-$T$ diagrams, shown for water in Figs. 1 and 2, are much used. Also common are the $T$-$s$ (temperature-specific entropy) and the $h$-$s$ (specific enthalpy-specific entropy) diagrams which are much used by engineers, the latter being known as Mollier diagrams. With some exceptions, a point of any one of these plots specifies a definite state for the substance considered. In this discussion of water, it is to be noted that, where a $p$ refers to a gas phase, the $p$ is that due to the water only and does not include that due to the air or other gas that may be present.

In the $p$-$v$ diagram of Fig. 1, several isothermal lines are shown. Also three regions are indicated, which meet at the point $P_c$, known as the

---

* Pierre Curie (1859–1906) was an able French physicist who, with his wife, Marie Sklodovska Curie (1867–1934), and A. Henri Becquerel (1852–1908), were awarded the Nobel prize in physics for 1903, for work done in radioactivity.

critical point.　The temperature, $T_c$, and the pressure, $p_c$, which define this point are known as the critical temperature and the critical pressure.　Physically, the former is defined as the highest temperature at which a gas may be liquefied, and the latter as the lowest pressure which will produce liquefaction at the critical temperature.　These two quantities serve to specify the critical state of the substance.　All other properties, such as density, and internal energy, for that state are then

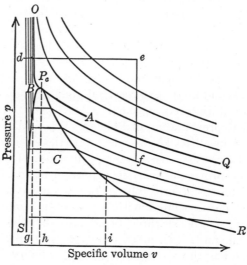

FIG. 1.　A $p$-$v$ plot for a substance such as water.　(To be true to scale, the horizontal distance from the pressure axis to the $P_cR$ line should be very greatly magnified.)

uniquely fixed.　All substances capable of existing as liquids and gases have critical point states.　More will be said about this later.

Of the three regions of Fig. 1 just referred to, region $A$ represents the gaseous phase.　With each point therein, there is associated a particular state for gaseous water, that described by the pressure and specific volume indicated by the point.　That portion of region $A$ below the isotherm corresponding to the critical temperature, $T_c$, that is, the region between the critical isotherm $OP_cQ$ and the saturated-vapor line $P_cR$ (to be discussed later) and extending indefinitely to the right, is sometimes referred to as the vapor region, while the remaining portion only of region $A$ is said to represent water in a gaseous state.　This distinction is highly artificial.　Nevertheless, it is customary to apply the term vapor to a gas whose condition or approximate condition is such that it could exist in equilibrium with its liquid.

Similarly region $B$ of Fig. 1 represents the liquid state. Often, however, the term is limited to the region bounded by the $p$-axis, the critical isotherm $OP_cQ$, and the saturated-liquid line $P_cS$. As will appear shortly, the use of the critical isotherm as a boundary here is also highly artificial. Finally, points in region $C$, between the saturated-liquid and saturated-vapor lines, represent mixtures of liquid and vapor in equilibrium, varying from 100% vapor on the right to 100% liquid on the left. The specific volume to be associated with a point in region $C$, where two phases exist, is an intermediate specific volume. When the separate values for the saturated vapor and the saturated liquid, $v_v$ and $v_l$ are known, the relative amounts of vapor and liquid, $m_v/(m_v + m_l)$ and $m_l/(m_v + m_l)$, corresponding to any intermediate specific volume may be determined. For example, at a temperature slightly above 0°C, the specific volumes of the saturated liquid and the saturated vapor for water are 1.00 cm³/gm and 200,000 cm³/gm. At the intermediate specific volume, 50,000 cm³/gm, we have

$$50,000 \ \frac{\text{cm}^3}{\text{gm}} = \frac{V_v + V_l}{m_v + m_l} = \frac{v_v m_v + v_l m_l}{m_v + m_l} = \frac{v_v \dfrac{m_v}{m_l} + v_l}{\dfrac{m_v}{m_l} + 1} \qquad (1)$$

Solution yields ⅓ for $m_v/m_l$, and the system is ¼ vapor. In the simplified graph of Fig. 1, the solid phase has not been included.

A striking feature of the $p$-$v$ diagram is the rapid rise of the isotherms in region $B$, a consequence of the relative incompressibility of liquid water. Also revealed here is the manner, not commonly realized, by which a liquid may be changed to a gas or a vapor without vaporization or boiling taking place. For this, a constant-pressure change $de$ followed by a constant-volume change $ef$ will suffice. Such a continuous and gradual change from the properties of the liquid to those of the vapor without any sudden change in any physical property demonstrates the principle of "continuity of state," concerning which more will appear later.

In Fig. 2, where the $p$-$T$ boundaries of the common phases of water are represented, three general regions are again suggested. In the interior of each, equilibrium occurs with only one phase present. At the boundaries of these regions, as represented by the three lines separating these regions in the figure, two phases may exist in equilibrium. Along one, the freezing or fusion curve, ice and liquid water are in equilibrium, and, along the sublimation curve or hoar-frost line, ice and water vapor. The one point where the three curves meet, $P_t$, the triple point, corresponds to the condition where the three phases of water are simultaneously in equilibrium. It is realized experimentally by placing ice and water in a flask and reducing the pressure therein to 4.579 mm-Hg. In this condition all three phases may be maintained indefinitely in equilibrium. All substances have triple points.

It is interesting to note that what is represented in Fig. 2 by the single finite curve $P_tP_c$ is represented in Fig. 1 by the area below the curve $SP_cR$. Of course, similar statements could be made of the liquid

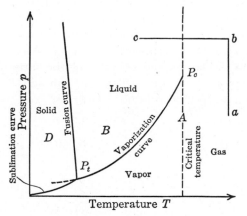

FIG. 2.   A $p$-$T$ plot for water.

solid and the frost lines, were Fig. 1 so magnified as to show the corresponding regions. Similarly, triple points may show up in certain graphs as lines or even as surfaces.

The vaporization curve for water, which includes as one of its points the normal boiling point, terminates at the high-temperature end at the critical point, $P_c$ (often reported as 374°C, 218 A, and 0.40 gm/cm³), and at the lower end at the triple point, $P_t$ (0.0075°C, 4.579 mm-Hg and 1.00021 cm³/gm for the liquid).

The advantages of both the $p$-$v$ and the $p$-$T$ diagrams may be combined by constructing a three-dimensional $p$-$v$-$T$ surface, as has been done for water at relatively low pressures in Fig. 3$A$ and for an extended range of pressures in Fig. 3$B$. Viewed parallel to the $T$-axis, Fig. 3$A$ appears as a $p$-$v$ diagram (Fig. 1); viewed parallel to the $v$-axis, it appears as a $p$-$T$ diagram (Fig. 2). On such a plot, transition lines of the $p$-$T$ diagram appear as surfaces and the triple point appears as a line extending, in the case of water, from a specific volume of 1.00 cm³/gm (saturated liquid) to 206,000 cm³/gm (saturated

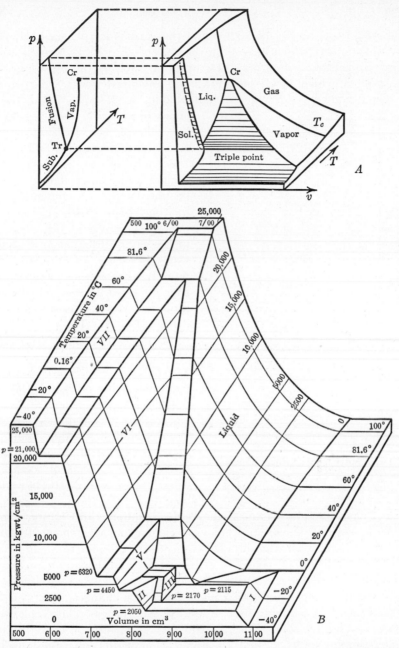

FIG. 3. A $p$-$v$-$T$ surface for water involving ($A$) only the ordinary ice phase, ($B$) many ice phases as constructed by Verwiebe on the basis of measurements by Bridgman (by permission, Zemansky, *Heat and Thermodynamics*, 2nd ed., p. 181, McGraw-Hill Book Co., 1943).

287

vapor). Incidentally, Fig. 3B shows the various ice phases I, II, III, V, VI, and VII which have been referred to above. Evidently other three-dimensional plots may be employed, such as the *u-v-s* and the *h-s-p* plots, which are discussed in more advanced works.

The fusion curve for water, as indicated in Fig. 2, shows that, with increase of pressure, there is a slight lowering of the freezing point. It amounts to only 0.0072 C°/A —enough for the production of certain interesting effects, as will be noted later. A change in the melting point with change in pressure is universal, but a change in the same direction as that for water is rather uncommon. Far more frequently the change is like that obtained by the Netherlands physicist W. H. Keesom for hydrogen (Fig. 4). For the pressure range indicated, that is from 0 to 450 kgwt/cm², about 435 A, the average rate of increase of freezing point with pressure is about 0.025 C°/A. Others have followed the curve for hydrogen up to 5000 A and a freezing point of about 75°K without any indications of other forms of solid hydrogen such as Fig. 3B shows for water.

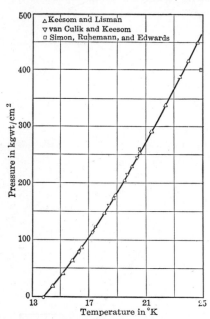

FIG. 4. The melting curve of hydrogen as obtained by Keesom and others (W. H. Keesom and J. H. C. Lisman, *Communication* 213 e, p. 43, *Physical Laboratory of the University of Leiden*, 1931).

3. **Phase Boundaries and Clapeyron's Equation.** In Chapter IX, a general relation, known as Clapeyron's equation, was shown to hold for a reversible transition of a substance from a liquid to a gas phase for the condition of constant temperature and constant pressure. Though derived for a transition involving a particular phase change, it is equally applicable to other reversible phase changes, such as from a solid phase to a liquid phase, a solid phase to a gas phase, one solid phase to another solid phase, or the reverse of any one. With this understanding let us consider the application of this equation, namely,

$$\frac{dp}{dT} = \frac{L}{T(v_A - v_B)} \qquad (2)$$

to the phase changes that occur along the three equilibrium boundaries of Figs. 1 to 3.

Consider, first, transitions which lead to the vapor phase. In Eq. 2, $v_A$, the specific volume for the higher-temperature phase, necessarily refers to the vapor phase while $v_B$ refers to a lower-temperature phase, that of the liquid or the solid. $L$ is the heat per unit mass required to bring about the transition from phase $B$ to phase $A$. Since all substances expand on boiling or vaporizing, $v_A$ will always exceed $v_B$, and, if $L$ is positive—as it always is—the coefficient $dp/dT$, which is the slope of the liquid-vapor or solid-vapor transition curve of Fig. 2, will always be positive. An increase of vapor pressure at equilibrium always accompanies an increase of the equilibrium temperature. This is in agreement with experiment.

Consider next a solid-liquid transition, in particular the ice-water change presented in Fig. 2. Here there is a contraction on melting, $v_A$ is less than $v_B$, and hence $dp/dT$ is negative. An increase of pressure lowers the freezing point. For this transition at 0°C, $v_A = 1.000$ cm$^3$/gm, $v_B = 1.087$ cm$^3$/gm, $L = 80.0$ cal/gm, and hence

$$\frac{dp}{dT} = \frac{L}{T(v_A - v_B)} = \frac{80\ \text{cal/gm}}{273°\text{K}\ (-0.087)\ \text{cm}^3/\text{gm}} \times \frac{10^3\ \text{cm}^3\ \text{A}}{24.1\ \text{cal}}$$

$$= -140\ \frac{\text{A}}{\text{K}°} \tag{3}$$

of which the term $10^3$ cm$^3$ A/24.1 cal is a conversion factor and is therefore equal to unity. As a more convenient expression for the ice-water line at ordinary pressures, we have,

$$\frac{dT}{dp} = -0.0072\ \frac{\text{C}°}{\text{A}} \tag{4}$$

An increase in pressure of 1 A lowers the freezing point by 0.0072 C°.

Two pieces of ice, both at or very close to the melting point, on being tightly pressed together and then released, solidify into a single piece. This phenomenon, known as regelation, is explained by the dependence of the freezing point on pressure outlined above. With the increased pressure and lowered freezing point, equilibrium can be maintained only by the melting of ice, by its cooling to a lower temperature, or by a combination of these two means. In fact, in the absence of a possible exchange of heat with other bodies, the combination effect actually occurs. Some ice melts. The heat required is furnished by the ice which does not melt and which in consequence cools to the new

melting point.   With release of the pressure, the liquid, now at a
temperature below the normal freezing point, freezes.   The surrounding ice is supplied some heat by the water that freezes, and its temperature is raised to the normal freezing point, but during the freezing the
two blocks in contact become united.

For substances which expand on melting, a far more common occurrence, the freezing curve has everywhere a positive slope.   With increase of pressure, there is then a raising of the melting-freezing point.
The steep slope of the solid-liquid curve is accounted for chiefly by the
fact that, compared with the liquid-vapor and solid-vapor transitions,
$v_A - v_B$ is very small, hence $dp/dT$ is large.

The Clapeyron equation, applied to the liquid-vapor transition, may
be regarded as the differential equation of the vaporization curve.   If
the heat of vaporization, $L$, were known as a function of temperature,
it would be possible to integrate this expression and obtain an equation
for the vaporization curve, and vice versa, as will appear later.   The
simple assumption that $L$ is constant, applied to cases where the specific
volume of the liquid may be neglected in comparison with that of the
vapor and where the vapor may be assumed to obey the ideal-gas law,
leads to a much-used, simple, but approximate relation.   From Eq.
2, one obtains directly

$$\frac{dp}{dT} = \frac{L}{v_A T} = \frac{Lp}{RT^2} \tag{5}$$

Separation of the variables followed by integration between the limits
$p_0$, $T_0$, and $p$, $T$ yields

$$\frac{dp}{p} = \frac{L}{R} \frac{dT}{T^2} \tag{6}$$

and

$$\ln \frac{p}{p_0} = \frac{L}{R} \left( \frac{1}{T_0} - \frac{1}{T} \right) \tag{7}$$

Conveniently $p_0$ may be taken as the saturated vapor pressure, or
vapor tension, corresponding to an arbitrarily chosen temperature $T_0$.

It is known that $L$ decreases as the temperature increases, becoming
zero at the critical point.   In partial recognition of this fact, the above
assumption of constancy for $L$ is frequently modified to take into
account the fact that its variation with $T$ may be approximated rather
well over a considerable range, well below the critical point, by the
linear relation

$$L = L_0 + B(T - T_0) \tag{8}$$

With this substitution and the other two assumptions given above, one obtains

$$\ln \frac{p}{p_0} = \frac{B}{R} \ln \frac{T}{T_0} + \frac{L_0 - BT_0}{R}\left(\frac{1}{T_0} - \frac{1}{T}\right) \qquad (9)$$

This expression has been widely used to represent vaporization curves. Eq. 9 is useful over a wider range than is Eq. 7. How well they fit for

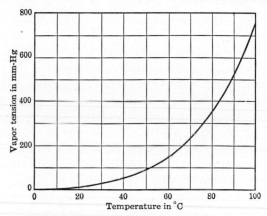

FIG. 5. Vapor tension of water for the temperature range 0°C–100°C.

water for the range 0°C to 100°C is shown in Table I. That the straight-line relation of Eq. 7 fails is shown by the column of the table

TABLE I

TEST OF THE APPLICABILITY OF EQS. 7 AND 9 TO WATER FOR THE RANGE 0°C TO 100°C

Data are those given by N. S. Osborne, H. F. Stimson, and D. C. Ginnings, *J. Research, Natl. Bur. Standards*, **13**, 1, 1934. For the standard condition, 1.00000 A and 373.16°K has been chosen. The constant determined for Eq. 7 is −5140 K°; those for Eq. 9 are −4.336 and −6585 K°. Computed pressures are indicated by $p_c$; those taken from the reported research by $p$.

| $T$ in °C | $p$ in A | $\frac{1}{T} \times 10^7$ in 1/K° | $\left(\frac{1}{T} - \frac{1}{T_0}\right) \times 10^7$ in 1/K° | $\ln \frac{p}{p_0}$ | $\ln \frac{T}{T_0}$ | $\ln \frac{p_c}{p_0}$ (Eq. 7) | $\frac{p - p_c}{p}$ (Eq. 7) | $\ln \frac{p_c}{p_0}$ (Eq. 9) | $\frac{p - p_c}{p}$ (Eq. 9) |
|---|---|---|---|---|---|---|---|---|---|
| 0 | 0.006027 | 36,609 | 9811 | −5.111 | −0.31195 | −5.0428 | −.071 | −5.1079 | −0.0036 |
| 10 | 0.012102 | 35,316 | 8518 | 4.4144 | .27600 | 4.3783 | −.037 | 4.4124 | −0.0020 |
| 20 | 0.023042 | 34,111 | 7313 | 3.7704 | .24128 | 3.7589 | −.012 | 3.7694 | −0.0010 |
| 30 | 0.041831 | 32,986 | 6188 | 3.1741 | .20776 | 3.1676 | +.007 | 3.1740 | −0.0001 |
| 40 | 0.072748 | 31,933 | 5135 | 2.6208 | .17531 | 2.6394 | +.019 | 2.6213 | +0.0005 |
| 50 | 0.12170 | 30,944 | 4146 | 2.1062 | .14388 | 2.1311 | +.025 | 2.1063 | +0.0001 |
| 60 | 0.19656 | 30,016 | 3218 | 1.6268 | .11341 | 1.6541 | +.028 | 1.6274 | +0.0006 |
| 70 | 0.30752 | 29,141 | 2343 | 1.1792 | .08381 | 1.2043 | +.025 | 1.1794 | +0.0002 |
| 80 | 0.46740 | 28,316 | 1518 | 0.7606 | .05510 | 0.7803 | +.020 | 0.7607 | +0.0001 |
| 90 | 0.69192 | 27,536 | 0738 | 0.3683 | .02717 | 0.3793 | +.011 | 0.3682 | −0.0001 |
| 100 | 1.00000 | 26,798 | 0000 | 0.0000 | .00000 | 0.0000 | 0.000 | 0.0000 | 0.000 |

headed $(p - p_c)/p$ (Eq. 7). How much better Eq. 9 satisfies the data is shown by the final column of the table. The value of $L_0$ which the best straight line predicts is about 568 cal/gm, which is not very far from the standard value for 100°C; that which results for 100°C using Eq. 9, a relation still to be viewed as an approximation, is about 548 cal/gm. Similar relations may be developed for the sublimation curves.

Eqs. 7 and 9, involving the heat of vaporization, are commonly used for the determination of that quantity. A more direct method, dependent only on Eq. 7 for a correction for departure from standard conditions as to pressure, will be discussed later.

**4. The Critical State.** Many important properties undergo changes or assume special values at the critical point. Here, $P_c$ of Fig. 1, not only are the densities of the liquid and the vapor phases equal, but also the two phases are indistinguishable in all respects. Further, since the critical isotherm is horizontal here, it follows that the heat supplied to a substance at the critical point, keeping the pressure constant, is for the instant completely used up in doing external work without raising the temperature. This means that the specific heat at constant pressure, $c_p$, at this point is infinite. Since $c_v$ is not infinite, their ratio, $\gamma$, must be infinite. A. Michels (1889– ) and his co-workers in the Netherlands have actually observed for carbon dioxide, at 31.18°C and at 79.0 A, a $\gamma$ of 28.1. Though this value is far from being infinite, it is sufficiently greater than ordinary values, which range from 1.0 to 1.7, that one feels that experimental limitations may be the explanation for failure to attain more nearly the expected value.

Consider what might be expected to happen when three glass tubes $g$, $h$, and $i$ of the same size, filled with a liquid and its vapor with initial specific volumes corresponding to the points $g$, $h$, and $i$ of Fig. 1, are evacuated, sealed off, and heated. One expects most of the substance of the $g$ tube to be in the liquid phase initially corresponding to its low average specific volume. On heating at constant volume, there will be vaporization of the liquid, but, because of the relatively large volume which it occupies, it will experience a net increase of volume with increase of temperature. With continued heating, a temperature is finally reached such that the liquid fills the tube completely and the meniscus disappears at the top. The reverse is expected for a tube whose initial state is represented by $i$, and a state is reached such that, with the vapor filling the tube completely, the meniscus disappears at the bottom. However, for a certain intermediate initial condition such as $h$ for which the average specific volume is the same as the critical specific volume, one may expect the meniscus in the tube neither to rise to the top nor to sink to the bottom of the tube even when heated to the critical temperature.   Yet, with passage through the critical state and the elimination of all distinctions between liquid and vapor, there is necessarily a disappearance of the meniscus.

Disappearance of the meniscus in a critical-state tube has generally been taken as evidence that the surface tension has become zero. Without question, the surface tension is zero when the true critical point has been reached.   However, as will be seen later, the disappearance of the meniscus by itself is not proof of the presence of a critical state.

**5. The Law of Rectilinear Diameters.**   The most commonly used method for determining critical values employs the law of rectilinear diameters which is ascribed to two French scientists, L. P. Cailletet (1832–1913) and Émile Mathias.   Using this method, one places in a furnace a number of thick-walled glass tubes which contain different known masses, $m$, of the substance under investigation.   For each tube, at any temperature, one may write

$$m = \delta_l V_l + \delta_v V_v \tag{10}$$

where $V_l$ and $V_v$ are the volumes of the liquid and the vapor and $\delta_l$ and $\delta_v$ the corresponding densities.   With the tubes previously calibrated by massing when filled with mercury or otherwise, a cathetometer may be used to determine the volumes occupied by the liquid and by the vapor.   For each of several temperatures near the critical point, a set of equations of the type of Eq. 10 is obtained, one for each tube.   Taken in pairs for any specified temperature, such equations yield desired values for $\delta_l$ and $\delta_v$ for that temperature.   When these densities are plotted as a function of temperature, it is found for each substance studied that points representing their averages fall very closely along a straight line.   The assumption that the line is truly straight even to the critical-point temperature is known as the law of rectilinear diameters.   Using this law, one finds it possible to make a determination of the critical density and the critical temperature by a short extrapolation from observed data.   Such a determination can then be verified with the aid of a new tube using a mass of the liquid equal to the product of the volume of the tube and the extrapolated critical density.   Fig. 6 shows how well the law applies to oxygen.   The critical pressure may be determined by extrapolation of the vaporization curve to the critical temperature.   Actually the so-called rectilinear diameters are not quite straight; and, unless the laws are known, extrapolations are dangerous.

Some critical constants for various substances are given in Table II. Here it is seen that the so-called permanent gases, those difficult to liquefy, are well above their critical temperatures under ordinary conditions. Also, with the possible exception of carbon dioxide, all those substances that we commonly recognize as vapors under ordinary conditions are below their critical temperatures when under such conditions.

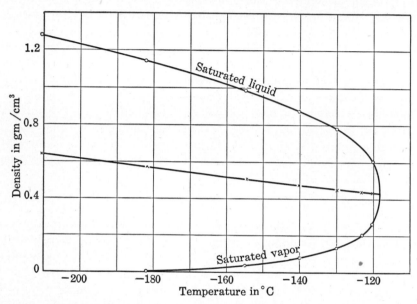

F i g. 6. The application of the Cailletet and Mathias law of rectilinear diameters in a determination of the critical density of oxygen by Mathias and Kammerlingh Onnes (*Communication* 117, *Physical Laboratory of the University of Leiden,* 1911).

**6. Critical-Region Difficulties.** The disappearance of a meniscus in a "critical-point tube" under the experimental conditions described above is frequently accepted as proof of the presence of the critical-point state. There is a fly in the ointment, however. Such disappearances are found actually to take place over a considerable range of average densities and not at just one average density which we would like to call the critical density. The range for carbon dioxide was found to vary from 0.341 $gm/cm^3$ to 0.589 $gm/cm^3$. This and related facts have led to the investigation of substances in the critical region at temperatures slightly above those at which menisci disappear.

For the purpose of studying possible density variations, G. Teichner, a German scientist, performed an experiment reported in 1904, in which several small solid spheres were included in a "critical tube" with the carbon tetrachloride which he studied. The densities of these spheres varied, but all were in the region of the expected critical density. Enclosed with the material in a tube, they might be expected to show by their positions and motions the existence of density differences and changes. Actually, considerable variations in density

## TABLE II

### CRITICAL CONSTANTS FOR VARIOUS SUBSTANCES

(Largely as reported in *International Critical Tables*, Vol. 3, p. 248.)

| | | $T_c$ in °C | $p_c$ in A | $\delta_c$ in gm/cm$^3$ | $\dfrac{RT_c}{p_c v_c}$ |
|---|---|---|---|---|---|
| Ammonia | $NH_3$ | 132.4 | 111.5 | 0.235 | 4.11 |
| Argon | A | −122 | 48. | 0.531 | 3.43 |
| Benzene | $C_6H_6$ | 288.5 | 47.7 | 0.304 | 3.76 |
| Carbon dioxide | $CO_2$ | 31.1 | 73.0 | 0.460 | 3.57 |
| Ethane | $C_2H_6$ | 32.1 | 48.8 | 0.21 | 3.60 |
| Ethyl alcohol | $C_2H_6O$ | 243.1 | 63.1 | 0.2755 | 4.09 |
| Ethylene | $C_2H_4$ | 9.7 | 50.9 | 0.22 | 3.58 |
| "Freon-12" | $CCl_2F_2$ | 111.5 | 39.6 | 0.555 | 3.66 |
| Helium | He | −267.9 | 2.26 | 0.0693 | 3.31 |
| Hydrogen | $H_2$ | −239.9 | 12.8 | 0.0310 | 3.28 |
| Neon | Ne | −228.7 | 25.9 | 0.484 | 3.38 |
| Nitrous oxide | $N_2O$ | 36.5 | 71.7 | 0.45 | 3.63 |
| Nitrogen | $N_2$ | −147.1 | 33.5 | 0.3110 | 3.43 |
| Oxygen | $O_2$ | −118.8 | 49.7 | 0.430 | 3.43 |
| Sulfur dioxide | $SO_2$ | 157.2 | 77.7 | 0.52 | 3.69 |
| Water | $H_2O$ | 374.0 | 217.7 | 0.4 | |
| | | 380.5 * | 248.* | 0.377 * | |

* As determined by Callendar, based on disappearance of the heat of vaporization rather than the disappearance of a meniscus. The $p_c$ and $\delta_c$ are approximate values only.

were found at temperatures above those corresponding to the disappearance of a meniscus. Just previous to the meniscus disappearance in any one instance, several spheres would be found at the meniscus, with varying portions protruding into the vapor region. Then, with a slight increase in temperature, first one and then another sphere would rise to the top of the tube or sink to the bottom as the density of the material in the upper portion of the tube became greater than that of a particular sphere or the density of that in the lower portion became less than that of another particular sphere. Not until a rise of about 2.5 C° above the temperature for meniscus disappearance had occurred did it appear that the density was uniform throughout the tube. Certain cloudlike forms present during intervening temperatures indicated that minute fog droplets were present in the vapor region.

An important study of the critical region for water was made by the English physicist Callendar (1863–1930) and reported in 1928. He showed the necessity of using very pure, air-free water. His work included determinations of density and of enthalpy, $H$ (see Chapter

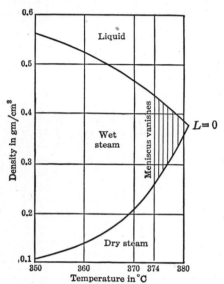

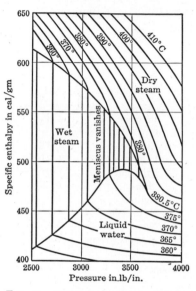

FIG. 7. Callendar's graph showing densities of saturated water vapor and of saturated water liquid in the critical point region (*Proc. Roy. Soc. London*, **A120**, 460, 1928).

FIG. 8. Callendar's graph showing enthalpy of water as a function of pressure at various temperatures, in the critical-point region (*Proc. Roy. Soc. London*, **A120**, 460, 1928).

IV). In various evacuated tubes of measured volumes, different known amounts of air-free water were sealed and heated. From the temperatures of disappearance of their menisci, in some at the tops of the tubes and in others at the bottoms, he determined with precision the densities along the saturated-vapor and the saturated-liquid curves (Fig. 7) for temperature below 374°C. He concluded that, at this upper limit of temperature as shown, saturated vapor has a density of about 0.264 gm/cm³ and saturated liquid a density of about 0.44 gm/cm³. The curves of constant enthalpy, $H$, were obtained by measuring temperatures and pressures when the water, either in liquid or vapor form at some high initial temperature and pressure, passed through a throttle (Fig. 8). With their aid he was able to make determinations of energy changes. Callendar stated that his results were highly consistent. Completely in agreement with Fig. 7, Fig. 8 indicates that, at 374°C where the meniscus vanishes, there is still a heat of vaporization, $L$, of 72.4 cal/gm and that only at 380.5°C is $L$ equal to zero. The corresponding pressures and densities are about 3660 lb/in.$^2$ or 249 A and about 0.38 gm/cm$^3$. Above 380.5°C, no indication of the coexistence of a liquid and a vapor was found. Despite the apparent definiteness of Callendar's results, they are questioned by several workers in the field.

It has been assumed that the surface tension of liquid water in contact with its vapor must be zero when the meniscus disappears. However, with a fog present at higher temperatures, this cannot be the case, for the existence of a water droplet depends on a positive value for the surface tension.

It would, in view of the foregoing, seem appropriate to regard the temperature at which $L$ becomes zero as the true critical temperature, but the difficulties of experimentation have resulted in rather few such determinations. Most tables of critical data seem to report the more easily determined temperature, that of meniscus disappearance, and with it corresponding pressures and extrapolated densities.

**7. Van der Waals' Equation and the Liquid State.** If, as in Fig. 9, isotherms are plotted on a $p$-$v$ diagram, in accord with the van der Waals * equation

$$\left(p + \frac{a}{v^2}\right)(v - b) = RT \quad (11)$$

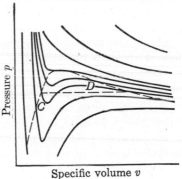

Fig. 9. A $p$-$v$ graph showing isotherms according to van der Waals' equation.

a definite resemblance to the experimental isotherms of Fig. 1 is observed, with, however, a gradual change from one type of variation to another. Isotherms corresponding to the higher temperatures approximate the familiar hyperbolas of the ideal-gas law. Those at lower temperatures resemble the isotherms of Fig. 1 which include the liquid state. The chief difference is in the behavior during the vapor-liquid transitions which appear in Fig. 1 as horizontal lines. Definitely separating two sets of isotherms is the critical isotherm which is characterized by a horizontal inflection at the critical point.

* J. D. van der Waals (1837–1923), winner of the Nobel prize in physics in 1910.

With attention fixed on the portion of the graph below the critical isotherm, it is instructive to discuss two experiments. (1) If we have a closed vessel completely filled with a pure liquid free from foreign matter, dissolved gases, and mechanical vibration, and if, without change of temperature for the liquid, we gradually and sufficiently reduce the pressure in the container, we may obtain the liquid in a superheated condition. Corresponding to a change along an isothermal of Fig. 10 from $A$ to $B$ to $C$, there is superheating as soon as the point $B$ is passed. At any given temperature in that range, the isothermal trace, ordinarily observed, is that of a part-liquid part-vapor

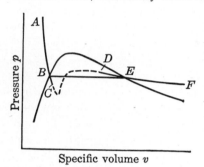

Specific volume $v$

FIG. 10. A diagram for illustrating the superheating of liquid water and the supercooling of water vapor.

isothermal which is horizontal and just below $BE$, and the condition as to $v$ and $p$ that actually occurs with the liquid thus superheated is that ordinarily found for a lower temperature. If, now, to the superheated liquid at $C$, a tiny bubble of the vapor is added, the liquid will change over at once by partial vaporization to a condition that is represented normally by a point on the horizontal, part-vapor part-liquid isotherm which is associated with its actual temperature.

(2) If the pressure experienced by a vapor, freed entirely of droplets of its own liquid and of possible nuclei for condensation, is increased carefully and without change of temperature the vapor may be supersaturated or, what is the same, supercooled. Corresponding to a change along the isotherm $FED$ of Fig. 10, the vapor becomes supercooled as soon as it enters the region to the left of the vapor-tension curve. At any given temperature the isothermal trace normally observed in that region is that of a part-liquid part-vapor isothermal which is horizontal and just above $EB$ and the condition as to $v$ and $p$ that actually occurs with the vapor thus supercooled is that ordinarily found for a higher temperature. If, now, a tiny droplet of the liquid or condensation nuclei are added to the supercooled vapor, that vapor will change over at once by partial condensation to a condition described normally by a point on a horizontal, part-liquid part-vapor isotherm which is associated with its actual temperature. Actually, in connection with demonstration experiments illustrating fog formation, a condition of supercooling, for a temperature lower than the starting temperature, however, is commonly obtained by an

adiabatic expansion, provided dust or ionic condensation nuclei are absent. The isothermal extensions $BC$ and $ED$ bear striking resemblances to the van der Waals isothermal predictions for these regions. Points $C$ and $D$ of a van der Waals isotherm of Fig. 9 have the same relations to it that $C$ and $D$ of Fig. 10 have to the isothermals to which they belong.

In Fig. 9, between points $C$ and $D$ of a van der Waals isotherm, an increase in volume accompanying an increase in pressure is shown. Such a change is highly improbable. Obviously a $p$-$v$ isotherm with a positive slope can have no physical meaning. Despite this, we are able to say that the description of the liquid-vapor transition given by the van der Waals equation—where that description has any possible reality—is in agreement with observation. To represent a van der Waals isotherm as normally observed, however, one should replace the section containing the double curve by a horizontal straight line at a pressure so chosen that the area between it and the upper loop equals the area between it and the lower loop. When this is done, the representation which the equation predicts is in good qualitative agreement with observed variations.

**8. Van der Waals' Equation and the Critical State.** The criteria for the selection of a critical point are

$$\left(\frac{dp}{dv}\right)_T = 0 \tag{12}$$

and

$$\left(\frac{d^2p}{dv^2}\right)_T = 0 \tag{13}$$

The first condition results from the fact that, on the ordinary $p$-$v$ plot, the critical isotherm is horizontal at the critical point. The second condition results from the fact that the critical point is at an inflection point of the critical isotherm. The curvatures of the critical isotherm above and below the critical pressure are opposite. Applying these conditions to the van der Waals equation, Eq. 11, rewritten for convenience in the following form

$$p = \frac{RT}{v - b} - \frac{a}{v^2} \tag{14}$$

leads to

$$\left(\frac{dp}{dv}\right)_T = -\frac{RT_c}{(v_c - b)^2} + \frac{2a}{v_c^3} = 0 \tag{15}$$

and

$$\left(\frac{d^2p}{dv^2}\right)_T = \frac{2RT_c}{(v_c - b)^3} - \frac{6a}{v_c^4} = 0 \tag{16}$$

where the subscript $c$ refers to a value at the critical point. Eliminating $RT_c/2a$ between Eqs. 15 and 16 leaves

$$\frac{(v_c - b)^2}{v_c{}^3} = \frac{3}{2} \frac{(v_c - b)^3}{v_c{}^4} \tag{17}$$

or

$$v_c = 3b \tag{18}$$

Substitution in Eq. 15 and then in Eq. 14 leads to

$$T_c = \frac{8a}{27bR} \tag{19}$$

and

$$p_c = \frac{a}{27b^2} \tag{20}$$

Knowing $a$ and $b$ for any gas, one may compute the critical constants. Conversely, if the critical constants have been otherwise determined, Eqs. 18 to 20 serve for determining $a$ and $b$.

A quantity of interest, which we may call a test criterion, is $RT_c/p_c v_c$. This criterion is dimensionless, and, if the van der Waals relation is generally applicable, its value should be constant and independent of the substance under consideration. Thus, for a van der Waals substance we should have

$$\frac{RT_c}{p_c v_c} = \frac{8a}{27b} \frac{1}{3b} \frac{27b^2}{a} = 2.67 \tag{21}$$

The last column of Table II shows how well the prediction checks with experiment. Note that, for the ideal gas, the value of this criterion is unity, a fact of small concern since an ideal gas has no critical state. All values are seen to be high, agreement being worse for the more complex molecules. Nevertheless, considering the wide range of critical constants included the approximation to constancy of $RT_c/p_c v_c$ is not to be ignored. Should one accept a zero value for the heat of vaporization of a substance rather than the disappearance of a liquid-vapor meniscus as the experimental criterion of the critical state for actual substances, the values obtained for $RT_c/p_c v_c$ would differ from those given in the table. Judged by Callendar's results for water, appreciable changes might be expected. $RT_c/p_c v_c$ is also a test criterion for the equation of C. Dieterici (1858–1929) (see p. 218), which predicts, instead of 2.67, a value of 3.69 which likewise is independent of the substance being considered. This agrees with experiment better than does van der Waals' predicted value.

**9. A Reduced Equation of State.** The above considerations, to-gether with certain remarks in Chapter VIII, suggest the formation of a reduced van der Waals equation, in which $p/p_c$, $T/T_c$, and $v/v_c$ are the variables. Such an equation should contain no parameters such as $a$ or $b$ which depend on the substance considered. To form it, solve Eqs. 18 to 20 for $b$, $a$, and $R$, thus,

$$b = \frac{v_c}{3} \tag{22}$$

$$a = 27 p_c b^2 = 3 p_c v_c^2 \tag{23}$$

$$R = \frac{8a}{27 b T_c} = \frac{8}{3} \frac{p_c v_c}{T_c} \tag{24}$$

Substitution of these values in the van der Waals equation yields

$$\left( \frac{p}{p_c} - 3 \frac{v_c^2}{v^2} \right) \left( \frac{v}{v_c} - \frac{1}{3} \right) = \frac{8}{3} \frac{T}{T_c} \tag{25}$$

which is the equation sought. Isothermals plotted on a $p$-$v$ diagram using reduced $p$- and $v$-axes should coincide for all substances if Eq. 11 is strictly true. How nearly this is fulfilled may be seen from Fig. 7, Chapter VIII. Strictly speaking, this graph is no more a test of the van der Waals equation than of certain other equations of state which likewise predict a common set of isothermals for all substances.

**10. Evaporation, Boiling, Vapor Pressure, and Vapor Tension.** Consider a vessel at room temperature containing water which is open to still air at atmospheric pressure. On a $p$-$T$ plot (Fig. 2) the condition is represented by some point such as $c$. Molecules of water, because of their thermal motions, will be constantly leaving and re-entering the liquid. If, however, a stream of air more or less dry is directed over the surface of the liquid, so that the evaporated molecules are removed as fast as they leave the surface, few molecules will have opportunity to re-enter the liquid. Two phenomena occur. Both are intensified by the stream of air. The more obvious occurrence is the gradual disappearance of the liquid, the familiar phenomenon of evaporation. Second, since at the surface only the faster-moving molecules have the requisite kinetic energy for overcoming the attraction of the liquid as they leave or attempt to leave, there is preferential vaporization for those faster-moving molecules. Those molecules which, though properly directed, are not able to escape, fail because of their lack of energy. As the process continues, the tendency is toward a residue of the more slowly moving molecules and a cooled liquid residue. Unless heat is supplied from some external source, the temperature of the liquid will drop. The heat per unit mass of vaporized material, which must be supplied under such conditions to maintain constant temperature of the liquid that remains, is the heat of vaporization of the liquid at the existing temperature.

In still air, at a liquid-air surface under equilibrium conditions, such as occur in closed vessels, molecules leave and re-enter the liquid at equal rates. Those in the vapor phase above the liquid displace some of the air molecules which would otherwise normally be there; and the pressure which exists there is consequently due partly to vapor molecules. Any contribution to the total pressure which is due to vapor molecules is termed vapor pressure. However, that which occurs when an equilibrium between the vapor and its liquid has been reached, that is, "saturated vapor pressure," is often referred to as a *vapor tension*. The vapor tension for a given liquid has definite values which depend only on the temperature. For instance, in still air just above a water surface in the open or better in the space above water in a closed vessel at 10°C, say, that portion of the atmospheric pressure, whatever it may be, which is due to water vapor is 9.2 mm-Hg, and at 20°C, 17.5 mm-Hg. (Unfortunately many use vapor pressure for this restricted term as well as for the general term. Of course, the term saturated vapor pressure is quite acceptable.)

Consider now what would happen were a minute bubble of vapor to form just below the liquid-air surface, within the body of a liquid exposed to the atmosphere at a temperature below the boiling point of the liquid. The pressure within the bubble would be the vapor tension for the temperature concerned and would be less than atmospheric pressure. The pressure in the liquid immediately surrounding the bubble would be approximately atmospheric. Hence the bubble, even if formed, would tend to collapse. However, as the temperature of a liquid is raised, its vapor tension increases and there is less tendency for bubbles that might form to collapse. Finally, when the vapor pressure becomes equal to—strictly, because of surface tension and other effects, somewhat greater than—the pressure outside the bubble, there is no collapsing tendency, boiling occurs, and the temperature of the saturated vapor just above the liquid-air surface is said to be the boiling-point temperature. In accord with this, normal boiling points for liquids are defined as the temperatures at which such saturated vapor pressures are equal to a standard atmosphere.

We frequently say that liquid that is boiling is at its boiling point. Actually, however, the temperature of a boiling liquid, in which the boiling is evidenced by rising bubbles of water vapor—not of air freed from solution—within the liquid, is always somewhat greater than that of the saturated vapor above. Accordingly in the precise deter- minations of boiling points, measurements are usually made of the temperature of the saturated vapor above the liquid.

Fig. 11 shows a particular type of instru- ment made of glass which may be used for determining the boiling points not only of water but also of such liquids as sulfur and naphthalene. It differs essentially from the common metal hypsometer used in connec- tion with the boiling point of water in having

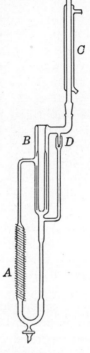

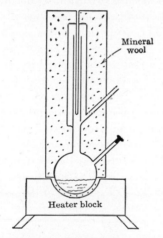

Mineral wool

Heater block

FIG. 11. Boiling-point ap- paratus for materials such as naphthalene and sulfur as well as water.

FIG. 12. An ebulliometer de- signed by W. Swictoslawski.

a shielded central tube into which the temperature-sensitive device is inserted. In use, the condition of vapor condensing at a reasonable uniform rate in the tube open to the air insures that the temperature in the space filled with vapor will have the necessary uniformity and that that space, after continued operation, is free from all gas but the vapor of the liquid under study. This condition must be fulfilled if the observed temperature is to correspond to the pressure of the atmosphere outside.

An interesting, rapid-acting, commercial device of high precision for the measurement of boiling points, known as an ebulliometer (from *ebullire*, meaning to boil up), is shown in simple form in Fig. 12. First proposed by F. G. Cottrell (1877–   ), chemist of the Fixed Nitrogen Research Laboratory of Washington, D. C., it was perfected by the Polish physical chemist W. Swietoslawski (1881–   ). Except for the heater, the device is made of glass. In use, much of it will be surrounded with thermally insulating material. The liquid under test is located in the U at the bottom. That which is in one arm at $A$ is heated electrically. When rather rapid boiling occurs, bubbles of vapor and drops of liquid are forced upward in the tube above $A$ as in a percolator and shot through an orifice against the thermometer well, $B$, over whose outer surface liquid is caused to spread rather uniformly by means of the externally fused, glass spiral. Normally the temperature of the water thus shot out is higher than the boiling point of the liquid; but, because of the vaporization which takes place at or on the surface of the well, the temperature assumed by the well is rather precisely that of the boiling point when the rate of boiling is properly adjusted.

The thermometer or other temperature-sensitive device in the thermometer well $B$ of the ebulliometer is normally surrounded by mercury or other liquid, to insure good thermal contact with the walls of the chamber. Vapor which does not condense in the neighborhood of $B$ will pass to the water-cooled condensing chamber $C$, which may be open at its upper end either to the atmosphere or to a chamber maintained at any desired pressure. The condensed liquid dripping down from $C$ enters the orifice of a drop counter at $D$. In practice it is found that, between rather wide limits of rates of passage of drops at $D$, the temperature indicated by a very sensitive thermometer in $B$ remains constant and is the same as that obtained with a thermometer immersed in a vapor above a boiling liquid as described above. For a particular ebulliometer, this temperature was found constant to within $0.001$ C° with drop rates varying from 10 to 25 per minute. So precise is this instrument that it may be and to some extent is used "in reverse" to measure atmospheric pressures.

A vapor-tension curve, such as shown on the $p$-$T$ plot of Fig. 2, is often referred to as a vaporization or a boiling-point curve.

**11. Methods of Determining Vapor Tensions.** Two distinct methods of measuring vapor tensions are suggested by the preceding section. In the first, or static, method, one measures the vapor tension as a function of temperature. In the second, or dynamic, method, one observes the temperature of the vapor above a boiling liquid as a function of pressure.

A simple, frequently used application of the static method employs the apparatus of Fig. 13. The U-tube, with air removed from the closed arm, is filled with boiled mercury to the extent desired, and a small amount of the substance to be investigated is introduced above the mercury in the closed arm. The tube is immersed in a well-stirred bath whose temperature can be varied by means of heater unit $H$ and observed by means of thermometer $T$. The vapor in $C$ will have a pressure $p$ which may be determined from

$$p = p_0 + p_m - p_l \tag{26}$$

where $p_0$ is the atmospheric pressure, $p_m$ is the pressure due to a column of mercury of height equal to the difference in level of the two

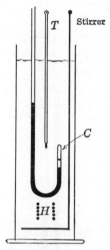

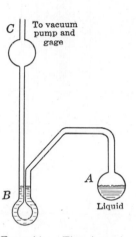

FIG. 13. Simple apparatus for the static method of determining vapor tensions.

FIG. 14. The isoteniscope of Smith and Menzies for measuring vapor tensions by a static method.

mercury menisci, and $p_l$, usually very small, is the pressure due to the liquid layer with which the vapor in $C$ is in equilibrium. A source of error in this method arises from having unsuspected dissolved gases in the liquid which are freed on heating. When this method is used, it is a common practice to free the liquid from dissolved air by boiling some of the liquid away after its introduction into the tube above the mercury. If, as is often the case, this boiling drives out dissolved gases from the liquid and from the space above, this method should yield accurate results.

An improvement over the simple static apparatus just described was (Fig. 14) devised at the University of Chicago in 1910 by the chemists Alexander Smith (1865–1925) and A. W. C. Menzies (1877– ). It is called an isteniscope, meaning an instrument in which equal tensions may be seen. The bulb $A$ and the twin side arms $B$ are partially filled with the liquid to be studied. At $C$ the apparatus is connected conveniently to a pump for producing the desired reduction in pressure and to a manometer for measuring the

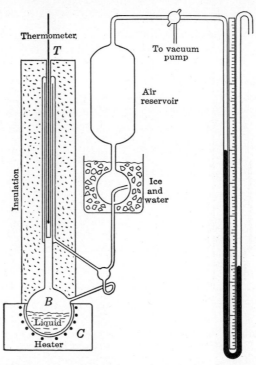

FIG. 15. Apparatus for determining vapor tensions by a dynamic method.

desired pressures. Air in the space between the liquids in $A$ and in $B$ must be driven out by boiling. With the apparatus, except for a portion near $C$, immersed in a constant-temperature bath, the pressure in the left arm above $B$ is reduced externally until the two liquid levels at $B$ are the same. The pressure above the liquid in $A$, that is its vapor tension, is then just equal to the pressure externally produced. Because of the location of the manometer outside the bath, measurements of the pressure will ordinarily be much more satisfactorily carried out than with the simple apparatus of Fig. 13. Further, this layout eliminates the unsatisfactory feature represented by $p_l$ of Eq. 26.

The dynamic method was used by the French physicist H. V. Regnault (1810–1878) in 1843 in a study of water. An apparatus employing this method is shown in Fig. 15. With the liquid in place the pressure is first reduced to some small desired value by means of a vacuum pump, after which the system is closed by means of the stopcock. The liquid being investigated is then boiled in a flask by a heater unit. The vapor flows up past the thermometer well containing the thermometer and over the internal shield, finally emerging to one side and thereafter returning to the flask. Reabsorption of air and other gases by the condensing or condensed vapors may be guarded against where necessary by collecting such liquids in a large reservoir, not shown, and returning it to the boiler only when desirable. With continued boiling, air and dissolved gases generally are driven off and away from the space above the liquid and around the thermometer well into the air reservoir so that the atmosphere in those regions tends towards one of pure vapor, a condition which is possible only when the surroundings are at the temperature of the vapor and the pressure in the system is that of the saturated vapor. When an equilibrium has been established, the temperature and pressure are noted. Together they determine a point on the vapor-tension curve. A small amount of air is now admitted to the system, and the process is repeated at the higher pressure.

Obviously the simple ebulliometer described above, when provided with means for producing various desired pressures and measuring them, may similarly be used for determining vapor tensions.

The vapor tensions of ethyl ether, water, and sulfur dioxide as functions of temperature are shown in Fig. 6, Chapter II.

**12. Determination of Vapor Tension by the Rate of Effusion through a Small Opening.** About 1909, from a study of the escape of gas molecules, through a small opening in the wall of a chamber containing the gas, into a highly evacuated space outside, Martin Knudsen (1871–   ), a Danish physicist, obtained for the expected rate of loss of mass (rate of loss of particles × mass per particle) per unit of area of the orifice, $E$,

$$E = \tfrac{1}{4}\delta\bar{c} \tag{27}$$

where $\delta$ represents the density and $\bar{c}$ the mean molecular velocity (not the root-mean-square speed $\tilde{c}$ discussed in Chapter VIII) of the gas in the chamber from which it is escaping. From the ideal-gas equation, we obtain

$$\delta = \frac{p}{RT} \tag{28}$$

and from kinetic theory, in case Maxwell's distribution law (see p. 206, Fig. 2, in which the distinction between $\bar{c}$ and $\tilde{c}$ is shown) is fulfilled,

$$\bar{c} = \sqrt{\frac{8p}{\pi\delta}} = \sqrt{\frac{8RT}{\pi}} \tag{29}$$

Finally, for the pressure in the chamber, we obtain

$$p = E\sqrt{2\pi RT} \tag{30}$$

Knudsen, using the mercury vapor above liquid mercury in a constant-temperature chamber, closed except for a minute opening in its wall, determined in accord with the above that the vapor tension of mercury at 0°C was 0.000185 mm-Hg. Others have used this method for a study of the vapor tensions of such metals as zinc, cadmium, lead, sodium, potassium, silver, gold, and copper.

**13. Determination of the Vapor Tension of a Metal from Its Rate of Vaporization in a Vacuum.** Adapting Knudsen's method just described to metals of low volatility, Irving Langmuir (1881– ) of the Research Laboratory of the General Electric Co. at Schenectady, winner of the Nobel prize in chemistry in 1932, developed an interesting and important method for the study of metals that, because of their exceedingly low rates of volatilization, cannot be studied by the Knudsen method. Langmuir assumed a rectangular enclosure, one wall of which was composed of the metal under consideration at some appropriate temperature, while the remaining walls were assumed perfectly reflecting. It is to be expected that an equilibrium would develop between the vapor in the enclosure and the metal of the wall under consideration. What the conditions for equilibrium would be is a matter of some speculation. Those assumed by Langmuir were: (1) that the atoms (molecules of metallic vapor are almost always monatomic) evaporating from the metal wall will have a Maxwellian distribution of velocities; (2) that all atoms, striking the metal wall on their returns from the opposite side of the enclosure, will condense on the metal and become a part of that wall; and (3) that the concentration of the atoms in the vapor will be so small that the interference of the returning atoms with the vaporization process will be entirely negligible. These assumptions seem not only reasonable but also to be in conformity with experiment as far as has been ascertained.

Under equilibrium conditions in an enclosure of the type assumed by Langmuir, the rate of vaporization, an experimentally determinable quantity, is necessarily the same as the rate of condensation, a quantity theoretically connected via kinetic theory with the vapor pressure in the enclosure (vapor tension). As it will appear, it is now possible, subject to the assumed conditions for equilibrium, to relate measured rates of vaporization to vapor-tension determinations.

The conditions occurring in the Langmuir enclosure are exactly parallel to those occurring in the Knudsen enclosure discussed in the previous section. That this is so becomes evident when one realizes that the atoms condensing on the metal wall of the Langmuir enclosure disappear from the enclosed space as truly as do those which pass through the opening in the Knudsen enclosure. It follows that Eq. 30 yields for the Langmuir enclosure the desired relation between the vaporization rate and the vapor tension. The vaporization of solids is often referred to as sublimation.

Langmuir and his colleagues studied the sublimation rates of tungsten, tantalum, molybdenum, and platinum by measuring the rates of loss of material from uniform filaments, composed of these materials, which were electrically heated in vacuo to known temperatures. Substitution of such values for $E$ in Eq. 30 gave the corresponding vapor tensions $p$. For example, at 2450°K, the approximate operating temperature for tungsten in a vacuum incandescent lamp, experiment shows that tungsten evaporates at a rate of about $3.6 \times 10^{-10}$ gm/(cm$^2$ sec). Substitution of this value for $E$ in Eq. 30 yields $3.0 \times 10^{-5}$ dy/cm$^2$ or $2.3 \times 10^{-8}$ mm-Hg for $p$. This is accordingly the vapor tension of tungsten at 2450°K.

A vapor tension determined as a function of temperature, as described above, combined with certain thermodynamic relations leads to the determination of an important constant for the substance in question, known as its chemical constant. The significance of this constant must be left to advanced thermodynamic treatises.

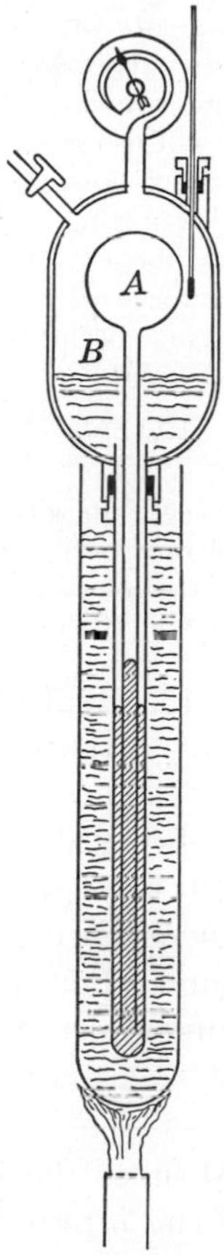

FIG. 16. Fairbairn and Tate's apparatus for determining saturated vapor densities.

**14. Determination of Saturated-Vapor Densities.** The line $P_cR$ of Fig. 1 is known as the saturated vapor line. Its exact position on such a $p$-$v$ diagram is of importance to the physicist, the chemist, and the engineer. The data involved consist of corresponding values of pressure, temperature, and specific volume or its inverse, density. Three methods of measurement are here noted, of which the first due to Cailletet and Mathias and the second due to Callendar have already been discussed in connection with the determination of critical points.

A third method, first described in 1860 in Great Britain by Sir William Fairbairn (1789–1874) and Thomas Tate (1807–1888), employs apparatus represented in Fig.

16. Two bulbs, both highly evacuated, are shown connected by concentric glass tubes filled with clean mercury. In use a small known mass $m$ of the substance being investigated is placed in $A$ and a somewhat larger amount in bulb $B$. The whole unit is then placed in a liquid bath and slowly heated. With liquid present in both bulbs, the pressures in both will be vapor tensions of the liquid corresponding to the temperatures of the bath and hence will be equal. The rate of increase of pressure with temperature in both bulbs will vary in accord with Clapeyron's equation. However, when the liquid in $A$ has completely evaporated, the rate of rise of pressure in $A$ with increase of temperature will follow a different law. If the pressure is not too great, the law followed will approximate the ideal-gas law, and the rate of rise of pressure with temperature will be much reduced. Since liquid will still be evaporating in $B$, the vapor there will still be saturated and no such decreased rate will be experienced there. Hence, with continued increase of temperature, the mercury will suddenly begin to fill vessel $A$. For the temperature at which this change occurs, the density of the vapor is obviously

$$\delta = \frac{m}{V_A} \tag{31}$$

Repetition with larger and smaller amounts of liquid initially in $A$ will mean complete vaporization at higher and at lower temperatures and lead to a determination of the complete dependence of density and of specific volume on temperature throughout the desired range.

**15. Heat of Vaporization and Internal Pressure.** It has been mentioned that, when a liquid is vaporized, a certain amount of heat per unit mass of vaporized material, its heat of vaporization, $L$, is required to bring about the transformation. For water at 100°C, this is about 540 cal/gm. Since there is expansion on vaporization, some of this energy is expended in doing external work against the external pressure. For water boiling at 100°C under atmospheric pressure, this amount of external work per unit of mass is

$$W_e/m = p(v_v - v_l) = 1 \text{ A } (1671 \text{ cm}^3/\text{gm}) = 40 \text{ cal/gm.} \tag{32}$$

Most of the heat supplied during vaporization is evidently spent in doing internal work against the forces that produce the internal pressure. For water at 100°C, the average internal pressure $\bar{p}_i$ that must exist during the vaporization process is accordingly

$$\bar{p}_i = \frac{L - W_e/m}{v_v - v_l} = \frac{500 \text{ cal/gm}}{1671 \text{ cm}^3/\text{gm}} = 0.299 \text{ cal/cm}^3 = 12.4 \text{ A} \tag{33}$$

Compared with internal pressures that ordinarily exist in liquids, this is very small. The explanation is that the value given is a particular type of average of a quantity that ranges from something of the order of 5000 A for boiling water to the nearly zero value for the saturated steam vapor. The actual value of 12.4 A has but little physical significance, for this average changes rapidly with the specific volume of the vapor formed.

**16. Direct Experimental Determination of the Heat of Vaporization.** Most commonly, heats of vaporization are determined from vapor-tension curves using Clapeyron's equation as indicated in Chapter IX.

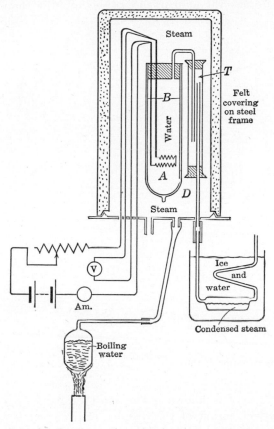

Fig. 17.  Apparatus for the direct determination of the heat of vaporization.  *B* is a Dewar flask containing water and an electric heater, *A*; *T* is a trap for liquid droplets coming from *B*.

Such determinations may conveniently be based on data obtained with apparatus such as is illustrated in Figs. 14 and 15 above.

A direct determination of the heat of vaporization for a liquid at atmospheric pressure may be made, however, with the aid of the apparatus shown in Fig. 17. A known quantity of electrical energy is supplied by means of heater *A* to the liquid in boiler *B*. That which evaporates passes through a trap, *T*, for holding back possible liquid droplets and is collected in the condenser and massed. By supplying vapor of the same liquid at atmospheric pressure, in the surrounding container $D$, surroundings having the temperature of the liquid in $B$ are obtained. This insures that all of the energy transferred in heater $A$ is utilized in evaporating the liquid, none being lost to the surroundings or used to raise the temperature of the liquid or the vapor. Temperatures are best obtained by means of measured pressures when the

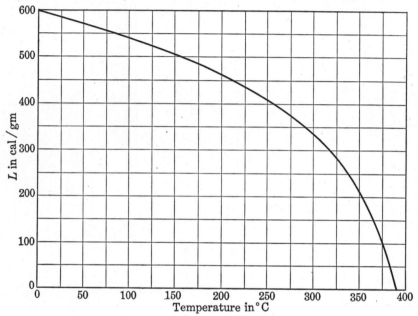

FIG. 18.   The variation of the heat of vaporization of water with temperature.

vapor-tension curve is known. The most probable sources of error are the imperfect action of the droplet trap and the pressure drop that occurs with passage of the vapor from the boiler to the condenser. In Fig. 18, the temperature variation of the heat of vaporization of water is shown. It is seen that $L$ falls to zero at the critical point.

**17. Direct Experimental Determination of the Heat of Fusion.** Like the heat of vaporization, the heat of fusion may be computed by means of Clapeyron's equation, if the specific volumes of the liquid and solid and the slope of the fusion curve are known.

A direct determination of a heat of fusion may be made with the aid of a time-temperature graph for a portion of the material under investigation as it cools slowly through the freezing point. For a pure substance cooling extremely slowly, a curve like that of Fig. 19 is obtained.

The depression at $b$ represents supercooling. The product of the mean of the slopes of the cooling curve just above and just below the solidifying temperature freezing the heat capacitance of the crucible and contents, $dQ/dt$, represents the rate of loss of heat by the system and consequently its rate of evolution of heat on solidification during the freezing interval, $t_{bc}$. The heat of fusion may be determined from

$$L = \frac{(dQ/dt)t_{bc}}{m} \tag{34}$$

where $m$ is the mass of material being investigated.

Fig. 19, drawn in the manner common to discussions of this kind, suggests that a freezing liquid will maintain a constant temperature during the freezing process. This is probably true for a process carried through infinitely slowly. However, the curve of $T = f(t)$ actually obtained in precise work rarely follows through in the idealized way. This is illustrated by some very precise work on the freezing point of benzoic acid carried out at our Bureau of Standards by chemists F. W. Schwab (1905– ) and Edward Wichers (1892– ), (Fig. 20). Consider the uppermost curve, which presents temperature measurements for three freezing runs

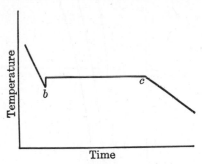

Fig. 19. The idealized cooling curve of a pure substance that undercools and then crystallizes at a definite single temperature.

with two standard samples. There was constant stirring by bubbles of dry air which entered through small capillary openings in the bottom of the freezing chamber. "Squinting" along the curve, with the eye at paper level, shows that the line is not straight through any considerable portion of its length. Were the temperature-measuring instruments noticeably less sensitive, however, a straight horizontal line would have been graphed. It is often the case that highly sensitive instruments under actual working conditions reveal the fact that the conditions are not ideal. Incidentally, undercooling previous to freezing is shown very nicely. The two lower curves, showing the effects of slight impurities on the freezing, need not interest us here.

In a somewhat more precise method for determining the heat of fusion, requiring no knowledge of specific heats, but limited in application for obvious reasons, one melts a known quantity of the substance being investigated and measures the heat transferred during the

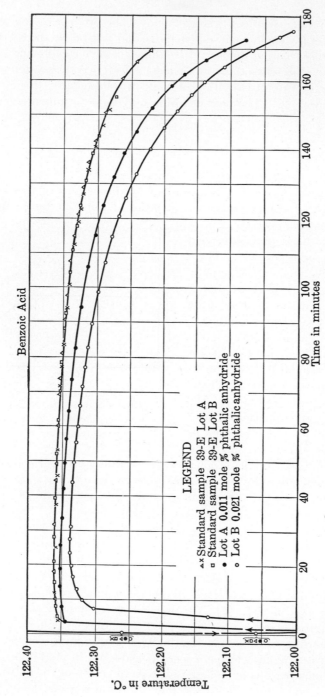

FIG. 20. The undercooling and freezing curves of some very pure and some slightly impure samples of benzoic acid as obtained at the Bureau of Standards during some tests that were carried through with care (courtesy of F. W. Schwab and Edward Wichers).

process. This method may be applied easily to water by drilling a hole to the center of a block of ice, at 0°C, swabbing it with cotton until dry, inserting an electric heater, previously cooled, melting some ice, and finally removing the melted ice with a pipette and a pad of absorbent cotton and determining its mass $m$. If the total energy input, $Q$, to the heater is measured, the heat of fusion may be found from

$$L = \frac{Q}{m} \tag{35}$$

The most satisfactory method for determining heats of fusion, aside from a few special cases, seems to be one in which the heat set free on freezing is measured with the aid of a standard compensated-loss calorimeter such as that described in Chapter V. In practice one makes, for each specimen tested, many individual determinations of the heat that is set free, corresponding to various starting temperatures both above and below the melting point. Fig. 21 shows the construction of a calorimeter used by the two English physicists J. H. Awberry and Ezer Griffiths (1888–  ) who reported the results of determinations for several metals in 1926. The specimen, shown as cross-hatched, fits snugly in a thin metal sheet container capable of withstanding the necessary high temperatures. Both specimen and container are shown inside a small tank immersed in the calorimetric fluid, water in the present study.

Two types of losses were guarded against by Awberry and Griffiths. One was the loss that occurred during the transfer of the specimen from the furnace to the calorimeter. This was accounted for by applying the difference principle. For each specimen test with container, a corresponding test using the container only was carried through in effect. Since the leakage losses in both cases were entirely from the external surface of the container, the differences in the amounts of heat given up for each high starting temperature gave the desired total amounts of heat yielded up by the specimen only.

The second type of loss to be guarded against was that due to the vaporization of the water of the calorimeter by the hot specimen. To eliminate such a loss a thread-supported tank in the calorimeter was introduced. By lowering the specimen into this tank, and keeping it from contact with the water until after the calorimeter cover was closed, no water vaporized by the specimen later could leave the container. After the cover was fastened, the tank, container, and specimen were drawn into the water by means of the wire shown.

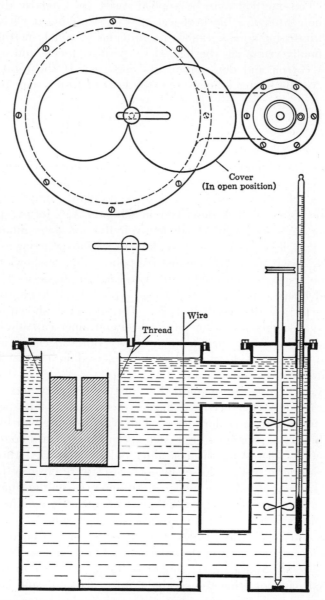

FIG. 21. Awberry and Griffiths' calorimeter for the study of heats of fusion (*Proc. Phys. Soc. London*, **A38**, 378, 1926).

For the procedure to be followed in determining the quantities of heat set free in the calorimeter, reference should be made to Chapter V. Awberry and Griffiths' data for several metals are shown graphed in

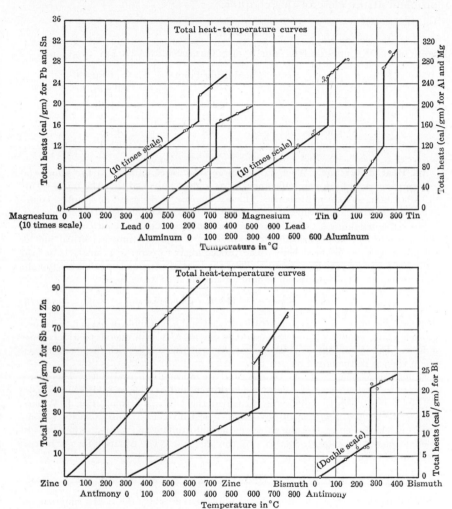

FIG. 22.   Graph of Awberry and Griffiths' data for determining the heats of fusion of aluminum, magnesium, lead, and tin (*Proc. Roy. Soc. London*, **A38**, 378, 1926).

Fig. 22.   The length of the vertical line at the temperature of solidification, as determined by other workers, connecting the two slanting lines for each particular substance indicates the total amount of heat set free per unit mass during solidification and, therefore, the heat of fusion of that substance. Note that the vertical scales are not all the same. Certain of the results of the study are given in Table III. Determinations for bismuth, zinc, and antimony form the basis for a problem at the close of this chapter.

TABLE III

SOME OF THE RESULTS ON HEATS OF FUSION OBTAINED BY AWBERRY AND GRIFFITHS

| Metal | Melting Point °C | Heat of Fusion cal/gm |
|---|---|---|
| Tin | 232 | 14.6 |
| Lead | 327 | 6.3 |
| Magnesium | 644 | 46.5 |
| Aluminum | 657 | 92.4 |

**18. Heat of Reaction.** When two or more substances, initially at the same temperature, react to form new substances, it is almost universal that the temperature of the reacting system will change. It may increase or decrease, and, unless conditions are adiabatic, heat will be given up to or absorbed from the surroundings.

Since the molal quantities of the different components entering into a reaction are different, the ordinary procedure for expressing a heat of transition in cal/mol or cal/gm cannot be followed here. The procedure is to express it, instead, in heat units for a given reaction as stated. Often the heat of reaction is made a part of the reaction equation. Thus, for an assumed reaction at 25°C we have

$$H_2(g) + \tfrac{1}{2}O_2(g) = H_2O(l) + 68,315 \text{ cal } * \tag{36}$$

The meaning of this is that a mole of hydrogen and a half mole of oxygen, both in a gaseous state, combining to form liquid water at 25°C will evolve 68,315 calories of heat. The (g) and the (l) indicate that the constituents to which they are annexed are in the gas or the liquid phase.

Reactions leading to heats of reaction are normally irreversible. There are, however, reversible ways of combining hydrogen and oxygen to form water vapor. For such cases, there is another term called the Gibbs function, after J. Willard Gibbs (1839–1903), professor of physics at Yale University. This quantity is commonly called free energy by the chemist—an unfortunate fact since another, closely related, quantity is called free energy by the physicist. The equation for the reversible reaction is often written as

$$H_2(g) + \tfrac{1}{2}O_2(g) \rightleftharpoons H_2O(l); \ \Delta G_{298°K} = -56,560 \text{ cal } \dagger \tag{37}$$

This means that, when the reaction takes place reversibly, the Gibbs function for the system decreases by 56,560 cal and that that amount of useful work may be accomplished under ideal circumstances in consequence thereof.

Emphasis should be placed on the idea of the useful work connected with Eq. 37 as against that of the available heat of Eq. 36, only a part of which can be used for

---

* B. L. Lewis and G. Von Elbe, *Combustion, Flames, and Explosions of Gases*, p. 384, Cambridge, England, The University Press, 1938.

† G. N. Lewis and M. Randall, *Thermodynamics and the Free Energy of Chemical Substances*, p. 485, New York, McGraw-Hill Book Co.

useful work. Not all reactions are exothermic, that is, yield heat when they take place. Many are endothermic instead.

Much of the work of the physical chemist is associated with heats of reaction and Gibbs' functions. Further discussion of this field must be left for other textbooks and treatises.

**19. Heat of Solution.** A heat of solution is in many respects a particular heat of reaction. When a solution of a crystalline solid in a pure liquid is made, a definite amount of heat per unit mass of solid is absorbed or evolved during the molecular rearrangement that occurs. This is known as the heat of solution. For sodium chloride in water at 18.0°C its value is $-1030$ cal/mol. This indicates that, when a gm-mole of sodium chloride is dissolved isothermally in water at 18°C to form an infinitesimally dilute solution, 1030 cal of heat must be supplied from an external source.

**20. Amorphous Solidification.** Most of the phase-change phenomena thus far considered have been concerned with pure substances that are crystalline in the solid phase. However, there exists a class of amorphous substances, of which certain glasses, waxes, and pitches are examples, for which the transitions from solid to liquid and the reverse are gradual rather than abrupt. The cooling curve for an amorphous substance during solidification as given in Fig. 23 shows distinct differences from the cooling curve of Fig. 19 which is typical of

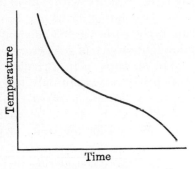

FIG. 23. The cooling curve of an amorphous substance.

the solidification of a crystalline solid. Such materials are characterized by a rather indefinite softening temperature (815°C for Pyrex glass) rather than a definite melting point. Many other dissimilarities suggest that a true phase change does not occur. In fact, X-ray investigations reveal that such amorphous substances are really supercooled liquids.

**21. Alloy Transitions.** Alloys are combinations of elements, usually metallic, which when solid are macroscopically (not necessarily microscopically) homogeneous and stable for widely varying concentrations of the constituents. Alloys of copper and zinc, for example, under the name of brass may be had in any proportion of the two constituents. That prepared with a zinc content ranging up to 40% is known as $\alpha$-brass. Commercially, a brass having approximately a 10% zinc content is often referred to as red brass. Brass with a 40% to 43% zinc content is known as $\beta$-brass and is generally yellow in color. The upper limit of zinc content commercially is about 65%. Great variations in mechanical and thermal properties accompany the change of constitution.

Fused metals are usually completely miscible in all proportions. As examples of exceptions, we have (1) aluminum and lead, which are almost immiscible at temperatures just above the melting point of aluminum, and (2) copper and lead, which are only partly miscible at temperatures just above the melting point of copper. A molten mixture of the two elements at that temperature will separate into two homogeneous components, copper with 38% of lead in solution and lead with 7.5% of copper in solution. Exactly similar conditions are presented by mixtures of non-metallic components.

The transition process from a metallic molten solution or melt to the alloy in a solid state varies greatly with the constitution of the melt and the rapidity with which the transition takes place. Obviously, heats of solution, heats of dilution, and ordinary heats of solidification are involved in varying amounts. Generally solidification takes place through a range of temperatures, which may be very great.

For an alloy melt, a cooling curve covering the interval of solidification will reveal not only the processes involved but also the extent to which they are involved. So definitely is this the case that analyses based on such curves, referred to as thermal analyses, represent a basic method for the study of the constitutional changes of alloys in general.

Here, before considering thermal analysis curves, we shall study in some detail what such an analysis has shown for a certain common type of alloy system, the copper-silver alloys.

A freezing-point diagram for copper-silver alloys is shown in Fig. 24. It is an equilibrium diagram and shows only in general outline what is obtained experimentally when the cooling process has been so slow that equilibrium conditions have prevailed throughout. Temperatures are shown as a function of constitution, ranging from 100% silver to 100% copper. The full lines represent normal transition temperatures for varying constitutions. Line $AE$ represents the initial freezing points, ignoring possible undercoolings, of cooling melts containing 71.9% or more by weight of silver and 28.1% or less of copper. Line $BE$ represents similar freezing points for copper-silver melts containing less silver. Point $E$ is referred to as a eutectic point, concerning which more will be said later. Lines $AS_1$ and $BS_2$, as will appear later, represent the temperatures at which various solutions of copper in silver and of silver in copper are in equilibrium with varying melts. The significance of the line $S_1 S_2$ will also appear later. The dashed lines beginning at $U$, $V$, $X$, $Y$, and $Z$ refer to different constitutions of melts and solidified alloys.

Consider first what happens when a melt, rich in silver as characterized by $U$, cools. No change occurs until it reaches a temperature of about 925°C, some 35 C° or so below the silver point. At this temperature freezing begins. The composition of that which freezes out, $C_1'$, however, is quite different from that of the freezing melt, $C_1$. As a result, the remaining melt becomes richer in copper and its freezing point is lowered. After a certain continuation of lowering of temperature, of freezing, and of enriching of the copper content of the melt, it occurs that the composition of the melt is $C_2$ and that of the frozen-out material is $C_2'$. The solid solution of copper in silver which was formed at higher temperatures has had its copper content increased by diffusion from the melt so that at this stage all of the solid alloy is characterized by $C_2'$. This process continues until a composition $C_3$ for the remaining

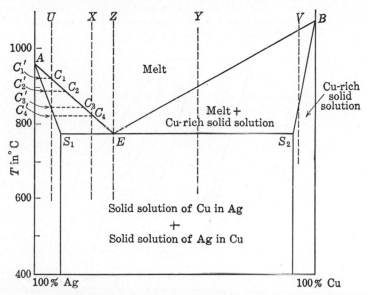

FIG. 24. A freezing-point diagram for the silver-copper system (by permission. Carpenter and Robertson, *Metals*, p. 248, London, Oxford University Press, 1939).

melt and a composition $C_3'$ for the solid is indicated. But with $C_3'$ the same at $C_1$ it follows that there is no remaining melt and freezing is over. From there down, the alloy, a particular solid solution of copper in silver, will cool like any other solid.

Consider next what happens when a melt, rich in copper and characterized by $V$, cools. Obviously the procedure is similar to what happens for the $U$ composition. The sole difference, aside from that of temperatures, is that the solution that freezes out is one of silver in copper instead of the reverse.

Consider now what happens for a melt characterized by $X$. After freezing sets in, with a melt composition of $C_4$ and a frozen component of composition $C_4'$, there is, as for the $U$ case, the same enrichment of the copper component of the melt and passage of the characterizing point along the line $AE$ toward $E$, the eutectic state. In this case point $E$ is actually reached by the remaining melt, and point $S_1$ by the solid alloy which has been frozen out. Also the amount of melt remaining is finite. Before further lowering of the temperature becomes possible, the whole of the melt must freeze. Should the melt initially have been characterized by $Y$, the only difference observed would be in the solid alloy formed, whose final condition would be a solution of silver in copper as represented by $S_2$.

The solid produced by the freezing of the eutectic is not microscopically homogeneous. Examination shows it to be an intermingling of crystals corresponding to states $S_1$ and $S_2$. State $S_1$ corresponds to a solution 91.2% silver, 8.8% copper; $S_2$, to 92.0% copper, 8.0% silver. If the initial condition of the melt is that of the eutectic, the final alloy will contain $S_1$ and $S_2$ crystals in such proportion as to yield an overall content of 71.9% silver and 28.1% copper. For a greater initial content of silver or of copper, there will be a correspondingly greater final content of $S_1$ or of $S_2$ crystals in the solid alloy. It appears that the eutectic liquid is that particular composition in liquid form which can exist in equilibrium with two different solid phases composed of the same initial simple components. The temperature at which this occurs, in copper-silver alloys, is about 778°C.

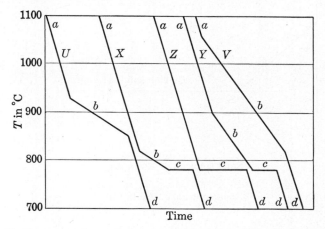

Fig. 25.   Cooling curves for various compositions of the binary copper-silver alloy.

$S_1S_2$ is a line drawn to separate regions of two phases, a solid solution and a remaining melt, from the region indicating a condition of intermingled crystals of compositions corresponding to $S_1$ and $S_2$.

Consider now the temperature variations that might be expected as one gradually cools various copper-silver melts corresponding to the initial conditions given by $U$, $V$, $X$, $Y$, and $Z$ of Fig. 24. The curves that one obtains for equilibrium cooling curves, during which the rate of loss of heat is substantially constant, are somewhat like those shown diagrammatically in Fig. 25. Obviously not all the lines will be straight, nor will corresponding slopes be equal for cases where conditions are chosen such that the total time intervals for cooling from 1100°C to 700°C are the same. Parts $a$ correspond to coolings at temperatures above those at which crystallization starts, parts $d$ to coolings at temperatures below which solidification is complete, parts $b$ to coolings during which freezing accompanies a gradual lowering of the temperature, and parts $c$ to the condition of eutectic freezing. Corresponding to what is indicated in Fig. 24, curve $U$ indicates that process $b$ extends from about 925°C to about 840°C and that there is no eutectic freezing. Similarly, curve $X$ indicates that part of the freezing is eutectic freezing and curve $Z$ that all freezing is eutectic freezing. How thermal analysis of such curves as these may be used to develop equilibrium phase diagrams such as that of Fig. 24 is beyond the scope of this book.

The equilibrium phase diagram of Fig. 24 is characteristic of many non-metallic combinations, as for instance that of oxygen and nitrogen (Fig. 26) obtained by the Russian physicists Ruhemann and Lichter. That for water and ordinary salt

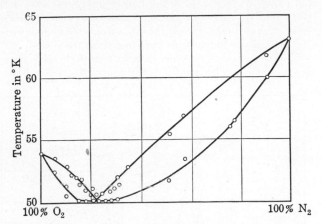

FIG. 26 Freezing-point diagram for the oxygen-nitrogen system (by permission, M. and B. Ruhemann, *Low Temperature Physics*, p. 100, Cambridge, England, University Press, 1937).

(Fig. 27) is quite similar, differing mainly in that the components which freeze out with cooling are nearly if not quite pure ice and pure salt. Similar considerations hold for lead-tin alloys. A much more complicated diagram is that which describes the copper-zinc system (Fig. 28) to which brass belongs.

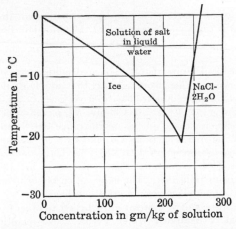

FIG. 27.    Freezing-point diagram for the water-sodium chloride system.

Another type of transformation occurring frequently in alloys, known as the order-disorder transition, is well illustrated by the change from $\beta'$-brass to $\beta$-brass (Fig. 28). X-ray studies have shown that both the $\beta$ and the $\beta'$ phases have body-centered cubic lattices. Further, in the $\beta'$ phase, the positions occupied by the copper and the zinc atoms separately are such that the positions taken by each kind of atoms alone form ordered arrays. However, in the $\beta$ phase, there are no such separate ordered arrays. Though an ordered array still occurs when both kinds of atoms are taken into consideration, the individual arrays are disordered. With transfer from the $\beta'$ phase to the $\beta$ phase there is a transition from order to disorder, hence the name given above for the type of change being considered.

An interesting characteristic of the order-disorder type of change is the gradualness of the transfer from one type to another. Starting with a well-ordered state, one

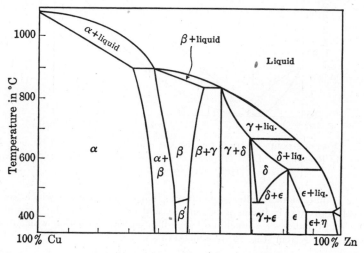

Fig. 28. Freezing-point diagram for the copper-zinc system (by permission, J. C. Slater, *Introduction to Chemical Physics*, p. 287, McGraw-Hill Book Co., New York, 1939).

finds, on raising the temperature, that there is no definite temperature for the starting of the disorder phenomena, though one may say that, at a fairly definite temperature, the phenomenon of complete disorder has been very nearly attained. This feature is well shown by the graph of Fig. 7 of Chapter VI, p. 148, which gives the specific heats of what is commonly called $\beta$-brass for the range 100°C and 600°C as obtained by C. S. Smith of the American Brass Co. and by C. Sykes and H. Wilkinson in England. The shape of the specific-heat curve in this critical region, with a sharp maximum at about 465°C, is much like the Greek letter $\lambda$, and the transition is often referred to as a $\lambda$-point transition. The explanation of such transitions as these is one of the great accomplishments of statistical mechanics.

Further consideration of alloy systems must be left to other books and treatises.

**22. Specific Heat of Saturated Water Vapor.** This quantity is of great importance to the steam engineer. Though generally beyond the scope of this book, certain points may be considered here. In the derivation of the Clapeyron equation (Chapter IX), we obtained

$$c_{AB} - c_{DC} + \frac{\Delta L}{\Delta T} - \frac{L}{T} = 0 \qquad (38)$$

of which $c_{AB}$ represented the specific heat for the $AB$ process shown in Fig. 5 of that chapter, and $c_{DC}$ that for the $DC$ process. Neither is at constant pressure or constant volume. Rearranging Eq. 38 and passing to the limit, we obtain for the specific heat of the saturated vapor

$$c_{DC} = c_{AB} + \frac{dL}{dT} - \frac{L}{T} \tag{39}$$

This equation is known as the Clausius (1822–1888) equation, after the German physicist who first pointed out its significance.

The value of $c_{AB}$ for water can differ but slightly from $c_p$ for water, which at 100°C is closely 1.006 cal/gm C°. Substituting this and known values for $L$, $dL/dT$, and $T$ we obtain

$$c_{DC} = (1.006 - 0.604 - \tfrac{540}{373}) \text{ cal/gm C}° = -1.046 \text{ cal/gm C}° \tag{40}$$

The interesting point is that $c_{DC}$ is negative. This means that heat must be actually withdrawn from water vapor that is being heated and maintained saturated.

Not all vapors are like water vapor in this respect. Different materials vary all the way from a considerable negative value to a considerable positive value.

**23. Effects of Dissolved Substances on Boiling and Freezing Points.** If a solid is dissolved in a liquid—salt in water, for example—we might expect that the pressure of the saturated vapor above the solution will be decreased, since some water molecules, which would normally escape, are then prevented from doing so by increased attractions due to the molecules of the dissolved solid. Whether or not this is a valid explanation, it seems to check with observations. Since the solution will not boil until its vapor tension equals the external pressure, it follows that the boiling point will be raised. Further, experiment shows that, for dilute solutions, the elevation of the boiling point is directly proportional to the particle concentration of the dissolved substance, the proportionality factor being the same for all substances. For electrolytes, like common salt, which break up into two or more ions when in solution, the concentration must be computed in terms of these elementary particles. For water at its normal boiling point, a boiling-point elevation of 0.0518 C° occurs if the concentration of dissolved material is 0.10 mol/(kg of solvent). For benzene at its boiling point, the corresponding figure is 0.26 C°.

The behavior of the freezing point, when there are dissolved substances, is quite similar to that of the boiling point, save that a lowering occurs. The freezing-point depression is again proportional to concentration, for dilute solutions. For water, the freezing-point depression is 0.1858 C° if the concentration is 0.10 mol/(kg. of solvent). The corresponding figure for benzene is 0.51 C°. It is this phenomenon that explains the melting—provided the temperature is not too low—of ice when salt is sprinkled on it.

Considerations of boiling-point elevation and freezing-point depression are of great importance to the chemist. Much in the form of theory, research, and application relating thereto has been developed. For such further considerations, however, the student must be referred to other textbooks and treatises.

**24. Change of Heat of Transition with Temperature at Constant Pressure.** Where a change of state from a crystalline solid of a pure substance to a liquid is involved, there is ordinarily a very definite fixed temperature for a given pressure. So definite is this that, as described in Chapter II, many of these temperatures are accepted as fixed points on our thermometer scales. Where alloys are involved, as has been noted, definite temperatures of transition generally do not occur. On the other hand, where the change of state for a pure substance is from one solid phase to another, as from rhombic sulfur to monoclinic sulfur, it sometimes happens that one may be undercooled below the normal transition point with transition carried out at the undercooled temperature in a more or less normal manner.  Similarly, it is possible to superheat the other phase beyond the normal transition point and to cause the

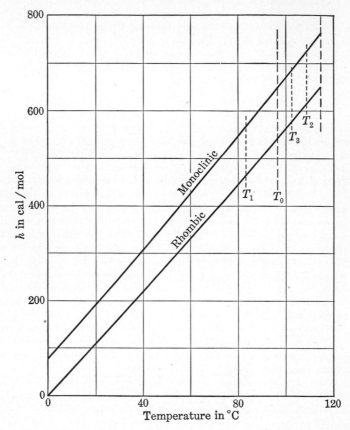

FIG. 29.  Heats of transition as a function of temperature for rhombic-monoclinic sulfur transitions.

phase change to go forward at this higher temperature.  In such cases, given certain appropriate data, the heat of transition at any temperature may be determined.

Under normal atmospheric pressure, rhombic and monoclinic crystals of sulfur can exist indefinitely in equilibrium only at 96.5°C.  At higher temperatures up to the melting point at 114°C, gradual transition to the monoclinic form takes place. At lower temperatures than 96.5°C, gradual transition to the rhombic form takes place.  Accordingly, heats of transition for rhombic-monoclinic changes for sulfur may be determined readily for various temperatures.

The theory underlying the variation in the heat of transition with temperature involves transferring a sample from one phase at temperature $T_1$ (Fig. 29) to another phase at temperature $T_2$ with the transition taking place at $T_0$, the normal transition point, in one case and at $T_3$ in another, and then applying the principle that the change in internal energy $\Delta U$, strictly the change in enthalpy $\Delta(U + pV)$, is independent of the path of transfer. Taking account of the fact that heat is absorbed on transition from the phase in equilibrium at the lower temperature to the phase in equilibrium at the higher temperature and, as will soon appear, that the specific heat of the former is less than that of the latter, we may write for cases where the change of volume on transition is negligible

$$L + c_M(T_3 - T_0) = c_R(T_3 - T_0) + (L + \Delta L) \tag{41}$$

where for obvious reasons the heats added in passing from $T_1$ to $T_0$ and from $T_3$ to $T_2$ are ignored. Obviously also $T_3$ cannot be lower than the normal transition temperature, $T_0$. Rearranging, we obtain

$$\Delta L = (c_M - c_R)(T_3 - T_0) = (c_M - c_R)\,\Delta T \tag{42}$$

For rhombic and monoclinic sulfur crystals, the accepted variations for $c_p$ are given by

$$c_R = 5.850 \text{ cal/(gm-atom C}°) + 0.0047 \text{ cal/gm-atom } (T - 96.5°C) \tag{43}$$

$$c_M = 6.280 \text{ cal/(gm-atom C}°) + 0.0072 \text{ cal/gm-atom } (T - 96.5°C) \tag{44}$$

Given further that the heat of transition at 96.5°C is 105 cal/gm-atom, one may compute the value for any other temperature and atmospheric pressure. Thus, the value for $L$ at 100°C is given by

$$L_{100°C} = L_{96.5°C} + \Delta L$$

$$= 105 \text{ cal/gm-atom} + [(6.293 - 5.858) \text{ cal/(gm-atom C}°)]3.5 \text{ C}°$$

$$= 120 \text{ cal/gm-atom} \tag{45}$$

**25. Trouton's Rule and Hildebrand's Modification.** A generalization of importance relating to heats of vaporization was presented by an Englishman named F. T. Trouton (1863–   ) in 1884. His work suggested that

$$\frac{L}{T_b} = S = \text{constant} \tag{46}$$

that is, that the ratios of heats of vaporization to their normal boiling-point temperatures was constant for all substances. The value of the constant was given as about 21 cal/mol K°.

Computed in accord with Eq. 46, the supposed constant shows a marked tendency to increase with temperature. To correct for this tendency J. H. Hildebrand (1881–   ), professor of chemistry at the University of California, proposed that comparison should be made, not for transitions at atmospheric pressure, but for transitions leading to a common value of the vapor molecule concentration. Using a concentration of 0.005 mol/l, he obtained the values given in Table IV, which show a reasonably high degree of constancy.

TABLE IV

HILDEBRAND'S VERIFICATION OF TROUTON'S RULE FOR COMPARISONS OF THE
QUOTIENT $S(= L/T_b)$ ON THE BASIS OF EQUAL CONCENTRATION OF VAPOR
MOLECULES

The following values correspond to a concentration of 0.005 mol/l (Lewis and
Randall, *Thermodynamics*, p. 145, McGraw-Hill Book Co.).

| Substance | S cal/mol K° | Substance | S cal/mol K° |
|---|---|---|---|
| Nitrogen | 27.6 | Fluorobenzene | 27.4 |
| Oxygen | 27.6 | Stannic chloride | 27.2 |
| Chlorine | 27.8 | Octane | 27.6 |
| Pentane | 27.0 | Bromonaphthalene | 27.6 |
| Hexane | 27.2 | Mercury | 26.2 |
| Carbon tetrachloride | 27.0 | Cadmium | 26.4 |
| Benzene | 27.4 | Zinc | 26.4 |

## PROBLEMS

**1.** Compute for boiling water at 100°C, for which $v_l = 1.09$ cm³/gm and $v_g = 1672$ cm³/gm, the fractional parts which have been vaporized when the intermediate specific volumes are 10 cm³/gm, 100 cm³/gm, and 1000 cm³/gm.

**2.** Given that the heat of vaporization of water at 20°C is 585 cal/gm and that the specific volume of the saturated vapor is 57.8 m³/kg, compute for the vapor the rate of increase of pressure with temperature (a) under the condition of constant saturation and (b) under the condition of constant volume, assuming the ideal-gas law.

**3.** By considering, on the p-T diagram of Fig. 2, the changes of heat supply for two constant-pressure processes, one *slightly* above the triple-point pressure and the other *slightly* below, show the relation that exists between the heats of fusion, vaporization, and sublimation at the triple point. Assume for convenience that both processes begin at the same temperature and end at the same temperature.

**4.** Given that the heats of fusion and of vaporization for water at the triple point are 80 cal/gm and 595 cal/gm respectively, and that the specific volume of the saturated vapor is 206,000 cm³/gm, compute for the triple-point state the heat of sublimation and the ratio of the slope of the freezing curve to that of the vaporization curve.

**5.** Using the data of problem 4, compute the amounts of external and internal work done per unit mass by water on subliming just below the triple point.

**6.** In a fruit cellar which, in a period of very cold weather, loses heat to the outside at the rate of 300 btu/hr, about how long may dangerous freezing temperatures be delayed by the freezing of 5.0 ft³ of water distributed about the cellar in pans?

**7.** Compute, using Clapeyron's equation, the effect of change of pressure on the sublimation temperature, near the triple point.

**8.** Using the following data, determine the heats of vaporization of water at 0°C, 50°C, and 100°C.  Use Clapeyron's equation.

| TEMPERATURE °C | VAPOR TENSION mm-Hg | TEMPERATURE °C | VAPOR TENSION mm-Hg |
|---|---|---|---|
| 0.0 | 4.569 | 60.0 | 148.9 |
| 10.0 | 9.140 | 70.0 | 233.3 |
| 20.0 | 17.36 | 80.0 | 354.9 |
| 30.0 | 31.51 | 90.0 | 525.4 |
| 40.0 | 54.87 | 100.0 | 760.0 |
| 50.0 | 91.98 | | |

**9.** Using Callendar's method for determining the densities of saturated liquid water and saturated water vapor, compute for a 10.0-cm$^3$ tube, with the aid of Fig. 7, the masses of water required for determinations at 360°C.

**10.** Using Callendar's data for water as presented in Fig. 7, determine what mass of water must be placed in a 10.0-cm$^3$ cylinder if the meniscus is to disappear at the middle of the cylinder on heating.  Note that the meniscus disappears at 374"C.

**11.** Determine the variation in the criterion $RT_c/p_c v_c$ for water using the data given in Table II.

**12.** The following properties are given for dichlorodifluoromethane ("Freon-12") refrigerant.

| $T$ °F | VAPOR TENSION lb/in.$^2$ | SPECIFIC VOLUMES, ft$^3$/pd Liquid | Vapor |
|---|---|---|---|
| −20 | 15.3 | 0.0108 | 2.474 |
| 0 | 23.9 | .0110 | 1.637 |
| 20 | 35.8 | .0113 | 1.121 |
| 40 | 51.7 | .0116 | 0.792 |
| 60 | 72.4 | .0119 | 0.575 |
| 80 | 98.8 | .0123 | 0.425 |
| 100 | 131.6 | .0127 | 0.319 |
| 120 | 171.8 | .0132 | 0.240 |
| 140 | 220.2 | .0138 | 0.180 |

What are the heats of vaporization at 0°F and 100°F in btu/pd?

**13.** The vapor tension of mercury at 0°C is $1.85 \times 10^{-4}$ mm-Hg.  How long a time is required for the vaporization of 1.0 mg of mercury from a 10-cm$^2$ surface of mercury at 0°C in a vacuum?  Mercury vapor is a monatomic gas.

**14.** The vapor tension of liquid sodium is approximately given by the following equation for the temperature range 180°C to 880°C, $\ln p/p_0 = L/R(1/T_0 - 1/T)$. Given that the vapor tensions at 500°K, 600°K, and 800°K in mm-Hg are $5.28 \times 10^{-4}$, $3.64 \times 10^{-2}$, and 6.44, compute three values for the heat of fusion of sodium by taking the data for two temperatures in pairs.

**15.** Langmuir's results for the rate of vaporization of tungsten at 2400°K, 2600°K, and 2800°K in gm/(cm$^2$ sec) are $1.58 \times 10^{-10}$, $4.64 \times 10^{-9}$, and $8.28 \times 10^{-8}$. How long will a tungsten filament whose diameter is 0.025 mm last in a vacuum at these temperatures if it ceases to operate when its diameter has been reduced by 8%?  As an approximation, assume the vaporization to go on as though the average diameter were to hold throughout.

**16.** Using the data of problem 15, compute (*a*) the vapor tension of tungsten at 2400°K and (*b*) the heat of sublimation of tungsten at 2500°K, using Eq. 5 or Eq. 7.

**17.** In a determination of the heat of sublimation of carbon dioxide a considerable amount of the solid was broken into small pieces and placed in an enclosed Dewar flask about a suitable electric heating device. The flask with contents was placed on the pan of a platform balance, and, after a suitable time had elapsed for the establishment of a steady rate of sublimation, the combined mass was noted at 5-min intervals, first, without electric heating, second, with electric heating, third, without electric heating. The heating began at the close of the second interval and continued for just 8 min at the rate of 125 watts. The data were

| TIME min | MASS kg | TIME min | MASS kg |
|---|---|---|---|
| 0.0 | 1.0504 | 20.0 | 0.9230 |
| 5.0 | 1.0442 | 25.0 | 0.9172 |
| 10.0 | 1.0383 | 30.0 | 0.9111 |
| 15.0 | No reading | | |

No reading was possible at the close of the third interval because of the rapid rate of variation of mass at that time. What is the heat of sublimation that results?

**18.** Using the value obtained from problem 17 for the heat of sublimation of carbon dioxide and 1.565 gm/cm³ as the density of the solid at the sublimation point −78.5°C, determine how much water may be frozen by the immersion of a block of Dry Ice 10 cm by 10 cm by 1½ cm, which is at that temperature, in water at 0°C. Disregard the heat that may be used in heating the bubbles of carbon dioxide which will rise to the top.

**19.** With the aid of Fig. 22, determine the heats of fusion of bismuth, zinc, and antimony.

**20.** Starting with a sodium sulfate, $Na_2SO_4$, solution at 20.00°C composed of 0.005366 mole of sodium sulfate and 1.0000 kg of water, one finds that 0.1535 cal of heat are evolved when the solution is diluted isothermally with 1.0000 kg of water at 20.00°C. What, in cal/(mole of sodium sulfate) is the heat of dilution of sodium sulfate in water at 20.0°C for the dilution indicated?

**21.** What depression of the freezing point is produced when 4.50 gm of sodium chloride, NaCl, which dissociates in water, are added to 500 gm of water? What depression results when 4.50 gm of urea, $CO(NH_2)_2$, which does not dissociate in water, are added to 500 gm of water? What elevations of the normal boiling point are produced by the same additions?

**22.** Given that the heat of fusion of monoclinic sulfur is 370 joules/gm, determine the heat of fusion of rhombic sulfur at the melting point 114°C.

# CHAPTER XI

## HEAT ENGINES, REFRIGERATORS, AND HUMAN POWER PLANTS

**1. Introduction.** The first record of the use of steam in the performance of work goes back to Hero of Alexandria. About 130 B.C., he described a primitive reaction turbine. A hollow spherical vessel pivoted along a central vertical axis was supplied with steam through one of its pivots. From the interior, the steam escaped to the air through orifices at the outer ends of two horizontal pipes, which left the spherical vessel at the opposite ends of a diameter perpendicular to the vertical axis. The outer ends of the pipes were so shaped that the steam issued from the orifices tangentially and in opposite directions. The spherical vessel was caused to whirl much after the manner of our whirling lawn-sprays and for the same reason.

Hero also described a toy in which air heated in a closed vessel was allowed to expand through a pipe into another vessel containing water and thereby forced the water out through a second pipe to produce a fountain. This was, in a sense, a forerunner of later engines which were put to actual tasks.

The first commercially successful steam engine was built in England by Thomas Savery (1650–1715) in 1698. It was used to lift water from a mine. The engine (Fig. 1), except for pipes leading from the mine and to the reservoir, consisted of two sets of duplicating parts, $ABCDE$ and $A'B'C'D'E'$, which acted cyclically, each 180° out of phase with the other. Starting with vessel $A$, filled with water from the mine, valve $B$ was opened by hand, letting in steam from the boiler. Much of the steam entering thus condensed on the top layer of water in vessel $A$ and raised it to the boiling temperature. Thereafter the pressure supplying the steam forced the water in $A$ out through pipe $C$ via self-acting valve $E$ and the outlet pipe to the reservoir above or elsewhere. With the water pushed out, further entry of steam from the boiler was prevented by operating valve $B$. The steam remaining in $A$ was then condensed, by water flowing over its outer surface, the pressure therein was reduced greatly, and water was forced up from the mine by atmospheric pressure forces via the self-acting valve $D$ into $A$ until the cycle was completed.

331

During operation, the cycle described was repeated in succession by both sets of duplicating parts. Because of the out-of-phase feature mentioned, however, there was a fairly constant stream of water being lifted from the mine and forced upward to the reservoir. Due to the condensation of steam on the cold water in the large vessels and to the

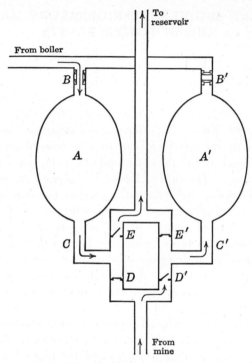

FIG. 1. Savery's pumping engine of 1698.

cooling of the vessel itself, much heat was lost, at least twenty times as much as in present-day practice.

Savery's invention was followed by Denis Papin's (1647–1712) safety valve, by Jean Desaugliers' condensation of the remaining steam in the emptied pump chamber by a jet of cold water within the chamber, and by Papin's floating diaphragm or piston. The last-mentioned invention necessitated replacing Savery's egg-shaped chambers by cylinders. Because of the prevention of direct contact between the steam from the boiler and cold pumped water, there was no longer need of heating the upper layers of water in the pump chamber up to the temperature of the entering steam. Following the displacement which it produced in the cylinder, the steam was allowed to escape to the air.   Papin's device has been described as a "non-condensing single-acting steam pump, with steam cylinder and pump cylinder in one."   There is some doubt that Papin ever had built one.

Thomas Newcomen's (1663–1729) atmospheric engine of 1705 (Fig. 2), also developed in England, represented the next considerable advance.   This engine included a cylinder with piston which was entirely separate from any pump cylinder.   Starting with piston $A$ at

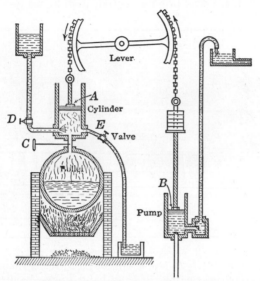

FIG. 2.   Newcomen's atmospheric engine of 1705 (courtesy of O. H. Blackwood).

the bottom of the cylinder, valve $C$ was opened and steam from the boiler entered the cylinder to force the piston upward against the downward-pressing force due to atmospheric pressure.   Next, with the closing of valve $C$ and the opening of valve $D$, the steam in the cylinder was condensed by a spray of cold water.   Piston $A$ was then forced down by the atmosphere above, and water was lifted by the pump.   The water of the condensing spray and that produced by the condensation of the steam later escaped through the tube containing valve $E$ when that valve was opened.   With the proper readjustment of valves $C$, $D$, and $E$, the device was returned to the initial state ready for another cycle.

Initially the valves of Newcomen's engine were operated manually. According to story a so-called "lazy" lad, charged with such work, devised the method of making the actions automatic in order that he might enjoy himself at play during working hours.   However true the story, this automatic feature has since been an important part of steam and other engines.

The actual lifting of water by Newcomen's engine occurred during the displacement of the piston by atmospheric pressure forces, hence the name, atmospheric engine. Of course, during the upward motion of the piston a certain amount of work was done by the steam. In that cylinder A was cooled during each cycle, in that the energy of the condensed steam was not recovered, in that no use whatever was

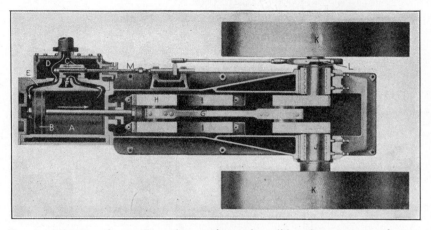

FIG. 3. Diagram of a small, modern, reciprocating, slide-valve, center-crank steam engine, showing: A, cylinder; B, piston with rings; D, steam chest; E, intake port; F, exhaust port; G, connecting rod; H, cross-head; I, cross-head guides; M, eccentric rod; J, journal in bearings; K, flywheels (courtesy of the Socony-Vacuum Oil Co.. New York).

made of the internal energy of steam which is made available by reversible adiabatic expansions, and in that the temperature and hence the pressure of the intake steam was low, the system, like Savery's, was wasteful of fuel. Newcomen engines were widely used for colliery pumps for about 75 years.

The greatest improvements in the steam engine were made by James Watt (1736–1819) of Scotland. Because of his manual dexterity he was trained as an instrumentmaker. His interest in steam engineering seems to date from 1763, when asked by the professor of physics at Glasgow University to repair a faulty Newcomen engine. While thus engaged, it is said, he perceived various features of the Newcomen engine which were wasteful of fuel and set about to remove them. He developed (see the modern steam engine shown in Fig. 3): (1) the separate condenser which conserved the heat otherwise lost in the repeated cooling of the cylinder into which the steam expanded; (2) jackets for preventing loss of heat from the steam cylinder to the outside by surrounding the cylinder with poorly conducting wood or with a steam-filled sleeve; (3) the double-acting or reciprocating feature in order that, without appreciable increase of machinery, an engine might perform useful work on the backward as well as on the forward stroke, thereby effectively doubling its output; (4) the adiabatic expansion feature, which was brought about by shutting off the steam supply to a cylinder when the power stroke was but partially completed and utilizing the internal energy released by the enclosed steam while expanding during the remainder of the stroke; (5) the flyball throttling governor, which tended toward constancy of speed of operation, and (6) the conversion from a reciprocating motion to and fro in a straight line to rotary motion. To this list of rather vital features is to be added Watt's straight-line mechanism, the float valve as a regulator to the water supply of the boiler, and an engine indicator. His engine of 1782 had a specific consumption of 8 lb of coal/hp-hr, in contrast with Savery's probable value of 30 lb/hp-hr and the value for our present best steam turbine of less than 1 lb/hp-hr.

Jonathan Hornblower, a contemporary of Watt, in 1781 patented a compound engine with two cylinders of different sizes. In use, steam was first admitted to the smaller cylinder, whose exhaust became the intake of the larger cylinder, which in turn exhausted into a condenser. Though not appreciated by Hornblower or those who followed him for a long time to come, the compound engine had an advantage over the single-expansion engine in that the changes of temperature to which the parts of each cylinder were subjected with the expansion of the steam were materially less in the compound engine. With improvements in design and construction and greatly increased steam pressures, triple- and even quadruple-expansion engines were found desirable.

Following Watt and Hornblower, the next major improvement, made in 1849 by an American named G. H. Corliss (1817–1888), provided special, quick-closing, intake valves in order to reduce the irreversible throttling and frictional flow effects associated with slow-closing slide valves (Fig. 4). The most recent development in reciprocating engines was made by the Dutchman, Johannes Stumpf (1863– ) who, in his uniflow engine of 1908, provided different ports for the inflow of hot steam and the outflow of cold steam in such manner that much of the cold exhaust steam passed directly to the condenser without flowing backward over surfaces which shortly thereafter would be reheated by steam entering at boiler pressure. As shown in

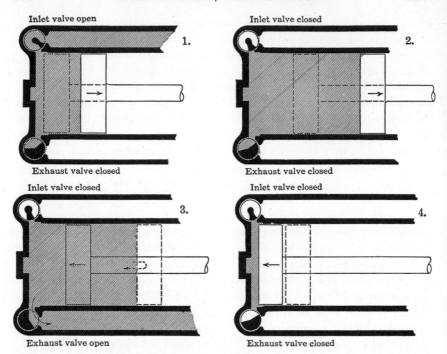

FIG. 4. Diagrams showing the positions of the quick-acting, rotary valves of Corliss engines for the characteristic four stages of a cycle. The initial position of the piston for each stage is shown in dashed (------) lines, the final position in full (——) lines. (Courtesy of the Socony-Vacuum Oil Co., New York.)

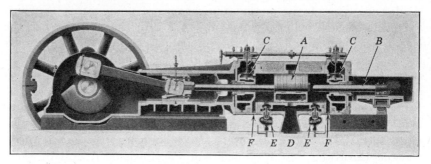

FIG. 5. Section of a universal, uniflow, reciprocating steam engine showing: *A*, piston, partly cut away, in the center of the cylinder; *B*, piston rods which, extending both forwards and backwards from the piston through fixed bearings, tend to keep the piston axially aligned with the cylinder; *C*, poppet intake valves; *D*, exhaust port; *E*, auxiliary exhaust valves which function only under certain conditions of engine operation; *F*, openings leading to safety valves for relieving occasional, otherwise dangerous, pressures that may develop (courtesy of the Skinner Engine Co., Erie, Pa.).

Fig. 5, the main exhaust port is near the center of the cylinder and the piston is rather long. Quick-acting valves give the desired quick opening and closing of ports.

The greatest development in the steam engine since the time of Watt, however, occurred in 1884 with the invention by the Englishman Sir Charles A. Parsons (1854–1931) of a non-reciprocating type known as the turbine. It had as its prototype the toy of Hero of

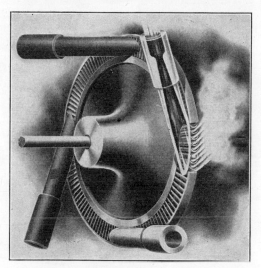

Fɪɢ. 6.   De Laval's single-stage impulse turbine (courtesy of the Dravo Corp., Pittsburgh, Pa.).

Alexandria of which mention has been made above. It may, in some instances only, be viewed as a multi-expansion, uniflow engine with a continuous exhaust from one cylinder to another, and thus a follow-up of the pioneer work of Hornblower.

There are two main types of turbines. (1) The single-stage impulse turbine (Fig. 6) invented by a Swedish engineer, Carl De Laval (1845–1913). It is characterized by a single rotating disk with turbine blades attached at its outer edge and an approximately complete drop of steam pressure and a huge change of steam velocity in the nozzles feed the incoming steam to the rotating blades. (2) The multi-stage reaction turbine, developed by Parsons is characterized by many parallel rings of blades, which gradually increase in size with change of location in the passage from the intake to the exhaust. Alternate rows (the flaring portion to the right of the center of Fig. 7) of these blades are attached to the rotating shaft and to the turbine frame. In contrast to what occurs in the impulse turbine, the pressure of the steam drops gradually as it passes through the turbine. A third type of turbine is known as the C. G. Curtis "velocity-compounded"

FIG. 7. A photograph of a 25,000-kw, 3,600-rpm combination turbine from which the upper portion of the casing has been removed. At $A$, the two movable disks of a "Curtis velocity-compounded" stage are shown. The nozzles, which are just to the left of these disks and similar to those of Fig. 6 in construction, cannot be seen in this view. Steam leaving these disks enters chamber $B$, after which it passes through the flaring "Parson's reaction" stage, $C$, into the exhaust passage $D$ which leads to the condenser. Small passages, as at $E$, serve to keep an atmosphere of steam in space $F$ whose pressure is the same as that in $B$. The end thrust on the balancing piston $G$ and hence on the rotating shaft, due to the steam in $F$, just counterbalances the thrust on the same shaft in the opposite direction exerted by the steam passing through the flaring set of turbine blades, $C$. Passages as at $H$ serve to "bleed off" limited amounts of steam at various temperatures for the partial reheating of the feedwater. Appreciable gains in efficiency result from their use.

(Courtesy of the Westinghouse Electric and Manufacturing Co., Pittsburgh, Pa.)

turbine. In principle it is much like the De Laval impulse turbine. It differs mainly in having the steam from the nozzles pass through three sets of blades. Two of the sets are movable and are separated by the third, which redirects the stream of steam so that both movable sets of blades are given impulses in the same direction. A fourth type is known as the Auguste Rateau (1863–1930) "pressure-compounded" turbine. In principle, it consists of two or more De Laval turbines in series with all the movable-bladed disks attached together to form a single rotating member in a single casing. There are just as many sets of nozzles as there are disks with turbine blades. Finally, certain other turbines are classed as combinations of the types described. Fig. 7 shows a combination of the velocity-compounded and the reaction types.

Comparing the steam turbine and the reciprocating steam engine, it is found that, at present, certain conditions of operating point to the steam turbine and others to the reciprocating steam engine as the more favorable engine. Generally speaking, high operating speeds, large power output, economy of space and cost, and freedom from vibrations are favored by steam-turbine installations. Low operating speeds, low power output, and large starting torques as characteristics favor the reciprocating steam engine.

Below we shall consider in more detail the operation of a reciprocating steam engine and a turbine, both mechanically and thermally. Special consideration will be given to the thermodynamic cycle through which the steam is carried in each.

We shall also consider in this chapter, in a similar way, the gasoline and the Diesel internal-combustion engines as well as those heat engines, commonly known as electric refrigerators, which date back to pioneer work by Jacob Perkins (1766–1849) and John Hague in Great Britain in 1834 on the production of ice and the cooling of liquids by evaporation.

Finally, we shall discuss in a broad way that most important engine of all, the human engine.

**2. Elements of a Steam Power Plant.** In Fig. 8 the important parts of a steam power plant are shown. Starting with the boiler, the course of the water, there generated as steam, is seen to be (1) to a prime mover, which is shown as a turbine though it may be a reciprocating engine, (2) to a condenser where, expanded at a low pressure and at a low temperature relatively, the steam comes in contact with water-cooled surfaces and is condensed to water, (3) to a condensate pump, (4) to a hot well at atmospheric pressure, (5) to a feedwater pump, and (6) to the boiler. From the boiler to the condenser, it passes as steam; from the condenser to the boiler, as liquid water. If the prime mover is a turbine, the movement is steady and continuous. If the prime mover is a reciprocating engine, the movement in the steam phase is not steady.

There are three features, in addition to those just noted, one or more of which are frequently found in steam power plants. They are (1) superheating, (2) reheating, and (3) regenerative heating. All tend to higher thermal efficiencies and are of importance particularly in large power plants where the energy cost is an appreciable factor. Superheating is usually accomplished by causing the steam, on leaving the boiler proper where it is in contact with boiling water, to enter tubes that pass through the furnace where it is heated to a substantially higher temperature than that of the steam in contact with the boiling liquid. Sometimes, however, in its course from the boiler to

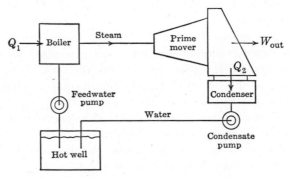

Fig. 8. The elements of a steam power plant.

the condenser, the steam is passed through a reheater (not shown in Fig. 7) located between two separate prime movers arranged in series. The purpose is the gaining of the advantage of a high temperature and the consequent elimination of condensed water droplets which at high speeds are detrimental to the blades of a turbine. Sometimes also, as noted, there is regenerative heating (see the "bleed off" passages $H$ of Fig. 7), a procedure which we shall discuss later (see p. 348).

**3. Processes Occurring in a Reciprocating Steam Engine.** With the reciprocating engine of Fig. 3 in mind, we shall give consideration only to what happens in the cylinder to the left of the piston. This is with the understanding that something is taking place simultaneously on the right side and that what is taking place there differs from what occurs on the left only in the time of actual occurrence. In the main theoretical outline, it makes little difference whether the valve is a slide valve or a poppet valve.

What the processes occurring in a cylinder of a steam engine are is best gained from a study of the engine's indicator diagram. As will be shown, this is a graph showing the steam pressure in the cylinder to one side of the moving piston as a function of that piston's position, or, what is effectively the same, the volume of the space occupied by that steam. Ordinarily such diagrams are automatically drawn by the engine in operation, making use of certain auxiliary apparatus. A common type of instrument for drawing indicator diagrams is shown

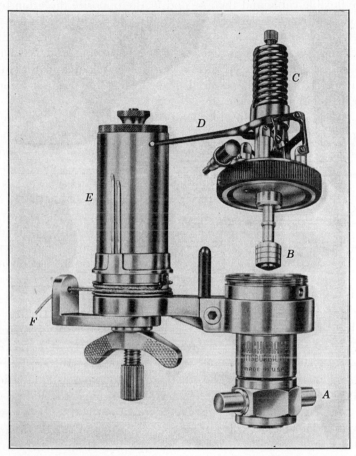

FIG. 9.  Apparatus for the drawing of an engine indicator diagram (courtesy of the W. S. Hill Co. and the Bachrach Industrial Instrument Co., Pittsburgh, Pa.).

in Fig. 9. The device is firmly attached at $A$ to a special outlet at the intake end of the cylinder to be studied. Through this outlet, steam under pressure comes in contact with the bottom of piston $B$, whose up-and-down motion, varying with the pressure, is controlled by spring $C$. A lever $D$, pinioned at one end and attached at one point to the piston, carries a pencil or a pen at its free end, which in use rests against paper fitted snugly about the cylindrical drum $E$. This drum, spring controlled, is provided with a flexible cable $F$ which in turn at its remote end is attached to a lever, one end of which is moved back and forth by the piston rod.  In operation, the paper-covered drum is rotated first in one direction about its central vertical axis by the flexible cable and then second in the opposite direction by the controlling spring as slack is provided by the cable.  Simultaneously the pen or pencil end of lever $D$ moves up and down corresponding to the varying pressures experienced at the base of piston $B$.  On the paper about drum $E$ in operation, a graph, an indicator diagram, is drawn which shows the desired pressure-volume relations for the steam in the cylinder under investigation.

Fig. 10 shows an idealized indicator diagram for an engine like that of Fig. 3.  Starting with the piston approximately as shown in that

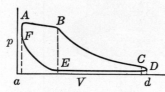

FIG. 10.   Indicator diagram for a steam engine.

figure in its extreme left position, we note a clearance space, indicated also in Fig. 10, which is never swept out by the piston.  At the right there is an equal clearance space.  As shown, the space at the left is fully open to the boiler, and the piston is being forced to the right by the incoming steam under boiler pressure.  With this movement, there is a gradual closing of the inlet port.  Up to the instant of complete closure, as shown by $AB$ on the indicator diagram, the pressure, though nearly constant, decreases somewhat because of the increasing resistance to the steam flow experienced at the port.  The process is nearly isothermal.  During most of the remainder of the stroke to the right, as shown by line $BC$, the enclosed steam expands adiabatically. Shortly before the completion of the stroke, however, the sliding valve starts to open the port through which steam entered, and it now becomes an exhaust port, connecting the space to the left of the piston with the condenser.  From $C$ to $D$, the pressure drops nearly to that of the condenser or of the atmosphere, if the exhaust is into the atmosphere.  An exhaust stage, $D$ to $E$, follows, during which the pressure is constant and about equal to that of the condenser.  Much of the steam remaining is forced at low pressure and constant temperature into the condenser.  With the closing of the port, what steam remains is compressed adiabatically for the remainder of the backward stroke, $EF$.  Its pressure and temperature are both increased accordingly. Finally the port is opened to the boiler, and the pressure and the temperature of the steam in the clearance volume change quickly to those occurring in the boiler. The cylinder is now ready for the start of another cycle.

Fig. 11 is a copy of three pairs of actual indicator diagrams taken for widely different load conditions. Those tapering to the right represent performance for the space on one side of the piston; those tapering to the left represent performance for the space on the other side.

The work done *by* the steam in the left compartment of Fig. 3 during a forward stroke is represented on the indicator diagram of Fig. 10 by the area $ABCDdaA$; that done *on* the steam in the same compartment by the steam in the right compartment during a backward stroke

FIG. 11. Indicator diagrams for a reciprocating universal uniflow steam engine. Three conditions of loading are shown. For each condition two indicator diagrams are given, one for the space to the left of the piston of Fig. 5, the other for the space to the right of the piston. 2 mep signifies that the mean effective pressure in the space to the left or the right of the piston was 2 lb/in.² The equality of the two areas in each of the three cases indicates that the rates of performing work by the steam on opposing sides of the piston were equal. (Courtesy of the Skinner Engine Co., Erie, Pa.)

is represented by $AFEDdaA$. The net work per cycle performed by the steam is, of course, represented by the area enclosed within $ABCDEFA$. Given the calibration data for the indicator apparatus, it is easy to determine the actual value of the work performed during a cycle. To illustrate, suppose that 1 in. taken vertically corresponds to a pressure change of 60 lb/in.², that 1 in. taken horizontally corresponds to a 300-in.³ displacement, and that the enclosed area for a given curve is 3.0 in.² The work per cycle performed by the steam on one side of the piston is then given by

$$\text{Work per cycle} = \frac{3.0 \text{ in.}^2}{\text{cycle}} \times \frac{60 \text{ lb/in.}^2}{1 \text{ in.}} \times \frac{300 \text{ in.}^3}{1 \text{ in.}}$$

$$\times \frac{1 \text{ ft}}{12 \text{ in.}} = 4500 \frac{\text{ft-lb}}{\text{cycle}} \quad (1)$$

The power expenditure by the steam in the engine is obtained by multiplying this value by twice the engine frequency. For an engine frequency of 5 cycles/sec, the steam power becomes 45,000 ft-lb/sec or 82 hp.  Because of friction the power delivery of the engine will be less.

In the foregoing, all changes of potential and kinetic energies due to changes in steam velocities and elevations have been neglected.  If, instead of slide valves, poppet valves or other quick-acting valves are used, the portions $AB$ and $DE$ of the indicator diagram will both be nearly parallel to the $V$-axis.  Such action would lead not only to greater power for an otherwise identical engine without such quick-acting valves but also to a greater thermal efficiency or ratio of work done to heat supplied.

**4. Processes Occurring in a Steam Turbine.**  Next, consider the passage of steam through a reaction turbine such as is pictured in Fig. 7.  The steam entry is at the small end; the exhaust, at the large end.  In between, there are two sets of curved blades.  One set is stationary and is attached to the turbine framework.  It is composed of several rings, each containing a large number of individual blades, all set with the same or about the same orientation radially with respect to the central rotating shaft.  The second set of blades differs from the first in that they are attached to the central rotating shaft with an orientation with respect to that central shaft that is just the reverse.  The rings of blades of one set mesh between those of the other set, and their shapes and orientations (Fig. 12) are such that, as the steam passes from the entrance to the exhaust, it meets each succeeding ring of blades at such an angle that the component of its velocity in the plane of rotation of the blades is reversed at the stationary blades though not completely so at the moving blades.  Actually the steam in its passage through the turbine tends generally to move in a gradually widening spiral whose direction of rotation is that of the central shaft.  The reactions to the forces exerted on the steam by the movable blades cause those blades and the shaft to which they are attached to rotate and, if external resisting torques are present, to perform external work.  The work so done is at the expense of the thermal energy of the steam and results in a lowering of both the temperature and the pressure of the steam as it passes through the turbine (see also Fig. 12).

As steam passes from the entrance to the exhaust of a turbine, the pressure decreases and the specific volume increases, both at more or less uniform rates; but, due to the lengthening of the blades and of the circumferences of succeeding rings, the speed of the steam lengthwise the turbine is kept approximately constant.  Of the energy carried in by the compressed steam, only that is carried out which it normally possesses by virtue of its reduced temperature and pressure and because of its kinetic energy of flow. To a considerable extent, the process undergone by the steam on passage through the turbine is much like a reversibly adiabatic expansion, in which, because of the fixed set of blades, expansion in one direction only is possible, that which results in motion of the rotating shaft. There is no cycle for the turbine by itself such as the indicator diagram gives for a recipro-

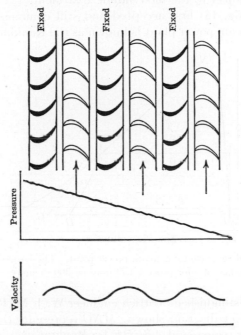

Fig. 12.  Blade orientations, pressure variations, and velocity variations along the length of a reaction turbine.

cating engine. However, for the steam plant as a whole, as indicated in the previous section, there is a cycle which will be discussed shortly.

Other turbines, known as impulse turbines, depend on the impulses from jets of steam which strike against blades fastened to rotating members (Fig. 6). The pressure change from high to low in this case takes place almost entirely within the nozzles from which the jets issue. Correspondingly, within those nozzles there is a great increase in steam velocity. Though commonly, in a single-impulse turbine, there is but one such pressure-drop stage, sometimes there are two or three and occasionally even more such stages. This type of turbine is especially favored in small sizes, and the number of them in use in the United States exceeds greatly the number of reaction turbines in use. Each type has certain advantages, and, as might be expected, many turbines have been built which combine the impulse and the reaction principles.

**5. The Rankine Cycle.** In a modern steam power plant the energy-conveying substance is carried through successive cycles involving changes of temperature and of pressure. Accordingly the processes involved are subject to thermodynamic treatment.

The cycle (Fig. 13) first accepted and still commonly used as descriptive of a steam power plant is known as the Rankine cycle after its

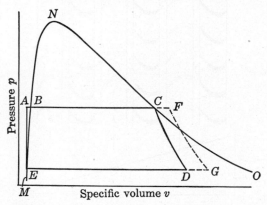

FIG. 13. The Rankine cycle for a steam power plant. The horizontal scale is badly distorted. The change of $v$ for process $CD$ may be 200 or more times that for $BC$.

proposer, the distinguished Scottish engineer W. J. M. Rankine (1820–1872). In the $p$-$v$ diagram shown, $MNO$ represents the boundary of the liquid-vapor region, and $ABCDEA$ a Rankine cycle for the simpler type of plant, involving none of the three supplemental features of superheating, reheating, and regenerative heating. In succession, we represent at $A$ the water entering the boiler just after leaving the feed-water pump (the pressure is that of the boiler, the temperature that of the hot well), at $B$ the water still in liquid form but at the boiling point, at $C$ the water as steam about to enter the prime mover, at $D$ the steam partially condensed at a low pressure and a relatively low temperature in the condenser, at $E$ the used steam completely condensed, ready to be transferred by the condensate pump to the hot well and then via the feedwater pump to the boiler and condition $A$ once more.

As water is carried about this idealized Rankine cycle, heat is supplied to it on passage from $A$ to $B$ and from $B$ to $C$. Correspondingly heat is removed during the condensing process $DE$. While processes

$AB$ and $BC$ are both at the same constant pressure, only $BC$ is isothermal. Process $CD$ is reversibly adiabatic; process $DE$ is reversibly
isothermal; and process $EA$ may be viewed as essentially reversibly
adiabatic. Except for the process $AB$, the cycle is essentially a Carnot
cycle, after Sadi Carnot (1796–1832). During the reversible adiabatic
expansion $CD$, much of the steam condenses to form water droplets.

As for the Carnot cycle, the area enclosed within $ABCDA$ represents the net work performed by the water vapor per unit mass of
vapor per cycle. The efficiency, $\eta$, of this cycle is given by the ratio
of the net work performed by the steam $W$ to the intake heat $Q_1$, thus

$$\eta = \frac{W}{Q_1} = \frac{Q_1 - Q_2}{Q_1} \tag{2}$$

of which $Q_2$ obviously represents heat delivered to the condenser.
Since not all of $Q_1$ was taken in isothermally, at temperature $T_1$, it is
not possible to equate $\eta$ to $(T_1 - T_2)/T_1$ as is done for the Carnot
cycle. Since that portion of $Q_1$ which is absorbed during the $AB$
process is a considerable fraction of the whole, we may expect the
theoretical efficiency to be appreciably less than the efficiency corresponding to a Carnot cycle employing the same high and low temperature. To illustrate, the idealized efficiency for the Rankine cycle using
water and operating with a boiler temperature of $401°F$ ($250$ lb/in.$^2$)
and a condenser temperature of $102°F$ ($1.0$ lb/in.$^2$) is $30.6\%$, whereas
the corresponding Carnot cycle efficiency for the same two temperatures is $34.7\%$. In reality any actual engine efficiency would be much
less on account of various heat losses and frictional resistances. Depending on conditions, an actual efficiency might range from $30\%$ to
$80\%$ of the $30.6\%$.

For a steam power plant using superheated steam, the Rankine
cycle is represented by $ABFGEA$ (Fig. 13), in which the extension of
the line $AC$ by $CF$ represents the change in the steam on passage
through the superheater. Note, as an important advantage, that,
during the reversible, adiabatic expansion, $FG$, less condensation
occurs than without superheating along $CD$. That is not the only
advantage, however. The efficiency of the cycle increases as well.
For operation at a boiler temperature of $401°F$, a condenser temperature of $102°F$, and a superheat temperature of $500°F$, the idealized
Rankine cycle efficiency becomes $31.1\%$, a slight but not-to-be-despised
gain over the $30.6\%$ value computed above.

**6. The Mollier Diagram and the Rankine Cycle.** Rather than the $p$-$v$ diagram of
Fig. 13, the engineer frequently uses a Mollier diagram, named after the German

engineer R. Mollier (1863–   ), such as that of Fig. 14 in which specific enthalpy, $h$, is plotted as a function of specific entropy, $s$. On this plot the lines $CD$ and $FG$ representing reversible adiabatic expansions are straight, vertical lines. One of the advantages of such a graph is that the available energy per cycle and unit mass

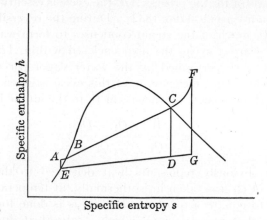

FIG. 14.   A Mollier diagram for water showing particular Rankine cycles outlined. The lettering of Figs. 13 and 14 is the same for corresponding states.

of water is given, except for the small correction $(h_A - h_E)$, by the difference between the $h$-values for $C$ and $D$ or for $F$ and $G$. The efficiency for the Rankine cycle, $\eta_R$, including the small correction just mentioned, is

$$\eta_R = \frac{h_C - h_D - (h_A - h_E)}{h_C - h_A - (h_A - h_E)} \tag{3}$$

All the quantities on the right may be read directly from the plot. The correction term $(h_A - h_E)$ is small and is often ignored. The derivation of Eq. 3 must be left for more advanced books.

**7. The Regenerative Steam Cycle.** For steam power plants employing turbines with "bleed-off" provisions (Fig. 7), the Rankine cycle, as an idealized unattainable cycle, is replaced by another idealized unattainable cycle, toward which construction and operating steam engineers may aim. Where there are several stages of bleeding, that which is bled off at the last stage is used to reheat the feedwater pumped from the condenser to a temperature near that of the bleed-off. That which is bled off at the next preceding stage is used to heat the partially reheated feedwater to a temperature near that of the reheating system, etc. (Fig. 15). The heat thus used, in what is called regenerative heating, is used under thermodynamically favorable conditions. Under idealized conditions in which, without superheating, a large number of bleed-offs of the right magnitude are employed to heat the feedwater completely to the boiling point and in which the externally supplied heat is used only to vaporize the boiling water, it can be shown that the conditions for a Carnot cycle are approached and that the corresponding Carnot efficiency rather than the Rankine efficiency becomes the idealized goal. Appreciable gains, of the order of a few per cent, justify the regenerative cycle.

**8. The Tendency toward Increased Operating Temperatures in Industry.** As shown in Chapter IX, Eq. 19, the efficiency of a Carnot engine, $\eta_C$, depends on the temperatures $T_1$ and $T_2$ of the two heat reservoirs and is given by

$$\eta_C = \frac{T_1 - T_2}{T_1} = 1 - \frac{T_2}{T_1} \tag{4}$$

where $T_1$ is the higher temperature. Both lowering the condenser temperature, $T_2$, and increasing the intake temperature, $T_1$, separately result in increases in the efficiency of the engine. The gain due to a change in $T_2$ is more pronounced than

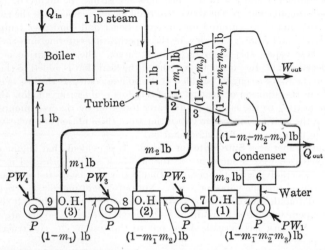

FIG. 15.   The layout of a regenerative heating steam plant (by permission, V.M. Faires, *Applied Thermodynamics*, New York, The Macmillan Co., 1938).

that due to an equal change in $T_1$. In industry, however, where attempts to approach the ideal $\eta_C$ are ever present, emphasis is directed largely toward increasing $T_1$. The temperature $T_2$, in accord with one of the ways of expressing the second law of thermo-dynamics (see p. 264), has the temperature of the surroundings as a theoretical lower limit. In contrast, for $T_1$, there is no theoretical upper limit.

In comparing Rankine and Carnot engine efficiencies, one must take account of the fact that, though both have constant condenser temperatures, only the Carnot engine has a constant intake temperature. As noted above, a consequence is that, for a given condenser temperature, $T_2$, and a given maximum intake temperature, $T_1$, the efficiency of the Rankine engine, $\eta_R$, as expressed in Eq. 3, is necessarily less than $\eta_C$ as expressed in Eq. 4. Other things unchanged, it is the case, however, that $\eta_R$, like $\eta_C$, increases with $T_1$. Always, of course, an efficiency realized in practice is less than the $\eta_R$ for the corresponding $T_1$ and $T_2$; but, for an assumed practical fixed condensing temperature $T_2$, such realized efficiencies, like the $\eta_R$'s and $\eta_C$'s, increase similarly with $T_1$.

On the basis of the foregoing, a tendency, in industrial steam plants, to transfer from standard carbon steel to stronger special alloy construction capable of standing up under higher temperatures is understandable. Let us compare the Rankine efficiencies for two plants having these constructions. For the former we may take, as among the best, a plant operating with a boiler temperature of 572°F, a maximum pressure of 1250 lb/in.$^2$, a condenser temperature of 102°F corresponding to a pressure of 1.0 lb/in.$^2$, and a superheat temperature of 725°F. For the latter, we take a recent installation with a boiler temperature of 660°F, a maximum pressure of 2365 lb/in.$^2$, a condenser temperature of 102°F, and a superheat temperature of 940°F. Their Rankine efficiencies are 38.1% and 41.2%. Their actual brake efficiencies are naturally much lower, though in about the same ratio. Such an increase of efficiency resulting from an increased operating temperature may well be the determining factor where a new construction is planned, even though scrapping of apparently good equipment and a high new installation cost may be involved.

It is interesting to compare the above two Rankine efficiencies with the two Carnot efficiencies that may be computed for the same boiler and condenser temperatures. They are 47.7% and 51.8%. In view of the superheating entering into the Rankine efficiency, these values may seem surprisingly large. The explanation is based on two considerations: (1) by far the larger part of the heat that is added to the working substance in the Rankine engine is added at the boiling point; (2) the loss in efficiency, resulting from the addition of heat at relatively low temperatures below the boiling point while heating to the boiling point water forced in by the feed pump, is much greater than the increase in efficiency resulting from the addition of a relatively small amount of heat in the superheating operation.

**9. Mercury Vapor as a Substitute for Steam.** It is evident that engine efficiency might be increased were a substance available which might be heated in its liquid state to a considerably higher temperature than water may be heated without exceeding some specified suitable vapor pressure. Not only might undue construction costs be eliminated, but also the condition of having the major intake of heat at the highest attained temperature might be realized. Diphenyloxide and mercury are two such substances. Mercury has actually been put to the test in the construction of at least three plants.

At 940°F, the vapor pressure of mercury is 124 lb/in.$^2$, a value which is about $\frac{1}{20}$ that of steam supplied by a boiler at 660°F. With 940°F and 80°F as $T_1$ and $T_2$, the Carnot efficiency, $\eta_C$, is 61.4%. Due to the elimination of the need of superheating, however, one might expect the Rankine efficiency, $\eta_R$, for such a mercury-vapor plant to be considerably greater than that for the steam plant noted above in which 940°F is reached by superheating. Actually, in the plants where mercury is used, it has been found desirable to operate binary systems. Because of the extremely great specific volume of mercury vapor at, say, 80°F, a condenser chamber for mercury vapor at this temperature would be much too large to be practical. In one plant the condenser temperature, $T_2$, for the mercury vapor has been fixed at 475°F and the heat transferred to the condenser by the mercury vapor, after having passed through a first-stage, mercury-vapor turbine, heats the water (later superheated) for a second-stage, normal, steam turbine which discharges into an ordinary, low-temperature, water-vapor condenser.

Some rather interesting features connected with mercury-steam systems follow. (1) For the transfer of heat from the mercury-vapor condenser to the steam boiler, a temperature difference is necessary. Mercury does not wet steel normally. Without a wetting agent, this failure to wet the steel would result in a large temperature difference and consequent loss in efficiency. To overcome this effect, a certain amount of magnesium and titanium are added. As a result, a temperature difference of less than 25 F° is obtained. (2) By having the mercury-vapor condenser at a reasonable elevation above the mercury boiler, the need for a condensate pump, returning the liquid to the boiler, is eliminated. In its place, one employs a 17-ft column of liquid mercury with the top open to the mercury condenser and the bottom below the upper mercury level in the mercury boiler. (3) Mercury vapor is poisonous, and certain rather costly provisions for the prevention of its escape are required. In practice, much consideration is given to ventilation. One plant, that at Schenectady, N. Y., is an out-of-doors station. (4) The amount of mercury required is based on the station output. In the present stations, it is said to range from 6.0 to 5.5 pd/kw. For a 15,000-kw station, this means a mercury supply of the order of 4 to 4.5 tons. (5) One system in operation yields an overall efficiency of more than 33% for the coal-to-electrical energy generated at the station bus. The best expectation for a similar all-steam plant, operating at 1200 lb/in.$^2$ gage pressure, is given as 32%.

**10. The Internal-Combustion Gasoline Engine.** The first suggestion for an internal-combustion engine seems to have been made in 1680 by the great Dutch physicist Christian Huyghens (1629–1695). His engine, consisting essentially of a vertical cylinder and piston, depended upon gunpowder as a fuel. The burning of the gunpowder forced the piston upward. Opening of the cylinder to supply a fresh charge of fuel gave opportunity for the return of the piston by gravity. The engine was not a success.

The first successful internal-combustion engine was patented in France in 1860 by E. Lenoir. It was a two-cycle engine. Coal gas was the fuel. In its general features, the engine was much like a common reciprocating steam engine with alternate power strokes from exploding gas on opposite sides of the piston. For the first half only of such a power stroke on one side, a mixture of gas and air was drawn into a cylinder. Then, with the closing of a valve, the mixture was fired by a spark and the hot burned gases pushed the piston the remainder of the way, performing external work. At the end of the stroke, the exhaust valve opened, and the piston, moving backward, cleared the cylinder of burnt gases in preparation for the closing of the exhaust valve and a repetition of the cycle. Neither the pressure nor the temperature of the fuel mixture was appreciably greater than atmospheric at the time of the ignition. Therein was a great weakness.

The first clear statement of principles underlying the operation of present-day gasoline engines was made by the French engineer A. Beau de Rochas in 1862. The first successful engine operating in accord with those principles, however, was not made until fourteen years later by the German engineers Nikolaus August Otto (1832–1891) and Eugen Langen (1833–1895). With many improvements as to details our present-day gasoline engines follow their general plan of operation, commonly described as the Otto cycle.

In comparing internal-combustion engines with steam engine plants, it must be kept in mind, as will be more apparent later, that the functions of the steam boiler and the steam engine in the one are united in the single engine of the other. Also, in the one case, the same working substance is treated to successive cycles, whereas, in the other, the working substance is rejected after being carried but once through a portion of a cycle.

**11. The Operation of a Gasoline Engine.** Most gasoline engines are said to be four-cycle engines (four-stroke-cycle engines would be more

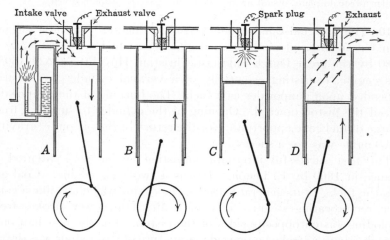

Fig. 16. A four-stroke-cycle gasoline engine showing: *A*, carburetor action and intake stroke; *B*, compression stroke; *C*, expansion stroke; and *D*, exhaust stroke (courtesy of O. H. Blackwood).

truly descriptive), meaning that, in each cylinder, there are four strokes, connected with essentially different processes, which are executed in order before a repeating cycle is recommenced. In order, they are known as (1) the intake stroke, (2) the compression stroke, (3) the expansion or power stroke, and (4) the exhaust stroke.

During the intake stroke, as shown at *A*, Fig. 16, the valve to the intake manifold is open and a certain portion of the mixture of air and gasoline at approximately atmospheric pressure is drawn in with the downward motion of the piston. The valve closes at the end of the stroke.

During the following compression stroke, both valves are closed. The contained mixture, except for losses to the cylinder wall, is compressed adiabatically and raised to a moderately high temperature, ready for firing. The minimum volume into which the gas is compressed varies, for ordinary engines, from about ¼ to ⅐ of the maximum volume. The inverse of this ratio which varies from 4 to 7 is spoken of as the "compression ratio."

During the third or expansion stroke, the valves are still closed. With the combustion of the fuel, which is started by a timed electric spark near the close of the preceding stroke but which takes place for the most part during the early part of this stroke, the pressure and the temperature inside the cylinder increase greatly until combustion is nearly complete. During this expansion, of which that following combustion is nearly reversibly adiabatic, the piston is shoved downward and work is done on the crankshaft, which in turn is able to perform external work.

During the fourth or exhaust stroke, the exhaust valve which ordinarily is opened near the close of the expansion stroke is kept open throughout and the burned gas initially at relatively low pressure and low temperature, but considerably above atmospheric values, is swept out. The valve is then closed, and the cylinder, with a cycle completed, is ready for another intake stroke.

**12. The Indicator Diagram for a Gasoline Engine.** In Fig. 17, there is given a pressure-angle diagram for a cylinder of a four-stroke-cycle, gasoline, airplane engine whose compression ratio is 5.3. Pressures in excess of atmospheric pressure are shown as a function of the crankshaft angular position for a part only of a whole revolution of the crankshaft. The portion of a cycle covered includes chiefly the compression and the expansion strokes. Zero position is labeled $TDC$ (top dead center), the position occupied just at the close of the compression stroke. Actually, pressures for only a portion of the compression stroke are shown, that from $-120°$ to $0°$. Pressures for the range $TDC$ or $0°$ to $BDC$ (bottom dead center) or $180°$ are for the expansion stroke. Those shown from $BDC$ or $180°$ to $-160°$ are for a portion of the exhaust stroke.

More in detail, as facts of interest in the analysis of engine performance to be gained in large part but not completely from the indicator diagram, we note (1) that the pressure increased during the compression stage, (2) that firing, $S$, took place about $27°$ previous to $TDC$, (3) that some of the increase in pressure due to combustion occurred previous to the expansion stroke, (4) that most of the combustion and the resulting pressure increase occurred during the early stage of the expansion stroke, (5) that the maximum pressure attained in the cylinder was more than 33 A above atmospheric pressure, (6) that the average pressure in the cylinder during the expansion stroke was several times that occurring during the compression stroke, (7) that the exhaust valve began to open, $X$, before the expansion stroke was two-thirds over, and (8) that during exhaust the pressure was greater than atmospheric.

Given the upswept volume of the cylinder, its cross section, the length of its stroke, and the length of the connecting rod (the rod reaching from the piston to the crankshaft), it is not difficult to present the data of Fig. 17 in the needed form for computing work done.

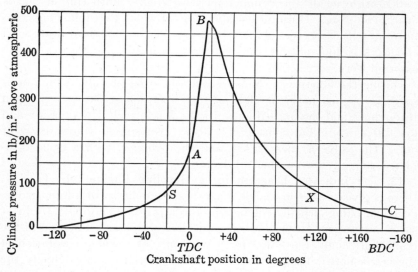

Fig. 17.   Pressure-angle diagram for a four-stroke-cycle, airplane, Otto engine whose compression ratio is 5.3.  Pressures for the compression and expansion strokes only are shown.

Fig. 18 shows the data of Fig. 17 thus transformed and is lettered to agree with it.  It includes additionally, however, idealized pressure variations for the exhaust and intake stages $CD$ and $DE$ for which little is shown in the first diagram.  As before, $S$ and $X$ indicate positions of firing and of opening of the exhaust valve.  Note that not all the burnt gases are removed on the exhaust stroke, also that, in accord with Fig. 17, the combustion process seems to last for a considerable time.  Though not as effective from the standpoint of work produced as instantaneous combustion, such gradual burning is obviously less dangerous from the standpoint of engine life.

Given that the swept volume of each cylinder is 184 in.$^3$, that the compression ratio is 5.3, that there are nine cylinders radially arranged, and that the crankshaft speed is 2000 rpm, it is not difficult to determine the indicated operating power.  Given further that a radial engine of the type discussed has a mechanical efficiency of about 90%, its actual operating power or brake horsepower may be determined. The carrying out of such computations is left to the student. If, in addition, the accompanying rate of supply of fuel and its heat of combustion are known it becomes possible to determine the efficiency of

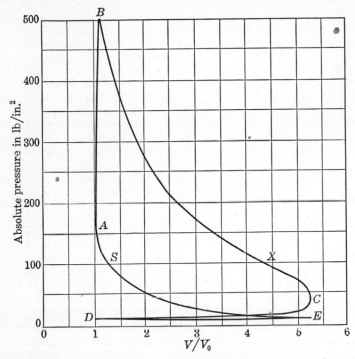

Fig. 18. Indicator diagram for the four-stroke-cycle, airplane, Otto engine, for which data are given in Fig. 17, arranged to show absolute pressures as a function of volume. $V_0$ is the unswept volume.

the engine, that is, $W/Q_1$. When $W$ is determined with the aid of the indicator diagram the efficiency is called an indicated thermal efficiency, $\eta_i$. When $W$ is determined with the aid of a brake meter, the efficiency is called a brake thermal efficiency, $\eta_b$. For well-built airplane engines, $\eta_b$ has been found to be about 90% $\eta_i$. For the $\eta_b$ of an automobile engine with a 6.7 compression ratio, Faires, in his *Applied Thermodynamics*, gives 23.1%; for the $\eta_b$ of a 6.1-compression-ratio airplane engine, he gives 26.5%. On the 90% basis mentioned, the corresponding indicated thermal efficiencies are 25.7% and 29.4%.

**13. The Air-Standard Otto Cycle.** For a comparison of the performance of an actual gasoline engine with the maximum that is ideally obtainable for the same compression ratio, engineers make use of the air-standard Otto engine. Like the Carnot and the Rankine engines, it is an engine impossible of actual realization. The working substance is air. As shown in Fig. 19, lettered to agree with Fig. 18, there are four stages. (1) Starting at $E$ with the volume enclosed by the cylinder a maximum, and with the contained air at atmospheric pressure and at temperature $T_E$, compress the gas adiabatically until it occupies the minimum volume indicated at $A$ and is at temperature $T_A$. During this process, work is done on the gas. (2) To the compressed air at constant volume, in whatever manner desirable, add an amount of heat, $Q_1$, equal to that set free by the combustion of the gasoline that is normally

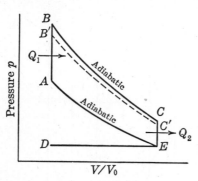

FIG. 19. The air-standard Otto cycle, $ABCEA$, and the fuel-air-standard cycle, $AB'$ $C'$ $EA$.

taken in during a single intake of the actual gasoline engine. This process is represented on the diagram by the line $AB$ and ends with the air at temperature $T_B$. (3) Next let the heated gas expand adiabatically from $B$ to $C$. During this process it will do external work and cool to temperature $T_C$. (4) Finally, cool the cylinder and contents from temperature $T_C$ to temperature $T_E$. In this process heat $Q_2$ is withdrawn from the gas. To make complete this comparison with the gasoline engine, one must include an exhaust stroke $ED$ followed by an intake stroke $DE$. Although these two last-mentioned strokes are important for the gasoline engine, they are of no consequence whatever to the Otto air-standard cycle and are frequently omitted in discussions.

Certain additional assumptions for the operation of the air-standard Otto engine are (1) that the air in the cylinder has the same specific heat and density during the $EA$ stage as does the mixture of fuel and air in an ordinary gasoline engine, and during the $BC$ stage the same values as do the burnt gases in the ordinary gasoline engine, (2) that there is no heat conduction into or out from the cylinder during the adiabatic stages $BC$ and $EA$, (3) that friction is negligible. Assumption 1 is not far from what is attained.

For the cycle described, the work done per cycle is represented by the area $ABCEA$ and, in accord with the first law of thermodynamics, is equal to the heat added during the process $AB$ less that removed during the process $CE$, that is $Q_1 - Q_2$. From the definition for efficiency, it follows that

$$\eta_i = \frac{W}{Q_1} = 1 - \frac{Q_2}{Q_1} \tag{5}$$

Further considerations, which we shall not develop here, lead to

$$\eta_i = 1 - \frac{T_C - T_E}{T_B - T_A} = 1 - \frac{1}{(V_A/V_B)^{\gamma-1}} \tag{6}$$

of which $\gamma$ represents the specific heat ratio for the gas in the engine. This shows that the efficiency of an Otto air-standard engine increases with an increase in the compression ratio. The same conclusion applies to the actual gasoline engine. An upper limit to the ratio $(V_A/V_B)$ is set in practice, however, by danger from preignition due to high compression temperatures and consequent "knocking."

In the rating of a real gasoline engine in terms of air-standard performance, the comparison should be made with an engine that has a $\gamma$ which is an effective average for the mixture of air, gasoline vapor, and burnt gases for the $EA$ and the $BC$ processes. Just what value to use is somewhat uncertain. One, a so-called cold-air-standard, value is 1.40. Another, a real-mixture-standard, is less. It varies with the fuel and conditions. A value of 1.35 seems reasonable from this point of view. Assuming 1.40 as correct, one obtains, for a compression ratio of 5.3, an efficiency of 51.4%. For a $\gamma$ of 1.35, one obtains 44.9%. It is interesting to compare the indicated thermal efficiencies, namely 25.7% and 29.4%, reported above for a real automobile and a real airplane engine with the 44.9% just determined for an air-standard Otto engine. They are respectively 57.5% and 65.5% of the 44.9%. Were the air-standard engine to have had the same compression ratio, the discrepancy would have been greater.

**14. The Fuel-Air-Standard Cycle.** Instead of the Otto, air-standard, engine as an ideal with which to compare real gasoline engines, many prefer the idealized fuel-air engine. Its operating cycle is much like though it differs from that of the air-standard engine. Instead of an all-air charge, its charge for any particular cycle consists of air, fuel, and some exhaust gases from the preceding cycle, just like the charge that occurs in a real engine. The heat added during a cycle is supplied by the burning of the fuel of the charge, which is assumed to take place completely at constant volume at the time when the charge occupies its minimum volume. The exhaust process likewise takes place completely when the cylinder volume is its maximum. Finally it presupposes no thermal leakage and no friction losses.

For any given compression ratio, the amount of heat generated by an idealized fuel-air engine will be less than that occurring in the Otto engine because the amount of oxygen present in the charge will be much less than if the charge were the all-air charge of the latter engine. Compared with the $EABCE$ Otto air-standard cycle of Fig. 19, its cycle is given by $EAB'C'E$. Obviously its efficiencies are much closer to those of real engines than are those of Otto air-standard engines.

With what is considered a correct fuel mixture for a real gasoline engine, the efficiency of the fuel-air idealized engine is said to be about 75% to 80% of that of the air-standard engine. In terms of the efficiency of the fuel-air standard, the indicated thermal efficiencies of the real automobile and real airplane engines mentioned above may now be seen to be roughly 76% and 88%.

Obviously, without some change in principle of operation, the fuel-air standard represents a limit of efficiency that cannot be surpassed.

## 15. The Operation of Diesel Engines.

The Diesel engine was the result of a search for an engine capable of operating with a fuel less refined and less costly than gasoline. The patent for it was obtained in 1893 by Rudolf Diesel (1858–1913), who, though born in France, was of German parentage and German educated. The fuel used is a slightly refined distillate of crude oil.

In general plan, the Diesel engine is much like the gasoline engine. It differs (1) in having no special ignition system, (2) in that the fuel in the form of a liquid spray is introduced under pressure only at the end or near the end of the compression stroke, and (3) in that the compression ratios are much larger, usually of the order of 12 to 15.

There are two main types of Diesel engines, which are generally known as two-cycle and four-cycle engines, corresponding to two strokes per cycle and four strokes per cycle. However, all processes present in one are present in the other.

As a description of the operation of a four-stroke-Diesel, we have for a single cylinder, beginning with the compression stroke: (1) A compression stroke, during which both intake and exhaust valves are closed and the air is compressed more or less adiabatically. The failure to be completely so is largely due to the heat exchange with the water-jacketed side walls. Both the end pressure and end temperature are high. For a compression ratio of 13, an initial temperature of 80°F (about 300°K), and a strictly reversible adiabatic process, values of about 36.3 A and 1050°F are expected. During the stroke, work is done upon the air in the cylinder at the expense of energy previously stored up. (2) An expansion stroke, with both intake and exhaust valves still closed, consisting of two stages. During the first, fuel oil is forced in under pressure as a fine spray and, igniting spontaneously, combines with the oxygen of the compressed air. The rate of supply of fuel is generally such as to yield a fairly constant pressure for this stage. Sometimes, in high-speed Diesels, fuel introduction begins during the compression stroke. The second stage of the expansion stroke begins with the cessation of the spray and consists mainly of an adiabatic expansion of burned gases though some combustion and some exchange of heat with the walls must take place. Near the end of this stage, the exhaust valve begins to open and a rapid fall of pressure takes place. During this stroke, the engine does work against outside forces and stores up energy for the future compression strokes. (3) An exhaust stroke, throughout which the exhaust valve only is open. The pressure is necessarily somewhat above atmospheric. (4) An intake stroke, during which the intake valve only is open. The pressure is necessarily somewhat less than atmospheric during this stroke.

Of the energy supplied by the fuel during combustion, normally about one-third is lost to the water jacket, about one-third is lost to the exhaust, and about one-third is utilized in the performing of external work.

Fig. 20 shows something of the construction and operation of a two-stroke-cycle Diesel engine. The following is a description of its action as given by the Fairbanks-Morse Company. "The cycle of events taking place in the two-cycle, airless injection, crankcase scavenging Diesel is illustrated in the accompanying diagram (Fig. 20). It may be said to begin with the closing of the exhaust ports by the piston on the compression or upstroke, approximately 50° past the bottom dead center, when the compression of the charge of fresh air begins. Compression continues to within a few degrees of top dead center when injection occurs and spontaneous ignition takes place due to the rise in temperature of the compressed air. After a momentary

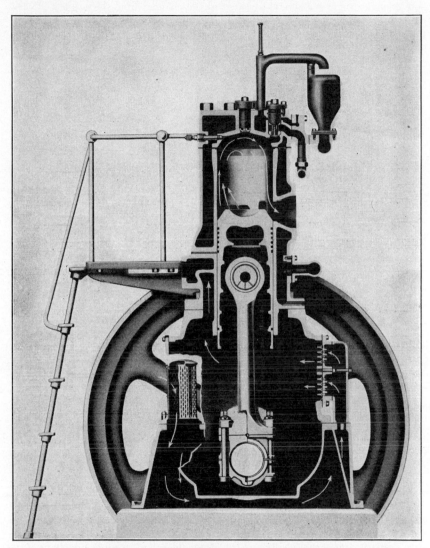

FIG. 20. Diagrams showing the construction and operation of a two-stroke-cycle Diesel engine (courtesy of the Fairbanks-Morse and Co.).

pressure rise above the compression pressure, during which the piston passes its top dead center position, the piston continues its accelerated downward movement on the working stroke due to expansion of the gases. When the piston has reached a point about 50° ahead of bottom center, the exhaust ports are uncovered and the burnt gases at a pressure slightly above atmospheric are released to the exhaust system. As the piston moves farther down, the scavenging air ports are uncovered and air under slight pressure is admitted to the cylinder from the crankcase. The entering air is deflected upward by the shape of the air passages and the contour of the piston head and thus drives the remaining burnt gases out the exhaust ports on the opposite side of the cylinder. On the next upstroke, first the air ports and then the exhaust ports are covered and compression begins."

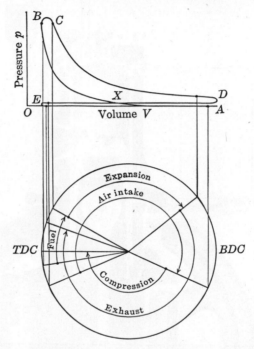

FIG. 21. The indicator diagram of a four-stroke-cycle Diesel engine.

Recently a new type of Diesel engine has been developed for heavy-duty, railroad locomotives. Each cylinder of the engine operates with two opposed pistons which are separately attached by piston rods and connecting rods to separate crankshafts. At all times during operation, the motions of the two pistons in a cylinder are opposite in direction or very nearly so. The fuel is injected at very nearly the instant that the pistons are nearest to each other. During their power strokes, which are of equal length, each piston recedes from the other. During their compression strokes, they similarly approach each other. The engine, like that shown in Fig. 20, is of the scavenging, two-cycle class. In addition to sharing in the beneficial features of that class, it possesses the great advantage of no heat loss at a cylinder head for it has no cylinder head.

**16. Indicator Diagrams for Diesel Engines.** A characteristic indicator diagram for a four-stroke-cycle Diesel engine is shown in Fig. 21. Line $AB$ represents the compression stroke, $BC$ the first or fuel-injection stage of the expansion stroke, $CD$

the second or adiabatic stage of the expansion stroke, $DE$ the exhaust stroke, and $EA$ the intake stroke. The heat, $Q_1$, taken in during the cycle is that yielded by the combustion of the fuel at the intake temperature; the work done, $W$, is represented by the area $DXBCD$ less the area $AXEA$. This latter area is small and necessarily negative because of the counterclockwise motion accompanying its description. The indicated thermal efficiency of the engine $\eta_i$ is given by $W/Q_1$, the brake efficiency by the product $\eta_m W/Q_1$, of which $\eta_m$, the mechanical efficiency of the engine, takes account principally of friction losses and is generally of the order of 80% to 85%.

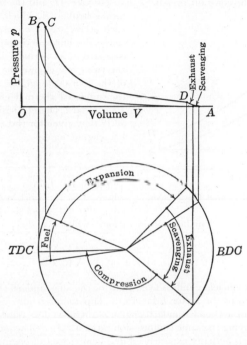

Fig. 22.   The indicator diagram of a two-stroke-cycle Diesel engine.

Experimentally and theoretically it has been found desirable to have a high compression ratio $V_A/V_B$ and a small cutoff ratio (the ratio of the volume of the gas in the cylinder at the cutoff of the fuel supply to the unswept volume) $V_C/V_B$. In practice, as already noted, $V_A/V_B$ ranges from 12 to 15 while the cutoff ratio is generally of the order of 2.

A characteristic indicator diagram for a two-stroke-cycle Diesel engine is shown in Fig. 22. It differs principally from that of Fig. 21 in that the exhaust and intake strokes $DE$ and $EA$ of that figure are replaced in Fig. 22 by the portions marked "Exhaust" and "Scavenging." The area enclosed, as in all indicator diagrams, corresponds to work performed per cycle of operation.

**17. The Air-Standard Diesel Cycle.** This cycle is related to the indicator diagram for a Diesel engine in just the same manner that the air-standard Otto cycle is related to the indicator diagram for a gasoline engine. Such a cycle is shown in Fig. 23, which is lettered to correspond to the indicator diagram of Fig. 21. Like the Carnot, the ideal Rankine, and the air-standard Otto engines, an air-standard Diesel engine is impossible as a practical engine.

The air-standard cycle requires a series of heat reservoirs. Beginning at $A$, Fig. 23, the air is heated adiabatically by compression to $B$. Next, with the aid of heat reservoirs, it is heated reversibly at constant pressure to $C$. Let $Q_1$ represent the amount of heat thus absorbed. Next the air is permitted to expand adiabatically to $D$. Then, with the aid of heat reservoirs, an amount of heat $Q_2$ is removed from the working substance and it is brought to condition $A$. Following this, there occurs for the four-cycle engine the constant-pressure exhaust stroke $AE$ and the constant-pressure intake stroke $EA$, which, since they annul each other, are of no real significance to the cycle, however important such processes are in an actual Diesel engine. For the two-cycle engine the last two strokes of the four-cycle engine are absent. For the indicated thermal efficiency $\eta_i$ of the air-standard Diesel engine, we have exactly that given for the air-standard gasoline engine, namely,

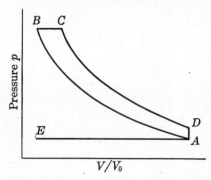

$$\eta_i = \frac{W}{Q_1} = \frac{Q_1 - Q_2}{Q_1} \qquad (7a)$$

Fig. 23.   The air-standard Diesel cycle.

where $W$ is the work represented by the area $ABCDA$ which is performed by the engine during a cycle.   Further considerations, which we shall not develop here, lead to

$$\eta_i = 1 - \frac{1}{(V_A/V_B)^{\gamma-1}} \, f\left(\frac{V_C}{V_B}\right) \qquad (7b)$$

This expression for efficiency differs from that for the air-standard Otto engine solely by the introduction of the factor $f(V_C/V_B)$.   This factor is always greater than 1, and the efficiency of a Diesel standard engine is therefore less than that for an Otto standard engine having the same compression ratio $V_A/V_B$.   The increased efficiency of the Diesel, that is actually experienced in a comparison of engines, arises accordingly from the fact that the compression ratio is much greater for the Diesel than for the gasoline engine.

In comparing actual Diesel engines with air-standard Diesel engines, there arises the same uncertainty regarding an acceptable value for $\gamma$ that appeared in connection with Otto engines.   Using 1.35 for $\gamma$, 2 for $V_C/V_B$, and 13 for $V_A/V_B$, leads to 1.15 for $f(V_C/V_B)$ and to 53% for $\eta_i$.   This efficiency is greater than the corresponding efficiency for an Otto engine with a 5.3 compression ratio, as computed above, by a factor of 1.15.   Had a compression ratio of 7.0 been used for the Otto engine, this factor would have been reduced to 1.07.   It appears that the Diesel engine has a definite advantage over the gasoline engine in addition to using a cheaper fuel.

For an actual four-stroke-cycle Diesel engine with a compression ratio of 13, Faires in his *Applied Thermodynamics* reports a brake thermal efficiency $\eta_b$ of 31.8%.   This value is only about 66% of the corresponding efficiency of the air-standard Diesel. Referring back to Faires' best quoted value for a gasoline engine, namely 26.5%, one sees that this value for the Diesel represents a considerable improvement.   An all-important question is how to change this 66% for Diesels to something much nearer

100%. The Diesel brake thermal efficiency of 31.8% which has been quoted is not the maximum that has been obtained. Other values well in excess of it have been measured.

As is obvious, fuel-air-standard cycles for Diesels, similar to those for gasoline engines, may be and are used as standards for comparisons. Naturally the real Diesel engines approach these standards in efficiency much more closely than they do the air-standard Diesel engine.

**18. The Gas Turbine.** The gas turbine is related to the steam turbine in much the same manner that gasoline and Diesel engines are related to the ordinary reciprocating steam engine. In a steam turbine system, the fuel is burned in a boiler, and liquid water is transformed into steam which passes through a pipe under pressure to

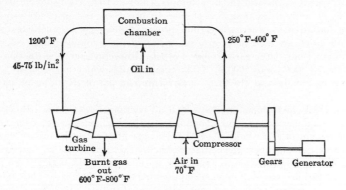

Fig. 24. Schematic diagram of the gas-turbine system.

the turbine, where it blows against alternate rows of fixed and movable blades and produces motion. In a gas turbine system, Fig. 24, the fuel, which may be oil, gas, or possibly powdered coal, is burned in a pipe leading to the turbine, and the products of combustion enter the turbine under pressure, blow similarly against the alternate rows of fixed and movable blades, and produce motion.

As in the steam turbine, where water is pumped under pressure into the steam boiler, in the gas turbine, the fuel including needed air is pumped under pressure into the pipe where it is burned. There is a decided difference, however, with regard to the aftertreatment of the material leaving the turbines. In the steam turbine, the steam goes to a condenser from which it is pumped as liquid water into the boiler. In the gas turbine, the burned gases are allowed to escape to the atmosphere. The work required to pump the liquid water into the boiler is relatively small; that required to pump the fuel and particularly the air needed for combustion into the pipe where combustion takes place is much greater because of the relatively great volume of air required.

A comparison of the gas turbine with the gasoline and the Diesel engines shows one very interesting feature. The gas turbine has only one moving member whereas the gasoline and the Diesel engines have many moving parts. Another interesting feature is that, for equally powered systems, the gas turbine occupies only a small fraction of the space occupied by the other engines. Certain railroad streamliners that are now drawn by four-car Diesel power plants could be drawn, it is said, by one-car gas turbine plants.

Interesting details for a gas turbine plant such as that shown in Fig. 24 are: (1) the normal gross output of the turbine proper was 15,660 kw; (2) the normal input power for the compressor was 11,480 kw; (3) the net supply power for the electric generator was 4180 kw; (4) the temperature of the burning fuel at the entry to the turbine was 1025°F; (5) the thermal efficiency was found to be 17.4%.

Although some thought was given to the gas turbine as long ago as 1791, the essential start with regard to its development was made about 1926 under the leadership of Aurel Stodola (1859–   ) in Switzerland. Stodola is also said to have run "the efficiency tests on the first successful experimental model" in 1936. Key accomplishments making the gas turbine possible were (1) the determining of the most efficient contours for airplane propeller planes and wings and turbine blades, (2) the development of alloys to withstand the high temperatures and the corrosive actions of the flaming gases, and (3) the designing of efficient blades for the air compressor.

Except for airplanes, where the turbine proper of small gas turbine units, powered by exhaust gases, are used to operate superchargers, it is found efficient, at present, to manufacture only large gas turbines. Most of those in operation develop powers of the order of 2000 hp to 5000 hp. The temperatures which must be sustained by their rotating members at the high-temperature end are of the order of 1000°C to 1200°C.

For the ideal gas turbine, one for which all friction losses and heat leakages are negligible, the upper limit to the amount of work performed with the combustion of a certain amount of fuel is given essentially by the product of the excess of pressure in the combustion chamber above atmospheric by the volume change on combustion plus the excess of work done as the burnt gases expand adiabatically on passage through the turbine over that done in compressing the air taken in by the compressor. Efficiencies for the gas turbines now obtainable are of the order of 22%. This is small compared with the 35% obtained for Diesels; but, taking into account the cheaper fuel burned and the lower first costs, they are able to compete with the Diesels in certain installations.

**19. The Jet Engine.** During World War II, a new type of engine, closely related to the gas turbine, was developed. It is the jet or rocket engine. Thus far it has been used for the propulsion of planes and projectiles. In one type, the fuel including the necessary air or oxygen is supplied under pressure. The energy made available by the release of the fuel and its burning is not used to drive the rotating member of a turbine but instead to force a jet of the products of combustion backward through an orifice into the atmosphere. The magnitude of the force that pushes the engine forward is equal or approximately equal to the product of the cross section of the jet and the difference of pressure between the flame end of the combustion chamber and the jet opening. In explanation one may also use the conservation of momentum principle. At present no estimates of efficiency or costs are available. In a second type of engine, the oxygen is taken from the atmosphere directly.

**20. Refrigeration.** In the discussion of the Carnot engine, considerable use was made of the idea of engines working "backward," rather than "forward," the direction of normal operation. In the forward operation there is absorption of heat from a hot reservoir and rejection of a part to a low-temperature reservoir by the working substance with a net performance of external work. In the backward operation, on the contrary, there is absorption of heat from a low-temperature reservoir, together with performance of work on the so-called working substance, and the transfer of heat from it to the hot reservoir. The backward operation results in further cooling of the cold reservoir. Such is the aim of the vapor-compression refrigerator, and the engine used in it is, in fact, a backward-working engine.

There are four classes of refrigerating machines. (1) The "compressed-air machine" was invented in 1862. It was much used in producing artificial ice and in protecting food. An efficiency of 4 lb of ice per lb of coal was reported. Such machines are practically non-existent now. (2) The "vacuum machine" dates from about 1755. The space above water in a boiler was evacuated by pumps. The loss of heat on vaporization was the cause of the cooling of the unvaporized water. With continued evaporation, it was possible to obtain about 5 lb of ice from 6 lb of water. This method is no longer used. (3) The vapor-compression machine, so named because in one process a vapor is compressed, is represented by the common electrically operated home refrigerator of today. It dates back to 1834 to a machine made by a John Hague in Great Britain after the designs of an American named Jacob Perkins (1766–1849). Various working substances or refrigerants have been used, among them ammonia, carbon dioxide, sulfur dioxide, methyl chloride, ethyl chloride, dichlorodifluoromethane, $CCl_2F_2$ (commonly called "Freon-12"), dichloromethane, $CH_2Cl_2$ (commonly called carrene), and dichlorotetrafluoroethane, $C_2Cl_2F_4$ (commonly called "Freon-114"). Of these some are objectionable because of effects due to leaky vapors. Some are toxic; some are offensive to smell; some attack metals common in the home; some have $p$-$T$ characteristics (Fig. 25) that are not so well suited as are those of others. On most counts, "Freon-12" seems to be quite acceptable and is now very much used for domestic purposes. In commercial installations, however, ammonia is the most common refrigerant. An efficiency of the order of 50 lb of ice per lb of coal is obtainable. (4) The vapor-absorption machine is represented by a single widely used make of home refrigerators. The principle dates back to 1867, when A. Rees Reece took advantage of the fact that two vapors of different boiling points can, when mixed, be separated by fractional condensation. In the well-known present-day machine, ammonia and water, along with hydrogen gas, form the working substances. Both of the latter two types will be discussed in more detail.

From the standpoint of capacity, certain refrigeration plants and machines are frequently rated in terms of tons-of-refrigeration. By a capacity of 5 tons-of-refrigeration, say, it is meant that the rate of production is such that in 24 hours the machine can freeze 5 tons of

liquid water at 32°F to ice at the same temperature.  Operation of a
5 tons-of-refrigeration machine for 10 days of time yields, obviously,
a quantity of refrigeration which is said to be 50 ton-days-of-refrigeration.  As may be easily verified, a ton-day-of-refrigeration is equivalent to a transfer of 288,000 btu or 2.24 × 10⁸ ft-lb of heat.  A ton-of-

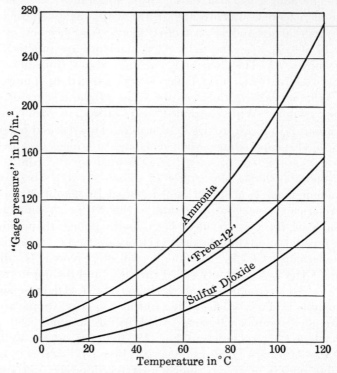

FIG. 25.   Vapor tensions as a function of temperature for some 1943 refrigerants.
"Gage pressures" are pressures in excess of atmospheric pressure.

refrigeration is similarly equivalent to a transfer rate of 12,000 btu/hr
or 200 btu/min.

Actually refrigerating plants seldom operate under the conditions
specified in the rating.  Accordingly in the production of a ton of ice
commercially about 1.6 ton-days-of-refrigeration are commonly
needed to take account of an initial water temperature of, say, 70°F–
75°F, a final average ice temperature of about 24°F, and an approximate 20% heat loss from various causes.  For the household refrigerator, appreciably wider extremes of temperature are experienced.  As
we shall see later, such refrigerators are rated on effects produced with
5°F (= −15°C) and 86°F (= +30°C) as assumed temperature limits.

**21. Operation of an Electrically Driven Vapor-Compression Refrigerator.** The layout of a vapor-compression refrigerator is shown in Fig. 26. A compressor, usually electrically driven, is connected through an intake valve with an evaporating chamber from which vapor of the refrigerating substance or refrigerant—"Freon," sulfur dioxide, or whatever it is—is pumped. Compressed and with temperature increased considerably beyond that of the air outside to which its heat must be transferred, the vapor is forced under pressure through

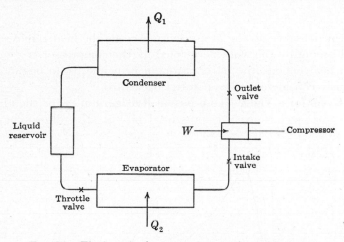

Fig. 26.   The layout of a vapor-compression refrigerator.

an outlet valve into a condenser. Here either by means of water or air currents, fan-driven or normal convection, the heated vapor is cooled and liquefied. As a liquid, it is passed on to a reservoir, still under the same high pressure. In the liquefying process, the heat supplied during vaporization is largely set free. From the liquid reservoir, the refrigerant passes through a throttling valve as needed into the evaporator where the pressure is kept low by means of the pumping action of the compressor. Expansion through the valve results in partial vaporization only. The heat needed is supplied by the portion that does not vaporize. The result is a lowering of the temperature. In practice, the temperature attained must be below that of the surroundings which are to be kept cool. Heat entering the evaporator from its surroundings causes further evaporation of the remaining liquid at a boiling-point temperature kept practically constant by the continued pumping action of the compressor.

Compressor and throttling valve action are controlled by a thermostat attached to the evaporator. The circulation processes are stopped when the temperature in the evaporator has reached a set minimum, only to start again when this temperature has reached a set maximum.

In the circulation process, a quantity of refrigerant of mass $m$ receives a quantity of heat $Q_2$ from the evaporator or cold room as it is often called, has performed on it an amount of work $W$ by the compressor, and delivers to the condenser a quantity of heat $Q_1$. In accord with the first law of thermodynamics, if various losses along the way are negligible, these energy exchanges are related as follows

$$Q_2 + W = Q_1 \tag{8}$$

The heat delivered to the atmosphere exceeds the heat removed from the cold room by the work performed by the compressor.

As a heat engine, the refrigerator, in principle, is an engine of the previously considered type operated backward.

**22. Cycle for a Vapor-Compression Refrigerator.** For the idealized refrigerator, such a cycle is presented in Fig. 27. Shown in a $p$-$V$

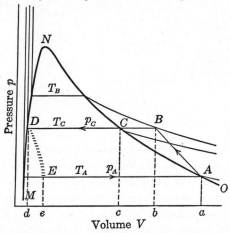

FIG. 27. A $p$-$V$ diagram (grossly distorted) for a vapor-compression refrigeration cycle.

diagram is the partial-liquid, partial-vapor region bounded by the line $MNO$ and crossed by three isothermals corresponding to the temperatures $T_A$, $T_B$, and $T_C$ which are of importance in the cycle. The cycle itself is described by $ABCDEA$. Let us start at $A$ with a mass $m$ of the working substance which has just been drawn into the compression chamber and consider the separate processes which it undergoes.

(1) The refrigerant is compressed adiabatically along $AB$. In the process, the pressure and temperature are raised from $p_A$ and $T_A$ to $p_C$ and $T_B$, and the work represented on the graph by the area $ABbaA$

is done on the refrigerant. This takes place completely within the compressor. In reality since the change in volume $V_A - V_B$ is relatively much greater than what is shown in the figure, and the work done during this process is correspondingly much greater than the figure seems to indicate.

(2) The refrigerant is cooled under constant pressure $p_C$ from $T_B$ to $T_C$. In this process, a portion of the heat $Q_1$ referred to above is transferred to the condenser. A small amount of work represented by the area $BCcbB$ is done on the vapor by the compressor as it is forced through the condenser tubes.

(3) The refrigerant is liquefied under constant pressure $p_C$ and constant temperature $T_C$ as described by the line $CD$. During this process, heat is transferred to the condenser. This heat, together with that transferred during the $BC$ process, goes to make up $Q_1$. Also work represented by the area $CDdcC$ is done on the refrigerant by the compressor.

(4) The refrigerant expands through the throttle valve. As represented by the broken line $DE$, this process is irreversible. Heat is neither added nor taken away. The process is one of constant enthalpy, and the net work done by the refrigerant, similar to that for all porous-plug processes, is given by $p_A V_E - p_C V_D$. We shall assume that the line $DE$ is so drawn that this difference is properly represented by the area $DdeED$. As shown at $E$ a portion is vaporized.

(5) The refrigerant receives a quantity of heat $Q_2$ from the cold room, and the remaining portion that is liquid is vaporized at pressure $p_A$ and temperature $T_A$. Work represented by the area $EeaAE$ is performed by the refrigerant.

During the cycle, the net amount of work done on the refrigerant $W$ is that represented by the area $ABCDEA$. Given the proper $p$-$V$ diagram and other appropriate data such as $p_A$, $p_C$, $T_A$, $T_B$, $T_C$, and heats of vaporization $L_A$ and $L_C$, one may compute the values of $W$, $Q_2$, and $Q_1$ per cycle or per unit mass of the refrigerant.

**23. The Coefficient of Performance of a Refrigerator.** The quantity used for comparing refrigerators is known as the coefficient of performance $K$. It is defined as the ratio of the heat removed from the cold room per cycle to the net work done per cycle by the compressor. For the ideal refrigerator, one whose mechanical efficiency is 100% and whose processes other than throttling are completely reversible, the value of this coefficient $K_i$ is given by

$$K_i = \frac{Q_2}{W} = \frac{Q_2}{Q_1 - Q_2} \tag{9}$$

One may express the performance coefficient of a refrigerator in terms of specific enthalpies as has been done in Eq. 3 for a heat engine.   Thus

$$K_i = \frac{H_A - H_E}{(H_B - H_D) - (H_A - H_E)} = \frac{h_A - h_E}{h_B - h_A} \tag{10}$$

This relation follows simply from Eq. 9, when one recognizes that a quantity of heat $Q$ added (or subtracted) during a constant-pressure reversible change is equal to the enthalpy, $H$, of the final state less that of the initial state, and that with passage of the material through the throttling valve the change in enthalpy is zero.   Given a graph of $p$ as a function of $h$ for a refrigerant, such as is given in Fig. 28—including the necessary adiabatics, determinations of $K_i$ become rather simple.

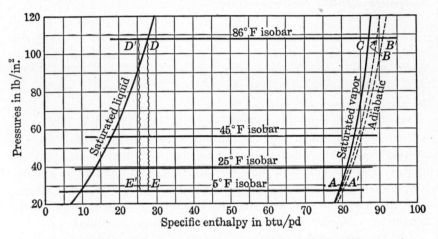

FIG. 28.   A pressure-enthalpy diagram for the refrigerant dichlorodifluoromethane, "Freon-12," showing particular refrigeration cycles.

To illustrate the foregoing we shall consider the following data for household refrigerators using "Freon-12."   Following standardized procedure, assume the pressures in the absorber and in the condenser to be the vapor tensions of the refrigerant at respectively 5°F (= −15°C) and 86°F (= 30°C).   For "Freon-12," these pressures are (Fig. 28) 26.51 lb/in.² (11.81 lb/in.² gage pressure) and 107.9 lb/in.² (93.2 lb/in.² gage pressure).   From tables giving the characteristics of "Freon-12," or using Fig. 28, wherein the particular cycle referred to is outlined by heavy lines, one may verif that $Q_2$ and $Q_1$ are 51.1 btu/pd and 61.9 btu/pd, and that consequently for the idealized cycle $K_i$ is 4.75.

Because of conduction of heat from the walls of the hot compressor to the incoming vapor, it appears that the initial temperature of the incoming vapor will be effectively higher than that which corresponds to point $A$ of Fig. 28.   How much higher depends on circumstances.   By agreement among refrigerating engineers, point $A'$, corresponding to an increase of temperature of 9 F° (= 5 C°), has been accepted as a good approximation.   Similarly, because of additional heat losses from the liquid in the condenser after liquefaction, the temperature of the liquid which enters the throttle is less than that corresponding to point $D$.   By agreement as before, point $D'$, corresponding to a decrease in temperature of 9 F° or 5 C°, has been accepted as a good compromise. With points $A'$ and $D'$ in the adjusted cycle replacing points $A$ and $D$ of the idealized cycle, obviously points $B$ and $E$ are replaced by points $B'$ and $E'$. Taking the foregoing adjustments into account, we obtain for an adjusted, indicated coefficient of performance, $K_i'$,

$$K_i' = \frac{h_A' - h_E'}{h_B' - h_A'} \tag{11}$$

How different $K_i'$ is from $K_i$ for the refrigerating cycle of Fig. 28 is the subject of a problem to be found at the end of the chapter.

Actual coefficients of performance, $K_a$, vary considerably from $K_i'$. By definition, we have

$$K_a = \eta_m K_i' \tag{12}$$

of which $\eta_m$ is the mechanical efficiency of the system, principally the compressing system. Again, $\eta_m$ varies with the installation and may range from 40% to 75% for the common installations in household refrigerators. Actual values of 2 or 3 for $K_a$ may be expected. It should be emphasized that $K_a$ may be used to rate the cooling system in a refrigerator and not the refrigerator as a whole. It is not concerned with how well or how poorly the cold room is insulated.

It is interesting to compare the $K_i$ computed above with what would be obtained with a Carnot engine working backward between the same two temperatures 5°F and 86°F. Here we should have

$$K_C = \frac{T_A}{T_C - T_A} = \frac{465°R}{86°F - 5°F} = 5.75 \tag{13}$$

This is larger than the 4.75 for $K_i$, despite $T_B$ being greater than $T_C$. A factor is the irreversibility of the throttling process $DE$. Comparative tests show that coefficients of performance depend but little on which one of the common refrigerants one uses.

**24. Operation of a Vapor-Absorption Refrigerator.** An early machine operating on the vapor-absorption principle was devised by the Frenchman Carré. It included a mechanical compressor. In 1926, however, two Swedes, V. Platten and Munter, devised an ingenious system which is now much used. It is marketed under the name Electrolux. It has no motor or mechanical pump and is accordingly free from certain objectionable noises common to the vapor-compression type. It requires for its operation a continuous supply of some source of heat such as illuminating gas or an electric current.

The layout of an Electrolux refrigerator is shown in Fig. 29. The system is closed. One portion only, the evaporator, is in the refrigerated space. Throughout, a substantially equal pressure of about 12 A is maintained. There are three working substances, water, ammonia, and hydrogen. The hydrogen with a partial pressure of about 9 A is confined to the evaporator, the gas heat-interchanger, and the absorber. In these chambers the remainder of the 12 A, or 3 A, is due almost wholly to the vapor pressure of ammonia; that due to the water vapor is entirely negligible. Elsewhere in the system where gas is present, the pressure is necessarily that due to heated ammonia.

In operation, liquid ammonia from the air-cooled condenser near the temperature of the surrounding air, say 30°C, flows under gravity into the evaporator. There,

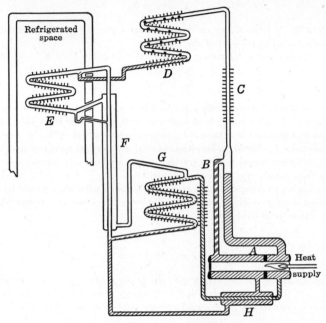

FIG. 29. The layout of a vapor-absorption refrigerator. In generator $A$, a weak solution of ammonia in water moves downward at the right; a strong solution moves upward at the left. Percolator pump tube $B$ contains hot, ammonia-rich liquid and bubbles of the vapors of water and ammonia. In air-cooled rectifier $C$, water vapor is condensed from the upward-moving ammonia and water vapors. Air-cooled condenser $D$ liquefies the oncoming ammonia vapor. In the evaporator cooling coils $E$, hydrogen moves upward over downward-moving ammonia liquid. Gas heat interchanger $F$ has hydrogen outside moving upward and hydrogen and ammonia vapor inside moving downward. In air-cooled absorber $G$, a weak water solution moving downward removes ammonia from the hydrogen-ammonia mixture moving upward. $H$ is a liquid heat interchanger with a weak solution inside and a strong solution outside.

because of the 9 A due to hydrogen, the vapor pressure of the ammonia is less than saturation pressure. The ammonia vaporizes and mixes with the upward-flowing hydrogen. This process is accompanied by the absorption of heat from within the refrigerated space. From the evaporator the hydrogen-ammonia mixture moves downward through the gas heat-interchanger to the air-cooled absorber. Circulation is produced by the variation in density between the inner and the outer columns of gas in the heat-interchanger. In the absorber, the upward hydrogen-ammonia stream encounters a weak solution trickling downward that absorbs or dissolves the ammonia. The liquid solution goes to the bottom; the hydrogen gas, however, passes to the top, ready, on passing through the heat-interchanger, to mix once more with ammonia in the evaporator. The concentrated ammonia solution at the bottom feeds by gravity through the liquid heat-interchanger into the strong-solution side of the generator, where, by percolator action, that is, by the forming of sufficient vapor bubbles in' the column rising from it, the liquid is caused to rise and to flow over into the generator at the top of the weak-solution side. The vapor, which is nearly all ammonia, rises to the condenser. That which does not vaporize, largely water, falls and becomes a part of the downward-moving weak solution. Under the influence of gravity, it enters the generator again at the top. The ammonia, which enters the condenser hot, is there cooled by the surrounding air and liquefied. It is then ready once more, on entering the evaporator, to pass through the cycle which has been described.

The thermodynamic cycle through which the ammonia passes is complicated and will not be considered here. We may only point out a similarity to the vapor-compression refrigerators. Like them a vapor-absorption refrigerator absorbs heat in an evaporator in a cold room, adds energy produced by burning gas or otherwise, and rejects the two at a higher temperature into a hot reservoir.

Since it is well-nigh impossible to evaluate the mechanical work performed, a coefficient of performance has little significance here. An efficiency comparison with other refrigerators must be made on the basis of the ratio of the heat removed from the refrigerated space to the energy supplied by the consumed fuel, going back to a common source such as coal, or on the basis of the costs per unit of refrigeration.

**25. Heating by Means of Refrigerators.** A somewhat obvious question arises when one considers actual coefficients of performance of refrigerating systems and finds that the amount of heat transferred from an absorber region to a condenser region may be several times the heat equivalent of the work performed. Why not use refrigerators to heat homes and buildings generally? In winter, why not, with the outdoors as our cold room, take heat $Q_2$ from it, perform work $W$ by means of a compressor, and transmit heat $Q_1$ $(= Q_2 + W)$ into the interior of our houses? Actually much thought and money have been spent in considering refrigerator heating. A few installations have been made. When the cost of ordinary fuel for heating becomes sufficiently high, such a method of heating may become common. Even now, in certain regions where coal is not readily available and where the temperature outside is only moderately low, it is said to be possible commercially. How the efficiency of such a system of heating varies with the temperature of the cold exterior is the subject of a problem at the close of the chapter.

**26. The Human Power Plant.** Human beings and other living animals are complex power plants containing fuel-refining apparatus, a multitude of simple elementary engines, and a large number of machines for the performing of external work of various types. However, its engines are not heat engines. Although heat is developed when they operate, there is no hot intake reservoir or any cold exhaust reservoir. They are more like electric batteries, though the analogy breaks down if one seeks to explain the mechanical work done on the basis of electromagnetic energy transformed into mechanical work and heat.

Following the statement of the first law of thermodynamics and its generalization to include all phenomena, it was natural to suppose that the intake of energy in the form of food and air by a living organism must equal the outgo in the form of mechanical work, heat, and excrement. This assumption was first verified by Max Rubner (1854–1932) in Germany in 1894. Using non-working dogs for a 45-day period, he found the intake energy, that which results from the complete oxidation of the food, to agree with the measured outgo to within 0.5%.

**27. Metabolism Rates.** The first really reliable and complete data relative to the energetics of living animals, including humans, however, were obtained by nutritionists, W. O. Atwater (1844–1907), F. G. Benedict (1870–   ), and associates, working at the Agricultural Experiment Station in New Haven, Connecticut, and elsewhere. The work undertaken by Atwater in 1892 made use of an adiabatic calorimeter, first described in 1897, whose construction was largely due to the physicist E. B. Rosa (1861–1921). How nearly perfect the calorimeter proved to be was shown by two calibration tests. In the first it was found that the outgo of heat measured for a given electrical input checked within 0.01%. In the second it was found, with the oxidizing of a certain amount of alcohol, that the carbon dioxide recovery was complete to within 0.2% and that the heat recovery was complete to within 0.1%. In this calorimeter human subjects were kept for days. Careful measurements were made of food and oxygen used, of mechanical work done, of heat developed, and of carbon dioxide, water vapor, and other products eliminated. From such studies performed there and elsewhere, including one of soldiers in training for the First World War, many definite conclusions have been drawn. Some, of particular interest here, follow:

1. The basal metabolism rate of an individual, that is his minimum rate of utilization of stored energy per unit surface area for just maintaining life, as when sleeping, a quantity usually expressed in $kcal/m^2$ hr (often, in certain fields, the calory is used where the physicist uses kilocalory), varies with his age, reaching, as shown in Fig. 30, a maximum at 5 years, after which there is a general decline.

2. The metabolism rates of individuals, not their basal rates, but their average daily rates of utilization of food energy to maintain constancy of condition, vary with the size of the individual and the type of work performed (Fig. 31).

3. The efficiency of the human power plant for the performing of various types of work, the ratio of the rate of performing work to the metabolism rate occurring during its performance less the metabolism

rate occurring when an individual is in a position to work but does not work, varies with the type of work and with the conditions occurring during its performance. Edgar Atzler (1887–   ), German nutritionist, found, from experiments in which a man rotated a crank attached to a bicycle ergometer (work meter), that the efficiency varied greatly with the location of the crank axis and with the torque required. For a crank axis at the waist-line level and an optimum torque, an efficiency of about 20% was found for the combination of arm and body muscles

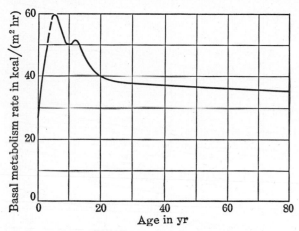

Fig. 30. Variation with age of the basal metabolism rate of a human male according to DuBois. The corresponding rate for women is about 7% less than for men. (By permission, Lusk, *The Elements of the Science of Nutrition*, 4th ed., p. 138, Philadelphia, W. B. Saunders Co., 1928.)

used. In a different test Rubner found an efficiency of 27%. Atzler also found in lifting tests that the efficiency is greatest when the bodies lifted are lifted from about the waist-line level to some level higher up. Benedict and E. P. Cathcart (1877–   ), English nutritionist, tested a professional bicycle rider who rode a stationary bicycle 4 hours and 22 minutes to exhaustion. The work done was 208,000 kgwt-m or about 409 kcal, the equivalent of a 100-mile ride, with the rate of performance of work equal to about 0.146 hp. The "no-work" metabolism rate used was that obtained when the man sat on the bicycle revolving the wheel but with the condition of no resistance. Certain of the data and computed results follow:

| | |
|---|---|
| "No-work" metabolism rate | 3.89 kcal/min |
| Average metabolism rate | 9.75 kcal/min |
| Metabolism rate associated with work performed | 5.86 kcal/min |
| Average rate of performance of work | 1.95 kcal/min |
| Average efficiency | 33.2% |

Throughout the whole time, all values were surprisingly near constant. This efficiency of 33% for the leg muscle has been verified by other work and is thought to be about the maximum of all muscular efficiencies. However, the efficiency computed on the basis used in a

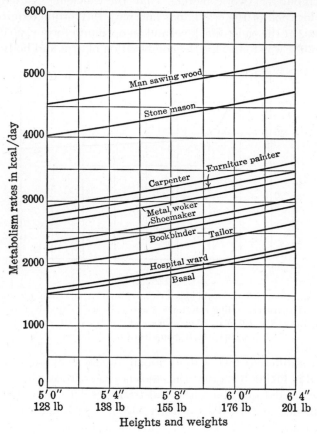

FIG. 31.   Metabolism rates for men of various statures and weights engaged for 8 hours daily in various pursuits, according to Lusk (by permission, Lusk, *The Elements of the Science of Nutrition*, 4th ed., p. 465, Philadelphia, W. B. Saunders Co., 1928).

brake thermal efficiency for a steam power plant is much less, viz., 1.95/9.75 or 20%.

4. The maximum metabolism rate maintainable for a considerable time is about 10 kcal/min, that of the bicycle rider discussed above. The maximum metabolism rate for a short period, corresponding to a 4-mile crew race "at home" in 22 min, was found to be about

19 kcal/min.   Average rates for hard workers range from 3500 kcal/day to 5000 kcal/day.

Let us consider the operation of the human power plant.   Fuel is taken in the form of food and drink.   Digested in the alimentary tract, much of it is taken up by the blood and transferred throughout the plant.   The refined fuel, that which is to be available later for the performance of work, is for the most part stored up as protein or muscle, glycogen (carbohydrate), and fat.   Other portions go to form bone, blood, nerve tissue, etc.   Whether an individual rests or not, work is being performed by some of the extremely numerous elementary engines of the power plant, that is the muscle fibers.   Their activity, which is continuous from the beginning of life until death occurs, results in the consumption of some of the stored refined fuel.   During an interval of complete rest, no external work is performed, although heat is developed and internal work is done.   When, however, external work is performed, the work so done and the extra heat so developed is in excess of that occurring with the system at rest.   With regard to the internal work, the external work, and the heat developed, the human system is somewhat like an automobile with engine running.   With the auto at rest there is a certain basal metabolism rate, that is, a certain rate of consumption of fuel and of development of heat.   When the car is moving under power and its engine is performing external work, there is an additional rate of consumption of fuel and of production of heat, corresponding to an increased metabolism rate.

**28. Operation of the Human Engine.**   The similarity between the human elementary engine and an automobile engine practically stops here.   When stimulated to work, a muscle fiber contracts and exerts a force through a distance, and the force exerted times such distance represents a small increment of work.   Muscle fibers do not continue to stay contracted, however.   With continued stimulation there is a succession of contractions and relaxations that are more or less regular in times of occurrence.

The total work done by a muscle fiber in a specified time is the sum of the small increments of work occurring during that time.   Steady action by a group of muscle fibers results only because of their great number and because their times of operation are distributed uniformly.   The needed energy is supplied by the oxidation of proteins, glycogen, and fats.   Because the contractions and relaxations are irreversible processes, the oxidized material is not recovered during relaxations.   The breakdown products become waste material which must be removed.   Somewhat as in primary electric cells, there is transfer of energy from a chemical form into a different form with the production of waste material, but without the increase in temperature customary in heat engines.

In order that muscles may exert forces, even without motion resulting, as when one holds his arm out horizontally from his body, work must be done by the component muscle fibers. Though no external work is done, such action is as conducive to fatigue as are some other actions in which external work is actually performed. The work done by a muscle is necessarily less than that done by its component fibers, the difference appearing generally as heat. Whether or not the difference between the two amounts of work accounts for the whole of the heat developed is not known.

Summarizing, we may say (1) that a human being is in essence a complex power plant containing fuel-refining apparatus, a multitude of simple elementary engines, and a large number of machines for the performing of external work; (2) that the refined fuel is distributed by the blood and stored up in the system as protein, glycogen, and fat; (3) that a simple elementary engine or muscle fiber in action contracts and relaxes irreversibly and intermittently; (4) that during such contractions mechanical forces are exerted and mechanical work is performed by muscle fibers at the expense of the refined fuel; (5) that the mechanical work thus performed in exerting forces on the machines belonging to the power plant does not depend on whether these machines are performing external work or not; (6) that the energy exchanges are precisely in accord with the first law of thermodynamics; and (7) that the efficiencies represented by the ratio of external work performed to stored energy used in the process may, under favorable conditions, become as high as 33%.

## PROBLEMS

**1.** Given that, as shown in Fig. 8, water is pumped from a hot well of a condensing power plant at a temperature of 80°F into the boiler at a temperature of 400°F, where it is vaporized, compute the ratio of the heat supplied to heat the water to the boiling point to that required to vaporize it and to that required to superheat the steam at constant pressure to 600°F. [Heat of vaporization at 400°F = 826 btu/pd, $\bar{c}_p$ of steam at 250 lb/in.$^2$ = 0.584 btu/(pd F°), $\bar{c}_p$ of liquid water between 80°F and 400°F = 1.022 btu/(pd F°).)]

**2.** In a certain power plant, the steam supplied by the boiler to the prime mover is just saturated and it has a pressure of 250 lb/in.$^2$ and a temperature of 401°F; the steam in the condenser enters at 0.90 lb/in.$^2$ and 98°F and has a moisture content of 20.0%. Given that $v$ of saturated steam at 98°F = 371 ft$^3$/pd; $\bar{c}_p$ for the liquid between 98°F and 401°F = 1.023 btu/(pd F°); heat of vaporization of water at 401°F = 825 btu/pd; heat of vaporization of water at 98°F = 1038 btu/pd. Compute, per pound of water, (a) the work done in condensing steam in the condenser,

(b) the heat to be added to raise the liquid to the boiling point, (c) the heat added to the water during a cycle, (d) the heat absorbed in the condenser, (e) the net work performed per cycle were no losses present, and (f) the efficiency of the system. (1 btu = 778 ft-lb.)

3. Assume that the steam, instead of being supplied saturated as in problem 2, is superheated to 800°F, and that the moisture content for that which enters the condenser drops to 10.0%. Given further that the average specific heat of the steam at constant pressure between 400°F and 800°F is 0.552 btu/(pd F°), compute the quantities asked for in problem 2.

4. Given that the brake engine efficiency of a certain 15,000-kw turbogenerator operating with a throttle pressure of 260 lb/in.$^2$, a throttle temperature of 620°F, and an exhaust temperature of 77°F is 26.2% and that the engine efficiency is 76%, determine the indicated thermal efficiency, $\eta_i$, that is, $W/Q_1$, where $W$ is determined from an indicator diagram. Compare this with the $\eta_R$ for the comparable Rankine cycle which gave 35.0%.

5. Using Figs. 17 and 18 and the data relating to them which are in the text, determine the indicated power and the brake horsepower of the engine.

6. In slightly more than a year's time, the Hartford mercury vapor-steam plant supplied $135 \times 10^6$ kwhr of electrical energy at the station bus using coal rated at 10,000 btu/pd. The overall efficiency is said to have averaged somewhat over 33%. How much coal was required for the time indicated?

7. The heat of combustion of commercial gasoline is given as about 125,000 btu/gal or 49 hphr/gal and the brake thermal efficiency of the automobile gasoline engine as about 23%. If a certain make of automobile driving across the country at 45 mi/hr uses gasoline at the rate of 14 mi/gal, what must be the average brake horsepower developed by the engine? What at 25 mi/hr and a gasoline consumption of 19½ mi/gal?

8. A new type of Diesel locomotive has 6 cylinders, each with an opposed pair of pistons as described in the text. The common cylinder diameter is 8⅛ in. The distance of closest approach for a piston pair is $^{15}/_{16}$ in. The stroke for each piston is 10 in. The engine operates normally at 850 rpm, uses a 19,000-btu/pd fuel, and possesses a brake efficiency of 35%. Determine the mean effective cylinder pressure during the power stroke and the rate of consumption of fuel per brake horsepower-hour when developing 1200 hp.

9. What is the adjusted ideal coefficient of performance $K_i'$ for a refrigerating system using "Freon-12," operating between the standardized temperatures 5°F and 86°F?

10. On the assumption that the highest room temperature that is to be encountered in household refrigeration is 100°F, that by ventilation the cooler part of the condenser may be maintained at a temperature not more than 10 F° in excess of the surrounding air, and that a factor of safety of 2½ for pressures in excess of atmospheric pressure must be provided for in construction, determine about what pressures must be provided for in systems using ammonia, sulfur dioxide, and "Freon-12."

11. With the aid of Fig. 28, determine the relative efficiencies of the refrigeration system of heating for a common high temperature of 86°F and low temperature of 5°F, 25°F, and 45°F. Assume the standard superheating and supercooling that are assumed in refrigeration determinations.

12. For a 60% mechanically efficient refrigerator using "Freon-12," at what rate must the refrigerant be pumped around the system when it operates between 5°F and 100°F (132 lb/in.$^2$) to yield $\frac{1}{20}$ ton-of-refrigeration? Assume the standard

superheating and supercooling. The specific volume of "Freon-12" vapor at 5°F is 1.485 ft$^3$/pd.

**13.** For a 60.6-kg man in a bed calorimeter, fasting for 31 days, distilled water only being taken, Benedict of the Carnegie Institution of Washington reported a roughly uniform rate of loss of mass of 0.43 kg/day with a total heat production of about 42,500 kcal. Determine the fuel value of the consumed flesh in cal/gm.

**14.** How much drinking water at 10°C must be taken in during an 8-hr working period by a workman in a room whose temperature, 35°C, is the same as that of the body surface of the workman, if during that period his metabolism rate is 350 kcal/hr? Assume that the temperature and the water content of the workman's body are to remain normal.

# CHAPTER XII

## CONVECTION

**1. Introduction.** Convection is the transfer of heat energy by means of the motion of matter. As used here it refers only to motions occurring in fluids, including liquids and gases. The motions referred to are those of sizable portions of fluid and must not be confused with random molecular motions which are constantly occurring in all bodies. The process is basically important in nature. How much so is suggested in part by the following from the British meteorologist Sir William Napier Shaw (1854– ): "There is nothing but thermal convection to act as the motive power for every drop of rain that ever fell and for every wind that ever filled a sail or wrecked a ship since the world began."

Convective circulation within a fluid is always associated with pressure differences, which may be brought about in many ways. A common one is by establishing a local change in density. Such a change is often associated with unequal heating or cooling of the fluid mass. For most liquids, a temperature gradient in which the temperature decreases upwards produces mechanical instability with heavier layers above lighter ones. As a result, relative motion can occur with the more dense cool liquid moving to regions occupied by the less dense warm liquid. Heat transfers ensue, and the process is described as convective. For substances like water between 0°C and 4°C, a temperature gradient of the opposite sign is required. Processes of this sort are called *natural convection*.

Another method of establishing pressure differences employs mechanical means, such as a pump or a blower. When heat transfers are associated with motions of this sort, the process is called *forced convection*.

As defined, heat transfer laterally into or out from the fluid stream must somewhere in its path accompany the fluid motion if the process is to be classed as convection. Such transfer may occur in many places. Illustrations are the passage of heat from the firepot of a furnace in the basement to the water flowing upward in the surrounding chamber preliminary to the passage of the water further by convection to the so-called radiators above. This is followed by the conduction of heat through those radiator walls into the convective air currents that heat up the surrounding space.

Examples of convection are everywhere at hand.  Most significant, as regards our personal welfare, are the large-scale, continuous convective processes of the atmosphere and the oceans known as winds and ocean currents.  Homelier examples are common.  The cooling fins on a soldering iron or engine cylinder and many types of central heating systems are devices for aiding natural convection.  One heat transfer commonly accomplished by forced convection is the cooling of a spoonful of hot soup by blowing.  One function of clothing in cool climates is to reduce heat transfer by convection.

In the field of industrial heat transfers, convection plays a large role. If the density of water, for example, were independent of temperature, thus preventing natural convective processes, the heating of large masses of water in boilers would be more difficult.  In the design of steam engines, heat exchangers, radiators, and many similar devices, heat engineers are constantly having to deal with the problem of transferring heat from a solid to a moving fluid.

One method used by several workers for the separation of isotopes depends in part on thermal convection.  In this method natural convection is used to set up a rising warm fluid stream and an adjacent falling cool fluid stream.  The isotope separation takes place by differential thermal diffusion across the vertical boundary between the two streams.

**2. Flow of Fluids.**  Frequently in industry there is transfer of heat from a wall, as of a boiler or pipe, to or from a fluid in forced motion along it and differing in temperature from it.  It is of advantage to discuss first the case where no such temperature difference exists.

It has long been known that there are two types of fluid motion. The first, occurring at lower velocities, is called laminar or streamline flow.  In this type of motion, particles of fluid move in orderly fashion with little sidewise motion or mixing.  A small tracer stream of colored fluid, of the same density as the fluid in which it is introduced, retains its identity for a considerable time, although finally it will be uniformly dispersed by molecular diffusion.  The second type of motion occurs at higher velocities and is called turbulent flow.  It is accompanied by constant mixing and turbulence.  A colored marker stream is very rapidly broken up.  Fig. 1a shows turbulence in the convection currents associated with a burner flame.  The photograph was taken by a special technique, known as the Schlieren method, which yields a so-called instantaneous picture of conditions.  Various parts of the irregularly heated column of gases, with corresponding variations in index of refraction, appear darker or brighter than other parts. Fig. 1b shows a direct photograph of the same flame taken in normal fashion.

As might be anticipated, laminar flow can be treated theoretically, whereas in general turbulent-flow problems are too difficult for rigorous analysis and require the use of approximate and empirical methods. The velocity with which the motion of a given fluid for a set of fixed geometrical conditions ceases to be laminar and becomes turbulent is not sharply defined. Rather, there is an intermediate region of velocities where the flow is a combination of the two types. For the case of fluid flow through pipes, the English engineer and physicist Osborne Reynolds (1842–1912), in his classical researches centering about 1883, arrived at a dimensionless grouping of characteristics of the fluid and the pipe on whose value the type of flow seemed to depend. This group has been called the Reynolds number $\eta$ and is defined as

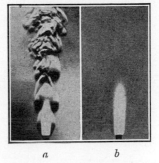

$$\eta = \frac{d\bar{v}\delta}{\nu} \tag{1}$$

where $d$ is the inside diameter of the circular pipe, $v$ is the average fluid velocity, $\delta$ the fluid density, and $\nu$ the fluid viscosity. Units that might be assigned to these

FIG. 1. Photographs of a burner flame taken (a) using the Schlieren method, and (b) in the normal fashion. Note the turbulent convection stream of heated gases which is revealed in (a). (Courtesy of D. B. Gawthrop.)

quantities are, in order, the cm, the cm/sec, the gm/cm³, and the poise or the gm/(cm sec), from which it is clear that $\eta$ is a numeric and that its value is independent of the system of units used. The Reynolds number has significance in other flow problems besides that of fluids through pipes. Another example is the falling of solid spheres through fluids, in which case $d$ and $\bar{v}$ represent the sphere diameter and velocity respectively.

Note that $\bar{v}$ in Eq. 1 is the average linear velocity over the cross section of the pipe. Actually the velocity starts from zero at the wall and increases to a maximum at the center of the pipe. The exact velocity distribution depends on the type of flow. For turbulent flow the velocity is more nearly uniform across the pipe than for laminar flow. If for any particular rate of flow of any fluid through any circular pipe the Reynolds number is below 2100, experiment shows the flow to be laminar. In the region of $\eta$ between 2100 and 3100, it is partly laminar and partly turbulent. For $\eta$ greater than

3100 the flow is wholly turbulent. Thus for water at 50°F flowing at a rate of 1.0 gal/min through a pipe ¾ in. I.D., the Reynolds number is 1900 and the flow is laminar. If, however, the rate be increased to 3.0 gal/min, the Reynolds number becomes 5700 and the flow is turbulent.

The British engineers T. E. Stanton and J. R. Pannell measured, in 1914, for both water and air flowing through smooth pipes, the ratio of the average linear fluid velocity $\bar{v}$ as defined above to the maximum linear fluid velocity $v_m$ at the center of the pipe, for various Reynolds numbers (Fig. 2). In the region to the left of $A$, the ratio is 0.5, a

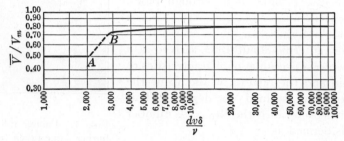

Fig. 2. The ratio of the average linear fluid velocity to the maximum linear fluid velocity for fluids flowing through smooth pipes (by permission, W. H. McAdams, *Heat Transmission*, p. 105, New York, McGraw-Hill Book Co., 1942).

value predicted by theory for laminar flow; in the region $AB$, the ratio changes rapidly; and in the region $BC$, the ratio increases slowly with increase in velocity, a characteristic of turbulent flow. The existence of two types of fluid flow in pipes is shown.

Other instances of laminar and turbulent flow may be cited. The linear velocities of fluids streaming along a flat plate as a function of the distance from the plate, for example, have been investigated by many workers. The results indicate that, for a certain distance in the region near the plate, the velocities start from zero at the surface and increase linearly outwards with laminar flow prevailing. There is then a thin buffer zone where the flow is intermediate between laminar and turbulent and the velocities increase less slowly. Beyond this region the flow is turbulent and the velocities increase still more slowly. This is shown in Fig. 3, taken from the 1924 data of the Dutch physicist Van der Hegge Zijnen for the forced flow of air parallel to a flat plate.

**3. Heat Transfer to a Moving Fluid.** When a cool fluid is streaming parallel to a heated wall, heat is transferred from the wall to the fluid. It is common practice, following I. Langmuir (1881–   ) of the General

Electric Research Laboratory, winner of the Nobel prize in chemistry in 1932, to regard this convective transfer as a first approximation to heat conduction through a thin layer of fluid close to the wall, roughly the laminar-flow region, to a region whose temperature distribution, after a steady state has been reached, is maintained by turbulent flow.

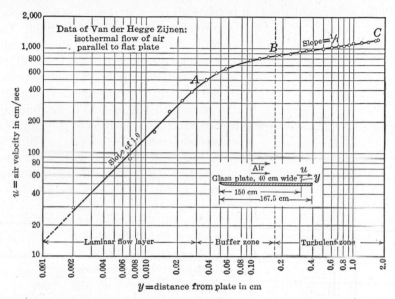

FIG. 3. Linear fluid flow velocities for a particular case of forced flow of air parallel to a flat plate (by permission, W. H. McAdams, *Heat Transmission*, p. 102, New York, McGraw-Hill Book Co., 1942).

Thus, an analysis of convective heat transfer of this type can be treated approximately in the same fashion as heat conduction, and heat engineers use the equation

$$\frac{dQ}{dt} = Ah\,\Delta T \qquad (2)$$

where $dQ/dt$ is the rate of heat transfer by convection from a heated wall of area $A$, $\Delta T$ is the temperature difference between the wall and the main body of the fluid, and $h$ is a *film coefficient*. A comparison of Eq. 2 and the basic equation for thermal conduction, Eq. 1 of Chapter VII as written for the case where the surface $A$ is perpendicular to the temperature gradient $dT/dl$, namely,

$$\frac{dQ}{dt} = -Ak\,\frac{dT}{dl} \qquad (3)$$

shows that $h$ is the average thermal conductivity for the fluid divided by the equivalent thickness of the conducting layer. This equivalent thickness is the thickness of a fluid layer with one face at wall temperature and the other at the temperature of the main body of the fluid under the artificial supposition that the temperature gradient actually existing at the wall persists all the way down to the tempera-

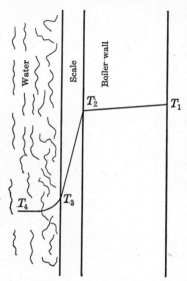

ture of the main body of the fluid. This equivalent thickness is always somewhat larger than the thickness of the laminar-flow region. The film coefficient, usually determined experimentally, varies with the speed of the fluid, the curvature and position of the fluid-wall surface, and other factors. Thus, for boiling water flowing with an average speed of 2.0 ft/sec through a smooth copper pipe 1.0 in. I.D., we find by experiment that $h$ is 560 btu/(ft² hr F°). Since the thermal conductivity of water at this temperature is 0.42 btu/(ft² hr F°/ft), the equivalent thickness of the conducting layer for these conditions is (0.42/560) ft or 0.009 in. For the conditions of Fig. 3, the equivalent thickness seems to be about 0.10 cm or 0.04 in. Note that heat transfers occurring under the conditions of Fig. 3 would be classed as

FIG. 4.  The temperature distribution for a case of heat transfer through a boiler wall with a layer of scale on the wall.

forced convection.  As might be expected, the equivalent thickness of the conducting layer decreases as the fluid velocity associated with forced convection increases.  For natural convection the layer is thickest, and for air it is about 0.17 in. thick under most conditions.

Industrially, heat transfer is often hindered by the presence of solid deposits on the heated wall.  Boiler scale on boiler pipes is an example (Fig. 4).  Here it is clear that the same rate of heat transfer occurs through all planes parallel to the wall, and we write for conduction through an area $A$ of the wall of thickness $d_w$

$$\frac{dQ}{dt} = \frac{k_w A (T_1 - T_2)}{d_w} \qquad (4)$$

for conduction through the scale of thickness $d_s$

$$\frac{dQ}{dt} = \frac{k_s A (T_2 - T_3)}{d_s} \tag{5}$$

and for the convective transfer

$$\frac{dQ}{dt} = hA(T_3 - T_4) \tag{6}$$

where $k_w$ and $k_s$ are the thermal conductivities of the wall and scale materials and $T_1$, $T_2$, $T_3$, and $T_4$ are the temperatures indicated in Fig. 4. From these equations $(1/A)(dQ/dt)$, $T_2$, and $T_3$ can be determined, provided $k_w$, $k_s$, $h$, $T_1$, and $T_4$ are known. For example, let a cast-iron boiler pipe wall 0.25 in. thick be maintained at an outside surface temperature $T_1$ of 300°F. Let $k_w$ and $k_s$ be 28 btu/(ft$^2$ hr F°/ft) and 0.4 btu/(ft$^2$ hr F°/ft) respectively. Assume a scale deposit $\frac{1}{16}$ in. thick and a water temperature of 200°F. Assume further that $h$ is 500 btu/(ft$^2$ hr F°) for the existing liquid flow conditions. Solving Eqs. 4, 5, and 6 for their temperature factors, and adding, we obtain

$$(T_1 - T_4) = \frac{dQ}{dt}\frac{1}{A}\left(\frac{d_w}{k_w} + \frac{d_s}{k_s} + \frac{1}{h}\right) \tag{7}$$

Substituting known values gives 6000 btu/(hr ft$^2$) for $(1/A)(dQ/dt)$. From Eqs. 4 and 6, 295°F and 212°F are obtained for $T_2$ and $T_3$.

In cases such as the above where one or more film coefficients and one or more thermal conductivities are involved, engineers often use an overall heat-transfer coefficient $h'$, which in the above example is defined by

$$\frac{dQ}{dt} = h'A(T_1 - T_4) \tag{8}$$

Obviously $(1/h')$ equals the parentheses-enclosed factor on the right of Eq. 7.

Very often there is convective heat transfer on both sides of the solid wall. Thus, in the preceding example, there might be convective transfer from the hot gases around the outside of the pipe to the pipe itself, as well as conduction through the pipe wall, through the scale, and convective transfer in the inside liquid.

In a convective transfer from a heated wall to a fluid under conditions for which the film coefficient is not known, the heat-transfer rate can still be calculated provided the thermal conductivity $k$ of the fluid and the fluid temperature gradient $dT/dl$ are known for all points in the fluid at the wall surface. For a section of plane wall of area $A$, the convective-heat-transfer rate is given by Eq. 3, which is applicable to objects of all shapes provided $(1/A)(dQ/dt)$ is interpreted as the rate of heat transfer per unit area at any point on the fluid-solid interface where the temperature gradient is $dT/dl$. It is a vector quantity and has the same orientation as $dT/dl$, normal to the interface, but is oppositely directed. With $\Delta A$ representing an element of surface, the total rate of heat transfer for a particular case is found by summing up, for the component elements of the surface, the corresponding products $(1/A)(dQ/dt)\,\Delta A$, i.e., by integration.

### 4. A Method for Measuring Temperatures in a Fluid Possessing Laminar Flow.

An ingenious method for determining air temperature distributions in the region

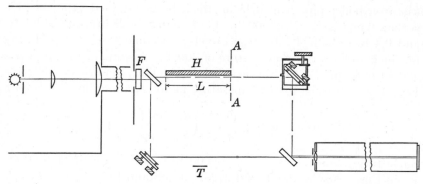

Fig. 5. A schematic diagram of Kennard's apparatus for studying thermal convection (by permission, *Temperature—Its Measurement and Control in Science and Industry*, p. 686, New York, Reinhold Publishing Corp., 1941).

about heated solids in air has been perfected by R. B. Kennard (1891–  ) of Wilson Teachers College and the Bureau of Standards in Washington, D. C. It makes use of the change of index of refraction of air with temperature and is an interferometer method. The apparatus is shown schematically in Fig. 5.

Light from the mercury lamp at the left of the figure is formed into a very slightly convergent beam by the lens system indicated. The light then passes through filter $F$, which permits only the strong mercury green line to enter the interferometer proper. The beam strikes first a half-silvered mirror, which separates it into a transmitted beam which continues parallel to its original direction and a reflected beam of approximately equal intensity which goes off at right angles to the original beam. The transmitted beam passes parallel and close to heated object $H$. After reflections at the adjustable mirrors, both beams finally recombine at a second half-silvered mirror and enter the camera which is focused on the plane $AA$ containing an end of the plate and, of course, on a plane $A'A'$, not shown in Fig. 5, which is equally distant from the second half-silvered mirror and perpendicular to the lower beam.

All rays making up the lower beam between the two half-silvered mirrors, provided the mirrors are parallel and the temperature throughout is uniform, contain exactly the same number of wavelengths of the mercury green line. However, the number of wavelengths in the various rays making up the upper beam between the two half-silvered mirrors depends upon what part of the beam one examines, because near the heated object the air temperature—hence the index of refraction and hence the wavelength in air—varies from ray to ray across the beam. In the recombined beam at the photographic plate, the phase distributions occurring in planes $AA$ and $A'A'$ are superposed and an interference fringe pattern is set up (Fig. 6). From photographs of these fringes and from certain other data, the air temperature at any point in the field can be determined.

For a vertical plate heated in air to a surface temperature of 118 C° above room air, Kennard determined the temperature-distance curve of Fig. 7, as described above.

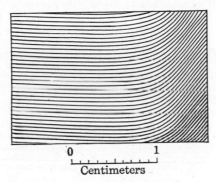

0        1

Centimeters

FIG. 6.   An interference pattern photographed by Kennard for the case of a vertical plate heated in air to a surface temperature of 118.1 C° above room air (by permission, *Temperature—Its Measurement and Control in Science and Industry*, p. 688, New York, Reinhold Publishing Corp., 1941).

The initial slope is $-246$ C°/cm. Knowing the thermal conductivity of air at the plate temperature to be 0.000308 watt/(cm² C°/cm), we find $(1/A)(dQ/dl)$ to be 0.076 watt/cm² by Eq. 3. The equivalent film thickness $l$, as defined in connection with Eqs. 2 and 3, is found from

$$l = \frac{-\Delta T}{(dT/dl)}$$

$$= -118 \text{ C°}/(-246 \text{ C°/cm})$$

$$= 4.8 \text{ mm}$$

(9)

Note that this film thickness for natural convection is considerably larger than the film thickness associated with Fig. 3, which is for forced convection. The film coefficient may be found from Eq. 2 to be 0.00064 watt/(cm² C°).

For a heated horizontal cylinder in air under natural convection conditions, Kennard obtained the fringe pattern of Fig. 8 and the isothermals of Fig. 9.

From classical electron theory the index of refraction of air, $n$, is related to its density, $\delta$, very closely by

$$\frac{n - 1}{\delta} = C$$

(10)

where $C$ is a constant. If $Q$ and $P$ refer to two points in the room on the same per-

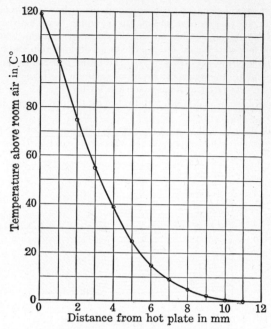

FIG. 7.   The temperature-distance curve corresponding to the interference pattern of Fig. 6.

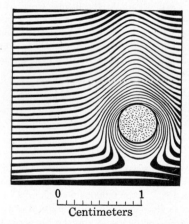

FIG. 8.   An interference pattern for the case of a horizontal cylinder heated in air to a surface temperature of 72.1 C° above room air (by permission, *Temperature— Its Measurement and Control in Science and Industry*, p. 701, New York, Reinhold Publishing Corp., 1941).

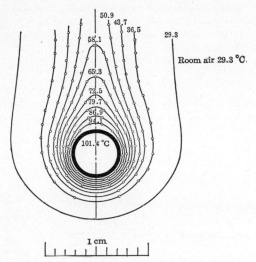

FIG. 9.   Some isothermals corresponding to the interference pattern of Fig. 8 (by permission, *Temperature—Its Measurement and Control in Science and Industry*, p. 703 New York, Reinhold Publishing Corp., 1941).

pendicular to the plate, one remote from and one near to the plate (Fig. 10), we have, substituting in Eq. 10,

$$\frac{n_Q - 1}{\delta_Q} = \frac{n_P - 1}{\delta_P} \tag{11}$$

or

$$n_Q - n_P = (n_Q - 1)\left(1 - \frac{\delta_P}{\delta_Q}\right) \tag{12}$$

In accord with Kennard's definitions we may write

$$n_Q = \frac{N_Q}{N_0} = \frac{N_Q \lambda_0}{L} \tag{13}$$

$$n_P = \frac{N_P}{N_0} = \frac{N_P \lambda_0}{L} \tag{14}$$

where $N_Q$ is the number of wavelengths along a horizontal line of length $L$ (see Fig. 5) perpendicular to the plane of Fig. 10 through point $Q$, $N_P$ is the corresponding number for point $P$, $N_0$ is the corresponding number for either point in a vacuum, and $\lambda_0$ is the wavelength in vacuum of the mercury green line. Substituting in Eq. 12, we get

$$N_Q - N_P = (n_Q - 1)\left(1 - \frac{\delta_P}{\delta_Q}\right)\frac{L}{\lambda_0} \tag{15}$$

Applying the ideal-gas law, representing $N_Q - N_P$ by $\Delta N$ and rearranging, this becomes

$$T_P - T_Q = \frac{\Delta N \lambda_0}{(n_Q - 1)L - \Delta N \lambda_0} \tag{16}$$

Because $\Delta N$ is the fringe displacement between $P$ and $Q$ measured in fringe widths and all other quantities may be known, we can determine $T_P - T_Q$ from Eq. 16. In this way, the temperatures for Fig. 7 were determined by Kennard for various points in the field next to the heated plate.

In applying Eq. 16, one must put

$$L = L_0 + \Delta L \tag{17}$$

where $L_0$ is the actual length of the heated plate and $\Delta L$ is a small end correction introduced because the air is heated laterally for a somewhat greater distance than $L_0$.

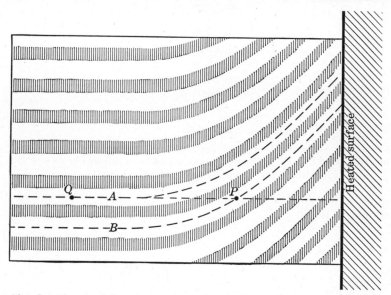

FIG. 10.   Interference fringes near a heated wall (by permission, *Temperature—Its Measurement and Control in Science and Industry*, p. 690, New York, Reinhold Publishing Corp., 1941).

It is evident that this technique may have practical applications in heat engineering.

**5. The Application of Dimensional Analysis.**   Problems in heat convection are quite often so involved that rigorous mathematical solutions are laborious, often prohibitively so.   In many instances, experiment is by far the quickest way to find an answer.   The methods of dimensional analysis are of great value in this field for providing partial theoretical solutions, coordinating experimental data, and extending the results of experiments made under certain conditions and with certain materials to other conditions and materials.   To illustrate the method, which, of course, is not restricted to the field of heat convection, consider the problem of determining the rate of heat transfer per unit area, $(1/A)(dQ/dt)$, for a long, heated, horizontal cylinder of diameter $d$ in a gas.   Let $\Delta T$ be the temperature difference between the cylinder and the surroundings.   Let us deal with the dimensions of mass $M$, length $L$, time $t$, and temperature $T$ as fundamental.   The starting point in dimensional analysis is to form a list of quantities  involved in the determination of an unknown, in this instance $(1/A)(dQ/dt)$, and assign dimensions to them. This is the most difficult step and often requires much thought. For this case the quantities and assigned dimensions are given in Table I.

## TABLE I

QUANTITIES INVOLVED IN HEAT TRANSFER FROM A HORIZONTAL CYLINDER TO A FLUID BY NATURAL CONVECTION

| Symbol | Quantity | Dimensions |
|---|---|---|
| $\Delta T$ | Temperature excess | $T$ |
| $k$ * | Thermal conductivity of fluid | $Mt^{-3}LT^{-1}$ |
| $d$ | Cylinder diameter | $L$ |
| $c$ † | Product of specific heat and density of fluid | $Mt^{-2}L^{-1}T^{-1}$ |
| $(\beta g)$ ‡ | Product of volume expansivity and acceleration of gravity | $Lt^{-2}T^{-1}$ |
| $\zeta$ § | Ratio of viscosity of fluid to its density | $L^2t^{-1}$ |

* The value of $k$ varies with temperature. For the accuracy involved in this discussion, it will be adequate to use the value corresponding to the mean of the cylinder temperature and that of the main body of the fluid.

† The thermal capacitance per unit volume, not per unit mass, is involved.

‡ This product is involved in setting up the pressure gradients in the fluid which are responsible for convection currents. Since the weight per unit volume of the heated fluid relative to that of the cooler surrounding fluid only is involved, $\beta$ should be evaluated at the temperature of the cooler surrounding fluid.

§ This is the so-called kinematic viscosity, which is involved in the viscous forces occurring during convection. It should be measured at the temperature at which $k$ is measured.

In the absence of more complete knowledge, let us then assume

$$\frac{1}{A}\frac{dQ}{dt} = k^u c^v (\Delta T)^w d^z (\beta g)^x \zeta^y \tag{18}$$

where the exponents are unassigned numbers. Because the dimensions of $(1/A)$ $(dQ/dt)$ are $Mt^{-3}$, we can write dimensionally, from Eq. 18,

$$Mt^{-3} = M^u t^{-3u} L^u T^{-u} M^v t^{-2v} L^{-v} T^{-v} T^w L^z L^x t^{-2x} T^{-x} L^{2y} t^{-y} \tag{19}$$

This yields four equations, because the exponents for $M$, $L$, $t$, and $T$ on each side must match,

$$1 = u + v \qquad \text{from } M$$
$$0 = u - v + z + x + 2y \quad \text{from } L$$
$$-3 = -3u - 2v - 2x - y \quad \text{from } t \tag{20}$$
$$0 = -u - v + w - x \qquad \text{from } T$$

From these we determine

$$w = 1 + x$$
$$v = 2x + y$$
$$u = 1 - 2x - y \tag{21}$$
$$z = 3x - 1$$

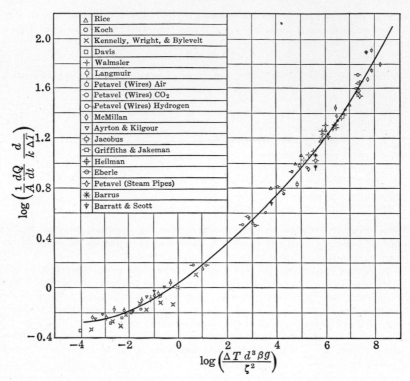

Fig. 11. Natural convection from horizontal cylinders of various diameters in various fluids (by permission, M. Fishenden and O. Saunders, *The Calculation of Heat Transmission*, p. 91, London, His Majesty's Stationery Office, 1932).

Substituting in Eq. 18 gives

$$\frac{1}{A}\frac{dQ}{dt} = k^{1-2x-y}c^{2x+y}\,\Delta T^{1+x}d^{3x-1}(\beta g)^x\zeta^y \tag{22}$$

or

$$\left(\frac{1}{A}\frac{dQ}{dt}\frac{d}{k\,\Delta T}\right) = (k^{-2}c^2\,\Delta Td^3\beta g)^x\left(\frac{c\zeta}{k}\right)^y \tag{23}$$

This expression can be simplified because from both kinetic theory and experiment the numeric $\frac{c\zeta}{k}$ is constant for gases. Thus,

$$\left(\frac{1}{A}\frac{dQ}{dt}\frac{d}{k\,\Delta T}\right) = B\left(\frac{\Delta Td^3\beta g}{\zeta^2}\right)^x \tag{24}$$

where $B$ is a numerical constant characteristic of natural convection phenomena in gases. This means that we can measure $(1/A)(dQ/dt)$ for various values of $d$ and $\Delta T$ and for gases having various values of $k$ and $\zeta$, and if the quantities in parentheses, or their logarithms, are plotted against each other, a single curve should result. The usefulness of this property in predicting the results of similar experiments is clear.

Fig. 11 shows such a plot. Table II shows the range of variables covered. Note that the quantities in parentheses in Eq. 24, like the Reynolds number, are dimensionless. The fact that the locus of Fig. 11 is not a straight line indicates that some assumption underlying Eq. 24 is not exact. Nevertheless for small ranges it serves fairly well.

## TABLE II

EXPERIMENTAL CONDITIONS UNDERLYING VARIOUS MEASUREMENTS OF HEAT TRANSFER BY NATURAL CONVECTION FROM HORIZONTAL CYLINDERS (SEE FIG. 11)

| Symbol | Worker | Diameters | Maximum Temperature Difference | Pressure | Gas |
|---|---|---|---|---|---|
| | | mm | F° | A | |
| △ | Rice | 40–113 | 270 | 1 | Air |
| o | Koch | 14–100 | 340 | 1 | Air |
| x | Kennelly, Wright, and Bylevelt | 0.1–0.7 | 400 | 0.3–2.5 | Air |
| □ | Davis | 0.08–0.16 | 400 | | Air |
| + | Walmsler | 21–90 | 300 | 1 | Air |
| ϕ | Langmuir | 0.04–0.5 | 2900 | 1 | Air |
| ♂ | Petavel | 1.1 | 1650 | 1–100 | Air |
| –o | Petavel | 1.1 | 1650 | 1–100 | $CO_2$ |
| o– | Petavel | 1.1 | 1650 | 1–100 | $H_2$ |
| ◇ | McMillan | 25–300 | 300 | 1 | Air |
| ▽ | Ayrton and Kilgour | 0.05–0.36 | 600 | 1 | Air |
| -⟨⟩- | Jacobus | 5 | | 1 | Air |
| -□- | Griffiths and Jakeman | 150 | 600 | 1 | Air |
| -⟨⟩- | Heilman | 25–250 | 750 | 1 | Air |
| -o- | Eberle | 76–160 | 320 | 1 | Air |
| -◇- | Petavel | 5–500 | 250 | 1 | Air |
| * | Barrus | 5–25 | | 1 | Air |
| ▽ | Barratt and Scott | 6–50 | 300 | 1 | Air |

As an example of the use of Fig. 11, let us compute the effect of changing the diameter of the cylinder alone on the heat-transfer rate per unit area, all other factors remaining unchanged. Representing the logarithm of the quantity in the parentheses on the right of Eq. 24 by $X$ and that on the left by $Y$ and expanding, we have

$$X = \log \frac{\Delta T \beta g}{\zeta^2} + 3 \log d \tag{25}$$

and

$$Y = \log \left( \frac{1}{A} \frac{dQ}{dt} \right) - \log (k \, \Delta T) + \log d \tag{26}$$

Taking differences for the two cases involving a change of $d$ only gives

$$\Delta X = 3\Delta \log d \tag{27}$$

and

$$\Delta Y = \Delta \log \left( \frac{1}{A} \frac{dQ}{dt} \right) + \Delta \log d \tag{28}$$

Combining gives

$$\Delta \log \left( \frac{1}{A} \frac{dQ}{dt} \right) = \left( 3 \frac{\Delta Y}{\Delta X} - 1 \right) \Delta \log d \tag{29}$$

The term $\Delta Y/\Delta X$, which in the limit is the slope of the curve of Fig. 11, varies from about 0.05 at the lower left-hand end of the curve, the region of small diameters, to an upper limiting value of $\frac{1}{3}$ at the upper right-hand end, the region of large diameters.

For a specific case, consider a wire of 10-mil diameter heated to 1950°C in air. For these conditions $\zeta$ is 1.8 cm²/sec and $\beta$ is 0.0033 1/C°. From Eq. 25, $-1.5$ is obtained for $X$. The slope $\Delta Y/\Delta X$ at the corresponding point on the curve of Fig. 11 is 0.10. Substituting in Eq. 29 gives

$$\Delta \log \left( \frac{1}{A} \frac{dQ}{dt} \right) = -0.70\Delta \log d \tag{30}$$

For a change of $d$ to 2 mil, a fivefold decrease, $\Delta \log d$ is $-0.699$ and the change in the rate of heat transfer *per unit area* is an increase of 3.1 fold. This fact, that as the diameter of a wire is reduced its convective-heat-transfer rate per unit area increases, is of great importance in the design of gas-filled incandescent lamps, as will appear in the next section. Also, it suggests that, if one is trying to measure the temperature of a gas with a thermocouple, it will be well to use very fine wires so as to increase the ease of heat exchange between the couple and the gas.

### 6. Gas Losses in Incandescent Lamps.

Most incandescent lamps are filled with an atmosphere of commercial argon—88% argon, 12% nitrogen—which is introduced at the time of manufacture at a pressure of 600 mm-Hg. Lamps of the 120-volt class with ratings of 25 watts and less and certain of the low-voltage lamps are exceptions to this general rule. The main purpose of the gaseous atmosphere is the securing of a higher possible temperature of operation without reduction of lamp life and the greater accompanying luminous efficiency which results, a consequence of the greatly decreased rate of vaporization of the tungsten filament. Under conditions occurring in lamps, this decrease in vaporization rate is of the order of 80. For the customary 1000-hr life of the standard 120-volt lamps of 1944–1945, the filaments of the gas-filled lamps may be operated at much higher temperatures than are possible for vacuum lamps. For example, the 40-watt, 120-volt, gas-filled lamp operates with a maximum temperature of about 2750°K while the 25-watt, 120-volt, vacuum lamp operates at about 2580°K. Their corresponding luminous efficiencies are 11.8 lum/watt and 10.5 lum/watt. Were a 40-watt, 120-volt vacuum lamp manufactured, its operating temperature would exceed that of the 25-watt, 120-volt lamp by only about 20 K°. Its luminous efficiency would be about 11.2 lum/watt, a value appreciably below that for the gas-filled lamp.

The obvious reason for the smallness of the increase in efficiency in going from the 25-watt to the 40-watt lamp, even with its greatly increased filament temperature, is the presence of a convection loss in the latter. First-hand evidence of this effect may be gained from the simple test of laying one's hand lightly first on top of an operating vacuum lamp and then on top of an operating gas-filled lamp. The deleterious effect of this gas loss, as it is called, so far as luminous efficiency is concerned, is more than overcome, however, in the 40-watt lamp by the favorable effect of the increase in operating temperature. An additional small gain from the presence of the gas results from the general tendency for the convection currents to carry the vaporized filament material toward the top of the lamp bulb where most of it is deposited, without cutting down appreciably the light output horizontally and downward where it is generally desired. In vacuum lamps, on the contrary, the material sent out on vaporization in any direction and deposited is roughly proportional to the light sent out in that direction. This results in the greatest cutting down where the output is greatest.

With 120 volts as standard for electric power systems and low wattages of the order of 6 watts to 2000 watts as desired lamp ratings for tungsten-filament lamps, only long filaments of small diameter are possible. The diameter of a 6-watt lamp filament is 0.47 mil (= 0.0119 mm), its length 360 mm, while corresponding values for the 2000-watt lamp are 17.7 mil (= 0.298 mm) and 1175 mm. Obviously with filaments of these sizes strung back and forth inside a glass bulb, as they were in the original vacuum tungsten lamps, gaseous atmospheres would be of no advantage except for the very large filaments. Convection losses would generally be so great that their deleterious effects from the standpoint of luminous efficiency could not be overcome by the increased temperatures of operation. To Irving Langmuir, who in 1914 was engaged in a study of the efficiencies of toasters, there came the simple but brilliant idea of how to reduce the convection effects without sacrificing those resulting from increases of temperature. It consisted of coiling the filaments and shifting from the vacuum surrounding, considered essential previously, to gaseous atmospheres. The outside diameters of the coils usually range from 5 to 6 times those of the filaments from which

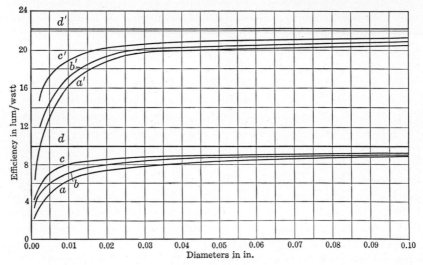

Fig. 12.   Gas losses for filaments of various diameters in nitrogen ($a$, $a'$), argon ($b$, $b'$), and mercury vapor ($c$, $c'$). The lower curves are for 2445°K; the upper curves are for 2885°K. Curves $d$ and $d'$ refer to operation in vacuo. (By permission, F. E. Cady and H. B. Dates, *Illuminating Engineering*, p. 111, New York, John Wiley & Sons, 1928.)

they are made. The result has been greatly increased luminous efficiencies, with the effect of increase of temperature now outweighing the gas-loss effect for lamps of the 120-volt class whose wattages are 40 watts or higher.

Just how much benefit may be expected by coiling the filament in particular cases can be obtained with some difficulty from Fig. 11. More directly we may make use of certain data originally reported by Langmuir which are here presented in graphical form in Fig. 12. For temperatures of 2445°K and 2885°K and for atmospheres of nitrogen, argon, and mercury vapor, there are shown curves of luminous efficiencies as functions of the diameters of tungsten filaments. Compared with vacuum lamp efficiencies of about 10.0 lum/watt, and about 22.2 lum/watt, all gas-filled lamp efficiencies are less, the more so the smaller the diameter of the filament and the less massive the

## TABLE III

### SOME CHARACTERISTICS OF EARLY 1945 INCANDESCENT TUNGSTEN LAMPS OF THE 120-VOLT CLASS

(Courtesy of W. E. Forsythe and associates of the Lamp Development Laboratory of the General Electric Company, Cleveland, Ohio.) Temperatures given for the filaments of the vacuum lamps, because of their smallness, are rather unreliable.

| Wattage (watts) | Type | No. of Supports (including leads) | Rated Life (hr) | Maximum Temperature °K | Filament Diameter (mils) | Filament Length (mm) | Coil Diameter (mils) | Coil Length (mm) | Loss to Supports % | Gas Loss % | Luminous Efficiency lum/watt | Type of Coiling |
|---|---|---|---|---|---|---|---|---|---|---|---|---|
| 6 | Vacuum | 8 | 1500 | 2400 | 0.47 | 360 | 3.33 | 29.5 | 2.6 | None | 7.0 | Single |
| 7½ | Vacuum | 5 | 1400 | 2400 | 0.53 | 390 | 3.50 | 35.0 | 1.6 | None | 7.5 | Single |
| 15 | Vacuum | 5 | 1000 | 2480 | 0.86 | 495 | 4.31 | 48.0 | 1.6 | None | 9.5 | Single |
| 25 | Vacuum | 5 | 1000 | 2580 | 1.20 | 565 | 6.59 | 48.0 | 1.6 | None | 10.5 | Single |
| 40 | Gas-filled | 5 | 1000 | 2750 | 1.29 | 380 | 7.83 | 39.0 | 1.6 | 24.5 | 11.8 | Single |
| 60 | Gas-filled | 3 | 1000 | 2770 | 1.83 | 535 | 29.5 | 24.0 | 1.0 | 15.0 | 14.0 | Coiled-coil |
| 100 | Gas-filled | 3 | 750 | 2850 | 2.48 | 580 | 42.7 | 28.0 | 1.0 | 13.7 | 16.3 | Coiled-coil |
| 200 | Gas-filled | 5 | 750 | 2890 | 4.00 | 625 | 20.0 | 68.0 | 1.7 | 13.7 | 18.2 | Single |
| 500 | Gas-filled | 5 | 1000 | 2940 | 7.10 | 815 | 40.8 | 80.5 | 1.8 | 9.2 | 19.7 | Single |
| 1000 | Gas-filled | 5 | 1000 | 3000 | 11.1 | 975 | 57.2 | 107.0 | 1.9 | 6.0 | 21.0 | Single |
| 2000 | Gas-filled | 11 | 1000 | 3050 | 17.7 | 1175 | 70.0 | 156.0 | 1.9 | 5.5 | 22.0 | Single |

molecules of the gaseous atmosphere. On a fractional basis these reductions in luminous efficiency are greater for the lower temperature.

Consider the coiling effect for the 200-watt, 120-volt lamp. As is shown in Table III, its filament, which has a diameter of 4.00 mil ($=$ 0.102 mm), is formed into a coil whose outer diameter is 20.0 mil ($=$ 0.51 mm) and is operated in commercial argon at 2800°K. On the assumption that the percentage gas losses for such a filament when uncoiled and when coiled and operated in commercial argon at 2800°K are about the same as for 4.00-mil and 20.0-mil uncoiled filaments in argon at 2885°K, we may determine the reduction in gas loss for the 200-watt lamp brought about by coiling. For the percentage gas loss of the uncoiled filament at 2800°K about 36% is obtained from Fig. 12. For the coiled filament, we obtain 13%, a value which checks well, differences considered, with the value 13.7% given in Table III. The comparison of 36% with 13% or 13.7% shows how effective is the coiling in the 200-watt incandescent lamp in decreasing gas losses and hence in increasing the luminous efficiency.

Two other effects that come with the coiling, namely, a blackening of the radiation (see Chapter XIII) and an increase of filament diameter, are both relatively small and tend to offset each other. So important is the coiling effect that, in certain lamps as shown in Table III, the filament is doubly coiled to yield what is known as a coiled-coil filament.

**7. Convection and the Weather—General.** The internal circulation of the earth's atmosphere, which is of worldwide extent, profoundly influences the weather at any spot. By this circulation, which is maintained fundamentally by temperature differences established between the poles and the equator by non-uniform solar heating, enormous convective heat exchanges take place. Atmospheric circulation embraces features of a continental or oceanic extent, such as monsoons and trade winds, and local features such as sea breezes, thunderstorms, and hurricanes. Although circulation is due chiefly to temperature differences caused by unequal heating or cooling, it is also affected by (a) local humidity changes which can appreciably affect the weight per unit volume of the air and thus cause pressure differences, and (b) mechanical effects associated with the rotation of the earth.

*The Atmosphere.* The atmosphere may be divided into three layers: (a) the troposphere, which extends from the earth's surface up to about 10–18 km; (b) the stratosphere, which extends from the top of the troposphere to about 80 km; and (c) the ionosphere, which lies above the stratosphere and extends to a great but undetermined altitude. Fig. 13, taken by means of sunlight scattered by the earth from

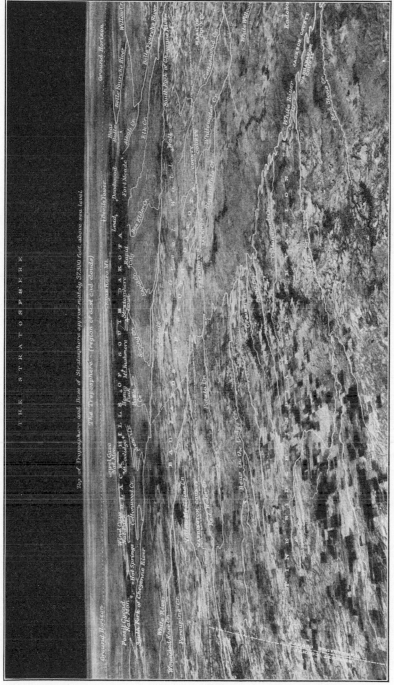

FIG. 13. A photograph taken from an altitude of 72,400 ft (by permission, *National Geographic Society*—*U. S. Army Air Corps Strato-sphere Flight of 1935 in the Balloon "Explorer II"*). Note straight line near the troposphere—stratosphere boundary.

401

a height of 72,400 ft during the 1935 ascent of the stratosphere balloon *Explorer II*, sponsored jointly by the National Geographic Society and the U. S. Army Air Corps, shows with remarkable clarity the sharp transition between the troposphere and the stratosphere. Similar photos have been taken from V-2 rockets at much greater altitudes.

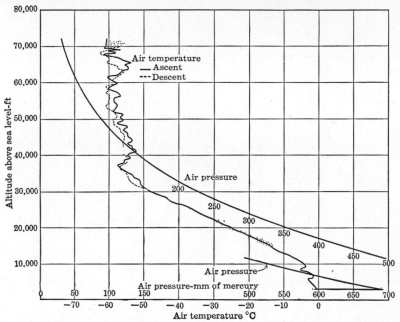

FIG. 14.   A characteristic plot of the temperature variation throughout the troposphere and the lower stratosphere (by permission, *National Geographic Society—U. S. Army Air Corps Stratosphere Flight of 1935 in the Balloon "Explorer II"*).

The transition is made apparent because of the presence of many dust particles in the comparatively turbulent troposphere and the comparative absence of dust in the calm, isothermal stratosphere. The troposphere is the region of convective motion, cloud formation, and ordinary weather phenomena as we know them. A plot of the temperature variation through the troposphere and part of the stratosphere representing measurements taken during the ascent of the balloon *Explorer II* is shown in Fig. 14. Up to about 37,000 ft, the base of the stratosphere, temperature decreases with altitude at a rate of about 7 C°/km. The mean rate for middle latitudes is about 6 C°/km. V-2 rocket researches for 1946–47 show an increase in temperature with altitude at still greater heights. At 120 km a temperature of about 60°C was obtained.

The composition of the atmosphere is given in Table IV.

TABLE IV

THE COMPOSITION OF THE ATMOSPHERE

(From W. J. Humphreys, *The Ways of the Weather*, p. 69, Jaques Cattell Press, Lancaster, Pennsylvania, 1942.)

| Substance | Volume Per Cent of Dry Air at Sea Level | Mass $10^8$ Tons |
|---|---|---|
| Nitrogen | 78.03 | 42,680,000 |
| Oxygen | 20.99 | 12,780,000 |
| Argon | 0.932 | 682,000 |
| Carbon dioxide | 0.03 | 24,000 |
| Hydrogen | 0.01 | 1,400 |
| Neon | 0.0018 | 760 |
| Krypton | 0.0001 | 140 |
| Helium | 0.0005 | 88 |
| Ozone | 0.00006 | 33 |
| Xenon | 0.000009 | 19 |

In addition to these constituents, water vapor may be present in amounts which vary from practically zero to about 4% by volume under tropical conditions. Neglecting water vapor and slight carbon dioxide variations, the composition of the atmosphere is remarkably uniform over the earth's surface and, with the further exception of ozone, throughout its height also to at least 27 km.

The stratosphere is a region of stable and uniform air conditions with very little temperature variation with altitude. Its mean temperature is about −55°C, although this varies somewhat with latitude, season, and time of day. A typical temperature altitude variation for the lower stratosphere is shown in Fig. 14.

The ionosphere is chiefly characterized by the presence of ionized layers such as the well-known Kennelly-Heaviside layer. It is the location of auroras. This discussion will be limited almost entirely to the troposphere, the region of convection phenomena.

The decrease in pressure with increasing altitude in the atmosphere, shown in Fig. 14, can be calculated. Consider two points separated vertically by a small distance $dh$. The pressure difference between them, as for the hydrostatic pressure of a layer of liquid of uniform density, is given by

$$-dp = \delta g \, dh \tag{31}$$

where $\delta$ and $g$ are the air density and the acceleration of gravity.

Assuming the ideal-gas law, this becomes

$$dh = -\frac{RT}{g}\frac{dp}{p} = -\frac{RT}{g}d(\ln p) \tag{32}$$

and finally, integrating for the condition of a constant $g$,

$$h = -\frac{R}{g}\int_{p_0}^{p} T\, d(\ln p) \tag{33}$$

where $p_0$ is the pressure at the earth's surface and $h$ is the height above it. Thus, if the variation of air temperature with pressure be known for any given vertical path into the atmosphere, the altitude-pressure relationship can be found by Eq. 33. The maximum altitude attained by the stratosphere balloon *Explorer II* was thus determined to be 69,139 ft above ground level, or 72,139 ft above sea level. Small corrections for humidity and variation of $g$ with altitude changed this latter figure to 72,395 ft, a value which was verified to 0.14% by a vertical photography method.

For ordinary aircraft use, barometric altimeters are calibrated, usually in feet, assuming that the atmosphere has a certain standard average variation of temperature with altitude. One such commonly used standard, that proposed by the International Commission for Air Navigation and in common use today, assumes a ground-level temperature of 15°C, a decrease of temperature with altitude of 6.5 C°/km up to 11 km, and a constant temperature of −56.5°C above this level. These temperature conditions are not usually met, and, to obtain precise results, readings of a barometric altimeter so calibrated must be corrected for departures of actual temperature conditions from this standard. In practice this correction is often made with the aid of a mechanical computer, into which the altimeter reading and the measured mean air temperature are set as known data.

*Atmospheric Convection.* The situation as regards natural convection is more complicated in gases than in liquids because of the relatively very much greater compressibility of gases. If a given portion of the liquid filling a deep container be moved under reversible adiabatic conditions from the bottom region to the top region of the liquid, i.e., from a higher-pressure to a lower-pressure region, the change in density of the portion so moved will be negligible for nearly all purposes. In a gas, however, a given portion moved under reversible adiabatic conditions from a higher- to a lower-pressure region will expand with a consequent reduction in density.

Consider a mass of dry air moving upward under reversibly adiabatic conditions from a point characterized by $p$, $T$, and $v$ to a near-by point characterized by $p + \Delta p$, $T + \Delta T$, and $v + \Delta v$. Recalling that Eq. 54, Chapter VIII, holds for the adiabatic process, and differentiating it, we obtain

$$\frac{dp}{dT} = -\frac{p}{T}\left(\frac{\gamma}{1-\gamma}\right) \tag{34}$$

Combining this with the ideal-gas equation and recalling Eq. 42, Chapter VIII, give

$$\frac{dp}{dT} = \delta c_p \tag{35}$$

Combining this with Eq. 31 finally gives

$$-\frac{dT}{dh} = \frac{g}{c_p} \tag{36}$$

Substitution of 0.240 cal/(gm C°) for $c_p$ and 980 cm/sec² for $g$ yields 9.8 C°/km for $(-dT/dh)$. This quantity is known as the *dry adiabatic lapse rate* and is of great meteorological importance.

For moist but not saturated air, the situation is slightly different in that $c_p$ of Eq. 36 must now be an average of the values for dry air and for water vapor, weighted according to their respective densities in the atmosphere. Because the specific heat at constant pressure for water vapor is about 0.47 cal/(gm C°) and that for dry air only 0.24 cal/(gm C°), the weighted mean value for moist air will be greater than that for dry air. In accord with Eq. 36, such air will cool less rapidly as it rises adiabatically. Since water vapor never constitutes more than about 4% of the atmosphere by volume at any locality, the lapse rate is never more than 1% smaller than the dry adiabatic lapse rate. For most purposes in meteorology, the difference between the two lapse rates can be neglected.

For moisture-saturated air, Eq. 36 no longer holds because condensation occurs as the air moves to a lower-temperature region. This releases heat of condensation and results in a lapse rate which is always lower than the dry adiabatic lapse rate. At high temperatures it may be considerably lower. The rate of decrease of temperature with increasing altitude for moisture-saturated air, or the *moist adiabatic lapse rate*, varies with temperature and pressure. At 1 A, for example, possible values are 9.5 C°/km at −30°C, 5.8 C°/km at 5°C, and 3.7 C°/km at 30°C.

*Atmospheric Stability.* The atmosphere is said to be stable for small changes at a particular place if a small mass of air, displaced vertically up or down under reversible adiabatic conditions, is acted upon by an unbalanced force tending to return it to its former position. The stability is neutral if the mass, when so displaced, is acted upon by no unbalanced force. The atmosphere is unstable if, when so displaced, an unbalanced force tends to displace the small mass still further. Vertical convection currents are necessarily present in an unstable atmosphere. The stability at a particular spot for such changes is determined by the temperature, the pressure, the density of water vapor in the air, and the existing lapse rate.

Two assumptions made in setting up the atmospheric stability criteria are (a) that the small displacement of the air mass considered was reversibly adiabatic, which will be generally true in a free atmosphere, and (b) that the initial temperature and pressure of the air mass considered were the same as those of its surroundings. Where there are significant departures from these assumptions, different stability criteria must be set up. In what follows, these assumptions are accepted.

Consider a portion of dry air, initially at the temperature of its surroundings, which is displaced adiabatically upward a small arbitrary distance. It will cool by an amount given by the product of the dry adiabatic lapse rate and the vertical displacement. If the resulting temperature is greater than that of the surrounding air at that level, the displaced portion will be less dense than its surroundings and will have an unbalanced upward force exerted on it. If the resulting temperature is the same or less than that of the surrounding air, the density will be the same as or greater than that of the surroundings and the unbalanced force will be either zero or downward. Thus, for dry air, a portion of the atmosphere will be in either stable, neutral, or unstable equilibrium, according to whether the lapse rate is less than, equal to, or greater than the dry adiabatic lapse rate. Downward displacements lead to the same conclusions.

For air containing water vapor but not saturated, the critical lapse rate will vary with humidity but will not differ from the dry adiabatic lapse rate by more than one per cent. For moisture-saturated air, the moist adiabatic lapse rate applies when upward displacements are considered. When downward displacements are considered, there is adiabatic heating of the displaced mass, and, unless water droplets are present so that evaporation can occur, the unsaturated moist adiabatic lapse rate applies.

The *average* lapse rate in mid latitudes, 6 C°/km, is less than the dry adiabatic lapse rate. The atmosphere there, when not saturated with moisture, is often stable. However, with varying local conditions, varying lapse rates also occur and result in neighboring "updrafts" and "downdrafts." Atmospheric instability is a very common cause of "bumpiness" sometimes experienced by air travelers. Under conditions of extreme instability, the air may become so violently turbulent that air travel becomes hazardous.

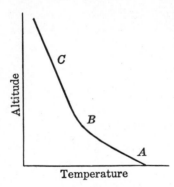

Fig. 15. A temperature-height curve of a sort usually associated with cumulus cloud formation.

Stability conditions usually vary with altitude. Fig. 15 shows a temperature-height curve of a sort usually associated with cumulous-cloud formation. In region $A$ the existing lapse rate is greater than the adiabatic lapse rate, so this is a region of instability with resulting vertical convection currents. In region $B$ the existing lapse rate is intermediate between the dry adiabatic rate and the moist adiabatic rate appropriate for the temperature and pressure in this region. In region $C$ the existing lapse rate is less than the appropriate moist adiabatic rate, so $C$ is a region of stable air conditions. If the air at ground level contains such an amount of moisture that it becomes just saturated on rising adiabatically to region $B$, conditions are very good for the formation of cumulous clouds of the "woolpack" or fair-weather variety in or close to region $B$.

A familiar proof of convection currents within cumulous clouds is furnished by hail formation. Initially a moisture droplet, rising in a vertical convection current within a cloud, freezes because of the adiabatic cooling of the surrounding air, then subsides, is caught in another rising current, and, if conditions are right, has another layer of ice frozen onto its surface. This process may be repeated several dozen times before eventual escape of the particle from the cloud as hail. The multiple-shell construction of large hailstones is evidence of this process.

Another rather common type of convective instability occurs in the layers of air, often only a few hundred feet thick, above the surface of a heated desert. Small sand whirls and the typical "shimmering" appearance of a distant object viewed over such a region are evidences of the existence of convective currents.

*Atmospheric Heat Balance.* If one considers the net rate of heat transfer into and out of a thin portion of the earth's crust of any arbitrary area including the atmos-

phere above it, important energy-transfer rates are (a) that from the sun by radiation, (b) that back into space by reflection and by reradiation at a longer wavelength, and (c) that by convection into or out of the region in question by atmospheric circulation.  A rate of somewhat less importance, though significant region-
ally, is (d) that by convection by ocean currents.  A rate that is practically negligible is (e) that by conduction from the hot interior of the earth.  Since the mean
annual air or surface temperatures for all points on the earth have remained essentially constant from year to year with no certain trend toward lower or higher
values, it follows that the mean annual heat-input rate into any given region of the
surface of the earth, including the atmosphere above it, must just equal, except for a
small storage in plant and animal growth, the mean annual net heat-output rate
from that region.  The British meteorologist G. C. Simpson, by making certain
assumptions about the distribution of water vapor and clouds and about the radiating
properties of various portions of the earth's surface, calculated, in 1929, expected
mean annual values of the rates mentioned in (a) and (b) above for various latitudes.
These are listed in Table V, along with the difference between them which must be
accounted for largely by convective heat transfers brought about by the circulation
of the atmosphere.  In accord with what has been stated above, the heat transfer
must occur from tropical regions to polar and subpolar regions.  It can be shown that,
choosing latitude 40° as an arbitrary dividing line, the mean heat-transfer rate across
it in a poleward direction must be $2.17 \times 10^{15}$ joules/sec.  The magnitude of this
transfer rate is very impressive when it is realized as an average transfer rate of about
6 kwhr/sec across each lineal foot of boundary.

TABLE V

Effective Net Heating and Cooling of the Earth's Surface at Various Latitudes

G. C. Simpson, *Memoirs of the Royal Meteorological Society*, vol. 3, No. 23, 1929,
*via* H. C. Willett, *Descriptive Meteorology*, p. 58, Academic Press, New York, N. Y.,
1944.

| Latitude | Mean Annual Rate of Input of Solar Radiant Energy per Unit Area cal/(cm² min) | Mean Annual Rate of Output of Terrestrial Radiant Energy per Unit Area cal/(cm² min) | Input Minus Output cal/(cm² min) |
|---|---|---|---|
| 0° | 0.339 | 0.271 | 0.068 |
| 10 | 0.334 | 0.282 | 0.052 |
| 20 | 0.320 | 0.284 | 0.036 |
| 30 | 0.297 | 0.284 | 0.013 |
| 40 | 0.267 | 0.282 | −0.015 |
| 50 | 0.232 | 0.277 | −0.045 |
| 60 | 0.193 | 0.272 | −0.079 |
| 70 | 0.160 | 0.260 | −0.100 |
| 80 | 0.144 | 0.252 | −0.108 |
| 90 | 0.140 | 0.252 | −0.112 |

*Atmospheric Circulation.*  Most simply one might imagine that convective heat transfer from the tropics toward the poles might be

accomplished by closed atmospheric convection loops formed by (*a*) descent of cool air at the poles, (*b*) horizontal transport to the tropics in the lower troposphere, (*c*) ascent of warmed air in the tropics, and (*d*) horizontal transport to the poles in the upper troposphere. The circulation that actually takes place, however, is much more complex, and, indeed, a mechanism accounting for it has not yet been firmly established. Important influences are known to be (*a*) deflections, due to the earth's rotation, of air currents moving horizontally between the poles and the equator; (*b*) effects due to temperature differences between portions of the continents and the oceans at the same latitude; and (*c*) frictional forces, which materially effect the winds in the lower troposphere.

Some average surface characteristics of the actual worldwide circulation are given below. These features represent yearly average conditions only, and great differences in the circulation will occur from day to day, as a continued inspection of the daily weather maps will reveal. Many of the features are greatly modified by the continental masses, and hence the description is more accurate for the southern hemisphere, which is largely water, than for the northern. Also, there are significant seasonal variations in the location and nature of many of the described characteristics.

(*a*) Around the earth at the thermal equator there is a narrow band containing several low-pressure regions known as the doldrums. It is a region of calms and rising air. Because of the adiabatic cooling of the rising moist air, condensation occurs and there is frequent rainfall.

(*b*) At about latitude 30° in each hemisphere there are several more or less permanent high-pressure areas or "highs" which are arranged side by side, forming two bands around the earth. They are known as the subtropical anticyclones. These regions, known to seamen as the "horse latitudes," are characterized by calms and descending air. Because the adiabatic heating of the descending air prevents condensation, there are few clouds and little rainfall. The importance of this region as a source region for warm tropical air to be transported convectively toward the poles in order to maintain the heat balance of the atmosphere will be mentioned later.

(*c*) At about latitude 60° north and south are belts of predominantly low-pressure regions known as the subpolar lows. One of the most prominent of these is the Icelandic low, centered over the North Atlantic.

(*d*) Over each pole there is a high-pressure zone, with descending air.

(*e*) From the horse latitudes, winds known as trade winds blow on the surface toward the doldrums. The trade winds blow from the northeast in the northern hemisphere and from the southeast in the southern. They are well defined only over the oceans. Above them, in the upper troposphere, winds called anti-trades blow in the opposite direction, forming in part the upper return current for the trades.

(*f*) From the horse latitudes, prevailing winds known as the prevailing westerlies blow poleward at the surface toward the subpolar lows. In the northern hemisphere the winds blow from the southwest and in the southern from the northwest. They are not so steady or so strong as the trades.

(*g*) Easterly winds blow from the poles toward the subpolar lows.

The mean circulation conditions described above do not make it very clear just how the large convective heat transfers from the tropics to the poles are accomplished. Much, though not all, of this transfer takes place by a mechanism which, because of its sporadic nature, does not appear as a prominent part of the yearly average circulation. A description of this mechanism, which involves heat transfer by means of huge traveling cyclonic and anticyclonic wind systems, the moving "lows" and "highs" which are so prominent on the daily weather maps of the temperate zone, is given below.

*Air Masses, Fronts, Extratropical Cyclones, and Anticyclones.* Most variations of weather from day to day in the middle latitudes are due to the movement of vast whirls which may easily have diameters of 1500 miles. These whirls, known commonly as "lows" or "highs," are more properly described as extratropical cyclones and extratropical anticyclones respectively. The former is a region of low pressure and rising air, surrounded, in the northern hemisphere, by counterclockwise winds. It is attended frequently by storms, high winds, and rain. The centers of these whirls generally travel from west to east and away from the tropical regions, following the prevailing westerlies. The anticyclone, however, is a region of high pressure and descending air surrounded, in the northern hemisphere, by clockwise winds. It is usually attended by fair weather and light winds. In the southern hemisphere the wind directions are reversed. These huge traveling whirls, several of which are usually present simultaneously in each hemisphere, are a fundamental part of the general circulation and an important factor in the heat interchange from lower to higher latitudes.

The origin of extratropical cyclones has been worked out in broad principle by the Norwegian school of meteorologists headed by the father and son V. Bjerknes (1862– ) and J. A. B. Bjerknes (1897–  ). It depends on the fact that, if a certain body of air remains for a considerable time in the same locality, over a heated continent, say, or a large ocean area, it becomes homogeneous as to surface temperature, lapse rate, humidity, and other characteristics. Such a body of air is known to meteorologists as an *air mass*. The permanent highs of the subtropical anticyclone belts are typical sources for such air masses. In these regions the air is warm and moist. Other air-mass source regions, productive of cold dry air masses, are the seasonal semipermanent highs that occur over the northern parts of the continents in winter.

The relatively sharp transition zone between one air mass and a neighboring air mass of uniform but different properties is known as a *front*. As a result of some local disturbance, a tongue of warm air may protrude into the cold air mass, the first step in the production of an extratropical cyclone or "low," according to the model originally proposed by V. Bjerknes. The tongue may travel along the front, in which case it is known as a cyclone wave, or it may enlarge and break away from it entirely, a process known as occlusion. The paths followed by the individual air particles during the formation and subsequent motion of such disturbances are not simple to discover or to describe. Suffice it to say that the net result of the motions of the front and of the cyclone waves moving along it is the necessary transport of warm air poleward and cool air equatorward.

For a specific example of the formation of extratropical cyclones, consider the winter cyclones of the north Atlantic and the southeastern United States. Most of them originate off the southeastern coast of the United States along a front whose mean position extends from Florida towards England, known as the Atlantic Polar Front. South of this front in winter is a permanent high, centered over the south Atlantic at latitude 30°, a member of the subtropical anticyclone belt. The air here is moist, warm, and generally vertically unstable. The winds are in a clockwise direction. North of this front is air of polar origin over parts of the North American continent. It is colder, drier, and possesses greater vertical stability. The front separating these two air masses is the origin of many migratory extratropical cyclones that sweep northeastward, transporting tropical air toward the poles. Many other extratropical-cyclone source regions in the world are also associated with the subtropical anticyclone belts.

Extratropical cyclones must not be confused with tropical cyclones, which are also known as hurricanes—much smaller disturbances, attended by higher winds and greater local precipitation rates.

*Monsoons.* These are winds of continental extent and, though strongest in Asia, occur to some extent on all continents. The heat convectively transferred by monsoons, in Asia, is the dominant factor in determining the seasonal weather pattern there. In the northern hemisphere they greatly modify the general circulation previously described. They are seasonal winds, blowing on the surface from continent to ocean in winter and in the reverse direction in summer. As with all convective circulations of this type there are return currents in the reverse direction at higher levels. The cause of monsoons is temperature differences between land masses and the surrounding ocean, due primarily to the fact that temperature changes of the land extend to a depth of only a few meters while those of the oceans, because of vertical mixing, extend to considerably greater depths. Thus, during summer, the continent heats up more rapidly than the ocean. The air mass over the continent is heated from below and, being lighter, volume for volume, than the surrounding air at the same level over the cooler oceans, rises slowly. In other words, a seasonal "low" forms over the continent. Cool moist air moving in from the ocean to replace the rising air constitutes the summer monsoon.

*Sea and Land Breezes.* These are winds of quite local character, seldom extending more than 25 miles from shore either inland or out to sea. They are associated with the diurnal heating cycle and at the surface blow from land to sea at night and in the reverse direction during the day. In each instance there is a return current above the surface current and in the reverse direction. The cause is, as for monsoons, land-sea surface-temperature differences. Both are rather shallow breezes, rarely more than 500 m high.

## PROBLEMS

**1.** Is the flow laminar or turbulent under the following conditions:

| SUBSTANCE | PIPE INTERNAL DIAMETER cm | AVERAGE SPEED cm/sec | DENSITY gm/cm$^3$ | VISCOSITY gm/(cm sec) |
|---|---|---|---|---|
| Water | 1.0 | 1.0 | 1.0 | 0.01 |
| Air | 10 | 200 | 0.0012 | $180 \cdot 10^{-6}$ |
| Castor oil | 30 | 10 | 0.91 | 9.9 |

**2.** Water is flowing through a circular pipe 5.0 mm in internal diameter at a rate of 4.0 gal/hr. The variations of viscosity and density with temperature are given below. Plot the Reynolds number as a function of temperature.

| Temperature (°C) | 0 | 10 | 20 | 30 | 40 | 50 | 60 | 70 | 80 | 90 | 100 |
|---|---|---|---|---|---|---|---|---|---|---|---|
| Viscosity (100 gm/cm sec) | 1.79 | 1.31 | 1.01 | 0.80 | 0.66 | 0.55 | 0.47 | 0.41 | 0.36 | 0.32 | 0.28 |
| Density (gm/cm$^3$) | 1.00 | 1.00 | 1.00 | 1.00 | 0.99 | 0.99 | 0.98 | 0.98 | 0.97 | 0.97 | 0.96 |

**3.** In the example worked on p. 387 relate the overall heat-transfer coefficient $h'$ to the constants $k_w$, $k_s$, $d_w$, $d_s$, and $h$.

**4.** In the example worked on p. 387, what rate of heat transfer per unit area would result if the boiler scale were removed, assuming $h$ to remain unchanged? What rate would result if the thickness of the boiler wall were doubled, assuming no other changes?

**5.** Compute the rate of heat transfer per unit area by convection and conduction from room air at 25°C through a glass window 2.0 mm thick to outside air at −15°C. The film coefficient for each convective transfer is $0.95 \times 10^{-4}$ cal/(sec cm$^2$ C°), and the thermal conductivity of glass is 0.0025 cal/(sec cm$^2$ C°/cm). What is the temperature difference between the window surfaces?

**6.** In problem 5, what would be the heat-transfer rate per unit area and the window-surface temperature difference if there was a wind blowing parallel to the window and of such a speed that the film coefficient for the external convective transfer became $9.0 \times 10^{-4}$ cal/(sec cm$^2$ C°)? Assume that the film coefficient for the internal convective transfer remains the same.

**7.** From the isotherms of Fig. 8 compute the surface-temperature gradients and the rates of convective heat transfer per unit area at points around the cylinder spaced 30° apart. The thermal conductivity of air near the wall is 0.017 btu/(hr ft$^2$ F°/ft). What is the heat-transfer rate per unit length for the cylinder?

**8.** From the curve of Fig. 11, what is the rate of heat transfer per unit area by convection from a wire of 50-mil diameter at a temperature of 1000°C in air. The temperature of the surroundings is 30°C. The thermal conductivity and kinematic viscosity of air at the mean temperature 515°C are $1.3 \times 10^{-4}$ cal/(cm$^2$ sec C°/cm) and 0.78 cm$^2$/sec.

**9.** Using the data given in Table III, compute and graph the effective radiancy per unit area of the filament coils and the gas loss per unit area—in watts/mm$^2$ in each case—as functions of coil diameter.

**10.** Derive an expression for the thermal expansivity of an ideal gas for possible use in connection with Eq. 24.

**11.** Corresponding temperature and pressure values obtained during the ascent of the stratosphere balloon *Explorer II* are:

| AIR PRESSURE mm-Hg | AIR TEMPERATURE °C |
|---|---|
| 687.6 | 0 |
| 575.4 | −4.9 |
| 478.6 | −8.5 |
| 363.1 | −23.3 |
| 208.9 | −50.5 |
| 166.0 | −56.7 |
| 131.8 | −54.5 |
| 100.0 | −56.1 |
| 69.2 | −59.7 |
| 52.5 | −59.4 |
| 43.7 | −55.9 |
| 36.3 | −58.8 |
| 30.1 | −59.0 |

Compute the altitude above ground level corresponding to 30.1 mm-Hg, using Eq. 33. Data from *National Geographic Society Contributed Technical Papers*, Stratosphere Series 2, p. 217, 1936.

**12.** Suppose a cu ft of dry air at 70°F and 760 mm-Hg and in equilibrium with its surroundings to be lifted under adiabatic conditions a vertical distance of 500 ft at a place where the lapse rate is 5.0 C°/km. What are the direction and magnitude of the resultant force on the displaced mass of air in its new position, considering only buoyancy and gravity as forces? The density of dry air under standard conditions is 1.293 kg/m³. Assume the ideal-gas law.

**13.** Using the data of Table V, show that the mean annual net rate of heat transfer, averaged over the globe, is zero.

# CHAPTER XIII

## RADIANT ENERGY

**1. Introduction.** It is universally recognized that our main source of energy is the sun. The effects of a long period of daylight in summer, a shortened period in winter, direct exposure under unclouded skies, the shade of a tree on a hot summer's day—all testify in a very direct way to the magnitude of its influence. What it means in measurable terms is not so generally understood. The earth's disposition of the energy received is much less known.

Thanks in a large measure to the initial work directed by S. P. Langley (1834–1906) at the Allegheny Observatory in Pittsburgh and later as director of the Smithsonian Institution of Washington and by his successor at that institution, C. G. Abbot (1872– ), we know with fair accuracy the rate at which the earth receives energy from the sun both at the limits of our atmosphere and at the surface where we live. From observations taken regularly for many years in Africa, South America, and the United States at sea level, at moderate elevations, and on the tops of mountains, the magnitude and something of the variations of a quantity known as the solar constant have been determined. Its average value is ordinarily given as 1.94 cal/(cm$^2$ min). This means that, at the upper limit of the earth's atmosphere, radiant energy from the sun is being received on each square centimeter oriented normally toward the sun at the rate of 1.94 cal/min.

The magnitude of the solar constant is better appreciated when it is stated that the rate of receipt of energy is such that, if the radiation were incident normally on a layer of ice and all the radiant energy received were used in melting it, that ice would melt at the rate of 1.6 cm of thickness per hour. Expressed still differently, it states that, in a yard 50 ft square at sea level with the sun directly overhead and a 70% transmission for the atmosphere, the rate of reception corresponds to 265 hp. Expressed thus the rate seems somewhat startling. When, however, one computes the total rate of emission of radiant energy from the sun by multiplying the solar constant by the area of a sphere with a radius equal to the mean distance from sun to earth, and obtains a rate of emission equivalent to the melting of ice at the

413

rate of a 12.5-km cube per second; and, when still further, one considers that the sun has sent out radiant energy at approximately this same rate for more than a billion years, he is somewhat appalled by the immensity of the sun's supply.

Of the radiant energy received during past geologic ages, the earth has saved but little. A large part of it is reflected into space. From brightness measurements of the sun and of the moon at times of solar eclipse and of full moon, 29% has been obtained for the fraction of the visible radiant energy which is reflected by the earth out into space to the moon. Nearly all the remaining 71% is reradiated into space. That which is stored during spring and early summer is very largely reradiated during fall and early winter. What there has been in the way of complete storage, a very small fraction of the whole, has been brought about largely by means of plant and animal life, and is represented by the fuel value of our forests, coal mines, and oil and gas fields. At a time when these natural fuel resources are being used so rapidly, it is comforting to know that some of the energy which is being reradiated into space may be trapped by artificial means and made to serve mankind. In fact, means for doing this economically are under study now.

Radiation as a process is universal, and it is to be expected that industry as well as nature would count on it. The most evident industrial example is our artificial light sources, but others occur in home-heating devices, in insect- and bacteria-killing devices, in the boilers of power plants, in the heating devices of distillation and fractionation systems, and elsewhere.

Radiation as a general term covers at least four separate divisions of study: (1) temperature radiation, that which is determined by the nature of the emitter and its temperature; (2) luminescent radiation, that which is determined by the nature of the emitter and of factors other than its temperature; (3) X-ray radiation; and (4) nuclear radiation, that which is associated with fundamental-particle emission, X-rays, and atomic nuclear structure. In this book, in conformity with the foregoing introductory remarks, we are concerned only with temperature radiation. Further, we shall limit ourselves largely to a discussion of the thermal or energy phases, ignoring except incidentally the luminous, the photoelectric, and other phases which are highly important in other fields.

In this chapter, we shall consider some of the principles and laws governing the radiation process, the distribution of the energy radiated with respect to frequency or wavelength, the absorption process, and associated methods of measurement.

**2. Electromagnetic Concept of Radiation.**   That radiant energy is electromagnetic in nature is a concept sponsored by the great Scotch physicist J. Clerk Maxwell (1831–1879).   Conceived in pre-quantum days, it is still found of great value and is much used.   As shown in Fig. 1, each wave train or photon is thought to consist of vibratory electric and magnetic disturbances which are in phase and move through space in a direction perpendicular to those disturbances. According to the quantum theory the region of appreciable disturbance for a single photon would seem to be rather limited.   A more exact statement of photon characteristics must be left for the future.

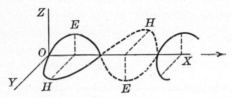

Fɪɢ. 1.   Diagram of an electromagnetic wave, moving in the positive direction along the $X$-axis of the coordinate system.   At all points, the electric field strength $E$, the magnetic field strength $H$, and the direction of propagation are at right angles to one another.

**3. Temperature Radiation a Universal Characteristic.**   The process of emission of radiant energy by a body which depends on its temperature is called temperature radiation.   More often the term is used to represent the radiant energy emitted.   The context will always indicate in which sense the term is being used.

To explain simply the phenomena of temperature radiation, it is universally assumed that all bodies at all times are emitting such radiations into the space about them and are absorbing, partially at least, those radiations originating elsewhere which are incident upon them. This assumption is often referred to as Prévost's theory of exchange after the Swiss physicist Pierre Prévost (1751–1839), who enunciated the theory in 1792.

Consider a body, hot or cold, suspended by a very fine thread or wire in an evacuated chamber with opaque walls maintained at a given constant temperature.   Experience indicates that the body will eventually assume the temperature of the enclosing walls.   This result is in no way dependent on the slight amount of heat which the thread may conduct from the body to the wall or in the reverse direction.   To account for this attainment of thermal equilibrium in a simple manner, Prévost's theory seems indispensable.   If the body inside the chamber is initially hot, relatively, it cools down because it radiates or emits energy to its surroundings more rapidly than it absorbs radiant energy which comes to it from its surroundings; if initially cool, it heats up because its rate of emission of energy is then less than its rate of absorption. When equilibrium is reached, the rates of emission and absorption are equal.

Nearly all the temperature radiation from ordinary terrestrial objects is infra-red, but many sources such as incandescent-lamp filaments, red-hot coals, and luminous gas flames yield radiations with appreciable but generally small portions in the visible region.

**4. Radiant-Energy Nomenclature and Definitions.** In the study of radiant energy, certain terms have been devised to describe certain measurable quantities expressible in terms of physical units. Of these,

TABLE

RADIANT ENERGY AND ANALOGOUS LIGHT

See footnote † for the significance of the various subscripts.

| Symbol | Term or Quantity | Definition | Common Units |
|---|---|---|---|
| $U$ | Radiant energy | | erg, joule |
| $u$ | Radiant energy density | $dU/dV$ | joule/m$^3$ |
| $\varphi, P$ | Radiant flux | $dU/dt$ | watt |
| $(\omega)$ | (Solid angle) ‡ | | (str) |
| $J$ | Radiant intensity of a source | $d\varphi_e/d\omega$ | watt/str |
| $\mathcal{R}$ | Radiancy § of a source | $d\varphi_e/dA$ | watt/cm$^2$ |
| $W$ | Radiant flux density (not cf a source) | $d\varphi/dA$ | watt/cm$^2$ |
| $\mathcal{B}, N$ | Steradiancy § of a source | $dJ/dA_p$ | watt/(cm$^2$ str) |
| | | $d\mathcal{R}/d\omega$ | |
| $\mathcal{E}, H$ | Irradiancy § of a surface | $J \cos \theta'/l^2$ | watt/cm$^2$ |
| | | $d\varphi_i/dA$ | |
| $\rho$ | Radiant total reflectance ‖ | $\varphi_r/\varphi_i$ | 1 |
| $\alpha$ | Radiant total absorptance ‖ | $\varphi_a/\varphi_i$ | 1 |
| $\tau$ | Radiant total transmittance ‖ | $\varphi_t/\varphi_i$ | 1 |
| $\epsilon$ | Radiant total emittance ‖ | $\mathcal{R}/\mathcal{R}_b$ | 1 |
| $\rho'$ | Radiant total reflectivity ‖ | $\varphi_r/\varphi_i$ | 1 |
| $\alpha'$ | Radiant total absorptivity ‖ | $\varphi_a/\varphi_i$ | 1 |
| $\epsilon'$ | Radiant total emissivity ‖ | $\mathcal{R}/\mathcal{R}_b$ | 1 |

* Obviously a similar table might be constructed which would involve spectral terms, their symbols, definitions, and units. In addition to having the word spectral appear before each term, the remaining principal differences consist in having $\lambda$ (wavelength) or $\nu$ (frequency) attached to all symbols and in having an appropriate $\lambda$ or $\nu$ interval included in the denominator of many units. In contrast to total transmissivity, spectral transmissivity has significance.

† Subscript $e$ indicates that the $\varphi$ or $F$ concerned is an emergent flux associated with a source. Subscript $i$ indicates that the $\varphi$ or $F$ concerned is an incident flux associated with a specified surface. Subscript $p$ indicates that the element of area concerned $dA_p$ is a projected area and is equal to the element of area $dA$ multiplied

those important in the discussion that follows are listed in Table I, together with their symbols, their definitions, and some of their more common units of measurement; and, because of the great similarity of its nomenclature structure, similar material is listed for the field of light. It is hoped that the parallel listings will help to fix better the material for both divisions in the minds of the readers.

For the sake of a better comprehension of the quantities in Table I, let us make application to a particular source of radiant energy and the radiant energy emitted by it. Consider a uniform, 100-watt, spherical source whose diameter is just 1.0 cm. Unless otherwise specifically stated, let the term source in what follows in this section refer to the one just described.

I

TERMS, SYMBOLS, DEFINITIONS, AND UNITS *

| Symbol | Term or Quantity | Definition | Common Units |
|--------|------------------|------------|--------------|
| $\int F\,dt$ | Light | $\int F\,dt$ | lumen-hour |
| $F$ | Luminous flux | | lumen |
| $(\omega)$ | (Solid angle) ‡ | | (str) |
| $I$ | Luminous intensity of a source | $dF_i/d\omega$ | lum/str, candle |
| $B$ | Brightness of a source | $dI/dA_p$ | c/cm$^2$, lambert |
| $E$ | Illumination of a surface | $I\cos\theta'/l^2$ | ft-c, lux |
| $\rho$ | Luminous total reflectance ‖ | $F_r/F_i$ | 1 |
| $\alpha$ | Luminous total absorptance ‖ | $F_a/F_i$ | 1 |
| $\tau$ | Luminous total transmittance ‖ | $F_t/F_i$ | 1 |
| $\epsilon$ | Luminous total emittance ‖ | $B/B_b$ | 1 |
| $\rho'$ | Luminous total reflectivity ‖ | $F_r/F_i$ | 1 |
| $\alpha'$ | Luminous total absorptivity ‖ | $F_a/F_i$ | 1 |
| $\epsilon'$ | Luminous total emissivity ‖ | $B/B_b$ | 1 |

by the cosine of the angle between its normal and the direction under consideration. Subscript $b$ refers to a corresponding quantity for a blackbody source at the same temperature. Subscripts $r$, $a$, $t$ indicate that the $\varphi$ or $F$ concerned are reflected, absorbed, or transmitted fluxes.

‡ The solid angle concept and the steradian (str) unit are included here because of the general unfamiliarity regarding them. See text for definitions.

§ The –ancy terms indicate a characteristic or an effect per unit surface area.

‖ The -ance terms strictly refer to bodies; the -ivity terms to substances and are independent of the sizes or shapes of bodies which are composed of them. Symbols are the same for the radiant and the luminous terms. A total transmissivity is without significance. Usually the words "Radiant" and "Luminous" are omitted when referring to these terms. The context is usually relied upon to show which is meant.

The terms radiant energy and radiant energy density hardly need discussion. The term radiant flux, however, needs some attention. Flux (from Latin *fluvius*, river) is used in science in several senses, not all of which are associated with concepts of something flowing. Here, however, there is a definite picture of radiant energy flowing out from a source, and the rate of that flow is the quantity which is spoken of as radiant flux. We may refer to the radiant flux through a specified opening or window, incident on a specified surface, or emergent from a source. Radiant flux is a power unit. The defining equation is

$$\varphi = \frac{dU}{dt} \tag{1}$$

A natural unit is the watt, and the radiant flux from our specified source is 100 watts. Unfortunately, many use the term radiant flux as though it were energy rather than a time derivative of energy. Regardless of this lack of a suitable language habit, the reader should keep in mind that radiant flux is a particular time rate.

Solid angle is the term used to denote the spacial opening subtended at the apex of a pyramid or cone which is bounded by its lateral surface. Its magnitude is determined by the ratio of the subtended portion of a spherical surface with center at the apex, which is determined by the intersection of that spherical surface with the sides of the cone or pyramid, $A$, to the square of the radius of that spherical surface, $r$. A section of the cone or pyramid may be highly irregular. The defining equation is

$$\omega = \frac{A}{r^2} \tag{2}$$

The normal unit for a solid angle is the steradian. It is a solid angle with a subtended spherical surface, whose center is at the apex of the angle, which is equal to that of a square one side of which is equal to the radius of the spherical surface. The solid angles determined by the walls and floor or ceiling of an ordinary room are all equal to $\pi/2$ steradians. A hemispherical solid angle is similarly equal to $2\pi$ steradians, and a total sphere angle (rather than a spherical angle, a term which has a different significance in solid geometry) equals $4\pi$ steradians. The steradian is often referred to as the unit solid angle. Another unit, much used in astronomy, is the square degree.

The radiant intensity of a source, $J$, is defined by

$$J = \frac{d\varphi_e}{d\omega} \tag{3}$$

of which $d\varphi_e$ represents the emergent flux from the source through the element of solid angle $d\omega$ in the direction determined by the axis of that $d\omega$. The $J$ of our specified 100-watt spherical source 1 cm in diameter is 100 watts/$4\pi$ str, or 7.96 watts/str. Had the source not been uniform, the $J$ would have varied with the direction under consideration. In such cases, particularly if the source is a plane source and $J$ is symmetrical with respect to the normal to the surface, the symbol used is $J_\theta$, the $\theta$ representing the angle between the normal and the direction concerned. The analogous light quantity $I$ is called luminous intensity.

The radiancy of a source, $\mathcal{R}$, is defined by

$$\mathcal{R} = \frac{d\varphi_e}{dA} \tag{4}$$

of which $d\varphi_e$ represents the emergent flux from an element of the source, all directions included, and $dA$ the area of that element. The $\mathcal{R}$ of our specified source is evidently 100 watts/$\pi$ cm$^2$ or 31.8 watts/cm$^2$. In connection with non-uniform sources, one speaks of average radiancies. The analogous light quantity is seldom used and has not received an accepted name.

Radiant flux density, $W$, is a term used to represent radiant flux per unit area in case the area selected is other than part of a source. A window through which radiant flux from the sun enters is an illustration. However, thinking of such a window as a secondary source emitting radiant energy throughout a limited solid angle, we may then speak of its radiancy, and the value of such radiancy would exactly equal the radiant flux density at the window.

The steradiancy of a source, $\mathcal{B}$ (or $N$), is defined by

$$\mathcal{B} = \frac{dJ}{dA_p} = \frac{1}{\cos\theta}\frac{dJ}{dA} \tag{5}$$

of which $dA_p$ represents an element of projected area, that is the projection of the element of area concerned on a plane surface perpendicular to the direction under consideration, and is equal to $dA\cos\theta$.

Combining Eqs. 3, 4, and 5 leads to another expression for $\mathcal{B}$, namely

$$\mathcal{B} = \frac{1}{\cos\theta}\frac{d\mathcal{R}}{d\omega} \tag{6}$$

This form is of importance when dealing with sources which do not conform with Lambert's cosine law (see p. 437). However, if the source conforms with Lambert's cosine law, as has been assumed tacitly for our special uniform source, Eq. 6 may be simplified to yield

$$\mathcal{B} = \frac{\mathcal{R}}{\pi \ \text{str}} \tag{6a}$$

Comparing $\mathcal{B}$ with $J$ and $\mathcal{R}$, we note that steradiancy, $\mathcal{B}$, differs from radiant intensity, $J$, in expressing the radiant intensity per unit projected area, and from radiancy, $\mathcal{R}$, in expressing the output rate of radiant energy per unit of projected area and unit solid angle rather than just the output rate per unit of actual area. We note further that, whereas the radiant intensity of a source is a function of the size of the source, its steradiancy and its radiancy are not. A small tungsten filament at 2500°K possesses the same steradiancy for a specified angle of emission and the same radiancy as does a large filament at the same temperature.

The steradiancy of our specified uniform source in accord with Eqs. 5 and 6a is either $\dfrac{7.96 \ \text{watt/str}}{\pi/4 \ \text{cm}^2}$ or $\dfrac{31.8 \ \text{watt/cm}^2}{\pi \ \text{str}}$, both of which reduce to 10.13 watt/(str cm²). It is interesting to note that, though there are $2\pi$ str to a hemispherical angle and though steradiancy is radiancy per unit solid angle, the steradiancy of a uniform source is the radiancy of the source divided by $\pi$ str. This is a consequence of the fact that an element of area seen from different directions varies in apparent size or projected area. As may be shown, the average value of the projected area of a plane source, viewed from all possible directions on one side, is just one-half of its actual area, hence the division by $\pi$ str, as shown in Eq. 6a, rather than by $2\pi$ str.

Most sources of radiation are not uniform and yield different steradiancies in different directions. The analogous light quantity is brightness $B$.

The irradiancy of a surface, $\mathcal{E}$ (or $H$), describes its rate of receiving radiant energy per unit of area. It is defined by

$$\mathcal{E} = \frac{d\varphi_i}{dA} \tag{7}$$

of which $d\varphi_i$ is radiant flux incident at the area $dA$ whose irradiancy is desired. Like radiancy it is measured in watt/cm². It is analogous to illumination in light, $E$. An irradiancy may be measured directly on the basis of Eq. 7 or it may be computed provided the radiant intensities of the sources irradiating it, their distances, and the orientations of the area $dA$ with respect to those directions are known.

Thus, for the irradiancy of an element of surface at a distance $l$ from a source whose radiant intensity is $J$, when the angle between the normal to the surface and the line joining the center of the surface and the source is $\theta'$, we have

$$\varepsilon = \frac{d\varphi_i}{dA} = \frac{J/l^2\, dA \cos\theta'}{dA} = \frac{J \cos\theta'}{l^2} \tag{8}$$

By means of Eq. 8, we may compute the irradiancy of a surface 2.0 m from our specified source when the orientation angle $\theta'$ is, say, 20°. Substitution yields (7.96 watt/str $\times$ .940)/4.0 m² or 1.87 watt/str m², or 1.87 watt/(m² of irradiated surface). Here, in accord with the definition of a solid angle which indicates that a solid angle times a radius squared equals the area of an intercepted spherical surface, we have replaced str $\times$ (1 m of radius)² by 1 m² of intercepted spherical surface. Irradiancies from various sources often add to produce a measured value.

The other radiant-energy terms of Table I will be taken up later as they are met in the chapter.

**5. Instruments for Measuring Radiant Energy.** We limit the discussion here to those instruments which respond to the energy or heating effects of radiant energy. Depending on circumstances we are sometimes interested in the heating effects of all wavelengths taken collectively, and, at other times, on the corresponding effects for limited ranges of wavelength including those ranges which are referred to as spectral. When spectral ranges are under consideration, spectrometers are generally used for their production.

There are two general groups of radiation detectors used in conjunction with radiation-measuring devices, the non-selective and the selective. As non-selective detectors, those whose efficiencies depend but little on the spectral characters of the radiation being measured, listed in the order of their invention, we have the thermocouple and thermopile, the radiometer, the bolometer, the radiomicrometer, and the pyrheliometer. As selective detectors, those whose efficiencies depend on the spectral character of the incident radiation, we have the eye, the photographic plate, the selenium cell, the photovoltaic cell, and the photoelectric cell. The former group of detectors may be and are used for the measurement of the radiation of all wavelengths taken together or spectrally, whereas the latter group may be used with safety only in measuring the radiation for limited ranges of wavelength or spectrally.

The *thermopile* is a combination of two or more thermocouples joined in series with all similar hot junctions close to one another in a line

or a plane and all similar cold junctions in another line or two lines
or in a plane or so disposed as to be protected from radiation that
should not impinge on them when the thermopile is in use.  Usually,
if high sensitivity is required, the thermocouple or thermopile is used
with a galvanometer.  Ordinarily the deflections are rather closely
proportional to the thermal emf's developed.  Where the demand for
sensitivity is not so great, the emf's are frequently measured with the
aid of a potentiometer.

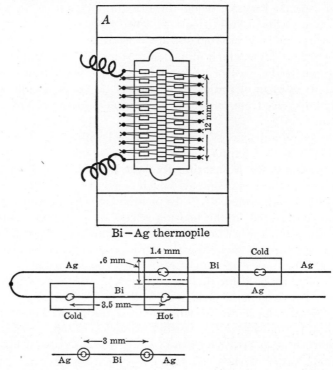

FIG. 2.  Details of a silver-bismuth linear thermopile as described by W. W. Coblentz (by permission, *Measurements of Radiant Energy*, ed. by W. E. Forsythe,
pp. 195–196, New York, McGraw-Hill Book Co., 1937).

In the construction of a thermopile, several factors are to be considered if great
sensitivity is demanded.  The choice of materials is most important.  At first thought,
one would be inclined to choose those two metals whose change of thermal emf per
unit change of temperature is greatest, but there are other features which may alter
one's considered choice.  Some conclusions arrived at from theoretical consideration,
as stated by the physicists Altenkirch and Johansen, indicate "that (1) the galvanometer resistance should be equal to the resistance of the thermo-elements; (2) the
radii of the two wires of the thermo-element should be so chosen that the ratio between the heat conductivity and the electrical resistance is the same in both; (3) the

heat loss by conduction through the wires must equal the heat loss by radiation from the junctions . . . ; (4) the radiation sensitivity is proportional to the square root of the exposed surface." It is apparent that dimensions as well as possible construction techniques are important.

Fig. 2 shows details of a highly sensitive silver-bismuth thermopile as described by Coblentz (1873–   ) of the Bureau of Standards in Washington. The wires are very small; the bismuth 0.1 mm in diameter is only 3.5 mm long, the silver 0.04 mm in diameter is only about 10 mm long. The thin receiver surfaces are of tin 0.18 to 0.20 mm thick. Each offers an exposed area 1.4 mm by 0.6 mm for the interception of radiation. The under surface of the receiving area and the wires are covered lightly with shellac. The receiving surface itself is blackened. For this purpose, camphor soot has been much used in the past, but a fine metallic powder appears to be better. A thin coating of zinc black is said by Pfund (1879–   ), of Johns Hopkins University, to have a fairly uniform absorptance of 98% from the ultraviolet to beyond 14 $\mu$ in the infra-red. For the highest sensitivity a thermopile should be mounted in a vacuum.

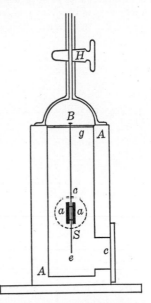

FIG. 3. E. F. Nichols' vane radiometer (by permission, *Measurements of Radiant Energy*, ed. by W. E. Forsythe, p. 198, New York, McGraw-Hill Book Co., 1937).

The *radiometer* dates back to 1876 to a study undertaken by the English physicist Sir William Crookes (1832–1919). Later, in 1900 and 1901, studies of radiation pressure using such an instrument were made by P. N. Lebedew (1866–1911) in Russia and E. F. Nichols (1869–1924) and G. F. Hull (1870–   ) at Dartmouth College in America. Fig. 3 shows a radiometer built by Nichols. As described by Spence (1883–   ) of Northwestern University, "The outer case consisted of a bronze cylinder bored to within a few millimeters of the bottom. A glass cover B fitted with a stopcock was ground to fit the top of the case. The suspended vane system consisted of two mica vanes a and a held together by small glass rods and the whole fastened to a vertical glass staff S. At the bottom end of the staff was a small mirror. This system with a mass of a few milligrams was hung (a very fine quartz fiber was used) from a glass strip placed across the top of the case. The bronze case was provided with two openings for windows: that indicated by the dotted circle was covered with a fluorite plate and that at c was covered with a glass plate to admit light for the illumination of the small mirror. The assembly was then pumped out to a pressure of about 0.02 mm-Hg.

"Radiation was allowed to fall on one vane only while the other was shielded and served as a compensator for stray radiation. Nichols found with this instrument that the radiation from a candle at a distance of 6 m gave a deflection of the vane system of 60 mm as registered on a scale at a distance of 1.3 m from the instrument."

Modifications of the Nichols radiometer have usually consisted of changes in vane construction, leading to lower moments of inertia, shorter periods, and higher sensitivities. At different times pearled mica, aluminum foil, thin paper, and fly wings

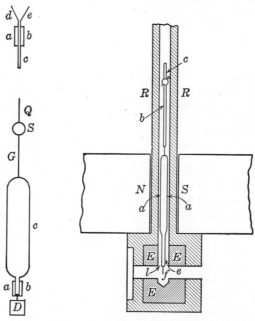

Fig. 4.   Paschen's radiomicrometer (by permission, *Measurements of Radiant Energy*, ed. by W. E. Forsythe, p. 205, New York, McGraw-Hill Book Co., 1937).

have been used as vanes. Suspended systems with masses less than a milligram have been obtained. Compared with the thermopile-galvanometer combination, the radiometer has both advantages and disadvantages. For a typical case, a sensitivity of $4.6 \times 10^{-9}$ watt/(mm deflection at 1 m) was obtained. The area of a vane was 5.02 mm$^2$.

The theory of operation of the radiometer is involved. In use, radiation is permitted to fall on one vane only, where, depending on the condition of the vane surface, it may be largely absorbed or reflected. In either case, provided the gas pressure is of the order of 0.02 to 0.03 mm-Hg, the net force experienced by the vane is directed toward the source of the incoming radiation and not oppositely as one might expect. If the pressure is considerably reduced and, in particular, if reduced to a high vacuum, the thrust experienced by the vane is oppositely directed and much smaller in magnitude. Radiometers have been much used in measuring radiation pressures, stellar spectra, and infra-red terrestrial spectra.

*The radiomicrometer* is essentially a moving-coil galvanometer with the coil of a single turn of wire supported between the poles of an electromagnet by a quartz fiber. A wire of copper or of silver ordinarily forms by far the larger part of the coil and connects near the bottom to the two cold junctions of a thermocouple which completes the circuit. The thermocouple wires of dissimilar metals which are fused together to form the hot junction are generally quite short.

Fig. 4 shows a radiomicrometer constructed by the German physicist Friederich Paschen (1865– ). The following is a brief description by Spence. "Two alloys were prepared, one of bismuth and antimony in the ratio of 10:1, and the other of equal parts of cadmium and antimony. A strip 0.3 by 0.5 by 5 mm was made from each of the alloys. One of each of these (*a* and *b*) is soldered to each end of a silver band *c* 0.5 mm wide and 0.03 mm thick and sufficiently long to make the galvanometer loop. The loop was formed and the strips of alloy soldered together to form a thermojunction just above *D*, the damping vane of thin mica. A very thin glass rod *G* is fastened to the upper end of the loop and carries a mirror *S*. The whole ensemble was supported by a fine quartz fiber, *Q*. The thermocouple was suspended in an iron block *E*, which in turn was enclosed in a copper block. A hole was drilled in the blocks to admit radiation. The silver loop was hung inside of a copper tube *R* which had a window for illumination of the mirror. Powerful magnetic pole pieces *N* and *S* were placed up against the copper tubing, but it was soon found that there was an optimum field strength for a particular instrument which gave the highest sensitivity."

In operation, radiant energy falling on the thermocouple hot junction produces an emf, and this, in turn, a current through the suspended coil. Because of the smallness of the resistance, relatively large currents and a fairly high sensitivity result. The instrument is little used.

*The bolometer*, as described by Aldrich (1884– ) of the Smithsonian Institution in Washington, "was devised by Langley (1834–1906) in 1880 when at the Allegheny Observatory in Pittsburgh. It consists essentially of two nearly identical, very thin strips of metal, usually platinum, which form two arms of a Wheatstone bridge. These strips are cut initially to correspond to a desired width of slit or purity of spectrum. They are blackened on one side only. In use one strip only is exposed to the radiation to be measured while the other is protected from it. With the bolometer bridge initially balanced, absorption of energy by one of the strips results in raising its temperature, increasing its electrical resistance, and destroying the bridge balance. A deflection of the galvanometer results. The shape of the absorbing surface of the bolometer, the narrow strip similar to a slit image, is decidedly favorable for spectroradiometry.

"In early work the bolometer was difficult to manipulate because of a very large uncontrolled drift of the galvanometer spot. Many improvements, mainly introduced by Abbot, have now made the bolometer a docile and easily handled instrument. One improvement—placing the bolometer strips inside a glass enclosure which is evacuated to less than 0.001 mm pressure—produced nearly tenfold increase in sensitiveness." A diagram showing the construction of a vacuum bolometer which has been much used by the Smithsonian Astrophysical Observatory is given in Fig. 5. The platinum strips are located in the evacuated chamber between the two short side tubes which have been sealed to the longer main tube that rises from the large spherical bulb. The ends of the side tube are optically figured glass plates. The radiation entering from one side passes through a tube provided with various sized slots to prevent radiation regularly reflected from the side walls from entering. The bolometer strips, made from 0.025-mm platinum wire, were hammered out between steel flats to a width of 0.12 mm. The lengths of strip used were 16 mm. Each

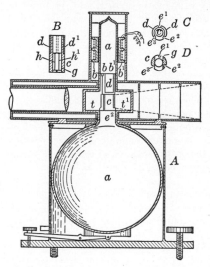

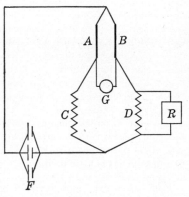

FIG. 5. Vacuum bolometer of the Smithsonian Astrophysical Observatory (by permission, *Measurements of Radiant Energy*, ed. by W. E. Forsythe, p. 208, New York, McGraw-Hill Book Co., 1937).

FIG. 6. Bolometer circuit (by permission, *Measurement of Radiant Energy*, ed. by W. E. Forsythe, p. 209, New York, McGraw-Hill Book Co., 1937).

had a resistance of about 3 ohms. The manganin wires of 54 ohms each shown at $C$ and $D$ in Fig. 6 are shown as two coils about the neck of the flask in Fig. 5 next to the side tubes mentioned above.

In operation the current passing through the bolometer bridge heats the platinum strips to about 50 C° above their surroundings. The bolometer, as a Wheatstone bridge, is balanced by varying $R$ of Fig. 6. One strip only, $A$ or $B$, is exposed at one time to the radiation being measured. The intensity of the entering beam may be measured in terms of the galvanometer deflection produced or of the change in the resistance of $R$ of Fig. 6 necessary for restoring balance. Calibration is made by exposing the bolometer to a source of known radiant intensity.

The *pyrheliometer* is an instrument for measuring solar radiation. At least four types of instruments have been used in conjunction with the solar observation work of the Smithsonian Institution. Two of them may be considered absolute instruments, whereas the other two are comparison instruments which are calibrated by comparing their indications with those of the absolute instruments. The two absolute instruments are known as the water-stir and the water-flow pyrheliometers. The other two are known as the Abbot silver-disk and the

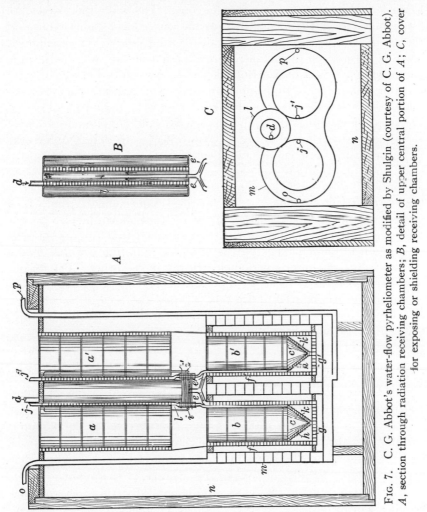

FIG. 7. C. G. Abbot's water-flow pyrheliometer as modified by Shulgin (courtesy of C. G. Abbot). *A*, section through radiation receiving chambers; *B*, detail of upper central portion of *A*; *C*, cover for exposing or shielding receiving chambers.

Knut Johan Ångström (1857–1910) electrically compensated pyrheliometers, the latter after the Swedish physicist of that name.

Of the two absolute pyrheliometers, the water-flow instrument, as designed by Abbot of the Smithsonian Institution and improved by Shulgin, is taken as the primary standard. It consists in part (Fig. 7) of two identical cylindrical chambers with blackened interior walls.

Each cavity is completely closed except for an opening at one end through which radiation may enter. The wall at the opposite end is cone-shaped to insure the practically complete absorption of radiant energy incident from the outside. A spiral coil of manganin wire is located next to and just outside the cone. The walls themselves are water-flow labyrinths so shaped that the water passes spirally around the cavity and absorbs from the walls of the chamber the heat developed by absorption of radiant energy. Each of the two chambers is mounted in a Dewar flask. Both flasks are maintained externally at a constant temperature by a separate stream of tapwater. A thermopile with its so-called hot junctions inserted near the outlet of one of the water-flow labyrinths and its so-called cold junction in a corresponding position in the other labyrinth serves to detect differences in temperature between the two heat-absorbing streams. In operation, while one and only one chamber is receiving radiant energy from the outside, the coil of manganin wire about the cone of the other is heated electrically. The rate of heating maintained is that which yields a zero deflection for a galvanometer (not shown in Fig. 7) connected with the thermopile. It is then assumed that the rate of heat production in one chamber by the entering radiation is equal to the corresponding rate of production electrically in the other. The former of these two rates is given by the product of the irradiancy of the chamber orifice produced by the sun, $\mathcal{E}_s$, and the area of that orifice, $A$. The latter of these two rates is given by the electrical power developed, $P$. Whence

$$\mathcal{E}_s = \frac{P}{A} \tag{9}$$

In practice, solar radiation is received alternately in one chamber and then in the other. For a series of readings, the first and the last measurements are made with the same chamber receiving radiation in order that the average value for one chamber as a radiation receiver shall correspond to the same instant of time as that for the other average value. Finally, of course, the average of the averages is accepted in determining the solar irradiancy. By this reciprocating arrangement of taking of averages, allowance is made for any possible differences in the magnitudes of the two heat-absorbing streams, variations in their entering temperatures, variations in the temperatures of their surroundings, and differences in the areas $A$.

The water-stir pyrheliometer differs from the water-flow instrument in that it has only one absorbing chamber and in that the same water is used throughout the experiment. This water is thoroughly stirred. Using this apparatus the rate of change of temperature of the stirred water $\Delta T/\Delta t$ is noted, when solar radiation is allowed to enter. Then one seeks the necessary electrical power, without solar radiation entering, to produce the same $\Delta T/\Delta t$.

The Abbot silver-disk pyrheliometer, as the name implies, has a silver disk as an important feature. As can be seen in Fig. 8, a thick disk which is well blackened on one face for radiation absorption has been drilled radially to receive the bulb of a mercury-in-glass thermometer. Actually the hole is closely fitted with a thin steel tube closed at the inner end, and mercury fills the space between the steel and the glass of the bulb. Some soft wick and wax are used to keep this mercury from leaking or spilling out. In use, one follows a certain program of temperature readings, involving alternate exposure of the disk to, and protection from, solar radiation. The temperature differences obtained, once the instrument has been calibrated with the aid of a water-flow pyrheliometer, can be translated into actual values for $\varepsilon_s$. The silver-disk instrument is thus a secondary instrument. The instrument is readily portable, relatively cheap, and quick operating, suited, where the absolute instrument is not, for the collection of data regularly at various stations in a broad program of study of solar radiation.

Ångström's electrically compensated pyrheliometer consists essentially of two equal platinum strips blackened on one side. At their centers on the unblackened sides, but separated from them by thin paper, the junctions of a sensitive thermocouple are attached. Either strip may be heated electrically. In operation one strip only is exposed

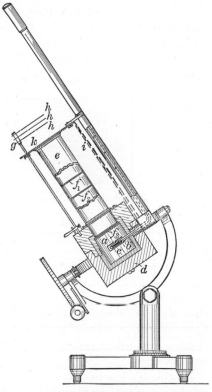

FIG. 8.   C. G. Abbot's silver-disk pyrheliometer (*Smithsonian Miscellaneous Collection*, **56,** 19, 1922).

to radiation while the other is heated electrically, until their central temperatures are the same as indicated by the thermocouple. As a first approximation, the rate of receipt of radiant energy per unit of area by the one strip is then equal to the rate of production of heat electrically per unit of area in the other strip. Failure of the blackening to yield complete absorption and failure to produce the same distribution of temperature along the strips by the two methods of heating accounts in a large measure for the failure of this pyrheliometer to yield satisfactory, absolute values. Calibrated against an absolute instrument it is a convenient instrument for actual observations.

### 6. Kirchhoff's Law.

This law stated in 1858 by the German physicist G. R. Kirchhoff (1824–1887), relates quantitatively the radiating and absorbing properties and processes of bodies. It is the most fundamental of all laws concerned purely with radiation. All others depend upon it. Its significance qualitatively may be shown readily. For this, we may use an ordinary electric hot plate whose heating element has been covered with a plate of unglazed porcelain and whose holes have been filled with a paste of water glass and Carborundum.* Viewed in a darkened room by its own light when heated, the Carborundum-filled portions appear bright against the dimmer background of unglazed porcelain. Viewed in a well-lighted room by the light of other sources, the Carborundum-filled portions appear, as

Fig. 9.    A piece of pottery viewed by reflected light (left) and by its own incandescent radiations (by permission, University of Pittsburgh Physics Staff, *An Outline of Atomic Physics*, 2nd ed., p. 54, New York, John Wiley & Sons, 1937).

ordinarily, dark against a relatively light background. The parts that are good absorbers of light and appear relatively dark by reflected light appear relatively bright by their own incandescent radiations. A piece of broken pottery (Fig. 9) is also convenient for the demonstration.

Kirchhoff's law may be derived theoretically and simply. It is based on the experimental fact that a body, inserted in a completely enclosed cavity whose walls are opaque and maintained at some constant temperature throughout, will eventually assume that temperature and thus come into equilibrium with those walls. Consider two opaque bodies in such an enclosure under equilibrium conditions. Let one body $b$ be a perfect or complete absorber of radiation, that is, a blackbody. Let the other body $n$ be only a partial absorber of radiation, therefore a non-blackbody. The reflectance of $b$, $\rho_b$, is necessarily zero while that of $n$, $\rho_n$, or simply $\rho$, must be finite. Since there is equilibrium, the rate of incidence of radiant energy at any given element of surface of $b$ or $n$ must equal the rate of departure of radiant energy

* Carborundum is a protected trade name for the product manufactured by the Carborundum Company, Niagara, New York.

from that same element of surface. Further, since equilibrium is in no way dependent on where bodies $b$ and $n$ may be in the enclosure, the rates of incidence and of departure per unit of area must be the same for all parts of both bodies. For the blackbody, this means that the irradiancy, $\mathcal{E}_b$—rate of incidence of radiant energy per unit of surface area—of its surface by radiant energy from the surrounding walls is equal to its own radiancy $\mathcal{R}_b$—its rate of emission of radiant energy per unit of area on account of its own temperature—that is,

$$\mathcal{E}_b = \mathcal{R}_b \tag{10}$$

a condition which insured that the radiation throughout the opaque enclosure at constant temperature is blackbody radiation. That this is the case will be made more evident later. For the non-blackbody, the relation is not so simple. Though the irradiancy of its surface is also $\mathcal{E}_b$, and though its *apparent* radiancy is equal to $\mathcal{R}_b$, only a portion of this latter quantity is ascribable to the non-blackbody. A certain part $\rho\mathcal{E}_b$ is due to the reflection of incident radiant energy. Here we may write

$$\mathcal{E}_b = \rho\mathcal{E}_b + \mathcal{R}_n \tag{11}$$

The remaining part of $\mathcal{E}_b$, namely, $(1 - \rho)\mathcal{E}_b$, is obviously associated with the absorption of radiant energy by the non-blackbody. With the aid of Eq. 10, Eq. 11 may be rewritten as

$$\mathcal{R}_n = (1 - \rho)\mathcal{R}_b = \epsilon\mathcal{R}_b \tag{12}$$

where $\epsilon$, a characteristic of the non-blackbody, is known as its total emittance. Eq. 12 rewritten as

$$\epsilon = \frac{\mathcal{R}_n}{\mathcal{R}_b} \tag{13}$$

shows that $\epsilon$, or $(1 - \rho)$, for a non-blackbody is the ratio of its radiancy to the radiancy of a blackbody at the same temperature. Further, since the non-blackbody is maintained in equilibrium with its surroundings, it must radiate energy to its surroundings at the same rate that it absorbs radiant energy that is incident. It follows, for the conditions in the cavity, where $\alpha$ represents the total absorptance of the non-blackbody, that

$$\alpha\epsilon_b = (1 - \rho)\mathcal{E}_b = \mathcal{R}_n \tag{14}$$

and, with the aid of Eqs. 10 and 13,

$$\epsilon = \alpha \tag{15}$$

This equation, the quantitative expression of Kirchhoff's law for the total radiation from a body, states that the total emittance of a non-blackbody at any given temperature is equal to its total absorptance for radiation from a blackbody at the same temperature.

To illustrate the meaning of Eq. 15, consider a piece of iron and a piece of blackbody material in a cavity with opaque walls at a uniform temperature of 1600°K. On all surfaces within the enclosure, radiant energy is incident at a rate of about 37.2 watts/cm².* The body of blackbody material absorbs all that is incident and emits radiant energy at the same rate per unit of area. Of the incident radiation, the iron, however, absorbs 29% or at a rate per unit area of 10.8 watts/cm². The iron also emits at a rate per unit area of 10.8 watts/cm². That which is reflected or 71% of the incident 37.2 watts/cm², that is 26.4 watts/cm², when added to the emitted 10.8 watts/cm² yields, of course, the 37.2 watts/cm² which is uniform throughout the enclosure. The total emittance of the iron at 1600°K, which is 10.8 watts/cm² divided by 37.2 watts/cm², or 0.29, is equal to its total absorptance, which is also 0.29. It must be emphasized that, were radiation different from that characteristic of a blackbody at 1600°K to fall on iron at 1600°K, the fractional part absorbed would probably not be 29%. This is a consequence, not of the fact that $\epsilon$ for iron varies with the temperature, but rather of the fact that $\epsilon_\lambda$ (see below) varies with the wavelength.

In the foregoing, all wavelengths of radiation have been included. It may be shown, however, that Kirchhoff's law is equally true for each wavelength, that is spectrally, and that

$$\epsilon_\lambda = \alpha_\lambda \tag{16}$$

For iron at 1600°K, in a region of the spectrum where the spectral emittance is 40%, say, the spectral absorptance is also 40%.

In what has been said thus far in this section, it has been tacitly assumed that the quantities $\alpha$, $\rho$, $\epsilon$, $\alpha_\lambda$, $\rho_\lambda$, and $\epsilon_\lambda$ are characteristics of the non-blackbodies rather than of the materials composing them. However, we are often concerned with the characteristics of materials. In order that such may be the case, some standard conditions must be established for the construction of the bodies that are studied with the characteristics of the material, not the body, in mind. The conditions agreed on are (1) that the body shall be of uniform composition throughout, (2) that it shall be opaque, and (3) that its surface shall be highly polished. Under the conditions of constant temperature required for measurements the reflectance, emittance, and absorptance,

* R. T. Birge's value for $\sigma$ is used. See p. 430.

$\rho$, $\epsilon$, and $\alpha$ then become the reflectivity $\rho'$, the emissivity $\epsilon'$, and the absorptivity $\alpha'$.

For tungsten at 2500°K, $\epsilon'$ is 0.303; and, at 0.665 $\mu$, $\epsilon'_\lambda$ is 0.425. For a tungsten body which is opaque but whose surface is not polished, $\epsilon$ may be anything between 0.303 and 1.00, and similarly $\epsilon_\lambda$ at 0.665 $\mu$ may be anything between 0.425 and 1.00. If, on the other hand, the body consists of a thin film of tungsten on quartz, its $\epsilon$ may be below 0.303 and its $\epsilon_\lambda$ at 0.665 $\mu$ may be below 0.425.

Though the appropriateness of the use of the "-ivity" and the "-ance" terms depends on the condition of the non-blackbody under discussion, such condition places no limitation on the application of Kirchhoff's law. The law as expressed in Eqs. 15 and 16 is strictly true.

**7. Blackbodies.** In the preceding section, a blackbody was defined as a body which absorbs all the radiant energy that falls upon it. It was pointed out that the rate of departure of radiant energy per unit of area from any portion of the opaque walls of the cavity at constant temperature or from any body within under equilibrium conditions is exactly equal to the radiancy of a blackbody at the same temperature. A conclusion that follows is that, for a given temperature, no body possesses a radiancy greater than that of a blackbody. Were, on the contrary, such a body possible, it would, if introduced into an opaque enclosure with walls at a uniform temperature, cool to a temperature lower than that of the walls, for, when at the same temperature as the walls, it would radiate faster than radiation would be received and hence would cool further. This would be contrary to the zeroth law of thermodynamics (see p. 21). The conclusion that a blackbody radiates energy at the maximum possible rate per unit of area for any given temperature is very important in the field of radiation.

Although we have very close approximations to blackbody sources for radiation, we have no blackbody material. Carbon black, platinum black, zinc black, and Carborundum are among the best approximations to such materials.

Our best approximations to sources that yield blackbody radiation are small apertures in the walls of enclosures of uniform temperature. At low temperatures, the obtaining of such cavities is simple. Any opaque material may be used. As shown in Fig. 10, radiation from $P$ outside the cavity entering at $O$ impinges on the wall at $A$, assumed polished, and is there partially absorbed. That which is reflected is in turn partially absorbed and partially reflected at $B$. Similar occurrences at $C$, $D$, $E$, etc., lead to the final practical absorption of the entering ray. Except for normal and near normal incidence on the back wall, such an aperture absorbs all entering radiation almost completely and hence satisfies the definition for a blackbody.

How the aperture can serve as a source of blackbody radiation is interesting. Let the opaque walls of such a cavity as is diagrammed in Fig. 10 be heated to incandescence. Let the aperture and its surroundings be regarded by an eye at $P$. Looking toward $Q$ the eye sees the material of the wall with the normal brightness $B_n$ characteristic of the material at the given temperature. Looking toward the aperture $O$, however, the eye sees not only the surface at $A$ with the brightness $B_n$ but also, superposed, the brightness of $B$ once reflected,

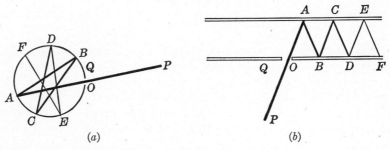

Fig. 10.  How non-blackbody radiation builds up in an opaque-walled, (a) spherical, (b) tubular, enclosure at constant temperature to yield blackbody radiation.

$\rho_l'B_n$, and of $C$ twice reflected, $\rho_l'^2 B_n$, etc., where $\rho_l'$ is the luminous reflectivity of the material of the polished opaque wall. For the brightness of the aperture $B_0$, which is made up of the various components, we have

$$B_0 = B_n + \rho_l'B_n + \rho_l'^2 B_n + \cdots = \frac{B_n}{1 - \rho_l'} \qquad (17)$$

and

$$B_n = (1 - \rho_l')B_0 = \epsilon_l'B_0 \qquad (18)$$

Eq. 18 is similar to Eq. 12. It differs in that we here deal with the brightness of a source rather than its radiancy. The $\epsilon_l'$, defined as $(1 - \rho_l')$, is similar to the $\epsilon$ of Eq. 12 and is to be interpreted similarly as an emissivity for emitted light. Likewise $B_0$ is the brightness of a blackbody at the temperature of the cavity walls, or, as we commonly say, of the cavity itself. As a source of radiation, the aperture is an exceedingly close approximation to a blackbody, regardless of the material used, because of the building-up process involved.

It can be shown, as might be inferred from what has been said in connection with Kirchhoff's law about the uniformity of distribution of radiation throughout a blackbody cavity, that, in such a cavity at incandescence, no detail may be seen even though different portions of the walls may be of widely different materials. This lack of detail is an important characteristic which is much used in practice for the determining of satisfactory blackbody conditions.

It is interesting to consider how many reflections are needed to yield an aperture that is 99.9% black. Consider cavities of copper, tungsten, and carbon whose reflectivities in the red region of the spectrum at incandescence are in order about 86%, 57%, and 15%. For the approximation to blackness in any case, we have, as may be obtained with the aid of Eq. 17,

$$X = \frac{B_n}{B_0} (1 + \rho_l' + \rho_l'^2 + \cdots \rho_l'^m)$$ (19)

in which the series terminates with $\rho'^m$, where $m$ represents the number of reflections considered. Now, it may be shown that, if the term $\rho_l'^{m+1}$ is less than 0.001, $X$ has a value of 99.9% or more. This occurs for copper, tungsten, and carbon respectively after 45, 12, and 3 reflections. If a value of 99.5% is acceptable, the required numbers of reflections are 33, 10, and 2.

For work at high temperatures, various types of blackbodies are used. A common, standard type is shown in Fig. 11. Fig. 12 shows

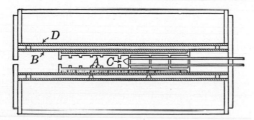

FIG. 11. A standard type of blackbody for use at incandescence with specifications by W. E. Forsythe. Tubes $A$, $B$, and $D$ are of Alundum or porcelain. Tube $A$ is wound uniformly with platinum ribbon 2 cm wide and 0.01 mm thick. Tube $B$ is wound with the same kind of ribbon but with a space between. $C$ is the blackbody. The space about D is packed with some good heat insulator, usually in powdered form.

a special type used at the Bureau of Standards in Washington, D. C., by H. T. Wensel (1893–   ), Wm. F. Roeser (1901–   ), and colleagues, in establishing, as a standard light source, 1.000 cm² of a blackbody at the melting point of platinum.

For the study of spectral emissivities, two types of miniature blackbodies have been used. The first of these, Fig. 13, the open-wedge blackbody, was described in 1911 by C. E. Mendenhall (1872–1935), physicist at the University of Wisconsin, in connection with a study of the emissivity of platinum. It consisted of two polished flat ribbons of the metal which were mounted to produce a very narrow wedge-shaped slot, with the two ribbons in contact along the sharp edge of the wedge. The method of building up radiation to produce a blackbody brightness is exactly the same as that described above in connection with Fig. 10. The outer side of the ribbons furnished the

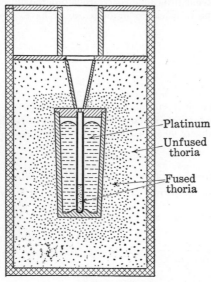

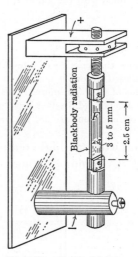

Fig. 12. A blackbody used at the Bureau of Standards in Washington, D. C., in the study of blackbody radiation at the platinum point (H. T. Wensel, Wm. F. Roeser, L. E. Borrow, and F. R. Caldwell, *J. Research, Natl. Bur. Standards,* **6**, 1103, 1931).

Fig. 13. C. E. Mendenhall's open-wedge blackbody (*Astrophys. J.*, **33**, 91, 1911).

natural platinum radiation; the wedge-shaped slot, the blackbody radiation having the same temperature.

A type of miniature blackbody which is more satisfactory for emissivity studies and now much more used was first presented by one of the authors in 1917 in a study of the emissivity of tungsten (Fig. 14*A*). There is shown an incandescent tubular filament of tungsten through whose wall a small hole was punched during an early stage of its manufacture by an extrusion process. The surface yielded normal tungsten radiation while the hole yielded blackbody radiation having the same temperature. Tubes of platinum as purchased have been drilled with small holes for a similar purpose. Similar tubes (Fig. 14*B*) have been formed by rolling thin but wide ribbons around small steel rods to yield closure along the length of the tube. A small opening to the interior is either drilled through the ribbon or filed at the edge in advance.

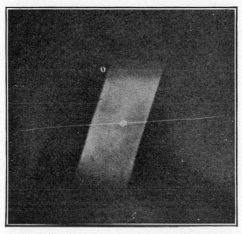

A

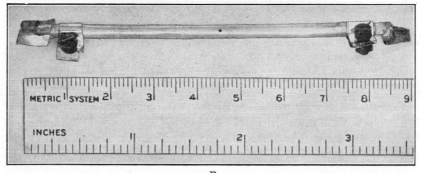

B

FIG. 14.  Miniature blackbodies consisting (A) of a tubular metallic filament with a small hole in its side wall (A. G. Worthing, *Phys. Rev.*, **10**, 377, 1917), and (B) of a tube formed from a metallic ribbon (H. B. Wahlin and L. V. Whitney, *Phys. Rev.*, **48**, 458, 1935).

**8. Lambert's Cosine Law.**  In what precedes, we have ignored, to a large extent, possible variations of the steradiancy and of the brightness of a radiating source with angle of emission. Actually, as will be noted later (see p. 452), non-blackbody sources show large variations. On the other hand, as a corollary of Kirchhoff's law, it may be shown that blackbody sources can have no variations whatever. This condition is usually expressed by saying that blackbodies obey Lambert's cosine law and that non-blackbodies do not.

Johann Heinrich Lambert (1728–1777), a famous German physicist, mathematician, and astronomer, is said to have concluded, from an inspection of an image of the sun formed on a garden wall, that the image was uniformly bright across the disk. With the knowledge that the light, yielding the various portions of the image, left the sun at various angles of emission, he further concluded that the brightness of any selected portion of the sun's surface does not vary with the direction of its viewing. It follows, in accord with Eq. 5, that the luminous intensity, $dI$, of an element of the sun's surface must vary as $\cos \theta$, the cosine of the angle of emission. The generalization that the luminous intensity and likewise the radiant intensity of a plane source of radiation, since brightness, $B$, is strictly analogous to steradiancy, $\mathcal{B}$, vary as the cosine of the angle of emission is known as Lambert's cosine law. In equation form the law is given by

$$\frac{I}{I_0} = \frac{J}{J_0} = \cos \theta \tag{20}$$

or by

$$\frac{B}{B_0} = \frac{\mathcal{B}}{\mathcal{B}_0} = 1 \tag{21}$$

Eqs. 20 and 21 are basic in the experimental determination of blackbody characteristic constants and in their theoretical connections with other physical quantities.

Actually, Lambert's original observation was faulty. The brightness of the sun's disk varies greatly between the center and the edge, not only for the total radiation but also spectrally. For $0.534 \mu$ in the green region, and an emission angle of $75°$, the brightness is about one-half that for normal emission. However, the concept of a strictly cosine variation, such as is realized in blackbody sources, is important, and the phrase Lambert's cosine law is much used. Speaking of non-blackbody sources, we frequently refer to deviations from the law.

### 9. Boltzmann's Fourth-Power Law.

Among the most important of radiation laws is that which was first established on a firm theoretical basis in 1884 by the Austrian physicist Ludwig Boltzmann (1844–1906). We shall refer to it as the Boltzmann fourth-power law.* Its

---

* This law is often referred to as the Stefan-Boltzmann fourth-power law on the basis that Stefan (1835–1893), an Austrian physicist, first gave an empirical statement of it and that Boltzmann's thermodynamic deduction followed later. When, however, one considers the basis for Stefan's deduction, it hardly seems fair to link his name with the law. The Irish physicist John Tyndall (1820–1893) had reported the ratio of the radiation output of a platinum wire at 1200°C to that at 525°C as 11.7. Stefan noticed that the ratio of (1473°K) to (798°K) raised to the fourth power is 11.6, and stated the law empirically. There were at least two errors, however. Later work has shown that the ratio of the two radiancies of platinum at these temperatures is more nearly 18.6 than 11.6, and that the radiation from platinum is far from blackbody radiation and should not be assumed to follow the laws of blackbody radiation. Actually Stefan applied his empirical law with some success to other data, but the same errors were always present. Stefan was an able physicist whose fame should rest on other accomplishments.

derivation is to be found in the chapter on thermodynamics. In equation form, it is

$$\mathcal{R}_b = \sigma T^4 \tag{22}$$

of which $\mathcal{R}_b$ is blackbody radiancy, a quantity commonly expressed in watts/cm$^2$, and $\sigma$ is Boltzmann's radiation constant, whose value, as recommended in 1941 by R. T. Birge (1887–   ) of the University of California, is $5.673 \times 10^{-12}$ watt/(cm$^2$ K$^{\circ 4}$).

In the experimental testing of the total radiation from a blackbody, the measuring instrument receiving the radiation never yields indications strictly proportional to the fourth power of the temperature of the blackbody. Instead, the indications are proportional to the differences between two such fourth-power terms. The blackbody under test replaces in the "field of view of the receiver," as we say, a portion of the field that otherwise would be occupied by surroundings at the normal surroundings temperature, and the net rate of reception of radiant energy varies as the excess of the steradiancy of the blackbody over that of the surroundings. With a receiver that is black and surroundings whose temperature is otherwise constant and equal to $T_0$, the indication given by the receiver, $D$, for a blackbody at the temperature $T$ is

$$D = k(T^4 - T_0^4) \tag{23}$$

of which $k$ is a constant for the instrument and the conditions of operation. Eq. 23 is the basic relation underlying total radiation pyrometry which is discussed later in this chapter.

The most extensive series of measurements for the testing of the Boltzmann fourth-power law was reported in 1897 by the German physicists Otto Lummer (1860–1925) and E. Pringsheim (1876–   ). The range of temperatures employed, which were based on the constant-volume, nitrogen-gas thermometer, was from 100°C to 1260°C, about 200 C° above the gold point. The apparatus used for the lower temperatures is shown in Fig. 15. $A$ is a cavity with a small opening on one side, whose temperature was maintained at a fixed value by means of boiling water. This cavity served as a blackbody comparison standard. $B$ is a cavity similar to $A$ which, however, was surrounded by a molten salt whose temperature was maintained at certain desired values by a regulated gas flame at $f$. The temperatures of the molten salt were measured by means of thermocouples. $G$ is a horizontally movable tube which, near the end opposite $A$, carries a bolometer for the measurement of radiant energy that may come to it from either $A$ or $B$. On the side toward $A$, the tube is diaphragmed to insure that the radiation from $A$ which was incident on the bolometer shall not include any that has been reflected from the side walls of the tube.

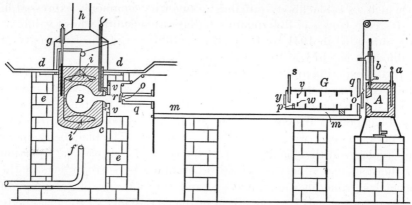

FIG. 15.    Apparatus used by Lummer and Pringsheim in testing Boltzmann's fourth-power law for blackbody radiation (*Ann. Physik*, **63**, 395, 1897).

In operation, radiant energy was admitted to the bolometer by shifting one or the other of the hand-operated, water-cooled shutters next to the water-cooled openings $o$, $o$ and shutter $y$ when working with radiation from $B$. To allow for gradual variations in the sensitivity and the zero drift of the bolometer and in the temperature of $B$, a series of galvanometer deflections, resulting from radiant energy received alternately from $A$ and $B$, was taken for each determination of the temperature of $B$, made in accord with Eqs. 22 and 23, the latter of which is based on the former.

The results of Lummer and Pringsheim are given in Table II. Although there is a certain tendency for values computed in accord with Eq. 23 to be too high, the results as a whole are taken as a very satisfactory check of the fourth-power law.

## TABLE II

### RESULTS OF A TEST OF THE FOURTH-POWER BOLTZMANN RADIATION LAW, BY O. LUMMER AND E. PRINGSHEIM

The observed temperatures, $T_o$, were measured with thermocouples in 1897 and adjusted later, in 1900, to the nitrogen, constant-volume, gas thermometer scale. The computed temperatures, $T_c$, were based on Eqs. 22 and 23.

| $T_o$ | $T_c$ | $T_o - T_c$ | $T_o$ | $T_c$ | $T_o - T_c$ |
|---|---|---|---|---|---|
| 373.1°K | 374.6°K | −1.5 K° | 1092°K | 1074°K | +18 K° |
| 492.5 | 492.0 | +0.5 | 1112 | 1095 | +17 |
| 723.0 | 724.3 | −1.3 | 1378 | 1379 | −1 |
| 745 | 749.1 | −4.1 | 1470 | 1468 | +2 |
| 789 | 778 | +11 | 1497 | 1488 | +9 |
| 810 | 806.5 | +3.5 | 1535 | 1531 | +4 |
| 868 | 867.1 | +0.9 | | | |

Simple apparatus for the testing of the fourth-power law and the measurement of $\sigma$ (Fig. 16) has been described by J. M. Cork (1894–   ) of the University of Michigan. For the testing of the law, it suffices to measure the necessary rates of supply of energy to maintain the ball, with a surface of some material such as zinc black, at

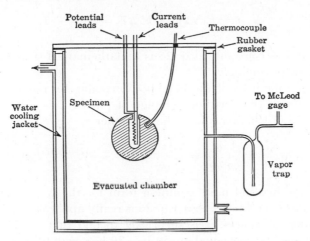

Fig. 16. Apparatus devised by Cork for a simple laboratory test of the Boltzmann fourth-power law for radiant energy and the measurement of $\sigma$ (by permission, J. M. Cork, *Heat*, 2nd ed., p. 158, New York, John Wiley & Sons, 1942).

various measured temperatures. For the measurement of $\sigma$, it is necessary to measure, with a thermocouple and timepiece, the rate of heating of the bath whose thermal capacitance must be known and to relate these to the radiant intensity of the ball.

**10. Newton's Law of Cooling.** This law, named after its proponent, the great English physicist Sir Isaac Newton (1642–1727), is much used in pure and industrial scientific research. It may be readily deduced with the aid of the Boltzmann fourth-power law. The rate of loss of energy by a blackbody of surface area $A$, at an elevated temperature $T$, on cooling in an evacuated blackbody enclosure at the temperature $T_0$, is obviously the difference between its own rate of emission of radiant energy and its rate of absorption of radiant energy incident on its surface, and is given by

$$\frac{dQ}{dt} = A\,(\mathcal{R}_b - \mathcal{R}_{b0}) = A\sigma(T^4 - T_0{}^4) \tag{24}$$

Replacing $T$ by $T_0 + \Delta T$ gives

$$\frac{dQ}{dt} = A\sigma[(T_0 + \Delta T)^4 - T_0{}^4]$$

$$= A\sigma\,\Delta T(4T_0{}^3 + 6T_0{}^2\,\Delta T + 4T_0\,\overline{\Delta T^2} + \overline{\Delta T^3}) \tag{25}$$

If $T$ is greater than $T_0$ by only a small amount, and to the extent that the part of the last term of Eq. 25, which is in parentheses, may be approximated by $4T_0{}^3$, that equation reduces to

$$\frac{dQ}{dt} = 4A\sigma T_0{}^3\,\Delta T = k'\,\Delta T = k'(T - T_0) \tag{26}$$

of which $k'$ is a constant. Eq. 26 is a mathematical statement of the Newton law of cooling.

If the specific heat of the blackbody, cooling by radiation only, is constant and it cools without change of phase, then, in accord with basic Eq. 18 of Chapter VI, we have further

$$\frac{dT}{dt} = \frac{1}{mc}\frac{dQ}{dt} = \frac{4A\sigma T_0{}^3}{mc}\,\Delta T = k''(T - T_0) \tag{27}$$

which is another and more common form for the cooling law. Contrary to the general belief that Eq. 26 is really applicable for moderate temperature differences, it is surprising to find that for $T_0 = 300°K$ and $\Delta T$ in succession equal to 50 K°, 20 K°, and 10 K°, the values yielded by Eqs. 26 and 27 are too low by about 22%, 9%, and 5%. For cases involving loss of heat by radiation only, the range of applicability of this law seems rather limited.

Actually, the law of cooling would follow as well for a fifth or any other power law for radiancy, such as we have for non-blackbodies generally. Further, since thermal conduction and thermal convection effects vary as the first power of temperature differences, Newton's law of cooling should be applicable to any real body in any atmosphere, except perhaps under some unusual circumstances.

Where the convection and conduction losses are combined with and predominate over radiation losses, as is frequently the case, the range of applicability of Newton's law becomes much greater than where the losses are due to radiation only. For the same temperature ranges, variations in fractions of a per cent rather than in per cent may be encountered.

It was, in fact, under just such conditions that the law was applied on p. 116 when the standard compensated-loss method of calorimetry was discussed.

**11. Blackbody Spectral Radiation Laws.** The next blackbody radiation law was announced in 1896 by the German physicist Wilhelm Wien (1864–1928), winner of the Nobel prize in physics in 1911, and is known as Wien's displacement law. Wien sought a relation to show how the heating effect of blackbody radiation varied with the wavelength, that is, an equation which would represent mathematically such curves as are shown in Fig. 17. He obtained one which gave accurately the changes occurring in the spectral radiancy curves of blackbodies with change in temperature. As an illustration, he was able to predict the curve for 4000°K if given the curve for 3000°K.

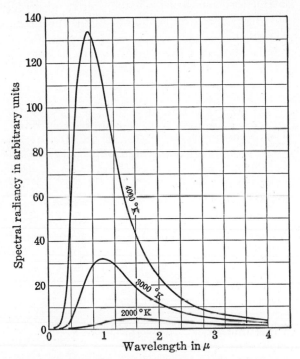

FIG. 17. Spectral distribution of the radiation from a blackbody at 2000°K, 3000°K, and 4000°K (by permission, University of Pittsburgh Physics Staff, *An Outline of Atomic Physics*, 2nd ed., p. 58, New York, John Wiley & Sons, 1937).

If, for instance, one contracts laterally the 3000°K curve of Fig. 17 in the ratio 3000/4000 and at the same time expands it vertically in the ratio $(4000/3000)^5$ he obtains at once the 4000°K curve. That this procedure, illustrating what is known as Wien's displacement law, is in accord with the fourth-power law for the total radiation is easily seen, for the ratio of the area beneath the new 4000°K curve, by virtue of its manner of derivation from the 3000°K curve, is greater than that under the 3000°K curve by the product $\frac{3}{4} \times (\frac{4}{3})^5$ or $(4000/3000)^4$. In equational form, this law is given by

$$\mathcal{R}_\lambda = T^5 f(\lambda T) \tag{28}$$

and states that, under circumstances so chosen that the product $\lambda T$ is constant, the spectral heating effects vary as $T^5$, as just illustrated.

A corollary of the Wien displacement law in the form of Eq. 28 follows readily. The $f(\lambda T)$ term indicates that the spectral radiancy distribution curves for blackbodies at different temperatures have the same general form, as has been illustrated. Further, it follows that, since the distribution for some one temperature shows a maximum spectral radiancy at some one wavelength (see Fig. 17), the other distributions must show corresponding maxima at other corresponding wavelengths, depending on their temperatures. With $\lambda_m$ representing the wavelength of maximum spectral radiancy, the corollary relation becomes

$$\lambda_m T = \text{constant} = 2884.1 \ \mu \ \text{K}° \tag{29}$$

The value of the constant given is that of the International Temperature Scale; that recommended by Birge and consistent with that given by him for $\sigma$ is 2897.2 $\mu$ K°. For a temperature of 2500°K, for instance, the maximum spectral radiancy is accordingly found at 1.1160 $\mu$. Obviously Eq. 29 with a different constant may be used to locate various other corresponding points, such as where $\mathcal{R}_\lambda$ equals 0.5, 0.8, or 0.9 of the maximum $\mathcal{R}_\lambda$.

Other laws relating to the spectral distribution of the energy radiated by blackbody sources are the Wien's distribution law

$$\mathcal{R}_\lambda = \frac{c_1 \lambda^{-5}}{e^{c_2/\lambda T}} \tag{30}$$

the Rayleigh distribution law after the great English physicist Lord Rayleigh (1842–1919), winner of the Nobel prize in physics in 1904,

$$\mathcal{R}_\lambda = \frac{c_1 \lambda^{-5}}{c_2/\lambda T} = \frac{c_1}{c_2} \lambda^{-4} T \tag{31}$$

and the Planck distribution law after the great German physicist Max Planck (1858–    ), winner of the Nobel prize in physics in 1918,

$$\mathcal{R}_\lambda = \frac{c_1 \lambda^{-5}}{e^{c_2/\lambda T} - 1} \tag{32}$$

of which $c_1$ and $c_2$ are often referred to as the first and the second radiation constants. There are very obvious similarities. The value of $c_2$ adopted for the International Temperature Scale is 14,320 $\mu$ K°. This seems to be too small, however, and probably will be revised upward. The value recommended by Birge, consistent with the value given above for $\sigma$, is 14,385 $\mu$ K°.

Wien's displacement law, as given in Eq. 28, seemed to be the limit of information regarding spectral distribution that may be obtained by thermodynamic reasoning alone.   In order to obtain an expression for an actual distribution at some one temperature, Wien accordingly introduced an assumption, namely, that the Maxwell distribution law for molecular velocities gave also the distribution of radiant energy with respect to frequency.   Eq. 30 followed, but, though it agreed with experiment in the short-wavelength region of the spectrum, it failed at the longer wavelengths.

Lord Rayleigh in 1900, perceiving certain inconsistencies resulting from Wien's use of the Maxwell distribution law, made instead the assumption that radiation within a blackbody cavity has degrees of freedom to correspond to the frequencies of standing waves that are possible in the cavity, and that, as with gases, there is equipartition of energy among these different degrees of freedom.   Eq. 31 resulted. Actually, Rayleigh erroneously included a factor of 8 in his evaluation of $c_1$.   The error was pointed out by the English physicist James Jeans (1877–   ).   For that reason, the law is often referred to as the Rayleigh-Jeans law.   Just the reverse of what occurred in connection with the Wien law, the Rayleigh law predicts correct values in the long-wavelength region but fails elsewhere.

Also in 1900, and with the successes and the failures of the Wien and the Rayleigh distributions in mind, Planck sought for the cause of the failures.   To his surprise, in his incompleted theoretical treatment, he arrived at an expression (Eq. 32) which yielded the Wien expression for short wavelengths and the Rayleigh expression for long wavelengths.   Seeking an explanation for what turned out to be the correct expression for a spectral distribution law, he was forced to the revolutionary and tremendously important theory of quanta.

How well the Planck law fits experimental data and how well the other two laws approximate it at the extremes of the spectrum is shown in Fig. 18.   One easily sees that the Wien and the Rayleigh approximations follow mathematically.   For small values of $\lambda T$, the $-1$ of Eq. 32 is negligible in comparison with $e^{c_2/\lambda T}$, and at once Eq. 30 results.   For large values of $\lambda T$, $e^{c_2/\lambda T}$ may be replaced by the first two terms of the expansion $1 + c_2/\lambda T + \dfrac{(c_2/\lambda T)^2}{2} + \cdots$   At once Eq. 31 results.

It is interesting to note that blackbody laws referring to measurements in terms of quantum or photon content rather than energy content have been derived.   A. Haas at Notre Dame University

(1884–1941) has shown that, corresponding to the Boltzmann fourth-power law, there is a third-power law for photons, while Frank Benford (1883–  ) of the General Electric Research Laboratory at Schenectady, N. Y., and one of the authors have pointed out certain other laws, among them a radiation efficiency and a photon law corresponding to the Wien distribution law.

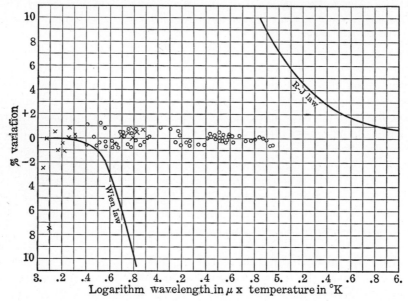

FIG. 18. Experimental tests of Planck's radiation law; ✕-points represent data by Coblentz; ◯-points represent data by Rubens and Michel (only about half of their points are shown). The variations from the Wien and the Rayleigh distributions are shown by the full-line curves. (Courtesy of W. E. Forsythe.)

## 12. Non-Blackbodies.

Since blackbody material does not exist, all real material is necessarily non-black, and all real bodies, if we may exclude cavities from the category of real bodies, are non-blackbodies. The particular characteristics of real bodies that interest us here are their abilities to reflect, transmit, and emit radiant energy.

In the discussion of Kirchhoff's law certain of the above terms were introduced and used. For an opaque non-blackbody, it was there shown that the sum of the reflectance, $\rho$, and the absorptance, $\alpha$, of the body for given incident radiation must be unity. For the general case including the non-opaque body, however, account must also be taken of the transmittance, $\tau$, and we have

$$\rho + \alpha + \tau = 1 \qquad (33)$$

a consequence of the fact that a body can only reflect, absorb, or transmit radiant energy that is incident on it.

For a body in equilibrium in an opaque-walled cavity, it was also shown that

$$(\alpha = \epsilon)_T \tag{15}$$

where $\epsilon$ is the total emittance of the body. If, however, the incident radiant energy is not that characteristic of a blackbody at the temperature of the body, as occurs when the temperatures of a body and its surroundings are different, Eq. 15 does not apply. The total absorptance of a body for incident radiation varies with the spectral distribution of that radiation. In general, $\epsilon$ varies with the temperature, though, in some instances, the rate of variation is small.

If the non-blackbodies are opaque and polished, we have to consider reflectivities $\rho'$, absorptivities $\alpha'$, and emissivities $\epsilon'$, rather than the -ance quantities; and we have analogous to Eqs. 33 and 15,

$$\rho' + \alpha' = 1 \tag{34}$$

and

$$(\alpha' = \epsilon')_T \tag{35}$$

These equations are important along with Eq. 22 in total radiation pyrometry and in industry where transfers of energy by radiation are concerned. In Figs. 19 and 20 there are shown certain interesting emittance and emissivity variations with material and with temperature. For temperatures between 100°F and 300°F as shown in Fig. 19, copper that is bright and freshly polished has a total emissivity, $\epsilon'$, of about 0.08. Much-tarnished copper, however, shows an $\epsilon$ between 0.4 and 0.5. Covering bright freshly polished copper with a single thin coat of clear lacquer raised its total emittance, $\epsilon$, to about 0.37; covering with two coats raised it to about 0.6. Covering the bright copper with a heavy coat of white lacquer produced an $\epsilon$ of about 0.93. It is interesting that, for radiation characteristic of a blackbody at from 100°F to 300°F, the white lacquer should be so nearly black. That many paints including white paints and white refractories may also be nearly black for these low-temperature radiations is shown in Fig. 20. That these same paints at higher temperatures tend to deviate from blackness in the directions expected is shown there also. For the white refractory in particular it seems that a close approach to real whiteness may be expected for high temperatures. That the white refractory and the white paint should be nearly black for 100°F radiation and nearly white when viewed in sunlight illustrates well the statement made above, namely, that "the absorptance of a body for

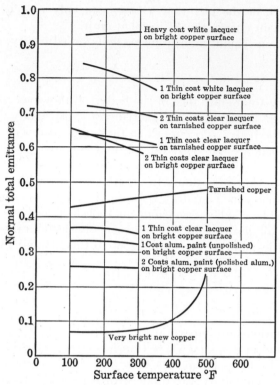

FIG. 19.   Normal total emittances at low temperatures for pieces of bright newly polished copper when uncoated and when variously coated (courtesy of R. H. Heilman).

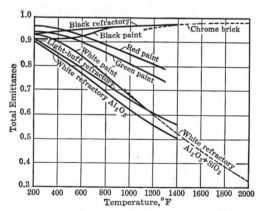

FIG. 20.   Some total emittances for a wide range of temperature (courtesy of R. H. Heilman).

incident radiation" and hence its reflectance also "vary with the spectral distribution of that radiation."

Various experimentally determined total emittances and emissivities are given in Table V of Appendix II. Wherever in industry heat interchanges between two systems at different temperatures are desired, of which there are a great number, or wherever it is sought to reduce to a practical minimum such heat interchanges, knowledge of such total emittances and emissivities is a factor of importance. Usually, in the search for a best solution, other factors such as shape, size, conduction, and convection enter and may or may not be of greater importance.

In much work involving radiation, we are concerned with a small range of wavelengths. Then, instead of the total -ance and -ivity quantities $\alpha\ \rho\ \tau\ \epsilon\ \alpha'\ \rho'\ \epsilon'$, we are interested in the corresponding spectral -ance and -ivity quantities $\alpha_\lambda\ \rho_\lambda\ \tau_\lambda\ \epsilon_\lambda\ \alpha_\lambda'\ \rho_\lambda'\ \epsilon_\lambda'$ ($\tau'$ and $\tau_\lambda'$ are zero by the definitions of the -ivity terms). We refer to these terms as spectral absorptance, spectral reflectance, etc. To correspond to certain relations for the total quantities, we have

$$\alpha_\lambda + \rho_\lambda + \tau_\lambda = 1 \tag{36}$$

$$\alpha_\lambda = \epsilon_\lambda \tag{36a}$$

$$\alpha_\lambda' + \rho_\lambda' = 1 \tag{37}$$

$$\alpha_\lambda' = \epsilon_\lambda' = \frac{\mathcal{R}_\lambda^*}{\mathcal{R}_{b\lambda}} \tag{37a}$$

The meanings of the above-named terms will be made clear by a consideration of Fig. 21, which shows certain spectral radiancy curves.

---

* Strictly the $\epsilon_\lambda'$ as here defined is a hemispherical spectral emissivity and for preciseness should be represented by $\epsilon_{\lambda h}'$. It differs from a normal spectral emissivity $\epsilon_{\lambda n}'$, which is a ratio of radiations emitted normally from the surfaces concerned. The defining equation differs from Eq. 37 in that the $\mathcal{R}$'s are replaced by $\mathcal{B}$'s. It is

$$\epsilon_{\lambda n}' = \frac{\mathcal{B}_{\lambda n}}{\mathcal{B}_{b\lambda n}} \tag{38}$$

of which $\mathcal{B}_{\lambda n}$ represents a spectral steradiancy, a quantity normally measured in watts/(cm$^2$ steradian micron), whereas $\mathcal{R}_\lambda$, the spectral radiancy, is normally measured in watts/(cm$^2$ micron). The subscript indicates that the steradiancies compared in Eq. 38 are normal steradiancies. Often values for $\epsilon_{\lambda n}'$ and for $\epsilon_{\lambda h}'$ are quoted and used indiscriminately. Usually they do not differ greatly. For tungsten at incandescence in the visible region an $\epsilon_{\lambda h}'$ is about 1.045 times the corresponding $\epsilon_{\lambda n}'$. In pyrometry (see later), $\epsilon_{\lambda n}'$ is much the more frequently used. In this book, in order to reduce the multiplicity of equations and qualifying terms otherwise necessary, we shall generally use but one subscript and trust to the context and the good sense of the reader to tell which is meant.

These curves indicate, per unit of area, the heating effects of which the emitted radiations are capable as a function of wavelength. Curve (a) is a spectral radiancy curve for polished, opaque tungsten at 2450°K; (b) and (c) are similar curves for a blackbody at 2450°K and at 2500°K. Certain relations are evident.

(1) The tungsten curve is seen everywhere to lie below that for the blackbody at the same temperature. Should the areas under the two

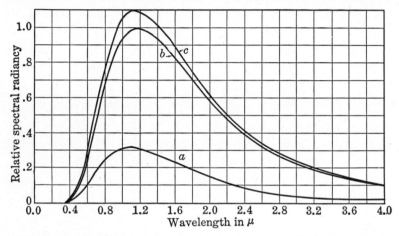

FIG. 21. Spectral radiancy curves for (a) tungsten at 2450°K, (b) a blackbody at 2450°K, and (c) a blackbody at 2500°K (*Pyrometry, The Papers and Discussions of a Symposium on Pyrometry*, p. 367, New York, Am. Inst. of Mining and Metallurgical Engineers, 1920).

curves, extended to $\lambda = \infty$, be compared, a ratio of about 0.300 would be obtained. In accord with Eq. 13, this indicates that the total emissivity of tungsten at 2450°K is about 0.300.

(2) The ratio of an ordinate of the tungsten curve to that of the blackbody curve at 2450°K at the same $\lambda$, that is the spectral emissivity $\epsilon_\lambda'$ of the tungsten as defined in Eq. 37, varies with the wavelength. For example, at 2450°K and at 0.5 $\mu$, $\epsilon_\lambda'$ for tungsten is about 0.47, while at 1.0 $\mu$ it is about 0.40, and at 2.0 $\mu$ about 0.26. Correspondingly, at 2450°K for these same wavelengths, the spectral absorptivities $\alpha_\lambda'$ are these same values, namely, 0.47, 0.40, and 0.26, while the spectral reflectivities $\rho_\lambda'$ in order are 0.53, 0.60, and 0.74. One consequence of this variation of $\epsilon_\lambda'$ with $\lambda$ is that the maximum $\mathcal{R}_\lambda$ for the tungsten curve is at a shorter wavelength than that for a blackbody at the same temperature. For 2450°K, $\lambda_m$ for tungsten is at 1.160 $\mu$, while for the blackbody, according to Eq. 29, it is at 1.182 $\mu$. Neces-

sarily the average $\epsilon_\lambda'$, when weighted according to the $\mathcal{R}_\lambda$ at each $\lambda$, must check with the total emissivity, 0.300.

(3) For tungsten, as for many metals, at a given temperature $T$, a temperature $T_c$ for a blackbody may be found such that the ratio $\mathcal{R}_\lambda/\mathcal{R}_{b\lambda}$ is constant for the visible and near infra-red regions. Thus, as shown in Fig. 21, with tungsten at 2450°K and a blackbody at 2500°K, this ratio is constant and equal to about 0.358. Such a ratio is called

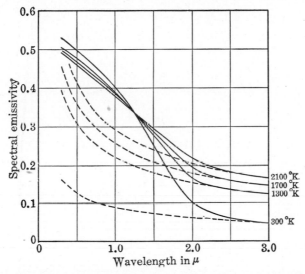

FIG. 22. Observed normal spectral emissivities for tungsten as a function of wavelength for several temperatures, and expected variations (----) as a function of wavelength were the Drude relation general.

a color emissivity. The qualifying word "color" is appropriate, since, for the conditions specified, there is obviously a match in color between the black and the non-black sources. For the region where a color emissivity applies, it is a simple matter to construct a desired spectral radiancy curve for the non-black source. One first constructs the appropriate blackbody spectral radiancy curve and then, using the color emissivity, constructs the curve desired. The temperature of the blackbody $T_c$ is referred to as the color temperature of the non-blackbody whose true temperature is $T$. Thus the color temperature of tungsten at 2450°K is 2500°K. The color temperatures of most incandescent metallic sources are greater than their true temperatures, though usually not much greater. For most solid incandescent sources, whether metallic or non-metallic, the differences $T_c - T$ are usually quite small. A consequence is that a rough, approximate measurement of the $T$ of any incandescent source may be obtained by matching the color of its light output with that from a calibrated tungsten lamp. How this may be done with ease and simplicity is discussed later under the heading color-match pyrometers and pyrometry.

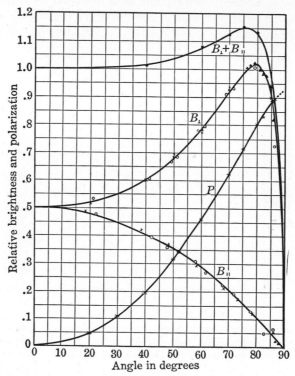

FIG. 23. For tungsten, at temperatures ranging from 1750°K to 2470°K, relative spectral brightnesses ($\lambda = 0.665\mu$) for the principal polarized-light components $B_\perp$ and $B_\parallel$ and the natural light ($B_\perp + B_\parallel$) and the polarization of the natural light $P$ as a function of the angle of emission. The variation from Lambert's cosine law is shown by the ($B_\perp + B_\parallel$) curve, as well as the variation of the emissivity with angle of emission. The $B_\perp$ and $B_\parallel$ curves show similarly emissivity variations for the two corresponding polarized components. (A. G. Worthing, *J. Optical Soc. Am.*, **13**, 635, 1926.)

How the spectral emissivity of tungsten, the substance most thoroughly studied, varies with temperature and wavelength is shown in Fig. 22. Certain interesting facts are indicated. (1) at $\lambda = 1.27\ \mu$, $\epsilon_\lambda'$ does not vary with temperature. (2) At all temperatures, there is a decrease in $\epsilon_\lambda'$ with increase in $\lambda$. (3) At $\lambda < 1.27\ \mu$, $\epsilon_\lambda'$ decreases with increase in $T$. (4) At $\lambda > 1.27\ \mu$, $\epsilon_\lambda'$ increases with increase in

$T$. (5) at $\lambda > 2.5\ \mu$, the values for and the variation of $\epsilon_\lambda'$ with changes in $\lambda$ and $T$ are closely predicted by a relation derived by the German physicist P. Drude (1863–1906), which is based on Maxwell's electromagnetic theory of light. It is

$$\epsilon_\lambda' = A \left(\frac{\zeta}{\lambda}\right)^{\frac{1}{2}} \tag{39}$$

of which $\zeta$ is resistivity and $A$ a constant having the value 0.365 ohm$^{-\frac{1}{2}}$.

Normal spectral emissivities $\epsilon_{\lambda n}'$ of various materials at about $0.665\ \mu$ are shown in Table VI of Appendix II.

For much that precedes, it has been tacitly assumed that the emissivity of a substance does not depend on the angle of emission, the angle between the direction of emission from an element of surface and its normal. That such is not the case is shown in Fig. 23. Starting with a certain value for normal emission, it is seen that, with increasing angle of emission, the spectral emissivity of tungsten increases by about 15% to a maximum at an emission angle of 75° and that it thereafter decreases to zero at grazing emission. How the two polarized-light components separately vary with angle is shown also. While many substances vary with angle in a similar manner, others such as carbon vary in just the reverse manner. Experiment has shown, as stated above, that the average emissivity for tungsten at $\lambda = 0.665\ \mu$, taking account of all directions, that is its hemispherical spectral emissivity, $\epsilon_{\lambda h}'$, is greater than its normal spectral emissivity $\epsilon_{\lambda n}'$ by the factor 1.045. For carbon the corresponding factor is 0.92.

The foregoing experimental facts regarding non-black materials and bodies have been obtained largely through pyrometry, a discussion of the theory and practice of which follow.

**13. Pyrometry.** Pyrometry is the theory and art of measuring temperatures considerably in excess of room temperatures. Although there is no definite lower temperature at which pyrometry takes over, its region is generally recognized as the region beyond that in which mercury-in-glass thermometers are practicable. There are several well-recognized methods, e.g., the Seger-cone, the gas-thermometer, the thermocouple, the electrical-resistance, the total-radiation, the spectral-radiation, and the color-match methods. There are other methods, such as the X-ray-diffraction, the electron-diffraction, and the velocity-of-sound methods, which are not so well recognized. Only the last three of the well-recognized methods will be discussed here, since they alone depend on temperature radiation processes and properties.

**14. Total Radiation Pyrometry.** The basic principles of total radiation pyrometry and the measurement of the temperatures of black-body sources with the aid of an idealized instrument were discussed in Chapter II. We shall now extend the treatment there given to non-black sources. This involves a knowledge of total emittances and emissivities, their measurement, and their application.

If a temperature is to be measured with the aid of a radiation pyrometer, a calibration must first be made. In what follows, we shall assume an idealized Féry pyrometer (Chapter II, Fig. 16) such that the total reflectance of its gold mirror and the total absorptance of the exposed thermojunction shall remain constant with change in the spectral character of the incoming radiation. In making the calibration, the pyrometer, in equilibrium in a room with surroundings at the constant temperature $T_0$, is first sighted on a blackbody at the known temperature $T_1$. Let $d_1$ be the galvanometer deflection; then

$$d_1 = c(T_1{}^4 - T_0{}^4) \qquad (40)$$

The constant $c$ includes among other things the radiation constant $\sigma$, the reflectance of the mirror, the absorptance of the thermojunction, and the sensitivity of the galvanometer. It may be regarded as the calibration constant of the instrument.

Let the pyrometer be now sighted on another blackbody at a temperature $T_2$ which is sought. Let the new deflection be $d_2$. Then

$$d_2 = c(T_2{}^4 - T_0{}^4). \qquad (41)$$

With the aid of the calibration constant, $T_2$ may be determined. Otherwise, substituting for $c$ from Eq. 40, one obtains the following relation,

$$T_2{}^4 = \frac{d_2}{d_1}(T_1{}^4 - T_0{}^4) + T_0{}^4 \qquad (42)$$

with the aid of which $T_2$ may be determined.

If, however, the second body is a non-blackbody, the $T_2$ thus obtained is not its true temperature. In place of the expression given in Eq. 41, we have

$$\tilde{d}_2 = c[\epsilon T_2{}^4 + \tilde{\rho} T_0{}^4 - T_0{}^4] \qquad (42a)$$

of which $\epsilon$ is the total emittance of the second body and $c\tilde{\rho}T_0{}^4$ represents the contribution to the deflection $\tilde{d}_2$ which results from radiation reflected to the pyrometer by that second body. In place of $\epsilon T_2{}^4$ we sometimes write $T_R{}^4$, which is known as the second body's radiation temperature, the temperature of a blackbody whose radiancy is equal to that of the second body. Replacing $\epsilon T_2{}^4$ by $T_R{}^4$ and rearranging, we have

$$T_R{}^4 = (1 - \tilde{\rho})T_0{}^4 + \frac{\tilde{d}_2}{d_1}(T_1{}^4 - T_0{}^4) \qquad (42b)$$

Eq. 42b obviously reduces to Eq. 42 for $\tilde{\rho}$ equals zero.

As may be verified, with $T_0$, $T_1$, $\tilde{d}_2/d_1$, and $\tilde{\rho}$ in turn equal to 300°K, 500°K, 2.00, and 0.42, $T_R$ becomes 574°K. If the $\tilde{\rho}$ term is ignored and Eq. 42 is applied, one obtains 580°K instead. The effect in this instance is small. How $\epsilon$ may be determined experimentally and applied to determine the true temperature $T$ follows.

A total emittance is conveniently obtained with the aid of a source such as is diagrammed in Fig. 10. With the temperature assumed constant throughout, let $d_3$ be the galvanometer deflection when the pyrometer is properly sighted on the surface and $d_4$ that when properly sighted on the hole. Proper sighting means in each instance that the image of the source, which is formed by the mirror or the lens of the pyrometer, must cover the receiving element completely. Further, the limiting diaphragm which determines the size of the solid angular aperture through which radiation passes to the receiving element should be in the pyrometer and not subject to change during any one test. There follows

$$\frac{d_3}{d_4} = \frac{\epsilon T^4 + \tilde{\rho}T_0^4 - T_0^4}{T^4 - T_0^4} = \frac{\epsilon T_0^4 - T_0^4(1 - \tilde{\rho})}{T^4 - T_0^4} \tag{43}$$

of which the term $\tilde{\rho}T_0^4$ corresponds to radiation from the surroundings at temperature $T_0$ which is reflected to the receiver by the hot body. $\tilde{\rho}$ represents the hot body's reflectance for the radiation in question. It differs from the $\rho(= 1 - \epsilon)$ of the hot body, which is defined for incident radiation from a blackbody source at temperature $T$. For bodies characterized by large $\epsilon$'s, the difference is usually small.

For the general case, Eq. 43 yields

$$\epsilon = (1 - \tilde{\rho})\frac{T_0^4}{T^4} + \frac{d_3}{d_4}\left(1 - \frac{T_0^4}{T^4}\right) \tag{44}$$

In case $\tilde{\rho}$ may be equated to $\rho$ or $1 - \tilde{\rho}$ to $\epsilon$, Eq. 44 reduces to

$$\epsilon = \frac{d_3}{d_4} \tag{44a}$$

Usually this procedure is justified. It is so assumed in what follows.

Let us next find $T$ for a non-blackbody whose $T_R$ and $\epsilon$ are known. The actual radiancy of the non-blackbody, in accord with Eqs. 13 and 22, is $\epsilon\sigma T^4$; but, since it is equal to that from a blackbody at temperature $T_R$, its radiancy is also $\sigma T_R^4$. Equating these two expressions, we obtain finally

$$T = T_R \left(\frac{1}{\epsilon}\right)^{\frac{1}{4}} \tag{45}$$

To illustrate the foregoing, consider a total radiation pyrometer which at 300°K and sighted on a blackbody at 500°K yields a galvanometer deflection of 5.00 divisions, and which yields a deflection of 25.0 divisions when sighted on another body whose total emittance, determined in accord with Eqs. 43 and 44, is 0.140. The true temperature for the body that yielded the 25.0 divisions deflection is desired. A substitution in Eq. 42b, with $\bar{p}$ taken as 0.86, yields

$$T_R{}^4 = 0.140(300°K)^4 + \frac{25.0}{5.00}[(500°K)^4 - (300°K)^4] \qquad (46)$$

and

$$T_R = 722.7°K \qquad (47)$$

Further substitution in Eq. 45 yields

$$T = 722.7°K \left(\frac{1}{0.140}\right)^{\frac{1}{4}} = 1182°K \qquad (48)$$

The values given are applicable to clean, polished tungsten.

Most total radiation pyrometers designed for industrial purposes are sealed to prevent dust and injurious vapors from coming in contact with the hot junction disk and the reflecting surfaces. Usually the incoming radiation enters through a glass lens. The lens absorbs much of the radiant energy located beyond about 2.7 $\mu$ so that the radiation that actually is directed to the receiving junction is far from blackbody radiation. An experimental calibration curve with the body of such a pyrometer at some fixed temperature as 100°F and pointed at blackbodies at various high temperatures will thereafter serve for determining certain unknown $T_R$'s.

The fact that the surroundings or pyrometer temperature enters into the calibration curve for a total radiation pyrometer represents a source of difficulty. In some industrial situations, considerable variations, of the order of 100 F°, may be expected for the pyrometer surroundings. Unless some correction is made for this variation, errors of the order of 200 F° or more may result in the $T_R$ which is computed. Some success in overcoming this difficulty has been obtained by having automatically operated shutters which reduce the size of the lens aperture. In 1940, T. R. Harrison (1891– ) and W. H. Wannamaker (1907– ) of the Brown Instrument Co. of Philadelphia (Chapter II, Fig. 17) reported that, with the so-called cold junctions of a total radiation pyrometer at the temperature of the pyrometer frame, the placing of a nickel wire resistance in parallel with the thermopile eliminated much of the uncertainty otherwise experienced in determined $T_R$'s for certain much-used temperature ranges.

**15. Spectral Radiation Pyrometers.** Spectral radiation pyrometers are commonly referred to as optical pyrometers. The construction of an optical pyrometer of the disappearing-filament type and its method of use in measuring the temperatures of blackbody sources have been discussed in Chapter II. We here extend the treatment to other types of optical pyrometers and to the measurement of the temperatures of non-black sources. This involves a knowledge of spectral emittances and emissivities, their measurement, and their application. Though there are many types of optical pyrometers differing in details of construction and operation, all are based on the same principles. Each contains a comparison lamp usually known as a pyrometer lamp. In each case, the brightness of the lamp's filament or the brightness of a spot illuminated by it in a chosen narrow band of wavelengths is matched with the corresponding brightness of the body whose temperature is sought. The temperatures themselves are obtained with the aid of calibrations against standard sources. Commonly, but not always, the chosen wavelength for the narrow spectral band centers about 0.66 $\mu$.

Of the particular designs, six may be mentioned. For the first four, rough approximations to monochromatic light are obtained by including, as parts of the pyrometers, filters of colored glass or other material so that from the standpoint of color little or no difficulty is experienced in matching a brightness produced by a lamp inside the pyrometer with the corresponding brightness of an external source.

1. The disappearing-filament optical pyrometer is the most important of the group. Morse in the United States obtained the first patent for an instrument of this type, though unknown to him, it is said, the principle was employed in industry earlier. Using instruments such as are shown in Figs. 18 to 20 of Chapter II, the observer sees the filament of the pyrometer lamp at $D$ projected against the body $A$ whose radiation is being studied. In making a measurement he varies the current through the filament of the pyrometer lamp, and thereby its brightness, and the filament is caused to disappear against the background at $A$, or, as is often said, to match the background in brightness. The appearances of the field of view at near match and at just match are shown in Fig. 21 of Chapter II. Details of the background and of the pyrometer filament, even at match, are readily distinguishable. The reading taken is that of the current in the pyrometer lamp filament. How such readings may be used will appear later.

2. The second design is also a disappearing-filament pyrometer. Disappearance, however, is produced with the aid of a graduated absorption disk, which, in position near $D$ between $C$ and $D$, Fig. 18 of Chapter II, may be gradually rotated, bringing into the path of the incoming beam from $C$ a darker or a less dark portion of the disk. In operation the current through the pyrometer lamp is adjusted to give a certain desired minimum brightness which is kept constant thereafter; and, when sighted on an object whose temperature is to be measured, the graduated absorption disk is rotated to the position where the filament disappears against the background. The angular position of the disk is then read. It is used much in the manner to be described for the current through the filament of the pyrometer lamp of design 1.

3. The third design (Fig. 24) is a disappearing-spot pyrometer. It differs from design 1 in that there is a small spot in the field of view which is illuminated uniformly

by the pyrometer lamp which is in a fixed position with respect to the spot. In use, the spot is caused to disappear against the body whose temperature is being

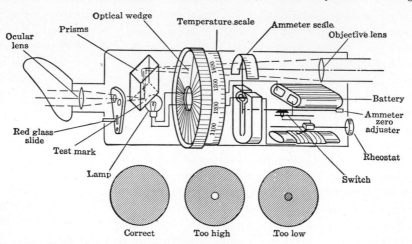

FIG. 24. Design of a disappearing-spot pyrometer (courtesy of the Pyrometer Instrument Co.).

measured, either by varying the current through the pyrometer lamp or by rotating in position a graduated absorption disk.

4. The fourth design (Figs. 25 and 26), usually known as the Wanner pyrometer, is an adaptation of the Arthur König (1856–1901) polarization spectrometer. Alto-

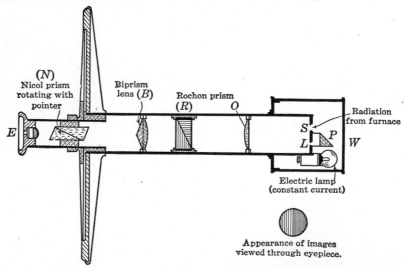

FIG. 25. Design of a Wanner polarization pyrometer. $S$ and $L$ are small openings for the admission of light from the sources to be compared; $O$, achromatic lens; $N$, analyzer for polarized light; $E$, eyepiece.

gether, by means of the polarizing prism $R$ and the biprism $B$, eight polarized images of the two slits or orifices $S_1$ and $L_2$ are formed in the plane of $B$. Only two of these, however, one of $S_1$, the other of $L_2$, fall on the opening of $E$. Adjustments are made so that each is half-moon in shape and so that their straight edges are just in contact.

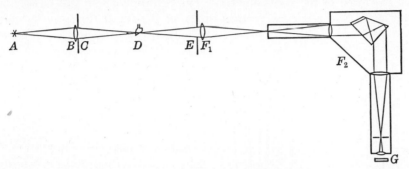

FIG. 26.   Diagram of a spectral pyrometer.   $A$, background body under investigation; $B$, objective lens; $C$, entrance cone diaphragm; $D$, pyrometer lamp; $E$, exit cone diaphragm; $F_1$, lens to focus light on the slit of spectrometer $F_2$; $G$, monochromatic filter for eliminating scattered light of other wavelengths than those desired.

Morcover, these two images are polarized at right angles to one another, so that, as the analyzer $N$ is rotated, the brightness of one image is increased while that of the other is dimmed in accord with the usual sine squared law for polarizing instruments. However differently the two slits $S_1$ and $L_2$ are illuminated, a brightness match for the two half-moon sections of the field is clearly possible. This pyrometer is, in effect, a disappearing-spot pyrometer. In use the position of the analyzer for match is noted. Further details as to theory and method of measuring temperatures, once given the ratio of brightnesses corresponding to the analyzer setting, are the same as for the first design described.

5. The fifth design differs from the first design essentially in that a spectrometer is used to obtain the monochromatic beam by which brightness matches are made. As is shown in Fig. 26, the eyepiece $F$ of Fig. 18 of Chapter II is replaced by a lens $F_1$ and a spectrometer $F_2$. The background $A$ is not a part of the instrument. Although at match the filament merges with the background, this pyrometer is not called a disappearing-filament pyrometer. Instead, because of the much better approximation to monochromatism, it is commonly called a spectral pyrometer. Naturally any wavelength of light in the visible region

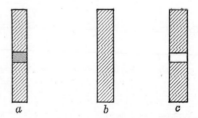

FIG. 27.   Appearance of the field of view of a spectral pyrometer when the pyrometer filament brightness is, $a$ too low, $b$ just right, $c$ too high, for matching the brightness of the background body on which it is sighted.

may be used in making a measurement of temperature or of other radiation characteristics. Often, as indicated in the figure, a pyrometer filter is added to eliminate much of the stray radiation that may be scattered in the spectrometer. The field of view in this case (Fig. 27) consists of a narrow vertical image of the slit of the spectrometer. The light from the upper and lower parts of the image comes from the background while that from a roughly square portion at the center comes from the pyrometer filament. The reading made at match is that of the current through the pyrometer filament. Further details as to method and theory are exactly the same as those for the first design described.

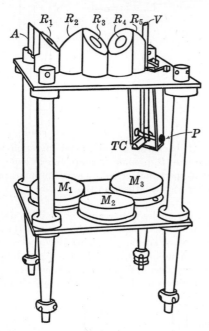

FIG. 28. Strong's infra-red spectral pyrometer. The characteristic wavelength is that of the residual rays of quartz, namely, 8.8 $\mu$. (*J. Optical Soc. Am.*, **29**, 520, 1939.)

6. The sixth design of spectral radiation pyrometers is due to J. D. Strong (1905–   ) of the California Institute of Technology and represents a radical departure from the other designs. It makes use of residual rays such as result from several successive reflections from polished surfaces of any one of many non-metallic materials. Strong used quartz whose narrow band of residual rays is located at 8.8 $\mu$. A portion of the apparatus is shown in Fig. 28; a short-focal-length reflecting telescope, not shown, focuses radiation onto aperture $A$, after which it is reflected in succession from quartz mirror $R_1$, concave aluminized mirror $M_1$, quartz mirror $R_2$, quartz mirror $R_3$, etc., finally to the thermocouple junction $TC$. The apparatus shown in Fig. 28 (but with shorter legs) is mounted in a box 5 in. by 6 in. by 8 in. This, as well as the telescope box to which it is attached, is exceedingly well insulated thermally. This instrument may be used for studying radiations from bodies at room temperature or higher or lower. Visible and near-infra-red radiations do not affect this 8.8 $\mu$ pyrometer. When sighted on an ordinary incandescent lamp that is lighted for a time and then turned off, it shows only a gradual heating of the glass envelope followed by a gradual cooling. It does not "see" the tungsten filament because at 8.8 $\mu$ the glass of the bulb is opaque. How useful this pyrometer may become remains to be seen.

**16. Spectral Radiation Pyrometry.** In what follows, we shall assume (1) that the radiation which is utilized is strictly monochromatic and (2) that, for the wavelengths and temperatures concerned, the spectral brightnesses or steradiancies of blackbodies predicted by the Wien spectral distribution law (Eq. 30) differ by negligible amounts from the true values as described by Planck's law (Eq. 32). The first assumption is realized actually in spectral pyrometers only. Where not realized, methods of correction for differences are available, though they will not be discussed here. The second assumption leads to a great simplification of calculations. How well it is justified is shown by the fact that, with its use, the error in temperatures measured at 3600°K (using $\lambda = 0.665\ \mu$) is only 1.5 K°, a quantity well within the uncertainties of measurement.

Wien's equation, as a sufficiently close approximation, is used almost exclusively in computing brightness and true temperatures. Given, for wavelength $\lambda$, a standard source whose spectral brightness $_0B_\lambda$, and hence also spectral brightness temperature, $_0S_\lambda$, are known, the corresponding spectral brightness temperature of an unknown source, $S_\lambda$, may be determined once its corresponding spectral brightness, $B_\lambda$, has been measured. Keeping in mind that $S_\lambda$ and $_0S_\lambda$ are the true temperatures of blackbodies with spectral brightnesses $B_\lambda$ and $_0B_\lambda$, we obtain for the ratio $B_\lambda/_0B_\lambda$, or what is its equal $\mathfrak{B}_\lambda/_0\mathfrak{B}_\lambda$, using Eq. 30

$$\ln \frac{B_\lambda}{_0B_\lambda} = \frac{c_2}{\lambda}\left(\frac{1}{_0S_\lambda} - \frac{1}{S_\lambda}\right) \tag{49}$$

and

$$\frac{1}{S_\lambda} = \frac{1}{_0S_\lambda} - \frac{\lambda}{c_2}\ln\frac{B_\lambda}{_0B_\lambda} \tag{50}$$

Eq. 50 is very much used in optical pyrometry. For the special case where $_0S_\lambda$ and $_0B_\lambda$ refer to a blackbody whose temperature $T$ is that of an unknown source, and the ratio $B_\lambda/_0B_\lambda$ is the spectral emittance of that source, $\epsilon_\lambda$, we have

$$\frac{1}{S_\lambda} = \frac{1}{T} - \frac{\lambda}{c_2}\ln\epsilon_\lambda \tag{51}$$

and

$$\frac{1}{T} = \frac{1}{S_\lambda} + \frac{\lambda}{c_2}\ln\epsilon_\lambda \tag{51a}$$

An application of the foregoing is well illustrated by a spectral emissivity determination using a polished, electrically heated, tubular filament of non-black material whose wall is pierced with small holes. Then $S_\lambda$ may represent the brightness temperature of the wall on the outside adjacent to a hole, while $_0S_\lambda$, representing that for the hole itself, is the same as the true temperature $T$ of the non-black material.

$B_\lambda$ and $_0B_\lambda$ will then represent the corresponding spectral brightnesses, and the ratio $B_\lambda/_0B_\lambda$ will be the spectral emissivity of the material $\epsilon_\lambda'$ (Eq. 38). To correspond to Eqs. 51 and 51a, we then have

$$\frac{1}{S_\lambda} = \frac{1}{T} - \frac{\lambda}{c_2} \ln \epsilon_\lambda' \qquad (52)$$

and

$$\frac{1}{T} = \frac{1}{S_\lambda} + \frac{\lambda}{c_2} \ln \epsilon_\lambda' \qquad (52a)$$

Eqs. 51a and 52a are basic for the determination of true temperatures.

FIG. 29. Photograph of a 90° rotating sectored disk mounted for use (courtesy of W. E. Forsythe).

For the convenience of having a definite instrument in mind, we shall assume for what follows a disappearing-filament pyrometer of the first design described, also a number of rotating sectored disks of varying transmittances (Fig. 29), 0.25 for the one shown in the figure. Neutral-tint, absorbing screens of measured transmittances will do as well. Let the wavelength of monochromatic light yielded by the pyrometer filter be 0.665 $\mu$.

**17. Calibration of a Disappearing-Filament Optical Pyrometer.** The pyrometer (Figs. 18 and 19 of Chapter II, or Fig. 26) is first sighted on a blackbody at the melting point of gold, 1336.0°K. Other standard temperatures such as the palladium point 1828°K * or the platinum point 2046°K* might be used instead. Note the pyrometer current at match, $i$ (Table III, part 1), which is given for a particular pyrometer lamp as 252.0 ma. Next, with rotating sectors, with varying transmittances somewhat as shown, introduced in succession between the blackbody source and the pyrometer, corresponding reduced pyrometer currents are obtained. Corresponding to them, in turn, reduced brightness temperatures $S_\lambda$ are to be computed using Eq. 50, of which $_0S_\lambda$ stands for the temperature of the blackbody source and the ratio $B_\lambda/_0B_\lambda$ is replaceable by the sector transmittance $t$. The computed

* These values are based on 14,320 $\mu$K° as an accepted value for $c_2$. Any change in the accepted value for the $c_2$ of the Wien equation as to 14,385 $\mu$K° will at once shift these values to 1825°K and 2041°K.

$S_\lambda$'s plotted as a function of the observed $i$'s form the basis for a temperature calibration curve of the pyrometer below the brightness temperature $_0S_\lambda$. A broad tungsten-ribbon filament which has been

### TABLE III

DATA OBTAINED IN THE CALIBRATION OF A PARTICULAR DISAPPEARING-FILAMENT OPTICAL PYROMETER USING $\lambda = 0.665\ \mu$ AND $c_2 = 14{,}320\ \mu K°$

*Part 1.   Temperatures below 1336°K*

| Temperature of Blackbody Source $T_0$ | Sectored Disk Transmittance $t$ | Pyrometer Current $i$ | Reduced Brightness Temperature $S_\lambda$ | $\log t$ | $\log i/i_0$ |
|---|---|---|---|---|---|
| 1336.0°K | 1.000 | 252.0 ma | 1336.0°K | 0.0000 | 0.0000 |
| 1336.0 | 0.500 | 230.1 | 1280.9 | −0.3010 | −.0394 |
| 1336.0 | 0.250 | 210.8 | 1230.2 | −0.6020 | −.0776 |
| 1336.0 | 0.125 | 193.8 | 1183.4 | −0.9031 | −.1141 |
| 1336.0 | 0.0625 | 178.8 | 1140.0 | −1.2040 | −.1490 |
| 1336.0 | 0.0312 | 165.6 | 1099.5 | −1.5051 | −.1823 |

*Part 2.   Temperatures above 1336°K*

In place of the blackbody source, a tungsten-ribbon filament is used which is capable of quick adjustment from one brightness temperature to another.

| Pyrometer Current $i$ | Sectored Disk Transmittance $t$ | Ribbon-Filament Current | Brightness Temperature of Ribbon Filament $S_\lambda$ | $\log 1/t$ | $\log i/i_0$ |
|---|---|---|---|---|---|
| 252.0 ma | 1.000 | $I_0$ | 1336.0°K | 0.0000 | 0.0000 |
| 252.0 | 0.500 | $I_1$ | 1396.1 | 0.3010 | .0000 |
| 277.1 | 1.000 | $I_1$ | 1396.1 | 0.0000 | .0412 |
| 252.0 | 0.250 | $I_2$ | 1461.8 | 0.6020 | .0000 |
| 305.8 | 1.000 | $I_2$ | 1461.8 | 0.0000 | .0840 |
| 252.0 | 0.125 | $I_3$ | 1534.0 | 0.9031 | .0000 |
| 338.5 | 1.000 | $I_3$ | 1534.0 | 0.0000 | .1282 |
| 252.0 | 0.0625 | $I_4$ | 1613.7 | 1.2040 | .0000 |
| 376.0 | 1.000 | $I_4$ | 1613.7 | 0.0000 | .1738 |
| 252.0 | 0.0312 | $I_5$ | 1702.1 | 1.5051 | .0000 |
| 419.5 | 1.000 | $I_5$ | 1702.1 | 0.0000 | .2213 |
| 252.0 | 0.0156 | $I_6$ | 1799.9 | 1.8062 | .0000 |
| 470.2 | 1.000 | $I_6$ | 1799.9 | 0.0000 | .2709 |
| 252.0 | 0.00781 | $I_7$ | 1909.5 | 2.1072 | .0000 |
| 529.2 | 1.000 | $I_7$ | 1909.5 | 0.0000 | .3222 |

accurately calibrated against a blackbody at the gold point may replace the blackbody in this part of the calibration.

If only one sectored disk is available, the above calibration may still be carried through, though not quite so satisfactorily because of the possibility of cumulative errors. This substitute method effectively requires a ribbon-filament lamp or other lamp as a substitute for the blackbody. Assume that we have a ribbon-filament lamp calibrated at the gold point, that the single sectored disk has a transmittance of 50%, and that the pyrometer lamp is the one used in obtaining the data of Table III. The procedure is the same as before for the determining of the first two pyrometer currents. Next, however, with the 50% sectored disk removed and with the pyrometer current maintained at 230.1 ma, the temperature of the ribbon-filament lamp is reduced until there is disappearance for the pyrometer filament in the regular manner. Now the ribbon-filament lamp is a substitute for a blackbody at 1280.9°K. Repeating the process, one can step down in brightness by another factor of one-half to a brightness that is one-fourth of the gold-point brightness, and obtain a corresponding new pyrometer current, etc.

The procedure for the calibration above $_0S_\lambda$ differs. Now it becomes necessary to replace the blackbody kept previously at $_0S_\lambda$, by a tungsten-ribbon or other lamp filament whose brightness temperature may be quickly changed from one value to another. First, with the pyrometer current at $i_0$, 252.0 ma for the pyrometer lamp referred to in Table III, part 2, and no sector in place, the matching current through the ribbon filament, $I_0$, is determined. At this current, its brightness temperature is $_0S_\lambda$. (This first step though desirable is not essential.) Then, with a 50% sectored disk introduced and in rotation and the pyrometer current unchanged, the matching current for the ribbon filament, $I_1$, is obtained. A corresponding $_1S_\lambda$ for the ribbon filament is then obtained with the aid of Eq. 50, using $1/t$ or 2.000 for the ratio $B_\lambda/_0B_\lambda$. Next, with the ribbon-filament current still $I_1$ and the sectored disk removed, a new corresponding pyrometer current $i_1$ for a match is obtained. This $i_1$ and the computed $_1S_\lambda$, 277.1 ma and 1396.1°K, as indicated in part 2 of Table III determine a point in the calibration at temperatures above $_0S_\lambda$. Using other sectored disks, somewhat as shown, various $i$'s corresponding to various computed $S_\lambda$'s are determined. These $S_\lambda$'s plotted as a function of $i$, as shown in Fig. 21 of Chapter II, together with those for values of $S_\lambda$ below 1336°K referred to above, form the desired brightness temperature calibration. It shows, for instance, for a particular pyrometer current, say 400.0 ma, that the brightness temperature of a body against which the pyrometer filament is seen to disappear when sighted on that body is 1672°K.  If only one sectored disk is available, a substitute procedure similar to the substitute procedure for the first part of Table III may be used for the second part.

Often, in pyrometry studies, we are interested in spectral brightness variations.  The calibration of a pyrometer for such purposes ordinarily shows spectral brightness as a function of pyrometer lamp

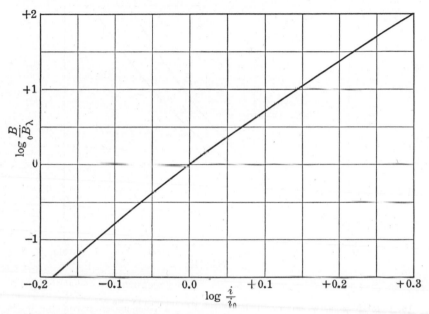

FIG. 30.   Spectral brightness calibration at $\lambda = 0.665 \mu$ for a particular disappearing-filament pyrometer.  The data for this curve are given in Table III.

current.  Since logarithmically the relation is nearly linear, it is customary, for this calibration, to plot $\log B_\lambda /_0 B_\lambda$ as a function of $\log i/i_0$ (Fig. 30).  The slope of the line varies from about 7.0 at $\log i/i_0 = -0.16$ or $S_\lambda = 1120°$K to about 5.9 at $\log i/i_0 = +0.30$ or $S_\lambda = 1850°$K. This means that, at those temperatures, the spectral brightnesses of the pyrometer filament vary about 7.0% and 5.9% for each 1.0% change in the pyrometer currents.

Were one dealing with blackbodies only, calibration curves similar to that shown on p. 51 would suffice for temperature measurements at incandescence.  Dealing with a non-blackbody, one requires the relation between its brightness temperature $S_\lambda$ and its true temperature $T$ or, what is effectively the same, its spectral emissivity or emittance

$\epsilon_\lambda{}'$ or $\epsilon_\lambda$ as a function of $T$ or $S_\lambda$. As described above, these are variously obtained, though most satisfactorily in the case of metals by observations on electrically heated tubular filaments whose walls are pierced with small holes. Granted $T$ or $T - S_\lambda$ as a function of $S_\lambda$, as in Fig. 31 for tungsten, it is a simple matter to obtain $T$ once $S_\lambda$ has been measured with a pyrometer. If, instead, $\epsilon_\lambda$ or $\epsilon_\lambda{}'$ is known, Eq. 49 may be used with $S_\lambda$ to obtain $T$.

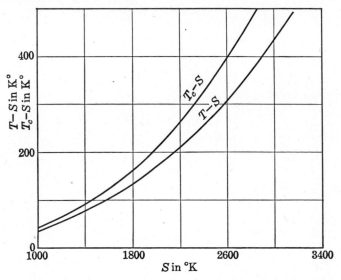

FIG. 31.   $T - S$ and $T_c - S_\lambda$ as a function of $S_\lambda$ for tungsten at wavelength 0.665 $\mu$.

**18. Color-Match Pyrometry.** The purpose of a color-match pyrometer is to determine the temperature of a blackbody whose spectral brightness or steradiancy distribution in the visible region or in the visible and near infra-red regions is like that of the particular source which is being studied. The temperature thus determined is, of course, the color temperature of that body, $T_c$. It is an experimental fact that, for a great many materials, particularly metals, like color temperatures indicate approximately equal true temperatures. Moreover, the color temperature usually is not greatly different from the true temperature, the quantity normally desired. Ordinarily it is much nearer than any spectral brightness temperature $S_\lambda$. To illustrate, for tungsten at 2450°K (see Fig. 21) the approximate operating temperature for the filament of a common, 115-volt, vacuum lamp, $T_c$, which is 2504°K, is but 54 K° greater. Compared, however, with the $S_\lambda$ at 0.665 $\mu$, which is 2233°K, one sees considerable difference. There are four methods which have been used in determining color temperatures.

The first and most direct, but until recently at least unduly long, method of obtaining a color temperature is that of comparing various spectral brightness curves for a blackbody at various known temperatures with the curve for the source in question. It involves the use of a spectrometer or of a spectrophotometer. Employing the recording spectrophotometer developed by A. C. Hardy (1895–   ) at the Massachusetts Institute of Technology, this method yields quick and reliable results and the work entailed is certainly far from being arduous.

The second method, developed by E. P. Hyde (1879–   ), at the General Electric Laboratories at Nela Park, Cleveland, who also introduced the color-temperature concept, consists of making a visual color comparison, using an ordinary photometer and the substitution method of comparison, of the source in question with a blackbody or a calibrated incandescent-lamp standard. A comparison incandescent lamp is required, and two individual color comparisons must be made for each color-temperature determination. Let $A$ be the source whose color temperature can be determined and is desired; $B$, a blackbody or a calibrated standard; and $C$, the comparison lamp. First mount $A$ and $C$ on a standard photometer frame with $A$, say, on the left, $C$ on the right, and a movable photometer head $D$ in between (Fig. 32). $A$ is operated

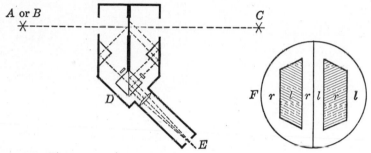

FIG. 32. The photometric arrangement for a color-temperature determination using the second method and the appearance of a balanced field in a good photometer head (contrast type). $A$ is the source whose color temperature is desired; $B$, a color-temperature standard; $C$, a comparison lamp; $D$, a photometer head; $E$, the opening through which the photometric field is viewed. $F$ shows the appearance of the photometric field at brightness match. Parts $l$ and $r$ are illuminated separately by the sources on the left and the right of the photometer head.

under the conditions desired, and $C$ is adjusted to any convenient temperature. Then, with the eye at $E$, the position of $D$ is shifted until the photometric field within is balanced and a judgment is made as to whether that portion illuminated by $C$ is of the same color as that illuminated by $A$ or is reddish or greenish in comparison. If reddish, it is necessary to raise the temperature of $C$ for another trial; if greenish, to lower the temperature. The procedure outlined is to be repeated until an operating condition for $C$ is reached which leads to a judgment of no color difference. Next, standard source $B$ is substituted for source $A$, and the color-matching process is gone through once more. But now $C$ is kept fixed at the previously determined operating condition while source $B$ is manipulated in the manner just described for source $C$. At the finally determined condition of operation for $B$, its color temperature will be the same as that for source $A$ for its condition of operation. This is the temperature sought. Curiously, different observers have different criteria regarding a color-matched photometric field, and only when the substitution method outlined is followed do various observers obtain consistent results.

A rough approximation to a determination of a color temperature by essentially this same second method may be obtained by simple means. The arrangement is shown in Fig. 33. As above, let $A$ be the source whose color temperature is desired, and $B$ a calibrated color-temperature standard. If the test is carried out in an otherwise darkened room, the shadows $M$ and $N$ of an opaque object such as a pencil at $E$ will be illuminated separately by sources $A$ and $B$. By changing the distances of the sources from $M$ and $N$ relatively, it is always possible to get a brightness balance for the shadows and then to determine whether $N$ is reddish or greenish in comparison with $M$ and to vary the temperature of $B$ accordingly. When the shadows have the same color, the sources are color matched and the color temperature of $A$ may be obtained from the calibration curve or chart of the standard $B$.

The third method is due to W. E. Forsythe (1881– ) of the General Electric Laboratories at Nela Park, Cleveland. An ordinary disappearing-filament pyrometer

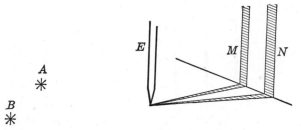

Fig. 33. Photometric arrangement for the rough determination of color temperatures by the comparison of shadows, a simplification of the more precise second method. $A$ is the source whose color temperature is desired; $B$ is a standard source; $E$ is an opaque object such as a pencil; $M$ and $N$ are shadows of $E$.

is used, first with one, say red, pyrometer filter and then another, say blue, filter. Let the effective wavelengths of transmission of these filters be $0.665\ \mu$ and $0.467\ \mu$. Theory shows that, when these red and blue brightnesses are expressed in terms of the corresponding brightnesses of a blackbody at the gold point seen through the same filters, we have

$$\ln\frac{(B/B_0)_r}{(B/B_0)_b} = c_2\left(\frac{1}{\lambda_b}-\frac{1}{\lambda_r}\right)\left(\frac{1}{T_c}-\frac{1}{T_0}\right)$$

$$= 9120\ \text{K}°\left(\frac{1}{T_c}-\frac{1}{1336°\text{K}}\right) \tag{53}$$

the constant of which is based on a value of $14{,}320\ \mu\text{K}°$ for $c_2$. One may, of course, select a different base temperature. In that case, the selected temperature replaces $1336°\text{K}$ in Eq. 53. When graphed, Eq. 53 yields a straight line with a zero value for the logarithm at $1336°\text{K}$ and a physical slope of $9120\ \text{K}°$. In making a $T_c$ determination for a source using Forsythe's method, one determines a "red-blue ratio" in the manner described and then reads the appropriate $T_c$ from a plot or computes it by means of Eq. 53.

The fourth method is due to H. W. Russell (1901– ) and C. F. Lucks of the Battelle Memorial Institute of Columbus, Ohio, and R. Turnbull (1905– ) of St. Lawrence Alloys and Metals, Ltd., Quebec, Canada. The principle is like that of Forsythe's method. The procedure, however, is much simplified. An instrument (Fig. 34) was devised for making the direct determination of the ratio of a red steradiancy to a green steradiancy.  Photoelectric cells with pyrometer filters are used as receivers.  In any particular case, the ratio of responses is determined electrically. A calibration curve showing this ratio as a function of temperature is obtained using a blackbody as a source.  Determining the color temperature of any source thereafter is a matter of finding its red-green ratio and then reading the proper color temperature from the calibration plot.

Though color temperatures determined by the various methods described will ordinarily check well they will not always do so, a consequence of the fact that the different methods assume different definitions for the term color temperature.

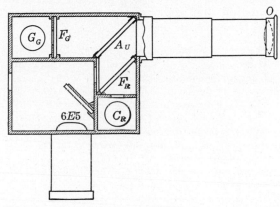

FIG 34.   The color-match pyrometer of Russel, Lucks, and Turnbull.  $A_U$ is a semi-transparent gold mirror; $F_R$ and $F_G$ are red and green filters; $C_R$ and $C_G$ are photoelectric cells responding essentially to the red and the green rays entering the instrument.  A resistance balancing arrangement is not shown   (*J. Optical Soc. Am.*, **30**, 248, 1940.)

Given a color temperature $T_c$ for a body, one cannot tell its true temperature $T$ without a calibration showing for the body $T = f(T_c)$ or $\epsilon_c' = f(T_c)$.  The quantity $\epsilon_c'$ of a source, called its color emissivity, is defined as the ratio of its brightness to that of a blackbody whose spectral brightness or spectral steradiancy distribution it matches.  In equation form this is

$$\epsilon_c' = \frac{\epsilon_\lambda' e^{-c_2/\lambda T}}{e^{-c_2/\lambda T_c}} \tag{54}$$

where for $\lambda$ any wavelength involved in the color match may be used.  Given the two comparison wavelengths, say $\lambda_r$ for the red and $\lambda_b$ for the blue, and the corresponding spectral emissivities $\epsilon_{\lambda r}'$ and $\epsilon_{\lambda b}'$, $\epsilon_c'$ may be determined from a relation derivable from blackbody and non-blackbody considerations.

$$\ln \epsilon_c' = \frac{\lambda_r \ln \epsilon_{\lambda}r' - \lambda_b \ln \epsilon_{\lambda}'b}{\lambda_r - \lambda_b} \tag{55}$$

Given the results of a spectral radiation pyrometry study of a source, both of the functions, $T = f(T_c)$ and $\epsilon_c' = f(T_c)$, follow directly.

In industry, determinations of $T_c$ often suffice as approximations for $T$ or in place of $T$.

**19. Measurement of Flame Temperatures.** In speaking of flame temperatures, one should keep in mind that the temperature of a single flame varies greatly from one region to another. All such temperatures measured are therefore average temperatures, or temperatures of some characteristic region, usually the region of the highest temperature. There are at least ten ways of measuring flame temperatures. Of these, only two will be described in some detail. See in this connection the excellent descriptions * given by H. C. Hottel (1903–   ) and F. P. Broughton, fuel engineers at the Massachusetts Institute of Technology. The methods are—

(a) *The "High-Velocity"-Thermocouple Method.* The gas flame is drawn past the hot junction of a thermocouple at a high speed. When, with further increase of speed, there is no appreciable increase of temperature of the junction, it is assumed to be at the temperature of the flame. The thermocouple is then used in the regular manner to determine the temperature.

(b) *The Shielded-Thermocouple Method.* The hot junction of a thermocouple is provided with shields whose construction should be such that both their outer and inner surfaces are bathed by the flames and are at about the temperature of the flames. The couple is then used in the ordinary manner.

(c) *The Thermocouple Extrapolation Method.* The smaller the thermocouple wires, the higher their temperatures when immersed in a flame. With many wires of different diameters it is possible to extrapolate temperatures to zero thickness of wire to obtain the flame temperature.

(d) *The Method Employing an Electrically Heated Thermocouple Junction.* One of the two junctions of a thermocouple is welded to a metal wire or ribbon that may be heated electrically without damage while in the flame. The thermocouple is then operated as a high-velocity thermocouple. The temperature of the junction which, for some particular heating current, is independent of the speed of the hot flame gases passing by is the temperature sought.

(e) *The Hot-Wire Extrapolation Method.* This method applies only to flames that are fairly transparent, whose temperatures are below the melting point of platinum, and whose component gases do not attack platinum. Into some specified region in such a flame, one introduces in succession several short lengths of small platinum wire which have different diameters. With the aid of an optical pyrometer, the temperatures of the wires are determined and then graphed as a function of the diameter of the wire. Such graphs always show an increase in temperature with decrease in wire diameter. The assumption is made that the temperature obtained by extrapolating the curve to zero wire diameter is the temperature of the flame in the region where the wires were located. That extrapolated temperature is then taken as the temperature sought.

(f) *The Method Employing an Electrically Heated Wire Calibrated in a Vacuum.* An alloy or platinum wire suitably mounted is first operated in a vacuum and its current-temperature calibration is obtained with the aid of an optical pyrometer. A similar calibration is then obtained with the wire in the flame. Plotted on the same graph the two calibration curves will cross. Obviously the temperature corresponding to the crossing point is the temperature of the flame. The nature of the wire's surface must remain unchanged if this method is to yield reliable results.

* H. C. Hottel and F. P. Broughton, *Ind. Eng. Chem.*, **4**, 166, 1932.

(g) *The Method Employing an Incandescent-Lamp Filament as Background.* This method is only applicable where the flame itself contains incandescent solid particles, as in luminous hydrocarbon flames. With the aid of an optical pyrometer, a brightness temperature of the lamp filament is sought for the condition where, for a given current through the lamp, the reading obtained with the optical pyrometer is the same whether or not the flame is present between the lamp and the pyrometer. In accord with the theoretically sound basis that the spectral absorptance of a flame equals its spectral emittance, this brightness temperature is the temperature of the flame.

(h) *The Mirror Method.* Like method g, this method is limited to flames containing incandescent particles. Using an optical pyrometer, the flame is first observed against a dark background and then with a mirror in place of the background so that then the observed flame brightness is increased by the reflected flame brightness, reduced, however, by the absorptance of the flame on the passage of the light backward through it. Assuming zero reflectance for the flame, but taking into account the reflectance of the mirror, it is easy to see how the spectral absorptance, hence also the spectral emittance, of the flame may be determined. Application of Eq. 51a to this spectral emittance and the brightness temperature of the unmirrored flame yields its temperature.

(i) *The Two-Color Optical Pyrometer Method.* This method, like methods g and h, is applicable only to flames containing incandescent particles. It is discussed in some detail below.

(j) *The Line-Reversal Method.* This method is particularly applicable to nonluminous flames, though it is not necessarily so limited. It is discussed in some detail below.

**20. Two-Color, Optical-Pyrometer Method of Determining Flame Temperatures.** This method applies only to flames in which very small solid particles are supplied to or are produced in the flame at a uniform rate, as occurs, for example, in the carbon-particle formation of gas flames burning hydrocarbon fuels. The method, which is described in detail by Hottel and Broughton in the paper referred to above, makes use of a disappearing-filament optical pyrometer with two separate color filters. It was developed especially for the measurement of temperatures in gas-fired furnaces, where the other methods listed above are thought, for the most part, to be very difficult to apply. Methods g and h listed above would seem to be possible exceptions, however.

The effective wavelengths of the color filters used by Hottel and Broughton, as determined for the region of temperatures common in hydrocarbon flames, were found to be about $0.6651 \mu$ and $0.5553 \mu$. The former filter was and here will be referred to as a red filter, the latter as a green filter.

Through an opening in the wall of the furnace, the pyrometer is sighted on a portion of the flame body seen against a completely dark background, which, if not normally present, must be provided. With the red and the green color filters in place, corresponding brightness temperatures of the flame $S_R$ and $S_G$ are determined. Their relation to the true temperature of the flame $T$ in accord with Eq. 51a are given by

$$\frac{1}{T} = \frac{1}{S_R} + \frac{\lambda_R}{c_2} \ln \epsilon_R \tag{56}$$

$$\frac{1}{T} = \frac{1}{S_G} + \frac{\lambda_G}{c_2} \ln \epsilon_G \tag{57}$$

of which $\epsilon_R$ and $\epsilon_G$ are spectral emittances. Since the flame is ordinarily far from opaque, these equations involve emittances rather than emissivities. Obviously, if $\epsilon_R$ and $\epsilon_G$ could be found, each of the two equations could be used separately to yield values for $T$. Obviously, also, if only a relation between $\epsilon_R$ and $\epsilon_G$ which does not involve other unknowns could be found, the two equations could be used simultaneously to yield a single value for $T$. In effect, Hottel and Broughton followed this

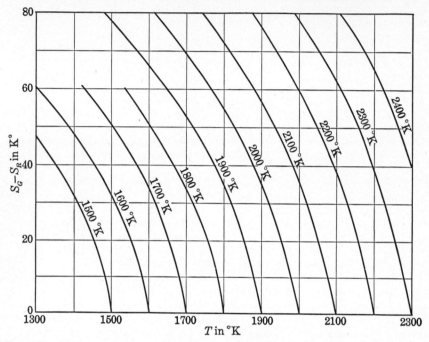

FIG. 35. A graph for hydrocarbon flames, which are luminous by virtue of incandescent carbon particles, showing, for various flame temperatures, the dependency on $S_R$ of $S_G - S_R$, the green brightness temperature for $0.5553\ \mu$ less the red brightness temperature for $0.6651\ \mu$. This graph is based on a graph published by Hottel and Broughton.

procedure. From measurements of the spectral absorptances of several thin layers of carbon soot of varying thickness from various sources, it was concluded that, throughout the visible spectrum, spectral absorptances for such flames were represented fairly well by $(1 - e^{-kL/\lambda^{1.39}})$ of which $k$ is an absorption constant characteristic of the flame under study and $L$ its thickness. Since, in accord with Eqs. 36a and 37a, spectral absorptances and spectral emittances are identical in value, we may write

$$\epsilon_R = 1 - e^{-kL/\lambda_R^{1.39}} = \alpha_R \tag{58}$$

$$\epsilon_G = 1 - e^{-kL/\lambda_G^{1.39}} = \alpha_R \tag{59}$$

Elimination of $kL$ leads at once to

$$\lambda_R^{1.39} \ln\ (1 - \alpha_R) = \lambda_G^{1.39} \ln\ (1 - \alpha_G) \tag{60}$$

Evidently Eq. 60 can serve as the third relation which, along with Eqs. 56 and 57, can be used in finding a flame temperature. The actual carrying out of a determination of $T$, once values for $S_R$ and $S_G$ have been obtained, is quite involved, and Hottel and Broughton have presented a graph which shows for various combinations of $S_R$ and $(S_G - S_R)$ the $T$'s that result. Fig. 35, plotted on a slightly different basis from that used by them, shows the interrelations expected.

In order to test their theory, Hottel and Broughton used six nearly identical acetylene flames whose $S_R$ and $S_G$ were determined singly, in twos, in threes, in fours, etc., always with all the flames being used in the line of sighting with the pyrometer. The results are shown in Table IV.

## TABLE IV

SUMMARY OF RESULTS FOR THE TEMPERATURE OF CERTAIN AMYL ACETATE FLAMES OBTAINED BY HOTTEL AND BROUGHTON IN THE APPLICATION OF THEIR TWO-COLOR, OPTICAL-PYROMETER METHOD OF MEASURING FLAME TEMPERATURES

All values have been rounded to eliminate tenths of degrees.

| No. of Flames | $S_R$ °K | $S_G$ °K | $T$ °K | Deviations K° |
|---|---|---|---|---|
| 1 | 1475 | 1528 | 1696 | + 1 |
| 2 | 1536 | 1582 | 1705 | -| 10 |
| 3 | 1583 | 1619 | 1696 | + 1 |
| 4 | 1600 | 1632 | 1693 | − 2 |
| 5 | 1621 | 1649 | 1697 | + 2 |
| 6 | 1635 | 1656 | 1685 | −10 |
| ∞ | 1696 | 1694 | | |
| Av. | | 1695 | 1695 | |

It is interesting to note how, with increasing thickness, there is a gradual approach to blackbody conditions. Assume $n$ equal flames in line of sight. Let $B_{\lambda 1}$ be the spectral brightness of each of the flames taken singly, and $\tau_\lambda$ the transmittance of each flame. Consider the addition to $B_{\lambda 1}$ of the first flame which each successive flame yields. Flame 2, for instance, adds to the luminous flux in the direction of the pyrometer only what is transmitted by flame 1. Its spectral brightness contribution is $\tau_\lambda B_{\lambda 1}$. Similarly, flame 3 contributes $\tau_\lambda^2 B_{\lambda 1}$; flame 4, $\tau_\lambda^3 B_{\lambda 1}$, etc. The spectral brightness for the $n$ flames $B_{\lambda n}$ is obviously

$$B_{\lambda n} = B_{\lambda 1}(1 + \tau_\lambda + \tau_\lambda^2 + \cdots \tau_\lambda^{n-1}) \qquad (61)$$

The method of building up the brightness is quite the same as the building up of the brightness of a small opening leading to a blackbody cavity (see Eq. 17). Actually it may be shown that, if the reflectance of the flame is zero, the spectral brightness $B_{\lambda \infty}$ for an infinite line-up of equal flames is that of a blackbody at the temperature of the flames.

Values in the column of Table IV headed $T$ were obtained, in effect, from a graph similar to that of Fig. 35. For example, for the case of one flame, one looks for the $T$ corresponding to the coordinates 1475°K for $S_R$ and 53 K° for $(S_G - S_R)$. The values for an infinite number of flames under $S_R$ and $S_G$ are average true temperatures based on an extension of method $h$ above. The precise agreement of the averages speaks well for the underlying theory.

Inspection of Table IV shows, for each combination of flames, a green brightness temperature which is considerably in excess of the red brightness temperature. Such an excess, by itself, does not prove that a green emittance is greater than the corresponding red emittance. Actually, however, the magnitudes of these excesses are sufficient to insure that the green emittances are the greater. What the emittances are for certain cases is the subject of a problem at the end of the chapter. On account of this variation of emittance with wavelength, one should not expect the color temperature of a flame to equal its true temperature.

In the original paper, it is shown how, with the aid of $k^L$ which the authors determined, it is also possible to determine total emittances.

In one small respect only does it seem possible to criticize the method. Throughout, it is assumed that the reflectance of a flame is zero. This is probably not true. On the other hand, the reflectance is very small, probably less than 1%, and the effect of this neglect is probably less than the uncertainties of measurement.

### 21. Line-Reversal Method of Determining Flame Temperatures.

This method has proved to be the most satisfactory for measuring flame temperatures. It was developed and first used by Féry in France in 1903. Whenever light from an incandescent source, as from an ordinary incandescent lamp, passes through a flame yielding a bright-line spectrum, the flame will absorb, from the light from the lamp passing through it, those radiations which the flame itself can and does radiate. If one then focuses the light under consideration upon the narrowed slit of a spectrometer (Fig. 36) and views it through the eyepiece, he will see, depending on conditions, the continuous spectrum of the incandescent filament crossed by (a) dark lines characteristic of the flame, (b) bright lines characteristic of the flame, or (c) no lines characteristic of the flame, when conditions are balanced.

The gas of a flame is like any solid in that it absorbs, emits, and transmits radiant energy. The underlying law relating the magnitudes of the effects produced is the Kirchhoff law discussed above in connection with solids. As a consequence, a flame, which is seen against a blackbody at the temperature that it possesses, disappears against its background. No detail can be seen, much as in the case of an object in equilibrium in a uniformly heated, opaque cavity. Actually this could be true only were the temperatures of the background and the flame both uniform. In the case of light focused as in Fig. 36 this condition of uniformity is effectively realized.

If now the temperature of the flame, which we shall assume in the further discussion to have been colored as is usually done by the introduction of a small amount of common salt, NaCl, is higher than the brightness temperature of the lamp filament, the flame, in accord with Kirchhoff's law, will emit more sodium light than it absorbs from the beam from the lamp filament; and, at the eyepiece of the spectrometer, one should see bright sodium lines crossing a continuous spectrum.

If, on the other hand, the temperature of the flame is lower than the brightness temperature of the lamp filament, the conditions are reversed and one should see dark sodium lines crossing a continuous spectrum. If, finally, the two temperatures are the same, one should see neither dark nor bright lines. Consequently, in making a flame-temperature measurement, one adjusts the temperature of the incandescent filament until the balanced brightness condition of neither dark nor bright sodium lines is seen by the eye at the spectrometer

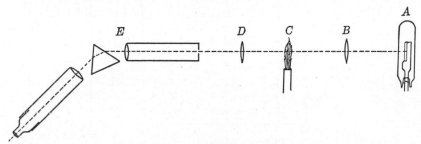

FIG. 36. Arrangement of apparatus for the line-reversal method of measuring flame temperatures. *A* is a ribbon filament incandescent lamp calibrated as to brightness temperature; *B* is a converging lens for focusing light from *A* onto some chosen portion of the flame *C* whose temperature is to be measured; *D* is a converging lens for focusing light from *A* and *C* on the slit of spectrophotometer *E*. In use it is necessary to have an eyepiece in the telescope of the spectrometer.

eyepiece. He then takes, as the temperature of the source, the brightness temperature of the filament for the wavelength characteristic of sodium light, a quantity which normally will be determined with an optical pyrometer following a method outlined above. In the seeking of the condition of balance, the greatest sensitivity is obtained when the slit is narrowed to a very fine line. In the discussion above, the brightness temperatures are strictly brightness temperatures as reduced by reflections at the bulb of the lamp and the lens between the lamp and the flame.

Fig. 37 shows results published in France in 1912 by A. Bauer. A special Meker burner with a rectangular, gauze-covered opening 8 mm by 40 mm burning commercial illuminating gas was used. The temperature distribution shown in the figure was obtained from sightings parallel to the 8-mm dimension. The temperatures found for the central part of the flame were remarkably constant. It is interesting that the highest temperatures occurred near the edges of the flame where the  as coming through the burner mixed with air diffusing into the flame from the outside. Of course the line of sight for positions between $-7$ mm and $+7$ mm included two such high-temperature regions, and, if these centrally observed temperatures were corrected for these outer regions, lower temperatures than those shown would have been obtained for the central region.

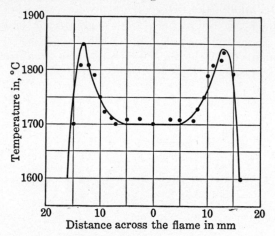

FIG. 37.   The temperature distribution for the flame from a special Meker burner with an opening 8 mm by 40 mm burning commercial illuminating gas, as obtained by M.E. Bauer, using the line-reversal method (*Ann. chim. phys.*, **29**, 372, 1913).

Fig. 38 shows some results obtained by H. Kaveler (1905–   ) and B. Lewis (1899–   ) at the Bureau of Mines in Pittsburgh in a line-reversal study of the effect on flame temperatures of a change in the

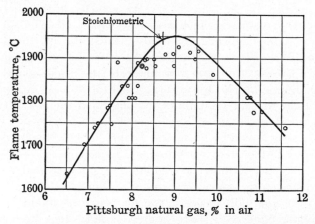

FIG. 38.   Graph of the results obtained by Kaveler and Lewis showing observed highest temperatures in flames burning natural gas as a function of the gas content of the fuel, natural gas, and air.   The full line represents theoretically computed temperatures.   (By permission, B. Lewis and G. von Elbe, *Combustion, Flames, and Explosions of Gases*, p. 342, Cambridge, England, University Press, 1938.)

relative amounts of air and gas supplied to a flame. It is interesting that the mixture yielding the highest temperature for the hottest portion of the flame should have a lower percentage of air (greater of gas) than that, the stoichiometric percentage, which yields complete combustion of the gas.

## PROBLEMS

**1.** A uniform spherical globule ($r = 2.0$ mm) of tungsten at its melting point, 3655°K, has a total radiant flux output of about 60 watts. What are its radiancy, its steradiancy, and the irradiancy which it will produce on a small, perfectly diffusing, plane surface 20 cm away when the incident angle is 30°?

**2.** Given that the total reflectance of the small plane surface of problem 1 is 60% and that its area is 5 cm², what are its reflected radiancy and average steradiancy as a secondary source due to the presence of the tungsten globule?

**3.** What are the radiant flux, the radiant intensity, the radiancy and the average steradiancy of the sun? The mean distance from the earth to the sun is $149.5 \times 10^6$ km. The sun's radius is $6.96 \times 10^5$ km.

**4.** In the text, it is stated that a certain typical radiometer with 5.0-mm² vanes mounted 1.5 mm from the central axis had a sensitivity of $4.6 \times 10^{-9}$ watt/mm deflection at 1-m scale distance. In order to have a radiometer deflection of just 1 mm at a meter's distance produced thereby, at what distance from one of the vanes would it be necessary to place a glowing Cuban firefly whose steady rate of emission of radiant energy is about 100 ergs/sec and whose luminous intensity is about $\frac{1}{1600}$ candle?

**5.** Given that a bolometer such as is diagrammed in Fig. 6 has approximately 8.6 ohms as the resistances of each of its two nearly equal platinum strips $A$ and $B$ when at its normal operating temperature, has 54 ohms as the resistances of each of the coils $C$ and $D$, and requires 5000 ohms as the resistance of $R$ when the instrument is balanced and ready for operation but not exposed to the radiation to be measured; determine the increase in temperature of one of the strips brought about by exposing it to an external source if when so exposed 5001 ohms are required at $R$ for a balance. The value of $(T\,dR)/(R\,dT)$ for platinum at 500°C, the assumed operating temperature, is about 1.078.

**6.** What are the solar constants at Mercury, Mars, and Neptune, whose mean distances from the sun are about 0.39, 1.52, and 30 times that of the earth?

**7.** The transmittance to sea level of a clear atmosphere for the sun's radiation with the sun at the zenith and at an elevation of 30°, as given by Abbot, are 70% and 56%; determine the actual rates of incidence of solar radiation for these conditions on a horizontal surface at sea level.

**8.** What must be the current passing through a 10-ohm manganin resistance in one of the two chambers of an Abbot water-flow pyrheliometer to balance, at sea level on a clear day at a time when the sun is overhead, the effect in the other chamber produced by solar radiation entering through a 10-cm² opening?

**9.** The total emissivity of tungsten at 300°K is about 0.018. At about what rates is radiant energy absorbed, reflected, and emitted by 1.00 cm² of polished tungsten in equilibrium with a closed chamber whose temperature is 300°K? What at 1000°K, at which temperature the total emissivity is about 0.115?

**10.** Two small metal pipes $A$ and $B$ of the same shape and size, which are used to carry water at 100°C through an evacuated chamber whose walls are at 25°C, differ only in that the surface of $A$ is polished copper and has a total emissivity of about 0.07 for the temperature range considered while the surface of $B$ is polished copper covered with clear lacquer and has a total emittance of about 0.7. What is the ratio of the radiation loss from $A$ to that from $B$?

**11.** A straight tungsten filament ($r = 0.0010$ cm) mounted in a large evacuated lamp bulb and heated to 2450°K is suddenly switched off. Given that the density of the tungsten is 19.2 gm/cm³, that its specific heat is 0.045 cal/(gm K°), and that its total emissivity at 2450°K is 0.300, determine the initial rate of cooling of the filament.

**12.** Using a Féry total radiation pyrometer in a room with surroundings at 300°K, a galvanometer deflection of 4.5 divisions is obtained when sighted on a blackbody at 500°K. What deflection is expected when sighted into a furnace at 1800°K?

**13.** A Féry total radiation pyrometer in a room at 90°F is sighted on a painted wall at 300°F and a deflection of 45 divisions is obtained. When it is sighted on a body at the same temperature whose known total emittance is 90%, the deflection is 55 divisions. What is the total emittance of the painted wall? Though it is ordinarily not strictly true, assume the objects at 300°F to have total reflectances of 100% less their emittances for the radiations from their surroundings.

**14.** In planning a Mendenhall open-wedge blackbody for the study of platinum, whose spectral emissivities are of the order of 0.29, it is desirable to provide for a blackness of 99.8%. How many components for $B_0$ must be provided? What is the largest wedge angle that may be used for symmetrical viewing?

**15.** Using data to be found elsewhere, as in the *International Critical Tables*, plot a spectral radiancy curve for a blackbody at 1200°K. Using Wien's displacement law, plot on the same sheet the spectral radiancy curve for 1336°K. Plan the scale in advance so that the maximum $\mathcal{R}_\lambda$ of the 1336°K curve will fall on the sheet.

**16.** Assuming that the brightness of a blackbody varies approximately as $\mathcal{R}_\lambda$ at 0.56 $\mu$, compute and plot the relative brightnesses of a blackbody at 1000°K, 1336°K, 1500°K, 2000°K, and 2500°K, expressed in terms of that at 1336°K, as a function of temperature. Use Wien's distribution law. Plot the data also with log $B$ as a function of log $T$.

**17.** Compute for $\lambda = 0.665$ $\mu$ the apparent brightness temperatures of a blackbody at 1336.0°K as seen through rotating sectored disks whose transmittances are 40% and 20%.

**18.** Compute for $\lambda = 0.665$ $\mu$ the brightness temperatures of sources which, when seen through rotating sectored disks whose transmittances are 20% and 40%, have apparent brightness temperatures of 1336.0°K.

**19.** The spectral emissivity of platinum for $\lambda = 0.665$ $\mu$ at its melting point 2046°K is about 0.300. What is the corresponding spectral brightness temperature?

**20.** The brightness temperature of polished silver for $\lambda = 0.665$ $\mu$ at its melting point is 1047°K. Given that its spectral emissivity is 0.044, what is the melting-point temperature that results?

**21.** Pyrometer currents of 196.2 ma and 252.0 ma were obtained when the pyrometer for which data are plotted in Fig. 22 of Chapter II was sighted on the surface and on the hole of a tubular filament of gold (see Fig. 14). What are the spectral brightness temperature, true temperature, and spectral emissivity that result?

**22.** Using the data for the tungsten pyrometer lamp given in part 2 of Table III, determine its $(dS_\lambda/S_\lambda)/(di/i)$, that is, its percentage change in brightness temperature per 1% change in heating current, at the middle of the range. For this purpose plot log $S_\lambda = f(\log i)$.

**23.** The color emissivity of tungsten at its melting point 3655°K is about 0.325. The spectral emissivity for 0.665 $\mu$ at this temperature is about 0.40. What is the corresponding color temperature?

**24.** For molybdenum at 2000°K, the spectral emissivities for 0.665 $\mu$ and 0.467 $\mu$ are 0.353 and 0.379; what are the corresponding color temperature and color emissivity?

**25.** In an experiment for determining the temperature of a gas flame by the line reversal method (Fig. 36), the pyrometer whose calibration is given in Table III was used. The pyrometer current for $\lambda = 0.665\mu$, obtained when the pyrometer was sighted on the background filament through a 90° rotating disk, was 540 ma. Given that, at each glass surface, as a consequence of light reflected, there is a reduction of about 4% in the apparent brightness of the source viewed, determine the flame temperature that is to be computed.

# APPENDIX I

## DERIVATION OF MAXWELL'S EQUATION FOR THE VELOCITY DISTRIBUTION OF THE MOLECULES OF AN IDEAL GAS COMPOSED OF IDENTICAL MOLECULES *

The distribution derived is based on probability considerations. The assumptions made are the following:

1. That, for the various elements of volume constituting the total volume of gas under consideration, if not chosen too small, the molecular velocity distributions do not differ perceptibly. Such elements of volume are called macroscopic.

2. That the molecular velocity distribution for any specified macroscopic element of volume does not change with time.

3. That $f(u)$, $f(v)$, and $f(w)$, the functional distributions of the $u$-, $v$-, $w$-velocity components, that is the $x$-, $y$-, $z$-velocity components, for all macroscopic elements are identical in form.

4. That changes in the $u, v, w$ for a particular molecule are independent of each other.

5. That the laws of impact obey the classical laws of mechanics and that there is conservation for both momentum and translational kinetic energy.

6. That the fractional number of molecules engaged in impacts at any instant is negligibly small.

With the possible exception of 6, all the foregoing assumptions seem very reasonable. In so far as that assumption is not fulfilled, the derivation here given is not valid. The failure of the assumption was pointed out by Boltzmann, who, in a separate derivation, took account of the impacts that occurred. The law derived was exactly that obtained by Maxwell. On the basis of the ideal gas law

$$pv = RT \qquad (1)$$

and the understanding that it applies not only to moderate and high densities but also to extremely low densities where the condition of a negligibly small number of impacts at any instant is realized, one

---

* See L. B. Loeb, *Kinetic Theory of Gases*, 1st ed., pp. 71 ff. New York, McGraw-Hill Book Co., 1927. The general method of treatment is much like that given there.

would normally expect that the law derived by Maxwell for negligible impacts would apply to conditions where the number of impacts at any instant are not negligible.

Let the various vectors of Fig. 1, all drawn with a common origin, represent in magnitude and direction a sample of the instantaneous

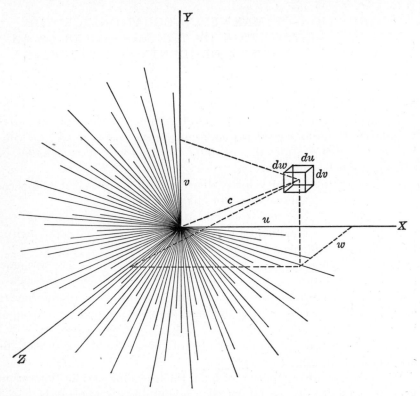

FIG. 1.  A velocity-space diagram representing in magnitude and direction a sample of an instantaneous distribution of the velocities of the molecules of a homogeneous gas in a microscopic element of volume under equilibrium conditions.

distribution of the velocities of the molecules in a macroscopic element of volume.   A vector whose outer terminus is given by $(u, v, w)$ has both its direction and magnitude $c$ determined thereby, $c$ being specified by the equation

$$c^2 = u^2 + v^2 + w^2 \tag{2}$$

In view of assumptions 1 and 2, Fig. 1 applies as well to the whole volume of gas under consideration at all times as to the gas in a particular macroscopic element of volume at some one instant.

For the probability that any velocity vector has an $x$-component lying between $u - \frac{1}{2}du$ and $u + \frac{1}{2}du$, let us write $f(u)\,du$. For the corresponding $y$- and $z$-components, let us similarly write, in view of assumption 3, $f(v)\,dv$ and $f(w)\,dw$. For the probability $dP$ that any single velocity vector shall simultaneously have the specified $x$-, $y$-, $z$-components, that is that, in the "velocity-space" diagram of Fig. 1, its velocity vector shall terminate in the element of volume of dimensions $du, dv, dw$ centered at $(u, v, w)$, we then have

$$dP = f(u)f(v)f(w)\,du\,dv\,dw \qquad (3)$$

Obviously corresponding to the specified $u, v, w$ combination, there is a definite $c$ as given by Eq. 2, and we may also write

$$dP = F(c)\,du\,dv\,dw \qquad (4)$$

of which, since $c$ is constant for the specified $du, dv, dw$ element, $F(c)$ is also constant. From Eqs. 3 and 4, there follows

$$f(u)f(v)f(w) = F(c) \qquad (5)$$

Consider next the change in the product $f(u)f(v)f(w)$ that results from the condition of changes in $u, v,$ and $w$ but no change in $c$ and hence in $F(c)$. Let $d'u, d'v, d'w$, primed to distinguish them from $du, dv, dw$ which are the dimensions of the "velocity-space" element, represent differential changes in $u, v,$ and $w$, subject as stated to no change in $c$. Forming the differential of $f(u)f(v)f(w)$, we have

$$f'(u)f(v)f(w)\,d'u + f(u)f'(v)f(w)\,d'v + f(u)f(v)f'(w)\,d'w = 0 \qquad (6)$$

Dividing through by $f(u)f(v)f(w)$, we obtain

$$\frac{f'(u)}{f(u)}\,d'u + \frac{f'(v)}{f(v)}\,d'v + \frac{f'(w)}{f(w)}\,d'w = 0 \qquad (7)$$

This condition of change of probabilities is necessarily accompanied by the added condition specified by Eq. 2, for the case of a constant $c$

$$u\,d'u + v\,d'v + w\,d'w = c\,d'c = 0 \qquad (8)$$

Multiplying Eq. 8 by an undetermined constant $\lambda$ and adding to Eq. 7, we obtain

$$\left(\frac{f'(u)}{f(u)} + \lambda u\right)d'u + \left(\frac{f'(v)}{f(v)} + \lambda v\right)d'v + \left(\frac{f'(w)}{f(w)} + \lambda w\right)d'w = 0 \qquad (9)$$

On the basis of assumption 4 above, it follows that the three portions of Eq. 9 inclosed in parentheses represent independent relations and that we may write

$$\frac{f'(u)}{f(u)} d'u = -\lambda u \, d'u \tag{10}$$

$$\frac{f'(v)}{f(v)} d'v = -\lambda v \, d'v \tag{11}$$

$$\frac{f'(w)}{f(w)} d'w = -\lambda w \, d'w \tag{12}$$

Integration yields

$$f(u) = A e^{-\frac{\lambda}{2} u^2} \tag{13}$$

$$f(v) = A e^{-\frac{\lambda}{2} v^2} \tag{14}$$

$$f(w) = A e^{-\frac{\lambda}{2} w^2} \tag{15}$$

The justification for a common integration constant leading to $A$ is a second consequence of assumption 3 above. Replacing the undetermined constant $\lambda$ by $2/\alpha^2$ ($\alpha$ will be given an interpretation later), we obtain

$$f(u) \, du = A e^{\frac{-u^2}{\alpha^2}} du \tag{16}$$

as the probability that a randomly chosen molecule shall have a velocity component between $u - du/2$ and $u + du/2$. If in a specified volume there are $N$ molecules the number that may be expected with such velocity components is

$$dN_u = \frac{\partial N}{\partial u} du = NA e^{\frac{-u^2}{\alpha^2}} du \tag{17}$$

Similarly we have

$$dN_v = \frac{\partial N}{\partial v} dv = NA e^{\frac{-v^2}{\alpha^2}} dv \tag{18}$$

$$dN_w = \frac{\partial N}{\partial w} dw = NA e^{\frac{-w^2}{\alpha^2}} dw \tag{19}$$

Once constants $A$ and $\alpha$ are evaluated, Eqs. 17 to 19 may be used to describe the distribution separately of the $u$-, $v$-, $w$-velocity components of the molecules of an ideal gas.

The evaluations of $A$ and $\alpha$ follow.   We have obviously

$$N = \int dN_u = NA \int_{-\infty}^{\infty} e^{-\frac{u^2}{\alpha^2}} du = NA\alpha\sqrt{\pi} \qquad (20)$$

$$A = \frac{1}{\alpha\sqrt{\pi}} \qquad (21)$$

The same value would have been obtained had we set $N$ equal to $\int dN_v$ or to $\int dN_w$.   It is now possible to write in place of Eqs. 17 to 19

$$N_u = \frac{\partial N}{\partial u} = Nf(u) = \frac{N}{\alpha\sqrt{\pi}} e^{-\frac{u^2}{\alpha^2}} \qquad (22)$$

$$N_v = \frac{\partial N}{\partial v} = Nf(v) = \frac{N}{\alpha\sqrt{\pi}} e^{-\frac{v^2}{\alpha^2}} \qquad (23)$$

$$N_w = \frac{\partial N}{\partial w} = Nf(w) = \frac{N}{\alpha\sqrt{\pi}} e^{-\frac{w^2}{\alpha^2}} \qquad (24)$$

The variation of $N_u$ with $u$ for an arbitrarily chosen $\alpha$, that for oxygen at 0°C, is shown in Fig. 2.   With zero values for $N_u$ at both extremes and a maximum value at zero $u$, the curve is seen in the form of its equation and its shape to be like that of the normal frequency

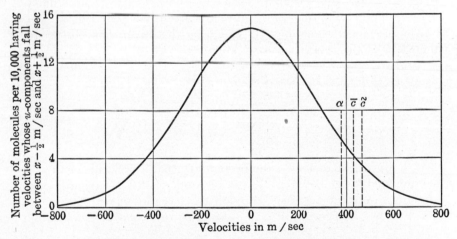

FIG. 2.   A diagram showing the frequency distribution of $u$-components of the velocities of 10,000 molecules of oxygen at 0°C.   The distributions for the $v$- and $w$-components are identical with that given for the $u$-component.   $\alpha = 377$ m/sec, $c = 425$ m/sec, $\bar{c} = 462$ m/sec.   See Fig. 2 of chapter VIII for the frequency distribution of their speeds.

distribution or "error curve." The significance of $\alpha$ remains to be seen. It should be emphasized that $N_u$ is not a number of molecules. Instead it is the number of molecules per unit change of $u$. One unit for its expression is the reciprocal cm/sec, that is $(cm/sec)^{-1}$. Only when one performs the integration $N_u \, du$ is a numeric obtained.

In view of Eqs. 2 to 5

$$dP = f(u)f(v)f(w) \, du \, dv \, dw = \frac{1}{(\alpha\sqrt{\pi})^3} e^{-\frac{u^2+v^2+w^2}{\alpha^2}} \, du \, dv \, dw$$

$$= \frac{1}{(\alpha\sqrt{\pi})^3} e^{-\frac{c^2}{\alpha^2}} \, du \, dv \, dw \quad (25)$$

Replacing the volume element in "velocity space" $du \, dv \, dw$ by the corresponding element in terms of spherical coordinates, that is by $dc \times cd\varphi \times c \sin \varphi \, d\theta$, of which $c$ corresponds to radial distance, $\varphi$ to colatitude, and $\theta$ to longitude, we may rewrite Eq. 25 as

$$dP = \frac{1}{(\alpha\sqrt{\pi})^3} e^{-\frac{c^2}{\alpha^2}} c^2 \sin \varphi \, dc \, d\theta \, d\varphi \quad (26)$$

where $dP$ now represents the probability that an arbitrarily selected molecule of the gas under consideration shall have a velocity such that its vector in the representation of Fig. 1 shall terminate in the element of volume now specified in spherical coordinates. The probability that the vector will terminate somewhere in velocity space is unity. That the total of all such probabilities as are specified by Eq. 26 turns out in agreement to be unity is shown by the integration of $dP$ over the whole of the velocity space. Thus

$$\int dP = \frac{1}{(\alpha\sqrt{\pi})^3} \int_0^\infty e^{-\frac{c^2}{\alpha^2}} c^2 \, dc \int_0^\pi \sin \varphi \, d\varphi \int_0^{2\pi} d\theta$$

$$= \frac{1}{(\alpha\sqrt{\pi})^3} \frac{\alpha^3\sqrt{\pi}}{4} \times 2 \times 2\pi = 1 \quad (27)$$

If, however, we seek $dP_c$, the probability that a molecule of the gas has a speed lying between $c - (dc/2)$ and $c + (dc/2)$ regardless of direction, we must not carry through the integration with respect to $c$ in Eq. 27. Integrating Eq. 27 subject to this condition, we obtain

$$dP_c = \frac{1}{(\alpha\sqrt{\pi})^3} c^2 e^{-\frac{c^2}{\alpha^2}} dc \int_0^\pi \sin \varphi \, d\varphi \int_0^{2\pi} d\theta$$

$$= \frac{4}{\alpha^3\sqrt{\pi}} c^2 e^{-\frac{c^2}{\alpha^2}} dc \quad (28)$$

For $N$ molecules the speed distribution is given by

$$N_c = \frac{dN}{dc} = \frac{4N}{\alpha^3\sqrt{\pi}} c^2 e^{-\frac{c^2}{\alpha^2}} \tag{29}$$

$N_c$ as a function of $c$ for oxygen at 0°C is shown in Fig. 2 of Chapter VIII, p. 206. Zero values for $N_c$ are shown at zero and infinite speeds. A maximum occurs at an intermediate speed.

The location of the maximum of the function of Eq. 29 is obtained by the standard process of equating the slope of the curve to zero, thus

$$\frac{dN_c}{dc} = 0 = \frac{4N}{\alpha^3\sqrt{\pi}} 2ce^{-\frac{c^2}{\alpha^2}}\left(1 - \frac{c^2}{\alpha^2}\right) \tag{30}$$

from which it follows that at the maximum

$$\alpha = c \tag{31}$$

and that $\alpha$ is that speed which is most common.

Consider next how $\alpha$ is related to $\tilde{c}$, which in the chapter on gases was defined as the root-mean-square molecular speed, that is,

$$\tilde{c} = \left(\frac{1}{N}\sum c^2\right)^{\frac{1}{2}} \tag{32}$$

In performing the summation, it is necessary to weight the $c^2$ corresponding to any infinitesimal range according to the frequency of occurrence of a $c$ within that range, that is according to $N_c\,dc$. Thus

$$\tilde{c} = \left(\frac{1}{N}\sum c^2 N_c\,dc\right)^{\frac{1}{2}} = \left(\frac{4}{\alpha^3\sqrt{\pi}}\int_0^\infty e^{-\frac{c^2}{\alpha^2}}c^4\,dc\right)^{\frac{1}{2}} \tag{33}$$

Tables of definite integrals show that the value of the integral is $(3/8)\alpha^5\sqrt{\pi}$. It follows that

$$\tilde{c} = \alpha\sqrt{\tfrac{3}{2}} = 1.225\alpha \tag{34}$$

In a similar manner, where $\bar{c}$ represents the average value of $c$, one may verify that

$$\bar{c} = \frac{2}{\sqrt{\pi}}\alpha = 1.128\alpha \tag{35}$$

This straight average is ordinarily of little concern in gas theory.

With the aid of Eq. 9 of Chapter VIII, p. 204, we obtain

$$\alpha = \sqrt{\frac{2}{3}}\,\bar{c} = \sqrt{\frac{2kT}{m}} \tag{36}$$

Substituting this value for $\alpha$ in Eq. 29 and multiplying both sides of the equation by $dc$ leads finally to

$$N_c\,dc = \frac{4N}{\sqrt{\pi}}\left(\frac{m}{2kT}\right)^{3/2} c^2 e^{-\frac{mc^2}{2kT}}\,dc \tag{37}$$

the form in which Maxwell's law is stated in the text on p. 201.

Assumption 5 underlies Eq. 36. Assumption 6 has been involved throughout.

# APPENDIX II

## TABLE I

### Some Basic Constants in Heat

The values given here are taken very largely from R. T. Birge's paper, "The General Physical Constants," *Reports on Progress in Physics*, **8,** 90, 1942, London, The Physical Society.

| Symbol | Quantity | Value |
|---|---|---|
| $T_0$ | Ice point | 0.000°C |
| $T_{100}$ | Steam point | 100.000°C |
| $T_{Au}$ | Gold point | 1336.0°K |
| $g_0$ | Standard gravity | 980.665 cm/sec$^2$ |
| $_0{}^\delta Hg$ | Density of mercury ($T_0$, 1 A) | 13.59504$_0$(1 ± 0.0$_5$4) gm/cm$^3$ |
| A | Standard atmosphere | 760.000 cm-Hg |
| | | 1.013246 × 10$^6$(1 ± 0.0$_5$4) dy/cm$^2$ |
| | | 1.033223(1 ± 0.0$_5$4) kgwt/cm$^2$ |
| gmv | Gram-molecular volume | 22.4146 × 10$^3$(1 ± 0.0$_4$3) cm$^3$ |
| | | 22.4140(1 ± 0.0$_4$3) l |
| $v_0$ | Molal volume of an ideal gas ($T_0$, 1 A) | 1.000000 gmv/mole |
| $j$ | Mechanical equivalent of heat | 4.1855 (1 ± 0.0$_3$1) abs j/cal$_{15}$ |
| $T_0 k$ | Absolute zero | −273.16 ± .01°K |
| $\beta_0$ | Volume expansivity of an ideal gas ($T_0$) | 3.66086 × 10$^{-3}$(1 ± 0.0$_4$3) 1/K° |
| R | Molal gas constant | 3.66086 × 10$^{-3}$(1 ± 0.0$_4$3) A gmv/(mol K°) |
| | | 8.31436(1 ± 0.0$_4$5) j/(mol K°) |
| | | 8.20545 × 10$^{-2}$(1 ± 0.0$_4$5) l A/(mol K°) |
| | | 1.98647(1 ± 0.0$_3$10) cal$_{15}$/(mol K°) |
| $N_0$ | Avogadro number | 6.0228 × 10$^{23}$(1 ± 0.0$_3$2) molecules/mole |
| $n^1(= N_0/v_0)$ | Loschmidt number (ideal gas, ($T_0$, 1 A) | 2.6870 × 10$^{19}$(1 ± 0.0$_3$2) molecules/cm$^3$ |
| $k(= R/N_0)$ | Boltzmann molecular constant | 1.38047 × 10$^{-16}$(1 ± 0.0$_3$20) erg/(molecule K°) |
| $E_0(= kT_0)$ | Average translational kinetic energy of an ideal gas molecule at 0°C | 5.6564 × 10$^{-14}$(1 ± 0.0$_3$20) erg/molecule |
| AMU | $\frac{1}{16}$ mass of $_8 O^{16}$ atom | 1.66035 × 10$^{-24}$(1 ± 0.0$_3$20) gm |
| $m_0$ | Mass of the electron at rest | 9.1066 × 10$^{-28}$(1 ± 0.0$_3$4) gm |
| $_1 M^1$ | Mass of the hydrogen atom | 1.67339 × 10$^{+24}$(1 ± 0.0$_3$20) gm |
| $c$ | Velocity of light in free space | 2.99776 × 10$^{10}$(1 ± 0.0$_4$13) cm/sec |
| F | Faraday constant | 9.6514$_7$ × 10$^4$(1 ± 0.0$_3$10) abs-coul/gm-equiv |
| $e(= F/N_0)$ | Electronic charge | 4.8025 × 10$^{-10}$(1 ± 0.0$_3$2) st-coul |
| | | 1.60203 × 10$^{-20}$(1 ± 0.0$_3$2) abcoul |
| $R_\infty$ | Rydberg's constant for infinite mass | 1.09737303 × 10$^5$(1 ± 0.0$_6$16) cycles/cm |
| $h\left(= \dfrac{2\pi^2 c^3 F^5}{R_\infty N_0{}^5 e/m_0}\right)$ | Planck's constant | 6.624 × 10$^{-27}$(1 ± 0.0$_3$6) erg sec |
| $\sigma\left(-\dfrac{2\pi^5 k^4}{15 c^2 h^3}\right)$ | First radiation constant | 5.672$_8$ × 10$^{-12}$(1 ± 0.0$_3$6) watt/(cm$^2$ K°$^4$) |
| $c_2(= hc/k)$ | Second radiation constant | 1.4384$_8$ × 10$^4$(1 ± 0.0$_3$24) $\mu$K° |
| | (International value accepted in 1927) | 1.4320 × 10$^4$ $\mu$K° |

489

## TABLE II

### PROPERTIES OF MATERIALS

Many values given in these tables are approximate only. Where properties vary with temperature, assigned values may be room temperature values or, in some cases, means over the range 0°C–100°C. Sources used in preparing the appendix are: *Handbook of Chemistry and Physics*, 25th ed., Chemical Rubber Publishing Co., 194; *International Critical Tables*, McGraw-Hill Book Co., 1926; and others.

*Part A.   Some Common Solids*

| Substance | Atomic Number | Molecular or Atomic Weight gm/mol | Crystal* Structure | Density gm/cm³ | Softening or Melting Point °C | Heat of Fusion cal/gm | Specific Heat cal/gm C° | Thermal Conductivity cal/(sec cm² C°/cm) | Linear Expansivity $10^{-6}$/C° | Boiling Point °C | Heat of Vaporization cal/gm | Compressibility $10^{-7}$ cm²/kgwt |
|---|---|---|---|---|---|---|---|---|---|---|---|---|
| Aluminum | 13 | 26.97 | FCC | 2.70 | 669.7 | 76.8 | 0.214 | 0.504 | 25.5 | 1800 | 2000 | 13.3 |
| Brass, yellow | | | | 8.40 | 900 | | .092 | .023 | 18.9 | | | |
| Cadmium | 48 | 112.41 | CPH | 8.65 | 320.9 | 13.7 | .0552 | .222 | 28.8 | 767 | 230 | 2.17 |
| Carbon, amorphous | 6 | 12.01 | ...... | 1.88 | | | .204 | .091 | 5.4 | 4200 | | 1.6 |
| Carbon, diamond | 6 | 12.01 | FCC | 3.51 | | | .17 | .360 | 1.18 | | 7200 | |
| Carbon, graphite | 6 | 12.01 | Hex | 2.25 | >3500 | | .12 | .34 | 7.86 | | | 30 |
| Cobalt | 27 | 58.94 | CPH; FCC | 8.71 | 1480 | 60.3 | .100 | .17 | 12.4 | 3000 | 1500 | 5.5 |
| Copper | 29 | 63.57 | FCC | 8.94 | 1083 | 42 | .092 | .918 | 16.8 | 2300 | 860 | 7.5 |
| Cork | | | ...... | 0.24 | | | | .00013 | | | | |
| Gold | 79 | 197.2 | FCC | 19.32 | 1063 | 15.8 | .0312 | .700 | 14.3 | 2600 | 330 | 6.0 |
| Glass, crown | | | | 2.6 | | | .161 | .0025 | 8.97 | | | 22 |
| Glass, Pyrex | | | ...... | 2.25 | 815 | | .20 | | 3.2 | | | |
| Ice | | 18.02 | Hex | 0.917 | 0.000 | 79.71 | .53 | .0022 | 41.7 | 100.00 | 539.55 | 120 |
| Iodine | 53 | 126.92 | R | 4.93 | 113.5 | 11.71 | .0523 | .0011 | 83.7 | 184.35 | 23.95 | 130 |
| Iron | 26 | 55.84 | BCC | 7.86 | 1535 | 478 | .107 | .161 | 12.1 | 3000 | 1600 | 6.1 |
| Magnesium | 12 | 24.32 | CPH | 1.74 | 651 | 29.9 | .25 | .376 | 26.1 | 1120 | 1110 | 29 |
| Mica | | | | 2.9 | | | .206 | .0018 | | | | |
| Molybdenum | 42 | 95.95 | BCC | 10.2 | 2620 | | .065 | .346 | 4.9 | 3700 | 830 | 4.6 |
| Lead | 82 | 207.21 | FCC | 11.35 | 327.4 | 5.86 | .0306 | .083 | 29.4 | 1620 | 230 | 22.7 |
| Nickel | 28 | 58.69 | CPH; FCC | 8.90 | 1455 | 73.8 | .105 | .142 | 12.8 | 2900 | 1010 | 4.3 |
| Palladium | 46 | 106.7 | FCC | 12.16 | 1545 | 36.3 | .054 | .168 | 11.0 | 2200 | 610 | 5.4 |
| Platinum | 78 | 195.23 | FCC | 21.37 | 1773.5 | 27.2 | .0324 | .166 | 8.99 | 4300 | 320 | 3.8 |
| Silver | 47 | 107.880 | FCC | 10.50 | 960.5 | 21.1 | .0558 | .990 | 18.8 | 1950 | 490 | 9.9 |
| Steel | | | | 7.83 | 1430 | 13.2 | .11 | .11 | 13.2 | | | |
| Sulfur, mono | 16 | 32.06 | M | 1.96 | 119.0 | | .181 | .00050 | 64 | 444.6 | 67 | |
| Sulfur, rh | 16 | 32.06 | R | 2.07 | 112.8 | | .176 | .00070 | 7 | 444.6 | 67 | 129 |
| Tantalum | 73 | 180.88 | BCC | 16.6 | 2850 | | .036 | .132 | 6.5 | 4100 | 480 | 5.3 |
| Tin, gray | 50 | 118.70 | FCC | 5.75 | 231.9 | 14.0 | .0542 | .155 | 26.9 | 2260 | 500 | 18.9 |
| Tungsten | 74 | 183.92 | BCC | 19.3 | 3370 | | .034 | .41 | 4.44 | 5900 | | 3.0 |
| Uranium | 92 | 238.07 | BCC | 18.7 | <1850 | | .028 | .048 | | | 305 | 10 |
| White oak ⊥ | | | ...... | 0.77 | | | .33 | | 54.4 | | | |
| Zinc | 30 | 65.38 | CPH | 7.14 | 419.5 | 28.1 | .0925 | .265 | 26.3 | 907 | 430 | 17.4 |

* FCC = face-centered cubic; BCC = body-centered cubic; CPH = close-packed hexagonal; R = rhombic; M = monoclinic.

*Part B. Some Common Liquids*

| Substance | Formula | Molecular or Atomic Weight gm/mol | Density gm/cm³ | Specific Heat cal/gm C° | Volume Expansivity 10⁻³/C° | Thermal Conductivity cal/(sec cm² C°/cm) | Boiling Point °C | Heat of Vaporization cal/gm | Freezing Point °C | Heat of Fusion cal/gm | Viscosity Centipoises |
|---|---|---|---|---|---|---|---|---|---|---|---|
| Alcohol, ethyl | $C_2H_5OH$ | 46.07 | 0.789 | 0.581 | 1.12 | 0.00043 | 78.3 | 204 | −117 | 24.8 | 1.72 |
| Alcohol, methyl | $CH_3OH$ | 32.04 | 0.796 | 0.600 | 1.20 | .0005 | 64.7 | 262.8 | −97.8 | 22.0 | 0.596 |
| Acetone | $(CH_3)_2CO$ | 58.08 | 0.792 | .528 | 1.49 | .0004 | 57.0 | 124.5 | −95 | 23.4 | 0.303 |
| Carbon tetrachloride | $CCl_4$ | 153.84 | 1.595 | .201 | 1.24 | .00026 | 76 | 46.5 | −22.8 | 4.15 | 0.975 |
| Carbon disulfide | $CS_2$ | 76.13 | 1.263 | | 1.22 | .00038 | 46.3 | 84.1 | −108.6 | | 0.376 |
| Castor oil | | | 0.969 | | | .00043 | | | −12 | | 986. |
| Ether ethyl | $(C_2H_5)_2O$ | 74.12 | 0.714 | .540 | 1.66 | .00033 | 34.6 | 83.8 | −117.6 | | 0.223 |
| Gasoline | | | 0.67 | | | | | | −130 | | 0.40 |
| Kerosene | | | 0.82 | | | | | | | | 2.0 |
| Mercury | Hg | 200.61 | 13.6 | 0.0333 | | .0197 | 356.9 | 60 | −38.87 | 2.78 | 1.55 |
| Sea water | | | 1.025 | | | | 80 | 65 | −2.5 | | |
| Water | $H_2O$ | 18.02 | 1.00 | 1.00 | 0.181 | .0014 | 100.00 | 539.55 | 0.00 | 79.8 | 1.01 |
| Toluene | $C_6H_5CH_3$ | 92.13 | 0.866 | 0.428 | | .00038 | 110.8 | 86.3 | −95 | | 0.590 |

*Part C. Some Common Gases*

| Substance | Formula | Molecular or Atomic Weight gm/mol | Density gm/l | $c_p$ cal/gm C° | $c_p/c_v$ | Thermal Conductivity 10⁻⁵ cal/(sec cm² C°/cm) | Molecular diameter 10⁻⁸ cm | Viscosity 10⁻⁶ poise | Critical Temperature °C | Critical Pressure A |
|---|---|---|---|---|---|---|---|---|---|---|
| Acetylene | $C_2H_2$ | 26.02 | 1.173 | 0.385 | 1.26 | 4.1 | | 73.5 | 36 | 62 |
| Air | ...... | 29 | 1.292 | 0.238 | 1.403 | 5.3 | 2.97 | 181 | −140.7 | 37.2 |
| Ammonia | $NH_3$ | 17.03 | 0.771 | 0.523 | 1.310 | 4.6 | 2.88 | 110 | 132.4 | 111.5 |
| Argon | A | 39.944 | 1.784 | 0.125 | 1.67 | 3.8 | 3.34 | 221 | −122 | 48 |
| Carbon dioxide | $CO_2$ | 44.00 | 1.977 | 0.199 | 1.304 | 3.4 | 3.19 | 148 | 31.1 | 73.0 |
| Carbon monoxide | CO | 28.00 | 1.250 | 0.248 | 1.404 | 5.3 | | 172 | −139 | 35 |
| Chlorine | Cl | 35.457 | 3.214 | 0.115 | 1.355 | 1.7 | | 130 | 144.0 | 76.1 |
| Helium | He | 4.003 | 0.178 | 1.31 | 1.66 | 33.6 | 1.90 | 109 | −267.9 | 2.26 |
| Hydrogen | $H_2$ | 1.0080 | 0.0899 | 3.389 | 1.410 | 38.6 | 2.40 | 88.7 | −239.9 | 12.8 |
| Neon | Ne | 20.183 | 0.900 | | 1.64 | 10.6 | | 312 | −228.7 | 25.9 |
| Nitrogen | $N_2$ | 14.008 | 1.251 | 0.248 | 1.404 | 5.5 | 3.15 | 176 | −147.1 | 33.5 |
| Oxygen | $O_2$ | 16.000 | 1.429 | 0.218 | 1.401 | 5.57 | 2.98 | 196 | −118.8 | 49.7 |
| Sulfur dioxide | $SO_2$ | 64.07 | 2.923 | | 1.29 | 1.84 | | 124 | 157.2 | 77.7 |
| Water vapor | $H_2O$ | 18.02 | | 1.52 | | 5.19 | | 98 | 374.0 | 217.72 |

## TABLE III

THERMOCOUPLE POTENTIAL DIFFERENCES DEVELOPED BY VARIOUS TYPES OF THERMOCOUPLES

The cold junction is assumed to be kept at 0.0°C.

| $T$ | Iron to Constantan emf | Copper to Constantan emf | Chromel to Alumel emf | Platinum to Platinum +10% Rhodium emf | Platinum to Platinum +13% Rhodium emf |
|---|---|---|---|---|---|
| 0°C | 0.00 mv | 0.00 mv | 0.00 mv | 0.000 mv | 0.000 mv |
| 20 | 1.04 | 0.79 | 0.80 | 0.114 | 0.113 |
| 40 | 2.08 | 1.61 | 1.61 | 0.235 | 0.234 |
| 60 | 3.14 | 2.47 | 2.43 | 0.365 | 0.364 |
| 80 | 4.21 | 3.36 | 3.26 | 0.500 | 0.500 |
| 100 | 5.28 | 4.28 | 4.10 | 0.643 | 0.646 |
| 20 | 6.38 | 5.23 | 4.92 | 0.792 | 0.798 |
| 40 | 7.47 | 6.20 | 5.73 | 0.946 | 0.957 |
| 60 | 8.57 | 7.21 | 6.53 | 1.105 | 1.121 |
| 80 | 9.68 | 8.23 | 7.33 | 1.269 | 1.290 |
| 200 | 10.78 | 9.29 | 8.13 | 1.436 | 1.464 |
| 20 | 11.88 | 10.36 | 8.93 | 1.606 | 1.642 |
| 40 | 12.99 | 11.46 | 9.74 | 1.779 | 1.825 |
| 60 | 14.09 | 12.57 | 10.56 | 1.956 | 2.011 |
| 80 | 15.20 | 13.71 | 11.38 | 2.134 | 2.201 |
| 300 | 16.30 | 14.86 | 12.21 | 2.316 | 2.394 |
| 20 | 17.40 | 16.03 | 13.04 | 2.498 | 2.590 |
| 40 | 18.51 | 17.22 | 13.87 | 2.684 | 2.789 |
| 60 | 19.61 | 18.42 | 14.71 | 2.871 | 2.990 |
| 80 | 20.72 | 19.64 | 15.55 | 3.060 | 3.193 |
| 400 | 21.82 | 20.86 | 16.39 | 3.251 | 3.398 |
| 20 | 22.92 | | 17.24 | 3.441 | 3.605 |
| 40 | 24.03 | | 18.08 | 3.634 | 3.816 |
| 60 | 25.14 | | 18.93 | 3.828 | 4.027 |
| 80 | 26.27 | | 19.78 | 4.023 | 4.239 |
| 500 | 27.39 | | 20.64 | 4.219 | 4.450 |
| 20 | 28.53 | | 21.49 | 4.417 | 4.671 |
| 40 | 29.68 | | 22.34 | 4.616 | 4.891 |
| 60 | 30.83 | | 23.20 | 4.817 | 5.113 |
| 80 | 32.00 | | 24.05 | 5.019 | 5.336 |
| 600 | 33.16 | | 24.90 | 5.222 | 5.561 |
| 20 | 34.35 | | 25.75 | 5.427 | 5.790 |
| 40 | 35.54 | | 26.60 | 5.633 | 6.020 |
| 60 | 36.74 | | 27.45 | 5.841 | 6.251 |
| 80 | 37.97 | | 28.29 | 6.050 | 6.485 |
| 700 | 39.19 | | 29.14 | 6.260 | 6.720 |
| 20 | 40.44 | | 29.98 | 6.471 | 6.958 |
| 40 | 41.69 | | 30.82 | 6.684 | 7.196 |
| 60 | 43.95 | | 31.65 | 6.898 | 7.438 |
| 80 | 44.22 | | 32.48 | 7.113 | 7.682 |
| 800 | 45.48 | | 33.31 | 7.330 | 7.927 |
| 20 | 46.75 | | 34.12 | 7.548 | 8.173 |
| 40 | 48.02 | | 34.94 | 7.768 | 8.421 |
| 60 | 49.28 | | 35.75 | 7.989 | 8.671 |
| 80 | 50.55 | | 36.56 | 8.211 | 8.923 |

## TABLE III (*Continued*)

THERMOCOUPLE POTENTIAL DIFFERENCES DEVELOPED BY VARIOUS TYPES OF THERMOCOUPLES

The cold junction is assumed to be kept at 0.0°C.

| $T$ | Iron to Constantan emf | Copper to Constantan emf | Chromel to Alumel emf | Platinum to Platinum +10% Rhodium emf | Platinum to Platinum +13% Rhodium emf |
|---|---|---|---|---|---|
| 900 | 51.82 | | 37.36 | 8.434 | 9.177 |
| 20 | 53.09 | | 38.16 | 8.658 | 9.432 |
| 40 | 54.36 | | 38.96 | 8.884 | 9.689 |
| 60 | 55.62 | | 39.75 | 9.111 | 9.947 |
| 80 | 56.89 | | 40.53 | 9.340 | 10.208 |
| 1000 | 58.16 | | 41.31 | 9.569 | 10.470 |
| 20 | 59.43 | | 42.08 | 9.800 | 10.733 |
| 40 | 60.70 | | 42.86 | 10.033 | 11.000 |
| 60 | 61.96 | | 43.62 | 10.266 | 11.269 |
| 80 | 63.23 | | 44.38 | 10.500 | 11.540 |
| 1100 | 64.50 | | 45.14 | 10.736 | 11.811 |
| 20 | | | 45.89 | 10.973 | 12.084 |
| 40 | | | 46.64 | 11.209 | 12.356 |
| 60 | | | 47.38 | 11.448 | 12.630 |
| 80 | | | 48.12 | 11.686 | 12.906 |
| 1200 | | | 48.85 | 11.924 | 13.181 |
| 20 | | | 49.57 | 12.163 | 13.456 |
| 40 | | | 50.29 | 12.402 | 13.733 |
| 60 | | | 51.00 | 12.642 | 14.010 |
| 80 | | | 51.71 | 12.881 | 14.285 |
| 1300 | | | 52.41 | 13.120 | 14.563 |
| 20 | | | 53.10 | 13.358 | 14.838 |
| 40 | | | 53.79 | 13.598 | 15.114 |
| 60 | | | 54.47 | 13.836 | 15.389 |
| 80 | | | 55.15 | 14.074 | 15.664 |
| 1400 | | | 55.81 | 14.312 | 15.940 |
| 20 | | | | 14.550 | 16.215 |
| 40 | | | | 14.787 | 16.493 |
| 60 | | | | 15.024 | 16.769 |
| 80 | | | | 15.261 | 17.043 |
| 1500 | | | | 15.498 | 17.316 |
| 20 | | | | 15.733 | 17.590 |
| 40 | | | | 15.969 | 17.864 |
| 60 | | | | 16.205 | 18.135 |
| 80 | | | | 16.440 | 18.407 |
| 1600 | | | | 16.674 | 18.680 |
| 20 | | | | 16.908 | 18.951 |
| 40 | | | | 17.142 | 19.222 |
| 60 | | | | 17.376 | 19.492 |
| 80 | | | | 17.608 | 19.762 |
| 1700 | | | | 17.841 | 20.032 |
| 20 | | | | 18.073 | |

APPENDIX II

## TABLE IV

Some Properties of Ice, Liquid Water, and Water Vapor at Saturation

Compiled from data given for the ice-vapor system by Keenan and Keyes, *Thermodynamic Properties of Steam*, New York, John Wiley & Sons, 1936, and for liquid water-vapor system by Osborne, Stimson, and Ginnings, *Journal of Research*, **23,** 261, 1939, National Bureau of Standards. A slight discrepancy is found for the specific enthalpy of the vapor at 0.0°C.

### Ice—Vapor

| Temperature $T$ °C | Vapor Tension $p$ mm-Hg | Specific Volume solid $v_s$ cm³/gm | Specific Volume vapor $v_v$ cm³/gm | Specific Enthalpy solid $h_s$ cal/gm | Specific Enthalpy vapor $h_v$ cal/gm | Heat of Vaporization $L$ cal/gm |
|---|---|---|---|---|---|---|
| −40 | 0.10 | 1.084 | 8,360 | −98.33 | 580.1 | 678.4 |
| −30 | 0.29 | .086 | 2,930 | −93.92 | 584.5 | 678.4 |
| −20 | 0.79 | .088 | 1,360 | −89.36 | 588.9 | 678.3 |
| −10 | 1.96 | .089 | 470 | −84.57 | 593.4 | 677.9 |
| 0 | 4.58 | .091 | 206.4 | −79.64 | 597.7 | 677.3 |

### Liquid Water—Vapor

| | | | | | | |
|---|---|---|---|---|---|---|
| 0 | 4.581 | 1.00021 | 206,288 | 0.000 | 597.3 | 597.3 |
| 10 | 9.204 | .00035 | 106,422 | 10.040 | 601.7 | 591.7 |
| 20 | 17.518 | .00184 | 57,836 | 20.040 | 606.1 | 586.0 |
| 30 | 31.816 | .00442 | 32,929 | 30.024 | 610.4 | 580.4 |
| 40 | 55.317 | .00789 | 19,546 | 40.006 | 614.7 | 574.7 |
| 50 | 92.52 | .0121 | 12,045 | 49.990 | 619.0 | 569.0 |
| 60 | 149.40 | .0171 | 7,677.6 | 59.981 | 623.2 | 563.2 |
| 70 | 233.72 | .0228 | 5,045.3 | 69.984 | 627.3 | 557.3 |
| 80 | 355.22 | .0290 | 3,408.3 | 80.002 | 631.3 | 551.3 |
| 90 | 525.85 | .0359 | 2,360.9 | 90.039 | 635.3 | 545.2 |
| 100 | 760.00 | .0435 | 1,673.0 | 100.102 | 639.1 | 539.0 |
| 120 | 1,489.5 | .0603 | 891.71 | 120.32 | 646.4 | 526.1 |
| 140 | 2,710.5 | .0798 | 508.66 | 140.72 | 653.0 | 512.3 |
| 160 | 4,635.7 | .1021 | 306.85 | 161.34 | 658.8 | 497.4 |
| 180 | 7,521 | .1275 | 193.85 | 182.28 | 663.5 | 481.3 |
| 200 | 11,664 | .1565 | 127.19 | 203.59 | 667.1 | 463.5 |
| 220 | 17,402 | .1900 | 86.062 | 225.40 | 669.1 | 443.7 |
| 240 | 25,112 | .2291 | 59.674 | 247.84 | 669.5 | 421.7 |
| 260 | 35,257 | .2755 | 42.149 | 271.09 | 667.9 | 396.8 |
| 280 | 48,147 | .3321 | 30.133 | 295.41 | 663.9 | 368.5 |
| 300 | 64,440 | .4036 | 21.643 | 321.22 | 656.6 | 335.4 |
| 320 | 84,680 | .4992 | 15.451 | 349.24 | 644.8 | 295.6 |
| 340 | 109,570 | .639 | 10.779 | 380.93 | 626.3 | 245.3 |
| 360 | 140,060 | .894 | 6.943 | 420.74 | 592.6 | 171.9 |
| 374.15 | 165,980 | 3.1 | 3.1 | 498. | 498. | 0.0 |

## TABLE V

### Some Measured Emissivities and Emittances

For additional data see W. H. McAdams, *Heat Transmission*, McGraw-Hill Book Co., and G. Ribaud, *Traité de pyrométrie optique*, published by *Revue d'optique théorique et instrumental*, Paris, 1931.

#### Metals

| Substance | Temperature | | Total Emissivity | |
|---|---|---|---|---|
| | °F | °K | Normal | Hemispherical |
| Aluminum, highly polished | 440–1070 | | 0.039 –0.057 | |
| Brass A, highly polished | 476–674 | | .028 – .031 | |
| Brass B, highly polished | 494–710 | | .039 – .037 | |
| Copper, polished | 176 | | .018 | |
| Gold, highly polished | 440–1160 | | .018 – .035 | |
| Iron, highly polished | 350–440 | | .052 – .074 | |
| Iron | | 1300–1700 | .08 – .13 | |
| Lead, unoxidized | 260–440 | | .057 – .075 | |
| Mercury, pure, clean | 32–212 | | .09 – .12 | |
| Molybdenum, filament | | 1000–2000 | | .096–.210 |
| Nickel, polished | 74 | | .045 | |
| Nickel | | 1300–1700 | .056 – .069 | |
| Platinum, polished | 440–1160 | | .054 – .104 | |
| filament | | 500–1500 | | .060–.190 |
| Silver, polished, pure | 440–1160 | | .0198– .0324 | |
| Tantalum, filament | | 1600–2500 | | .194–.278 |
| Tin, tinned iron sheet | 76 | | .043 – .064 | |
| Tungsten, filament | | 1000 | | .114 |
| "          " | | 2000 | | .260 |
| "          " | | 3000 | | .334 |
| Zinc, pure, polished | 440–620 | | .045 – .053 | |

#### Non-Metals

| Substance | | Total Emittances | |
|---|---|---|---|
| Asbestos board | 74 | .96 | |
| Brick, red, rough | 70 | .93 | |
| Carbon, filament | 1300–1800 | | .52 |
| Lamp black and water glass | 260–440 | .957 – .952 | |
| Enamel, white | 66 | .897 | |
| Glass, smooth | 72 | .937 | |
| Marble, polished | 72 | .931 | |
| Paints, lacquers, varnishes | 70 | .82 – .92 | |
| Plaster, rough lime | 50–190 | .91 | |
| Porcelain | 72 | .924 | |
| Water | 32–212 | .95 – .963 | |
| Zinc black | | .997 | |
| Nickel oxide | 900–1600 | .54 – .87 | |
| Iron oxide | 800–1500 | .85 – .89 | |
| Copper oxide | 1100–1400 | .66 – .54 | |
| Magnesia | 2000 | .18 | |
| Thoria | 1100–2000 | .22 – .24 | |
| Zirconia | 2000 | .43 | |

#### Spectral Emissivities of Selected Materials for $\lambda = 0.665\ \mu$

| Substance | T in °K | $\epsilon\lambda'$ | Substance | T in °K | $\epsilon\lambda'$ |
|---|---|---|---|---|---|
| Carbon | 1600 | 0.89 | Palladium | 1275 | 0.35 |
| | 2500 | 0.84 | | 1805 | 0.33 |
| Copper | 1275 | 0.105 | Platinum | 1200 | 0.285 |
| | 1350 | 0.120 | | 1800 | 0.295 |
| Copper (liq) | 1375 | 0.15 | Silver (liq) | 1215 | 0.044 |
| Gold | 1275 | 0.14 | | 1255 | 0.072 |
| Iron | 1000 | 0.27 | Tantalum | 1400 | 0.44 |
| Molybdenum | 1300 | 0.378 | | 2800 | 0.39 |
| | 2750 | 0.332 | Tungsten | 1200 | 0.45 |
| Nickel | 1200 | 0.375 | | 2200 | 0.43 |
| | 1600 | 0.375 | | 3200 | 0.41 |

## TABLE VI *

### Properties of Tungsten

The data for this table are taken from (1) W. E. Forsythe and A. G. Worthing, *Astrophys. J.*, **61**, 152, 1925; (2) W. E. Forsythe and E. M. Watson, *J. Optical Soc. Am.*, **24**, 114, 1934; (3) R. H. Osborn, *J. Optical Soc. Am.*, **31**, 428, 1941.

| Temperature Degrees K $T$ | Spectral Emissivity $\epsilon_{0.665\,\mu}$ | Spectral Emissivity $\epsilon_{0.467\,\mu}$ | Average Luminous Emissivity $\epsilon_v$ | Color Emissivity $\epsilon_c$ | Total Emissivity $\epsilon_t$ | Brightness Temperature $S_{0.665\,\mu}$ | Color Temperature $T_c$ | Radiation Temperature $T_R$ | Relative Lengths at Different Temperatures $L/L_o$ | Thermal Conductivity watt/(cm² K°/cm) $k$ | Atomic Heats cal/gm-atom K° $C_p$ |
|---|---|---|---|---|---|---|---|---|---|---|---|
| 273 | 0.470 | 0.505 | ..... | ..... | 0.024 | ..... | ..... | ..... | 1.0000 | ..... | ..... |
| 300 | .468 | .501 | ..... | ..... | .034 | ..... | ..... | ..... | 1.0005 | ..... | ..... |
| 400 | .466 | .498 | ..... | ..... | .042 | ..... | ..... | ..... | 1.0010 | ..... | ..... |
| 500 | ..... | ..... | ..... | ..... | ..... | ..... | ..... | ..... | ..... | ..... | ..... |
| 600 | .464 | .495 | ..... | ..... | .052 | ..... | ..... | ..... | 1.0014 | ..... | ..... |
| 700 | .462 | .492 | ..... | ..... | .062 | ..... | ..... | ..... | 1.0018 | ..... | ..... |
| 800 | .460 | .490 | ..... | ..... | .074 | ..... | ..... | ..... | 1.0023 | ..... | ..... |
| 900 | .458 | .488 | ..... | ..... | .089 | ..... | ..... | ..... | 1.0028 | ..... | ..... |
| 1000 | .456 | .486 | 0.464 | 0.396 | .105 | 966 | 1006 | 581 | 1.0032 | ..... | 6.20 |
| 1100 | .454 | .484 | .463 | .393 | .121 | 1058 | 1108 | 659 | 1.0036 | 1.170 | 6.35 |
| 1200 | .452 | .482 | .462 | .391 | .138 | 1149 | 1210 | 738 | 1.0041 | 1.153 | 6.50 |
| 1300 | .450 | .480 | .460 | .388 | .156 | 1240 | 1312 | 819 | 1.0046 | 1.138 | 6.65 |
| 1400 | .448 | .478 | .459 | .386 | .174 | 1330 | 1414 | 905 | 1.0052 | 1.122 | 6.80 |
| 1500 | .445 | .476 | .457 | .383 | .192 | 1420 | 1517 | 991 | 1.0057 | 1.106 | 6.95 |
| 1600 | .443 | .475 | .456 | .381 | .207 | 1509 | 1619 | 1080 | 1.0063 | 1.089 | 7.10 |
| 1700 | .441 | .473 | .455 | .378 | .222 | 1597 | 1722 | 1167 | 1.0069 | 1.073 | 7.25 |
| 1800 | .439 | .472 | .454 | .376 | .236 | 1684 | 1825 | 1254 | 1.0075 | 1.058 | 7.40 |
| 1900 | .437 | .470 | .453 | .373 | .248 | 1771 | 1929 | 1342 | 1.0081 | 1.042 | 7.55 |
| 2000 | .435 | .469 | .452 | .370 | .259 | 1857 | 2033 | 1428 | 1.0088 | 1.026 | 7.70 |
| 2100 | .433 | .467 | .450 | .367 | .269 | 1943 | 2137 | 1514 | 1.0094 | ..... | 7.85 |
| 2200 | .431 | .466 | .449 | .364 | .278 | 2026 | 2242 | 1601 | 1.0101 | ..... | 8.00 |
| 2300 | .429 | .464 | .448 | .362 | .286 | 2109 | 2347 | 1688 | 1.0108 | ..... | 8.15 |
| 2400 | .427 | .463 | .447 | .359 | .294 | 2192 | 2452 | 1775 | 1.0116 | ..... | 8.30 |
| 2500 | .425 | .462 | .446 | .356 | .301 | 2274 | 2557 | 1859 | 1.0124 | ..... | 8.45 |
| 2600 | .423 | .460 | .444 | .353 | .308 | 2356 | 2663 | 1945 | 1.0132 | ..... | ..... |
| 2700 | .421 | .459 | .443 | .350 | .315 | 2437 | 2770 | 2031 | 1.0140 | ..... | ..... |
| 2800 | .419 | .458 | .442 | .347 | .321 | 2516 | 2878 | 2116 | 1.0149† | ..... | ..... |
| 2900 | .417 | .456 | .441 | .345 | .328 | 2595 | 2986 | 2202 | 1.016† | ..... | ..... |
| 3000 | .415 | .455 | .440 | .343 | .334 | 2673 | 3094 | 2286 | 1.017† | ..... | ..... |
| 3100 | .413 | .454 | .438 | .341 | .337 | 2750 | 3202 | 2371† | 1.018† | ..... | ..... |
| 3200 | .411 | .452 | .437 | .338† | .341† | 2827 | 3311† | 2465† | 1.019† | ..... | ..... |
| 3300 | .409 | .451 | .436 | .335† | .344† | 2903 | 3422† | 2538† | 1.020† | ..... | ..... |
| 3400 | .407† | .450† | .434† | .333† | .348† | 2978 | 3533† | 2621† | 1.021† | ..... | ..... |
| 3500 | .405† | .449† | .434† | .329† | .351† | 3053 | 3646† | 2704† | 1.023† | ..... | ..... |
| 3655 † | .402† | .447† | .433† | .324† | .354† | 3165 | 3817† | ..... | ..... | ..... | ..... |

* Data given in this table apply to aged tungsten filaments.
† These values are extrapolated.
‡ Melting point.

## TABLE VI * (Continued)

### PROPERTIES OF TUNGSTEN

| Temperature Degrees K, $T$ | Resistivity micro-ohms cm $\rho$‡ | $\frac{T}{\rho}\frac{d\rho}{dT}$ §‡ | Normal Brightness candles per cm² $B_n$ | $\frac{T}{B_n}\frac{dB_n}{dT}$ | Crova Wave-length $\lambda_c$ || | Total Radiancy watt/cm² | $\frac{T}{R}\frac{dR}{dT}$ | Luminous Efficiency lumens per watt eff. | $\frac{T}{(\text{eff.})}\frac{d(\text{eff.})}{dT}$ | Electron Emission amp/cm² $i$ | $\frac{T}{i}\frac{di}{dT}$ | Rate of Vaporization gm/(cm² sec) $v$ | $\frac{T}{v}\frac{dv}{dT}$ |
|---|---|---|---|---|---|---|---|---|---|---|---|---|---|
| 273 | 5.05 | 1.209 | | | | 0.00070 | | | | | | | |
| 300 | 5.65 | 1.209 | | | | 0.00110 | | | | | | | |
| 400 | 8.00 | 1.209 | | | | 0.00495 | | | | | | | |
| 500 | 10.48 | 1.209 | | | | 0.0150 | | | | | | | |
| 600 | 13.07 | 1.209 | | | | 0.0385 | | | | | | | |
| 700 | 15.75 | 1.209 | | | | 0.0850 | | | | | | | |
| 800 | 18.51 | 1.209 | | | | 0.1730 | 5.47 | | | | | | |
| 900 | 21.35 | 1.209 | | | | 0.333 | 5.50 | | | | | | |
| 1000 | 24.26 | 1.209 | | | 0.6077 | 0.600 | 5.51 | | | | | | |
| 1100 | 27.23 | 1.209 | | | .6038 | 1.01 | 5.53 | | | | | | |
| 1200 | 30.26 | 1.195 | | | .6004 | 1.63 | 5.53 | | | | | | |
| 1300 | 33.29 | 1.195 | | | .5971 | 2.54 | 5.52 | | | | | | |
| 1400 | 36.37 | 1.195 | | | .5934 | 3.82 | 5.48 | 0.09 | 11.8 | $5.75 \times 10^{-9}$ | 39.6 | | |
| 1500 | 39.50 | 1.195 | | | .5902 | 5.54 | 5.41 | 0.20 | 10.8 | $7.58 \times 10^{-8}$ | 37.1 | | |
| 1600 | 42.67 | 1.195 | 0.94 | 15.2 | .5874 | 7.74 | 5.31 | 0.40 | 10.0 | $8.05 \times 10^{-7}$ | 34.9 | $3.7 \times 10^{-20}$ | 67 |
| 1700 | 45.88 | 1.195 | 2.30 | 14.4 | .5850 | 10.58 | 5.18 | 0.71 | 9.3 | $6.31 \times 10^{-6}$ | 33.0 | $1.92 \times 10^{-18}$ | 63 |
| 1800 | 49.12 | 1.195 | 5.15 | 13.7 | .5826 | 14.15 | 5.02 | 1.16 | 8.7 | $3.92 \times 10^{-5}$ | 31.3 | $6.22 \times 10^{-17}$ | 59 |
| 1900 | 52.40 | 1.195 | 10.40 | 13.0 | .5806 | 18.45 | 4.89 | 1.88 | 8.1 | $2.04 \times 10^{-4}$ | 29.7 | $1.41 \times 10^{-15}$ | 56 |
| 2000 | 55.71 | 1.195 | 20.00 | 12.3 | .5785 | 23.65 | 4.80 | 2.78 | 7.5 | $8.92 \times 10^{-4}$ | 28.3 | $2.32 \times 10^{-14}$ | 53 |
| 2100 | 59.05 | 1.195 | 35.9 | 11.7 | .5769 | 29.85 | 4.73 | 3.95 | 6.9 | $3.46 \times 10^{-3}$ | 27.1 | $2.91 \times 10^{-13}$ | 50 |
| 2200 | 62.42 | 1.195 | 61.0 | 11.2 | .5753 | 37.20 | 4.68 | 5.47 | 6.4 | $1.14 \times 10^{-2}$ | 25.9 | $2.90 \times 10^{-12}$ | 48 |
| 2300 | 65.82 | 1.195 | 100.1 | 10.8 | .5737 | 45.70 | 4.64 | 7.25 | 6.0 | $3.63 \times 10^{-2}$ | 24.9 | $2.34 \times 10^{-11}$ | 46 |
| 2400 | 69.25 | 1.195 | 156.0 | 10.3 | .5724 | 55.70 | 4.61 | 9.37 | 5.6 | $1.02 \times 10^{-1}$ | 24.0 | $1.58 \times 10^{-10}$ | 44 |
| 2500 | 72.71 | 1.195 | 234.0 | 9.9 | .5711 | 67.2 | 4.59 | 11.67 | 5.3 | $2.67 \times 10^{-1}$ | 23.1 | $9.18 \times 10^{-10}$ | 42 |
| 2600 | 76.20 | 1.195 | 345 | 9.6 | .5701 | 80.6 | 4.57 | 14.28 | 5.0 | $6.48 \times 10^{-1}$ | 22.3 | $4.64 \times 10^{-9}$ | 40 |
| 2700 | 79.71 | 1.195 | 495 | 9.3 | .5691 | 95.6 | 4.55 | 17.26 | 4.7 | 1.47 | 21.5 | $2.08 \times 10^{-8}$ | 38 |
| 2800 | 83.25 | 1.195 | 690 | 8.9 | .5682 | 112.5 | 4.55 | 20.43 | 4.4 | 3.21 | 20.8 | $8.29 \times 10^{-8}$ | 36 |
| 2900 | 86.81 | 1.195 | 950 | 8.6 | .5674 | 132.0 | 4.54 | 23.80 | 4.1 | | | $2.99 \times 10^{-7}$ | 35 |
| 3000 | 90.40 | 1.195 | 1270 | 8.3 | .5666 | 154.5 | 4.53 | 27.10 | 3.8 | | | $9.92 \times 10^{-7}$ | 34 |
| 3100 | | 1.195 | | | .5659 | | | 31.0 | 3.6 | | | $3.01 \times 10^{-6}$ | 33 |
| 3200 | | 1.195 | | | .5652 | | | 34.6 | 3.4 | | | $8.79 \times 10^{-6}$ | 32 |
| 3300 | | 1.195 | | | .5645 | | | 38.5 | 3.3 | | | $2.29 \times 10^{-5}$ | 31 |
| 3400 | | 1.195 | | | .5638 | | | 42.6† | 3.1† | | | $5.74 \times 10^{-5}$ | 30 |
| 3500 | | 1.195 | | | .5628 | | | 45.9† | 3.1† | | | $1.36 \times 10^{-4}$ | 30 |
| 3655 ¶ | | | | | .5621 | | | 53.1† | 3.0† | | | $4.70 \times 10^{-4}$ | 28 |

In intercomparing values for the various properties, account should be taken of the thermal expansion as well as the variation from Lambert's cosine law.

* Data given in this table apply to well-aged tungsten.
† These values are extrapolated.
‡ These values depend on the dimensions at room temperature.
§ The constancy of this quantity at high temperatures makes temperature determinations from resistance measurements simple, since the temperature corresponding to any resistance can then be computed from resistances at two known temperatures.
|| The values of the Crova wavelengths given are the limiting values. The Crova wavelength between two temperatures is the average of the two corresponding limiting Crova wavelengths.
¶ Melting point.

## TABLE I

### Logarithms to the Base $e$

These two pages give the natural (hyperbolic, or Napierian) logarithms of numbers between 1 and 10, correct to four places. Moving the decimal point $n$ places to the right (or left) in the number is equivalent to adding $n$ times 2.3026 (or $n$ times 3.6974) to the logarithm.

| 1 | 2.3026 | 1 | 0.6974-3 |
| 2 | 4.6052 | 2 | 0.3948-5 |
| 3 | 6.9078 | 3 | 0.0922-7 |
| 4 | 9.2103 | 4 | 0.7897-10 |
| 5 | 11.5129 | 5 | 0.4871-12 |
| 6 | 13.8155 | 6 | 0.1845-14 |
| 7 | 16.1181 | 7 | 0.8819-17 |
| 8 | 18.4207 | 8 | 0.5793-19 |
| 9 | 20.7233 | 9 | 0.2767-21 |

| | 0 | 1 | 2 | 3 | 4 | 5 | 6 | 7 | 8 | 9 | 10 | Tenths of the Tabular Difference 1 | 2 | 3 | 4 | 5 |
|---|---|---|---|---|---|---|---|---|---|---|---|---|---|---|---|---|
| **1.0** | 0.0000 | 0100 | 0198 | 0296 | 0392 | 0488 | 0583 | 0677 | 0770 | 0862 | 0.0953 | 10 | 19 | 29 | 38 | 48 |
| 1.1 | 0953 | 1044 | 1133 | 1222 | 1310 | 1398 | 1484 | 1570 | 1655 | 1740 | 1823 | 9 | 17 | 26 | 35 | 44 |
| 1.2 | 1823 | 1906 | 1989 | 2070 | 2151 | 2231 | 2311 | 2390 | 2469 | 2546 | 2624 | 8 | 16 | 24 | 32 | 40 |
| 1.3 | 2624 | 2700 | 2776 | 2852 | 2927 | 3001 | 3075 | 3148 | 3221 | 3293 | 3365 | 7 | 15 | 22 | 30 | 37 |
| 1.4 | 3365 | 3436 | 3507 | 3577 | 3646 | 3716 | 3784 | 3853 | 3920 | 3988 | 4055 | 7 | 14 | 21 | 28 | 34 |
| 1.5 | 4055 | 4121 | 4187 | 4253 | 4318 | 4383 | 4447 | 4511 | 4574 | 4637 | 4700 | 6 | 13 | 19 | 26 | 32 |
| 1.6 | 4700 | 4762 | 4824 | 4886 | 4947 | 5008 | 5068 | 5128 | 5188 | 5247 | 5306 | 6 | 12 | 18 | 24 | 30 |
| 1.7 | 5306 | 5365 | 5423 | 5481 | 5539 | 5596 | 5653 | 5710 | 5766 | 5822 | 5878 | 6 | 11 | 17 | 23 | 29 |
| 1.8 | 5878 | 5933 | 5988 | 6043 | 6098 | 6152 | 6206 | 6259 | 6313 | 6366 | 6419 | 5 | 11 | 16 | 22 | 27 |
| 1.9 | 6419 | 6471 | 6523 | 6575 | 6627 | 6678 | 6729 | 6780 | 6831 | 6881 | 0.6931 | 5 | 10 | 15 | 21 | 26 |
| **2.0** | 0.6931 | 6981 | 7031 | 7080 | 7129 | 7178 | 7227 | 7275 | 7324 | 7372 | 7419 | 5 | 10 | 15 | 20 | 24 |
| 2.1 | 7419 | 7467 | 7514 | 7561 | 7608 | 7655 | 7701 | 7747 | 7793 | 7839 | 7885 | 5 | 9 | 14 | 19 | 23 |
| 2.2 | 7885 | 7930 | 7975 | 8020 | 8065 | 8109 | 8154 | 8198 | 8242 | 8286 | 8329 | 4 | 9 | 13 | 18 | 22 |
| 2.3 | 8329 | 8372 | 8416 | 8459 | 8502 | 8544 | 8587 | 8629 | 8671 | 8713 | 8755 | 4 | 9 | 13 | 17 | 21 |
| 2.4 | 8755 | 8796 | 8838 | 8879 | 8920 | 8961 | 9002 | 9042 | 9083 | 9123 | 9163 | 4 | 8 | 12 | 16 | 20 |
| 2.5 | 9163 | 9203 | 9243 | 9282 | 9322 | 9361 | 9400 | 9439 | 9478 | 9517 | 9555 | 4 | 8 | 12 | 16 | 20 |
| 2.6 | 9555 | 9594 | 9632 | 9670 | 9708 | 9746 | 9783 | 9821 | 9858 | 9895 | 0.9933 | 4 | 8 | 11 | 15 | 19 |
| 2.7 | 0.9933 | 9969 | {0006 | 0043 | 0080 | 0116 | 0152 | 0188 | 0225 | 0260 | 1.0296 | 4 | 7 | 11 | 15 | 18 |
| 2.8 | 1.0296 | 0332 | 0367 | 0403 | 0438 | 0473 | 0508 | 0543 | 0578 | 0613 | 0647 | 4 | 7 | 11 | 14 | 18 |
| 2.9 | 0647 | 0682 | 0716 | 0750 | 0784 | 0818 | 0852 | 0886 | 0919 | 0953 | 1.0986 | 3 | 7 | 10 | 14 | 17 |
| **3.0** | 1.0986 | 1019 | 1053 | 1086 | 1119 | 1151 | 1184 | 1217 | 1249 | 1282 | 1314 | 3 | 7 | 10 | 13 | 16 |
| 3.1 | 1314 | 1346 | 1378 | 1410 | 1442 | 1474 | 1506 | 1537 | 1569 | 1600 | 1632 | 3 | 6 | 10 | 13 | 16 |
| 3.2 | 1632 | 1663 | 1694 | 1725 | 1756 | 1787 | 1817 | 1848 | 1878 | 1909 | 1939 | 3 | 6 | 9 | 12 | 15 |
| 3.3 | 1939 | 1969 | 2000 | 2030 | 2060 | 2090 | 2119 | 2149 | 2179 | 2208 | 2238 | 3 | 6 | 9 | 12 | 15 |
| 3.4 | 2238 | 2267 | 2296 | 2326 | 2355 | 2384 | 2413 | 2442 | 2470 | 2499 | 2528 | 3 | 6 | 9 | 12 | 14 |
| 3.5 | 2528 | 2556 | 2585 | 2613 | 2641 | 2669 | 2698 | 2726 | 2754 | 2782 | 2809 | 3 | 6 | 8 | 11 | 14 |
| 3.6 | 2809 | 2837 | 2865 | 2892 | 2920 | 2947 | 2975 | 3002 | 3029 | 3056 | 3083 | 3 | 5 | 8 | 11 | 14 |
| 3.7 | 3083 | 3110 | 3137 | 3164 | 3191 | 3218 | 3244 | 3271 | 3297 | 3324 | 3350 | 3 | 5 | 8 | 11 | 13 |
| 3.8 | 3350 | 3376 | 3403 | 3429 | 3455 | 3481 | 3507 | 3533 | 3558 | 3584 | 3610 | 3 | 5 | 8 | 10 | 13 |
| 3.9 | 3610 | 3635 | 3661 | 3686 | 3712 | 3737 | 3762 | 3788 | 3813 | 3838 | 1.3863 | 3 | 5 | 8 | 10 | 13 |
| **4.0** | 1.3863 | 3888 | 3913 | 3938 | 3962 | 3987 | 4012 | 4036 | 4061 | 4085 | 4110 | 2 | 5 | 7 | 10 | 12 |
| 4.1 | 4110 | 4134 | 4159 | 4183 | 4207 | 4231 | 4255 | 4279 | 4303 | 4327 | 4351 | 2 | 5 | 7 | 10 | 12 |
| 4.2 | 4351 | 4375 | 4398 | 4422 | 4446 | 4469 | 4493 | 4516 | 4540 | 4563 | 4586 | 2 | 5 | 7 | 9 | 12 |
| 4.3 | 4586 | 4609 | 4633 | 4656 | 4679 | 4702 | 4725 | 4748 | 4770 | 4793 | 4816 | 2 | 5 | 7 | 9 | 11 |
| 4.4 | 4816 | 4839 | 4861 | 4884 | 4907 | 4929 | 4951 | 4974 | 4996 | 5019 | 5041 | 2 | 4 | 7 | 9 | 11 |
| 4.5 | 5041 | 5063 | 5085 | 5107 | 5129 | 5151 | 5173 | 5195 | 5217 | 5239 | 5261 | 2 | 4 | 7 | 9 | 11 |
| 4.6 | 5261 | 5282 | 5304 | 5326 | 5347 | 5369 | 5390 | 5412 | 5433 | 5454 | 5476 | 2 | 4 | 6 | 9 | 11 |
| 4.7 | 5476 | 5497 | 5518 | 5539 | 5560 | 5581 | 5602 | 5623 | 5644 | 5665 | 5686 | 2 | 4 | 6 | 8 | 11 |
| 4.8 | 5686 | 5707 | 5728 | 5748 | 5769 | 5790 | 5810 | 5831 | 5851 | 5872 | 5892 | 2 | 4 | 6 | 8 | 10 |
| 4.9 | 5892 | 5913 | 5933 | 5953 | 5974 | 5994 | 6014 | 6034 | 6054 | 6074 | 1.6094 | 2 | 4 | 6 | 8 | 10 |

## TABLE I (*Continued*)

### Log$_e$ (Base $e$ = 2.718284)

| | 0 | 1 | 2 | 3 | 4 | 5 | 6 | 7 | 8 | 9 | 10 | Tenths of the Tabular Difference 1 2 3 4 5 |
|---|---|---|---|---|---|---|---|---|---|---|---|---|
| **5.0** | 1.6094 | 6114 | 6134 | 6154 | 6174 | 6194 | 6214 | 6233 | 6253 | 6273 | 6292 | 2 4 6 8 10 |
| 5.1 | 6292 | 6312 | 6332 | 6351 | 6371 | 6390 | 6409 | 6429 | 6448 | 6467 | 6487 | 2 4 6 8 10 |
| 5.2 | 6487 | 6506 | 6525 | 6544 | 6563 | 6582 | 6601 | 6620 | 6639 | 6658 | 6677 | 2 4 6 8 10 |
| 5.3 | 6677 | 6696 | 6715 | 6734 | 6752 | 6771 | 6790 | 6808 | 6827 | 6845 | 6864 | 2 4 6 7 9 |
| 5.4 | 6864 | 6882 | 6901 | 6919 | 6938 | 6956 | 6974 | 6993 | 7011 | 7029 | 7047 | 2 4 6 7 9 |
| 5.5 | 7047 | 7066 | 7084 | 7102 | 7120 | 7138 | 7156 | 7174 | 7192 | 7210 | 7228 | 2 4 5 7 9 |
| 5.6 | 7228 | 7246 | 7263 | 7281 | 7299 | 7317 | 7334 | 7352 | 7370 | 7387 | 7405 | 2 4 5 7 9 |
| 5.7 | 7405 | 7422 | 7440 | 7457 | 7475 | 7492 | 7509 | 7527 | 7544 | 7561 | 7579 | 2 3 5 7 9 |
| 5.8 | 7579 | 7596 | 7613 | 7630 | 7647 | 7664 | 7681 | 7699 | 7716 | 7733 | 7750 | 2 3 5 7 9 |
| 5.9 | 7750 | 7766 | 7783 | 7800 | 7817 | 7834 | 7851 | 7867 | 7884 | 7901 | 1.7918 | 2 3 5 7 8 |
| **6.0** | 1.7918 | 7934 | 7951 | 7967 | 7984 | 8001 | 8017 | 8034 | 8050 | 8066 | 8083 | 2 3 5 7 8 |
| 6.1 | 8083 | 8099 | 8116 | 8132 | 8148 | 8165 | 8181 | 8197 | 8213 | 8229 | 8245 | 2 3 5 7 8 |
| 6.2 | 8245 | 8262 | 8278 | 8294 | 8310 | 8326 | 8342 | 8358 | 8374 | 8390 | 8405 | 2 3 5 6 8 |
| 6.3 | 8405 | 8421 | 8437 | 8453 | 8469 | 8485 | 8500 | 8516 | 8532 | 8547 | 8563 | 2 3 5 6 8 |
| 6.4 | 8563 | 8579 | 8594 | 8610 | 8625 | 8641 | 8656 | 8672 | 8687 | 8703 | 8718 | 2 3 5 6 8 |
| 6.5 | 8718 | 8733 | 8749 | 8764 | 8779 | 8795 | 8810 | 8825 | 8840 | 8856 | 8871 | 2 3 5 6 8 |
| 6.6 | 8871 | 8886 | 8901 | 8916 | 8931 | 8946 | 8961 | 8976 | 8991 | 9006 | 9021 | 2 3 5 6 8 |
| 6.7 | 9021 | 9036 | 9051 | 9066 | 9081 | 9095 | 9110 | 9125 | 9140 | 9155 | 9169 | 1 3 4 6 7 |
| 6.8 | 9169 | 9184 | 9199 | 9213 | 9228 | 9242 | 9257 | 9272 | 9286 | 9301 | 9315 | 1 3 4 6 7 |
| 6.9 | 9315 | 9330 | 9344 | 9359 | 9373 | 9387 | 9402 | 9416 | 9430 | 9445 | 1.9459 | 1 3 4 6 7 |
| **7.0** | 1.9459 | 9473 | 9488 | 9502 | 9516 | 9530 | 9544 | 9559 | 9573 | 9587 | 9601 | 1 3 4 6 7 |
| 7.1 | 9601 | 9615 | 9629 | 9643 | 9657 | 9671 | 9685 | 9699 | 9713 | 9727 | 9741 | 1 3 4 6 7 |
| 7.2 | 9741 | 9755 | 9769 | 9782 | 9796 | 9810 | 9824 | 9838 | 9851 | 9865 | 1.9879 | 1 3 4 6 7 |
| 7.3 | 1.9879 | 9892 | 9906 | 9920 | 9933 | 9947 | 9961 | 9974 | 9988 | 0001 | 2.0015 | 1 3 4 5 7 |
| 7.4 | 2.0015 | 0028 | 0042 | 0055 | 0069 | 0082 | 0096 | 0109 | 0122 | 0136 | 0149 | 1 3 4 5 7 |
| 7.5 | 0149 | 0162 | 0176 | 0189 | 0202 | 0215 | 0229 | 0242 | 0255 | 0268 | 0281 | 1 3 4 5 7 |
| 7.6 | 0281 | 0295 | 0308 | 0321 | 0334 | 0347 | 0360 | 0373 | 0386 | 0399 | 0412 | 1 3 4 5 7 |
| 7.7 | 0412 | 0425 | 0438 | 0451 | 0464 | 0477 | 0490 | 0503 | 0516 | 0528 | 0541 | 1 3 4 5 6 |
| 7.8 | 0541 | 0554 | 0567 | 0580 | 0592 | 0605 | 0618 | 0631 | 0643 | 0656 | 0669 | 1 3 4 5 6 |
| 7.9 | 0669 | 0681 | 0694 | 0707 | 0719 | 0732 | 0744 | 0757 | 0769 | 0782 | 2.0794 | 1 3 4 5 6 |
| **8.0** | 2.0794 | 0807 | 0819 | 0832 | 0844 | 0857 | 0869 | 0882 | 0894 | 0906 | 0919 | 1 2 4 5 6 |
| 8.1 | 0919 | 0931 | 0943 | 0956 | 0968 | 0980 | 0992 | 1005 | 1017 | 1029 | 1041 | 1 2 4 5 6 |
| 8.2 | 1041 | 1054 | 1066 | 1078 | 1090 | 1102 | 1114 | 1126 | 1138 | 1150 | 1163 | 1 2 4 5 6 |
| 8.3 | 1163 | 1175 | 1187 | 1199 | 1211 | 1223 | 1235 | 1247 | 1258 | 1270 | 1282 | 1 2 4 5 6 |
| 8.4 | 1282 | 1294 | 1306 | 1318 | 1330 | 1342 | 1353 | 1365 | 1377 | 1389 | 1401 | 1 2 4 5 6 |
| 8.5 | 1401 | 1412 | 1424 | 1436 | 1448 | 1459 | 1471 | 1483 | 1494 | 1506 | 1518 | 1 2 4 5 6 |
| 8.6 | 1518 | 1529 | 1541 | 1552 | 1564 | 1576 | 1587 | 1599 | 1610 | 1622 | 1633 | 1 2 3 5 6 |
| 8.7 | 1633 | 1645 | 1656 | 1668 | 1679 | 1691 | 1702 | 1713 | 1725 | 1736 | 1748 | 1 2 3 5 6 |
| 8.8 | 1748 | 1759 | 1770 | 1782 | 1793 | 1804 | 1815 | 1827 | 1838 | 1849 | 1861 | 1 2 3 5 6 |
| 8.9 | 1861 | 1872 | 1883 | 1894 | 1905 | 1917 | 1928 | 1939 | 1950 | 1961 | 2.1972 | 1 2 3 4 6 |
| **9.0** | 2.1972 | 1983 | 1994 | 2006 | 2017 | 2028 | 2039 | 2050 | 2061 | 2072 | 2083 | 1 2 3 4 6 |
| 9.1 | 2083 | 2094 | 2105 | 2116 | 2127 | 2138 | 2148 | 2159 | 2170 | 2181 | 2192 | 1 2 3 4 5 |
| 9.2 | 2192 | 2203 | 2214 | 2225 | 2235 | 2246 | 2257 | 2268 | 2279 | 2289 | 2300 | 1 2 3 4 5 |
| 9.3 | 2300 | 2311 | 2322 | 2332 | 2343 | 2354 | 2364 | 2375 | 2386 | 2396 | 2407 | 1 2 3 4 5 |
| 9.4 | 2407 | 2418 | 2428 | 2439 | 2450 | 2460 | 2471 | 2481 | 2492 | 2502 | 2513 | 1 2 3 4 5 |
| 9.5 | 2513 | 2523 | 2534 | 2544 | 2555 | 2565 | 2576 | 2586 | 2597 | 2607 | 2618 | 1 2 3 4 5 |
| 9.6 | 2618 | 2628 | 2638 | 2649 | 2659 | 2670 | 2680 | 2690 | 2701 | 2711 | 2721 | 1 2 3 4 5 |
| 9.7 | 2721 | 2732 | 2742 | 2752 | 2762 | 2773 | 2783 | 2793 | 2803 | 2814 | 2824 | 1 2 3 4 5 |
| 9.8 | 2824 | 2834 | 2844 | 2854 | 2865 | 2875 | 2885 | 2895 | 2905 | 2915 | 2925 | 1 2 3 4 5 |
| 9.9 | 2925 | 2935 | 2946 | 2956 | 2966 | 2976 | 2986 | 2996 | 3006 | 3016 | 2.3026 | 1 2 3 4 5 |

## APPENDIX III

### TABLE II

LOGARITHMS TO THE BASE 10

| | 0 | 1 | 2 | 3 | 4 | 5 | 6 | 7 | 8 | 9 | 10 |
|---|---|---|---|---|---|---|---|---|---|---|---|
| **1.00** | 0.0000 | 0004 | 0009 | 0013 | 0017 | 0022 | 0026 | 0030 | 0035 | 0039 | 0043 |
| 1.01 | 0043 | 0048 | 0052 | 0056 | 0060 | 0065 | 0069 | 0073 | 0077 | 0082 | 0086 |
| 1.02 | 0086 | 0090 | 0095 | 0099 | 0103 | 0107 | 0111 | 0116 | 0120 | 0124 | 0128 |
| 1.03 | 0128 | 0133 | 0137 | 0141 | 0145 | 0149 | 0154 | 0158 | 0162 | 0166 | 0170 |
| 1.04 | 0170 | 0175 | 0179 | 0183 | 0187 | 0191 | 0195 | 0199 | 0204 | 0208 | 0212 |
| 1.05 | 0212 | 0216 | 0220 | 0224 | 0228 | 0233 | 0237 | 0241 | 0245 | 0249 | 0253 |
| 1.06 | 0253 | 0257 | 0261 | 0265 | 0269 | 0273 | 0278 | 0282 | 0286 | 0290 | 0294 |
| 1.07 | 0294 | 0298 | 0302 | 0306 | 0310 | 0314 | 0318 | 0322 | 0326 | 0330 | 0334 |
| 1.08 | 0334 | 0338 | 0342 | 0346 | 0350 | 0354 | 0358 | 0362 | 0366 | 0370 | 0374 |
| 1.09 | 0374 | 0378 | 0382 | 0386 | 0390 | 0394 | 0398 | 0402 | 0406 | 0410 | 0414 |
| **1.10** | 0.0414 | 0418 | 0422 | 0426 | 0430 | 0434 | 0438 | 0441 | 0445 | 0449 | 0453 |
| 1.11 | 0453 | 0457 | 0461 | 0465 | 0469 | 0473 | 0477 | 0481 | 0484 | 0488 | 0492 |
| 1.12 | 0492 | 0496 | 0500 | 0504 | 0508 | 0512 | 0515 | 0519 | 0523 | 0527 | 0531 |
| 1.13 | 0531 | 0535 | 0538 | 0542 | 0546 | 0550 | 0554 | 0558 | 0561 | 0565 | 0569 |
| 1.14 | 0569 | 0573 | 0577 | 0580 | 0584 | 0588 | 0592 | 0596 | 0599 | 0603 | 0607 |
| 1.15 | 0607 | 0611 | 0615 | 0618 | 0622 | 0626 | 0630 | 0633 | 0637 | 0641 | 0645 |
| 1.16 | 0645 | 0648 | 0652 | 0656 | 0660 | 0663 | 0667 | 0671 | 0674 | 0678 | 0682 |
| 1.17 | 0682 | 0686 | 0689 | 0693 | 0697 | 0700 | 0704 | 0708 | 0711 | 0715 | 0719 |
| 1.18 | 0719 | 0722 | 0726 | 0730 | 0734 | 0737 | 0741 | 0745 | 0748 | 0752 | 0755 |
| 1.19 | 0755 | 0759 | 0763 | 0766 | 0770 | 0774 | 0777 | 0781 | 0785 | 0788 | 0792 |
| **1.20** | 0.0792 | 0795 | 0799 | 0803 | 0806 | 0810 | 0813 | 0817 | 0821 | 0824 | 0828 |
| 1.21 | 0828 | 0831 | 0835 | 0839 | 0842 | 0846 | 0849 | 0853 | 0856 | 0860 | 0864 |
| 1.22 | 0864 | 0867 | 0871 | 0874 | 0878 | 0881 | 0885 | 0888 | 0892 | 0896 | 0899 |
| 1.23 | 0899 | 0903 | 0906 | 0910 | 0913 | 0917 | 0920 | 0924 | 0927 | 0931 | 0934 |
| 1.24 | 0934 | 0938 | 0941 | 0945 | 0948 | 0952 | 0955 | 0959 | 0962 | 0966 | 0969 |
| 1.25 | 0969 | 0973 | 0976 | 0980 | 0983 | 0986 | 0990 | 0993 | 0997 | 1000 | 1004 |
| 1.26 | 1004 | 1007 | 1011 | 1014 | 1017 | 1021 | 1024 | 1028 | 1031 | 1035 | 1038 |
| 1.27 | 1038 | 1041 | 1045 | 1048 | 1052 | 1055 | 1059 | 1062 | 1065 | 1069 | 1072 |
| 1.28 | 1072 | 1075 | 1079 | 1082 | 1086 | 1089 | 1092 | 1096 | 1099 | 1103 | 1106 |
| 1.29 | 1106 | 1109 | 1113 | 1116 | 1119 | 1123 | 1126 | 1129 | 1133 | 1136 | 1139 |
| **1.30** | 0.1139 | 1143 | 1146 | 1149 | 1153 | 1156 | 1159 | 1163 | 1166 | 1169 | 1173 |
| 1.31 | 1173 | 1176 | 1179 | 1183 | 1186 | 1189 | 1193 | 1196 | 1199 | 1202 | 1206 |
| 1.32 | 1206 | 1209 | 1212 | 1216 | 1219 | 1222 | 1225 | 1229 | 1232 | 1235 | 1239 |
| 1.33 | 1239 | 1242 | 1245 | 1248 | 1252 | 1255 | 1258 | 1261 | 1265 | 1268 | 1271 |
| 1.34 | 1271 | 1274 | 1278 | 1281 | 1284 | 1287 | 1290 | 1294 | 1297 | 1300 | 1303 |
| 1.35 | 1303 | 1307 | 1310 | 1313 | 1316 | 1319 | 1323 | 1326 | 1329 | 1332 | 1335 |
| 1.36 | 1335 | 1339 | 1342 | 1345 | 1348 | 1351 | 1355 | 1358 | 1361 | 1364 | 1367 |
| 1.37 | 1367 | 1370 | 1374 | 1377 | 1380 | 1383 | 1386 | 1389 | 1392 | 1396 | 1399 |
| 1.38 | 1399 | 1402 | 1405 | 1408 | 1411 | 1414 | 1418 | 1421 | 1424 | 1427 | 1430 |
| 1.39 | 1430 | 1433 | 1436 | 1440 | 1443 | 1446 | 1449 | 1452 | 1455 | 1458 | 1461 |
| **1.40** | 0.1461 | 1464 | 1467 | 1471 | 1474 | 1477 | 1480 | 1483 | 1486 | 1489 | 1492 |
| 1.41 | 1492 | 1495 | 1498 | 1501 | 1504 | 1508 | 1511 | 1514 | 1517 | 1520 | 1523 |
| 1.42 | 1523 | 1526 | 1529 | 1532 | 1535 | 1538 | 1541 | 1544 | 1547 | 1550 | 1553 |
| 1.43 | 1553 | 1556 | 1559 | 1562 | 1565 | 1569 | 1572 | 1575 | 1578 | 1581 | 1584 |
| 1.44 | 1584 | 1587 | 1590 | 1593 | 1596 | 1599 | 1602 | 1605 | 1608 | 1611 | 1614 |
| 1.45 | 1614 | 1617 | 1620 | 1623 | 1626 | 1629 | 1632 | 1635 | 1638 | 1641 | 1644 |
| 1.46 | 1644 | 1647 | 1649 | 1652 | 1655 | 1658 | 1661 | 1664 | 1667 | 1670 | 1673 |
| 1.47 | 1673 | 1676 | 1679 | 1682 | 1685 | 1688 | 1691 | 1694 | 1697 | 1700 | 1703 |
| 1.48 | 1703 | 1706 | 1708 | 1711 | 1714 | 1717 | 1720 | 1723 | 1726 | 1729 | 1732 |
| 1.49 | 1732 | 1735 | 1738 | 1741 | 1744 | 1746 | 1749 | 1752 | 1755 | 1758 | 1761 |

## TABLE II (*Continued*)

### Logarithms to the Base 10

|       | 0      | 1    | 2    | 3    | 4    | 5    | 6    | 7    | 8    | 9    | 10   |
|-------|--------|------|------|------|------|------|------|------|------|------|------|
| **1.50** | 0.1761 | 1764 | 1767 | 1770 | 1772 | 1775 | 1778 | 1781 | 1784 | 1787 | 1790 |
| 1.51 | 1790 | 1793 | 1796 | 1798 | 1801 | 1804 | 1807 | 1810 | 1813 | 1816 | 1818 |
| 1.52 | 1818 | 1821 | 1824 | 1827 | 1830 | 1833 | 1836 | 1838 | 1841 | 1844 | 1847 |
| 1.53 | 1847 | 1850 | 1853 | 1855 | 1858 | 1861 | 1864 | 1867 | 1870 | 1872 | 1875 |
| 1.54 | 1875 | 1878 | 1881 | 1884 | 1886 | 1889 | 1892 | 1895 | 1898 | 1901 | 1903 |
| 1.55 | 1903 | 1906 | 1909 | 1912 | 1915 | 1917 | 1920 | 1923 | 1926 | 1928 | 1931 |
| 1.56 | 1931 | 1934 | 1937 | 1940 | 1942 | 1945 | 1948 | 1951 | 1953 | 1956 | 1959 |
| 1.57 | 1959 | 1962 | 1965 | 1967 | 1970 | 1973 | 1976 | 1978 | 1981 | 1984 | 1987 |
| 1.58 | 1987 | 1989 | 1992 | 1995 | 1998 | 2000 | 2003 | 2006 | 2009 | 2011 | 2014 |
| 1.59 | 2014 | 2017 | 2019 | 2022 | 2025 | 2028 | 2030 | 2033 | 2036 | 2038 | 2041 |
| **1.60** | 0.2041 | 2044 | 2047 | 2049 | 2052 | 2055 | 2057 | 2060 | 2063 | 2066 | 2068 |
| 1.61 | 2068 | 2071 | 2074 | 2076 | 2079 | 2082 | 2084 | 2087 | 2090 | 2092 | 2095 |
| 1.62 | 2095 | 2098 | 2101 | 2103 | 2106 | 2109 | 2111 | 2114 | 2117 | 2119 | 2122 |
| 1.63 | 2122 | 2125 | 2127 | 2130 | 2133 | 2135 | 2138 | 2140 | 2143 | 2146 | 2148 |
| 1.64 | 2148 | 2151 | 2154 | 2156 | 2159 | 2162 | 2164 | 2167 | 2170 | 2172 | 2175 |
| 1.65 | 2175 | 2177 | 2180 | 2183 | 2185 | 2188 | 2191 | 2193 | 2196 | 2198 | 2201 |
| 1.66 | 2201 | 2204 | 2206 | 2209 | 2212 | 2214 | 2217 | 2219 | 2222 | 2225 | 2227 |
| 1.67 | 2227 | 2230 | 2232 | 2235 | 2238 | 2240 | 2243 | 2245 | 2248 | 2251 | 2253 |
| 1.68 | 2253 | 2256 | 2258 | 2261 | 2263 | 2266 | 2269 | 2271 | 2274 | 2276 | 2279 |
| 1.69 | 2279 | 2281 | 2284 | 2287 | 2289 | 2292 | 2294 | 2297 | 2299 | 2302 | 2304 |
| **1.70** | 0.2304 | 2307 | 2310 | 2312 | 2315 | 2317 | 2320 | 2322 | 2325 | 2327 | 2330 |
| 1.71 | 2330 | 2333 | 2335 | 2338 | 2340 | 2343 | 2345 | 2348 | 2350 | 2353 | 2355 |
| 1.72 | 2355 | 2358 | 2360 | 2363 | 2365 | 2368 | 2370 | 2373 | 2375 | 2378 | 2380 |
| 1.73 | 2380 | 2383 | 2385 | 2388 | 2390 | 2393 | 2395 | 2398 | 2400 | 2403 | 2405 |
| 1.74 | 2405 | 2408 | 2410 | 2413 | 2415 | 2418 | 2420 | 2423 | 2425 | 2428 | 2430 |
| 1.75 | 2430 | 2433 | 2435 | 2438 | 2440 | 2443 | 2445 | 2448 | 2450 | 2453 | 2455 |
| 1.76 | 2455 | 2458 | 2460 | 2463 | 2465 | 2467 | 2470 | 2472 | 2475 | 2477 | 2480 |
| 1.77 | 2480 | 2482 | 2485 | 2487 | 2490 | 2492 | 2494 | 2497 | 2499 | 2502 | 2504 |
| 1.78 | 2504 | 2507 | 2509 | 2512 | 2514 | 2516 | 2519 | 2521 | 2524 | 2526 | 2529 |
| 1.79 | 2529 | 2531 | 2533 | 2536 | 2538 | 2541 | 2543 | 2545 | 2548 | 2550 | 2553 |
| **1.80** | 0.2553 | 2555 | 2558 | 2560 | 2562 | 2565 | 2567 | 2570 | 2572 | 2574 | 2577 |
| 1.81 | 2577 | 2579 | 2582 | 2584 | 2586 | 2589 | 2591 | 2594 | 2596 | 2598 | 2601 |
| 1.82 | 2601 | 2603 | 2605 | 2608 | 2610 | 2613 | 2615 | 2617 | 2620 | 2622 | 2625 |
| 1.83 | 2625 | 2627 | 2629 | 2632 | 2634 | 2636 | 2639 | 2641 | 2643 | 2646 | 2648 |
| 1.84 | 2648 | 2651 | 2653 | 2655 | 2658 | 2660 | 2662 | 2665 | 2667 | 2669 | 2672 |
| 1.85 | 2672 | 2674 | 2676 | 2679 | 2681 | 2683 | 2686 | 2688 | 2690 | 2693 | 2695 |
| 1.86 | 2695 | 2697 | 2700 | 2702 | 2704 | 2707 | 2709 | 2711 | 2714 | 2716 | 2718 |
| 1.87 | 2718 | 2721 | 2723 | 2725 | 2728 | 2730 | 2732 | 2735 | 2737 | 2739 | 2742 |
| 1.88 | 2742 | 2744 | 2746 | 2749 | 2751 | 2753 | 2755 | 2758 | 2760 | 2762 | 2765 |
| 1.89 | 2765 | 2767 | 2769 | 2772 | 2774 | 2776 | 2778 | 2781 | 2783 | 2785 | 2788 |
| **1.90** | 0.2788 | 2790 | 2792 | 2794 | 2797 | 2799 | 2801 | 2804 | 2806 | 2808 | 2810 |
| 1.91 | 2810 | 2813 | 2815 | 2817 | 2819 | 2822 | 2824 | 2826 | 2828 | 2831 | 2833 |
| 1.92 | 2833 | 2835 | 2838 | 2840 | 2842 | 2844 | 2847 | 2849 | 2851 | 2853 | 2856 |
| 1.93 | 2856 | 2858 | 2860 | 2862 | 2865 | 2867 | 2869 | 2871 | 2874 | 2876 | 2878 |
| 1.94 | 2878 | 2880 | 2882 | 2885 | 2887 | 2889 | 2891 | 2894 | 2896 | 2898 | 2900 |
| 1.95 | 2900 | 2903 | 2905 | 2907 | 2909 | 2911 | 2914 | 2916 | 2918 | 2920 | 2923 |
| 1.96 | 2923 | 2925 | 2927 | 2929 | 2931 | 2934 | 2936 | 2938 | 2940 | 2942 | 2945 |
| 1.97 | 2945 | 2947 | 2949 | 2951 | 2953 | 2956 | 2958 | 2960 | 2962 | 2964 | 2967 |
| 1.98 | 2967 | 2969 | 2971 | 2973 | 2975 | 2978 | 2980 | 2982 | 2984 | 2986 | 2989 |
| 1.99 | 2989 | 2991 | 2993 | 2995 | 2997 | 2999 | 3002 | 3004 | 3006 | 3008 | 3010 |

## TABLE II (Continued)

### Logarithms to the Base 10

These two pages give the common logarithms of numbers between 1 and 10, correct to four places. Moving the decimal point $n$ places to the right (or left) in the number is equivalent to adding $n$ (or $-n$) to the logarithm. Thus, log $0.017453 = 0.2419 - 2 \ [= \bar{2}.2419]$.

To facilitate interpolation, the tenths of the tabular differences are given at the end of each line, so that the differences themselves need not be considered. In using these aids, first find the nearest tabular entry, and then add (to move to the right) or subtract (to move to the left), as the case may require.

| | **0** | **1** | **2** | **3** | **4** | **5** | **6** | **7** | **8** | **9** | **10** | Tenths of the Tabular Difference 1 2 3 4 5 |
|---|---|---|---|---|---|---|---|---|---|---|---|---|
| **1.0** | 0.0000 | 0043 | 0086 | 0128 | 0170 | 0212 | 0253 | 0294 | 0334 | 0374 | 0414 | |
| 1.1 | 0414 | 0453 | 0492 | 0531 | 0569 | 0607 | 0645 | 0682 | 0719 | 0755 | 0792 | |
| 1.2 | 0792 | 0828 | 0864 | 0899 | 0934 | 0969 | 1004 | 1038 | 1072 | 1106 | 1139 | To avoid Interpolation in the first |
| 1.3 | 1139 | 1173 | 1206 | 1239 | 1271 | 1303 | 1335 | 1367 | 1399 | 1430 | 1461 | ten lines, use the |
| 1.4 | 1461 | 1492 | 1523 | 1553 | 1584 | 1614 | 1644 | 1673 | 1703 | 1732 | 1761 | special table on the |
| 1.5 | 1761 | 1790 | 1818 | 1847 | 1875 | 1903 | 1931 | 1959 | 1987 | 2014 | 2041 | preceding page. |
| 1.6 | 2041 | 2068 | 2095 | 2122 | 2148 | 2175 | 2201 | 2227 | 2253 | 2279 | 2304 | |
| 1.7 | 2304 | 2330 | 2355 | 2380 | 2405 | 2430 | 2455 | 2480 | 2504 | 2529 | 2553 | |
| 1.8 | 2553 | 2577 | 2601 | 2625 | 2648 | 2672 | 2695 | 2718 | 2742 | 2765 | 2788 | |
| 1.9 | 2788 | 2810 | 2833 | 2856 | 2878 | 2900 | 2923 | 2945 | 2967 | 2989 | 3010 | |
| **2.0** | 0.3010 | 3032 | 3054 | 3075 | 3096 | 3118 | 3139 | 3160 | 3181 | 3201 | 3222 | 2 4 6 8 11 |
| 2.1 | 3222 | 3243 | 3263 | 3284 | 3304 | 3324 | 3345 | 3365 | 3385 | 3404 | 3424 | 2 4 6 8 10 |
| 2.2 | 3424 | 3444 | 3464 | 3483 | 3502 | 3522 | 3541 | 3560 | 3579 | 3598 | 3617 | 2 4 6 8 10 |
| 2.3 | 3617 | 3636 | 3655 | 3674 | 3692 | 3711 | 3729 | 3747 | 3766 | 3784 | 3802 | 2 4 5 7 9 |
| 2.4 | 3802 | 3820 | 3838 | 3856 | 3874 | 3892 | 3909 | 3927 | 3945 | 3962 | 3979 | 2 4 5 7 9 |
| 2.5 | 3979 | 3997 | 4014 | 4031 | 4048 | 4065 | 4082 | 4099 | 4116 | 4133 | 4150 | 2 3 5 7 9 |
| 2.6 | 4150 | 4166 | 4183 | 4200 | 4216 | 4232 | 4249 | 4265 | 4281 | 4298 | 4314 | 2 3 5 7 8 |
| 2.7 | 4314 | 4330 | 4346 | 4362 | 4378 | 4393 | 4409 | 4425 | 4440 | 4456 | 4472 | 2 3 5 6 8 |
| 2.8 | 4472 | 4487 | 4502 | 4518 | 4533 | 4548 | 4564 | 4579 | 4594 | 4609 | 4624 | 2 3 5 6 8 |
| 2.9 | 4624 | 4639 | 4654 | 4669 | 4683 | 4698 | 4713 | 4728 | 4742 | 4757 | 4771 | 1 3 4 6 7 |
| **3.0** | 0.4771 | 4786 | 4800 | 4814 | 4829 | 4843 | 4857 | 4871 | 4886 | 4900 | 4914 | 1 3 4 6 7 |
| 3.1 | 4914 | 4928 | 4942 | 4955 | 4969 | 4983 | 4997 | 5011 | 5024 | 5038 | 5051 | 1 3 4 6 7 |
| 3.2 | 5051 | 5065 | 5079 | 5092 | 5105 | 5119 | 5132 | 5145 | 5159 | 5172 | 5185 | 1 3 4 5 7 |
| 3.3 | 5185 | 5198 | 5211 | 5224 | 5237 | 5250 | 5263 | 5276 | 5289 | 5302 | 5315 | 1 3 4 5 6 |
| 3.4 | 5315 | 5328 | 5340 | 5353 | 5366 | 5378 | 5391 | 5403 | 5416 | 5428 | 5441 | 1 3 4 5 6 |
| 3.5 | 5441 | 5453 | 5465 | 5478 | 5490 | 5502 | 5514 | 5527 | 5539 | 5551 | 5563 | 1 2 4 5 6 |
| 3.6 | 5563 | 5575 | 5587 | 5599 | 5611 | 5623 | 5635 | 5647 | 5658 | 5670 | 5682 | 1 2 4 5 6 |
| 3.7 | 5682 | 5694 | 5705 | 5717 | 5729 | 5740 | 5752 | 5763 | 5775 | 5786 | 5798 | 1 2 3 5 6 |
| 3.8 | 5798 | 5809 | 5821 | 5832 | 5843 | 5855 | 5866 | 5877 | 5888 | 5899 | 5911 | 1 2 3 5 6 |
| 3.9 | 5911 | 5922 | 5933 | 5944 | 5955 | 5966 | 5977 | 5988 | 5999 | 6010 | 6021 | 1 2 3 4 6 |
| **4.0** | 0.6021 | 6031 | 6042 | 6053 | 6064 | 6075 | 6085 | 6096 | 6107 | 6117 | 6128 | 1 2 3 4 5 |
| 4.1 | 6128 | 6138 | 6149 | 6160 | 6170 | 6180 | 6191 | 6201 | 6212 | 6222 | 6232 | 1 2 3 4 5 |
| 4.2 | 6232 | 6243 | 6253 | 6263 | 6274 | 6284 | 6294 | 6304 | 6314 | 6325 | 6335 | 1 2 3 4 5 |
| 4.3 | 6335 | 6345 | 6355 | 6365 | 6375 | 6385 | 6395 | 6405 | 6415 | 6425 | 6435 | 1 2 3 4 5 |
| 4.4 | 6435 | 6444 | 6454 | 6464 | 6474 | 6484 | 6493 | 6503 | 6513 | 6522 | 6532 | 1 2 3 4 5 |
| 4.5 | 6532 | 6542 | 6551 | 6561 | 6571 | 6580 | 6590 | 6599 | 6609 | 6618 | 6628 | 1 2 3 4 5 |
| 4.6 | 6628 | 6637 | 6646 | 6656 | 6665 | 6675 | 6684 | 6693 | 6702 | 6712 | 6721 | 1 2 3 4 5 |
| 4.7 | 6721 | 6730 | 6739 | 6749 | 6758 | 6767 | 6776 | 6785 | 6794 | 6803 | 6812 | 1 2 3 4 5 |
| 4.8 | 6812 | 6821 | 6830 | 6839 | 6848 | 6857 | 6866 | 6875 | 6884 | 6893 | 6902 | 1 2 3 4 4 |
| 4.9 | 6902 | 6911 | 6920 | 6928 | 6937 | 6946 | 6955 | 6964 | 6972 | 6981 | 6990 | 1 2 3 4 4 |

# APPENDIX IV

## PROPERTIES OF DETERMINANTS

A determinant is a particular grouping of numbers and/or symbols. It has a definite value in terms of other, conventionally arranged, numbers and/or symbols. For example, the two simple determinants

$$\begin{vmatrix} -3 & 5 \\ -6 & 1 \end{vmatrix} \quad \text{and} \quad \begin{vmatrix} 2 & x \\ 5 & y \end{vmatrix} \tag{1}$$

are equal to $+27$ and $(2y - 5x)$ respectively. Determinants can form parts of equations, and we may have, for example,

$$\begin{vmatrix} x & y \\ 3 & 2 \end{vmatrix} = 5 \tag{2}$$

which, expanded, yields the conventionally written equation

$$2x - 3y = 5 \tag{3}$$

In Chapter I a determinant equation method was introduced as a means of obtaining equations from plotted or tabulated data. The question arises as to the method of expanding the determinants involved. It will be clear from the above examples that the expansion of a simple two-row-two-column determinant is given by

$$\begin{vmatrix} a & b \\ c & d \end{vmatrix} = ad - bc \tag{4}$$

Determinants with more than two rows and columns may be reduced to these simpler types by a method that will be clear from a study of the application of it to a particular third-order determinant.

$$\begin{vmatrix} a_1 & a_2 & a_3 \\ b_1 & b_2 & b_3 \\ c_1 & c_2 & c_3 \end{vmatrix} = a_1 \begin{vmatrix} b_2 & b_3 \\ c_2 & c_3 \end{vmatrix} - a_2 \begin{vmatrix} b_1 & b_3 \\ c_1 & c_3 \end{vmatrix} + a_3 \begin{vmatrix} b_1 & b_2 \\ c_1 & c_2 \end{vmatrix} \tag{5}$$

The right-hand member of Eq. 5 may be written, if desired, as

$$-b_1 \begin{vmatrix} a_2 & a_3 \\ c_2 & c_3 \end{vmatrix} + b_2 \begin{vmatrix} a_1 & a_3 \\ c_1 & c_3 \end{vmatrix} - b_3 \begin{vmatrix} a_1 & a_2 \\ c_1 & c_2 \end{vmatrix}$$

or as

$$c_1 \begin{vmatrix} a_2 & a_3 \\ b_2 & b_3 \end{vmatrix} - c_2 \begin{vmatrix} a_1 & a_3 \\ b_1 & b_3 \end{vmatrix} + c_3 \begin{vmatrix} a_1 & a_2 \\ b_1 & b_2 \end{vmatrix}$$

505

It is seen that the determinant multiplying any coefficient in the last equation above (that multiplying $a_2$, for example) is formed from what remains of the original determinant when the row and column containing the coefficient in question ($a_2$) are struck out. Note also that the signs of successive coefficients alternate as one proceeds across any row in the expansion process. The generalization to higher orders of determinant is not difficult.

A property of determinants that often results in much saving of labor in their evaluation is the fact that, if every member of any row (horizontal) or any column (vertical) be divided (or multiplied) by any quantity, the process is equivalent to dividing (or multiplying) the entire determinant by that same quantity. (See p. 15.)

An additional property of determinants that also often results in a saving of labor is the fact that any row (or column) may be subtracted from, or added to, any of the remaining rows (or columns) without altering the value of the determinant. For example, if the bottom row of the two determinants in Eq. 1 be subtracted from the remaining row, we obtain

$$\begin{vmatrix} 3 & 4 \\ -6 & 1 \end{vmatrix} \quad \text{and} \quad \begin{vmatrix} -3 & x-y \\ 5 & y \end{vmatrix} \tag{6}$$

The values of these determinants, $+27$ and $(2y - 5x)$ respectively, remain unchanged in this process. The usefulness of this determinant rule is plain where two identical numbers or symbols are contained in the same column (or row). Subtracting the rows (or columns) involved in accord with the above rule will then introduce a zero into the determinant. The presence of such zeros reduces the labor of evaluation of a determinant, as will be evident by trial.

Illustrating some of the above principles, we have

$$\begin{vmatrix} y & 1 & x & x^2 \\ 2 & 1 & 1 & 1 \\ 2 & 1 & 2 & 4 \\ 6 & 1 & 3 & 9 \end{vmatrix} = \begin{vmatrix} y-2 & 0 & x-1 & x^2-1 \\ 2 & 1 & 1 & 1 \\ 0 & 0 & 1 & 3 \\ 4 & 0 & 2 & 8 \end{vmatrix} = \begin{vmatrix} y-2 & x-1 & x^2-1 \\ 0 & 1 & 3 \\ 4 & 2 & 8 \end{vmatrix}$$

$$= 2 \begin{vmatrix} y-2 & x-1 & x^2-1 \\ 0 & 1 & 3 \\ 2 & 1 & 4 \end{vmatrix} = 2 \begin{vmatrix} y-2 & x-1 & x^2-1 \\ 0 & 1 & 3 \\ 2 & 0 & 1 \end{vmatrix}$$

$$= 2 \left[ 2 \begin{vmatrix} x-1 & x^2-1 \\ 1 & 3 \end{vmatrix} - 0 \begin{vmatrix} y-2 & x^2-1 \\ 0 & 3 \end{vmatrix} + 1 \begin{vmatrix} y-2 & x-1 \\ 0 & 1 \end{vmatrix} \right]$$

$$= 2(y - 6 + 6x - 2x^2)$$

## ANSWERS TO PROBLEMS

### Chapter I

**1.** 760.00 mm-Hg, $1.0132 \times 10^6$ dy/cm$^2$ 14.696 lb/in.$^2$

**2.** 732.77 mm-Hg, 0.96417 A.       **3.** 754.40 mm-Hg.

**4.** 2.3262 gm.
**6.** $T = T_0 - 0.03682(\text{C}°/\text{mm-Hg})(p_0 - p) - 0.0000219(\text{C}°/\text{mm-Hg}^2)(p_0 - p)^2$.

**7.** $+0.31$ C°, $+0.66$ C°.       **8.** $-1.02$ C°.

### Chapter II

**1.** 1336.2°K, 1945.4°F, 2405.1°R.       **2.** 10,340°F.

**3.** 7.54°R, $-452.15$°F, 36.72°R, $-422.97$°F, 162.34°R, $-297.35$°F.
**4.** 1.30%, 1.02%.
**5.** 15.34 mm-Hg, 74.68 mm-Hg, 2627.6 mm-Hg, 4517 mm-Hg.

**6.** $+26.7$ mm-Hg.       **7.** 440.9°C, 443.91°C.

**8.** 42.5°C, 67.5°C, 95.0°C, 112.5°C.
**9.** $E = 6.260$ mv $+ 0.01053$ mv/C°$(T - 700$°C$) + 0.00000166$
mv/C°$^2$$(T - 700$°C$)^2$.
**11.** $R = R_0[1 + 3.96 \times 10^{-3}$ 1/C°$(T - 0$°C$) - 5.6 \times 10^{-7}$ 1/C°$^2$$(T - 0$°C$)^2]$.
**12.** $2.6 \times 10^{-7}$ C°.

**13.** 24.2 div, 178 div, 1260 div.       **14.** 1764°K, 1075°K.
**15.** 76.7, 268.       **16.** 2.54 km/sec.

### Chapter III

**1.** $4.40 \times 10^{-6}$ 1/C°, $0.27 \times 10^{-9}$ 1/C°.
**2.** $4.45 \times 10^{-6}$ 1/C°, $4.58 \times 10^{-6}$ 1/C°, $4.40 \times 10^{-6}$ 1/C°, $4.50 \times 10^{-6}$ 1/C°,
$4.78 \times 10^{-6}$ 1/C°.

**3.** 6250.       **4.** 2.533 cm, 0.32%.

**5.** $\Delta V/V = 181.1 \times 10^{-6}(1/\text{C}°)(T - 0°\text{C}) + 11 \times 10^{-9}(1/\text{C}°)^2(T - 0°\text{C})^2$.
**6.** 1.00145 kg, 0.9608 kg.
**7.** 1.18 gm too much, 4.59 gm too little.

**8.** $56.2 \times 10^{-6}$ 1/C°.       **9.** $25.0 \times 10^{-6}$ 1/C°.
**10.** 1.2 sec of arc, 0.2 C°.       **11.** $9.00 \times 10^{-6}$ 1/C°.
**12.** $50.6 \times 10^{-6}$ 1/C°.       **13.** 65°3.4′.
**14.** 3.95 ft, 6.30 ft.       **15.** 0.832.
**16.** 7.0 tons wt/in.$^2$       **17.** 9.4%.
**18.** 8.28 tons wt/in.$^2$

## Chapter IV

1. 4.192 joules/cal.
3. 777 ft-lb/btu.
5. 2.74 amp.
9. 0.076.
11. 3650 joules.
13. 47,000 btu, 11,850 kcal.

2. 0.248 m-kgwt/rad, 2.43 joules/rad.
4. 2.12 cal/sec.
6. $18 \times 10^{-6}$.
10. 118 joules.
12. 0.21 F°.

## Chapter V

1. 10.78 C°.
6. 0.140 cal/(mg hr), 0.162 C°.

3. 28.0°C.
7. 13.0 A, 94.08 kcal.

## Chapter VI

1. 0.0114 cal/(gm C°).
2. 0.00184 gmv A/(gm K°), 0.00085 gmv A/(gm K°), 0.000200 gmv A/(gm K°).

3. 62.4 btu, 26.4 btu, 53.1 btu.    4. $9.7 \times 10^{-6}$.

5. 6.70 cal/(gm-atom K°), 5.88 cal/(gm-atom K°).
6. 3.10 cal/(gm-atom K°), 5.05 cal/(gm-atom K°).

7. Pb 4.85 kcal, Cu 9.92 kcal.    8. 0.162 cal/(gm C°).

9. 0.233 cal/(gm C°), 0.318 cal/(gm C°), 0.405 cal/(gm C°).
10. 0.0334 cal/(gm C°), 0.0350 cal/(gm C°), 0.0361 cal/(gm C°).
11. 0.0417 cal/(gm C°), 53.4% Pb, 46.6% Sn.

12. 0.635 cal/(gm C°).    14. 0.454 cal/(gm C°).

15. 0.419 cal/(gm C°).
16. 0.048 cal/(gm K°), 0.111 cal/(gm K°).
17. 0.0425 cal/(gm K°), 0.0386 cal/(gm K°).

18. 0.0420 cal/(gm C°).    19. 78.3 gal/min.

20. 98 kcal/hr, 1.3, 2.6 F°/hr.

## Chapter VII

2. 11,000.
4. 0.0239 btu/(in.² hr F°/in.).
6. 18.6 cal/(cm² day C°/cm).

3. 0.129 watt, 1.04%.
5. 0.242 cal/(cm² sec C°/cm).
7. 760 days.

8. 18.4 amp, 0.142 cal/(cm² sec C°/cm).

9. 2030°K, 1.12 watt/(cm² K°/cm).    10. 0.0645 cal/(cm² sec C°/cm).

11. 2.4 min, 0.072 F°.
12. 3.18 K°/watt, 0.472 K° cm/watt, 2.090 watt/(cm² K°/cm).

**13.** 9.36 cal/(cm² hr C°/cm). **14.** 3.08 pd.
**15.** 4.97 cal/(cm² hr C°/mm). **16.** 0.061 in./hr.

**17.** 3.67 cal/(cm² hr C°/mm).
**18.** 0.322 btu/(ft² hr F°/in.), 0.40 cal/(cm² hr C°/cm).

**19.** 3.43 F°/watt. **20.** 0.06 F°, 700 F°, 39.3 btu/(hr ft).

**21.** 1.238 cal/(cm² hr C°/cm).

## Chapter VIII

**1.** 1712°K, 341°K.
**3.** 161.6 m/sec, 502.6 m/sec, 265.1 m/sec, 262.3 m/sec.
**4.** 11.6 × 10⁻⁶ cm, 93 × 10⁻⁶ cm, 2.4 × 10⁻⁶ cm.
**5.** For $CO_2$ 0.00717 A, 71.7 A, 7170 A; for $H_2$ 0.00042 A, 4.2 A, 420 A.

**6.** 31.8 A, 0.795. **7.** 2.93Å, 3,73Å.
**9.** About 27%, about 60°C. **10.** 6.05 × 10⁻⁵ cal/(cm² sec C°/cm).
**12.** About −39°C, about +32°C. **13.** 26.5 C°, 30.3 C°.
**14.** 3.405 cal/(gm C°). **16.** 4.44 C°.
**17.** 5.82 mm-Hg, 8.22 mm-Hg.

## Chapter IX

**1.** 0.969 A, 1.032 gmv, 300°K; 0.867 A, 1.108 gmv, 288°K; 17.04 cal, 16.36 cal, 0.68 cal, 0.040.
**3.** −17.04 cal, −71.30 cal, +54.26 cal; −16.36 cal, −70.62 cal, +54.26 cal; −0.0568 cal/K°.

**4.** 2.048 kcal/K°. **5.** 498.7 cal, 1.444 cal/K°, 539.2 cal.
**6.** +3.714 cal/K°, −0.047 cal/K°. **7.** +3.559 cal/K°.
**8.** +0.00018 cal/(K° gm). **9.** +0.109 cal/K°.
**10.** 596.6 cal/gm.

## Chapter X

**1.** 0.00534, 0.0591, 0.598.
**2.** 1.083 mm-Hg/K°, 0.00606 mm-Hg/K°.

**4.** 675 cal/gm, 320,000. **5.** 30 cal/gm, 645 cal/gm.
**6.** 6¼ days. **7.** 0.0020 C°/(dy/cm²).
**9.** 1.40 gm, 5.25 gm. **10.** 3.38 gm.
**12.** 77.0 btu/pd, 69.2 btu/pd. **13.** 11 sec.

**14.** 1100 cal/gm, 1085 cal/gm, 1070 cal/gm.

**15.** 3380 hr, 115 hr, 6.5 hr. **16.** 13.0 × 10⁻⁶ dy/cm², 1140 cal/gm.
**17.** 138.7 cal/gm. **18.** 408 gm.

**19.** 13.0 cal/gm, 26.6 cal/gm, 24.3 cal/gm.
**20.** 28.6 cal/(mole of $Na_2SO_4$).
**21.** 0.573 C°, 0.279 C°, 0.159 C°, 0.078 C°.
**22.** 2950 cal/gm-atom.

## Chapter XI

1. 1.000 : 2.537 : 0.359.
2. 49 btu/pd, 310 btu/pd, 1135 btu/pd, 830 btu/pd, 256 btu/pd, 22.5%.
3. 56 btu/pd, 310 btu/pd, 1355 btu/pd, 934 btu/pd, 365 btu/pd, 26.9%.

5. 625 hp, 562 hp.
7. 36.2 hp, 14.4 hp.
9. 4.95.
11. 4.75: 6.65: 10.40.
13. 3190 cal/gm.

6. 69,200 tons.
8. 82.3 lb/in.$^2$, 0.383 pd/bhp-hr.
10. 580 lb/in.$^2$, 210 lb/in.$^2$, 340 lb/in.$^2$
12. 0.184 pd/min, 0.273 ft$^3$/min.
14. 4.65 kg.

## Chapter XIII

1. 1.19 watt/mm$^2$, 0.380 watt/(mm$^2$ str), 0.0103 watt/cm$^2$.
2. 0.0062 watt/cm$^2$, 0.00197 watt/(cm$^2$ str).
3. 1.055 × 10$^{20}$ kwhr/sec, 8.38 × 10$^{18}$ kwhr/(sec str), 6230 watts/cm$^2$ 1980 watts/(cm$^2$ str).

4. 29.5 mm.

5. 1.5 × 10$^{-3}$ C°.

6. 12.8 cal/(cm$^2$ min), 0.84 cal/(cm$^2$ min), 0.0022 cal/(cm$^2$ min).
7. 1.36 cal/(cm$^2$ min), 0.54 cal/(cm$^2$ min).
8. 0.308 amp.
9. 8.3 × 10$^{-4}$ watt, 0.0451 watt, 8.3 × 10$^{-4}$ watt; 0.664 watt, 5.01 watt, 0.664 watt.

10. 10.0%.
12. 870 div.
14. 19, 9.5°.
18. 1484.2°K, 1416.5°K.
20. 1234°K.
22. 48.5%.
24. 2032°K, 0.298.

11. 34,300 K°/sec.
13. 73.6%.
17. 1264.2°K, 1214.7°K.
19. 1836°K.
21. 1191°K, 1336°K, 0.140.
23. 3788°K.
25. 2186°K.

# AUTHOR INDEX

# SUBJECT INDEX

Internal-combustion engine, gasoline, 351
Internal energy, 101, 103
Internal pressure, 310
Ionosphere, 400
Irradiancy, 416, 420
Isentropic processes, 103
Isobaric processes, 103
Isometric processes, 103
Isopiestic processes, 103
Isothermal processes, 103, 106
Isovolumic processes, 103

Jet engine, 364
Joule's experiment, 94, 220
Joule's law, 201
Joule-Thomson experiment, 222

Kennard's experiment, 388
Kinetic theory of gases, 202
Kirchhoff's law, 429

Laboratory procedures, some, 1
Lambert's cosine law, 437
Laminar flow, 383
Lapse rate, 405
Leakage modulus, 117

Mass, units of, 105
Massing, 6
    correction for buoyancy effects, 8
    double, 7
    single, 6
Maxwell equations for molecular speeds, derivation of, 481
Maxwell speed distribution, 201, 205
Mean free path, 209
Mechanical equivalent of heat, accepted values and significance of $J$, 99
    defining equation for, 93
    Joule's experiment, 94
    magnetic and electric methods, 96
    Mayer's computations, 94
    Rowland's experiment, 96
Mercury columns, reading positions of tops of, 2
    similarity of menisci at tops of, 3
Mercury vapor as substitute for steam, 350
Metabolism rates, 374

Metabolism rates, variation with age, 375
    variation with size and occupation, 376
Michels' experiments, 213
Microcalorimeter methods, Swietoslawski's, 123
Molecular heat, definition, 112
Molecular sizes, 211
Molecular velocities, Maxwell's equations for, derivations of, 481
Mollier diagram and the Rankine cycle, 347
Molybdenum, expansion with temperature, 12
Monsoons, 410

Newtonian leakage, 116
Newton's law of cooling, 441
Non-blackbodies, 446
    reflectances, absorptances, emittances, and transmittances, 431
    reflectivities, absorptivities, and emissivities, 447

Operating temperatures for steam engines, tendency for increased, 349
Order-disorder phenomenon in brass, 148
Otto cycle, air-standard, 355
    fuel-air-standard, 356

Perpetual motion, of first kind, 101
    of second kind, 262
    of third kind, 263
Phase, change of, 282
Phase boundaries, 288
Phases, graphical representation of, 283
Planck spectral distribution law, 444
Platinum, specific heats between 0°C and its melting point, 142
Poisson's equation, 162
Porous plug expansion, 103, 109, 222
Pound force (lb), 93
Pound mass (pd), 93
Pound-mole, 105
Pressure, atmosphere a unit of, 2
    cm-Hg a unit of, 1
    correction to standard conditions, 4
    correctness of the length-measuring instrument, 4
    definition, 1
    determining, 1